ELEMENTARY CRYSTALLOGRAPHY

ELEMENTARY CRYSTALLOGRAPHY

An introduction to the fundamental geometrical features of crystals

M. J. Buerger

Professor of Mineralogy and Crystallography Massachusetts Institute of Technology

John Wiley & Sons, Inc., New York

Chapman & Hall, Limited, London

Library of Congress Catalog Card Number: 55-9511

PRINTED IN THE UNITED STATES OF AMERICA

Dedicated
to
Helen Evans

Preface

Nearly every mineralogy, metallurgy, chemistry, and physics textbook now contains a short section on crystallography. These abbreviated treatments can hardly be expected to present more than some of the conclusions of the science. Something was plainly needed to explain the reasoning leading to these conclusions. This book was written to supply a fuller account of the subject.

Crystallography is a large science, and it is impossible to discuss all of it adequately in a single volume. This volume is concerned with the symmetry properties of crystals, which are fundamental to all other phases of crystallography. It is necessary to have a firm foundation in symmetry theory in order to make any further intelligent study of crystals or of the parts of other sciences which deal with crystals.

The subject matter of this volume falls naturally into three sections. About the first half of the book is devoted to a rational development of the megascopically observable symmetries of crystals. A second part of the book is devoted to a discussion of the internal symmetries of crystals. A third section contains some advanced material.

The fundamental ideas concerning crystal symmetry are inherently simple. They require no complicated mathematics, and can be understood by anyone whose background includes high school mathematics. In fact, they fall into the category of an interesting kind of solid geometry. Accordingly, elementary methods are used in most of the book. But, as a kind of appendix on advanced methods, the book ends with three chapters which are concerned with group theory and its application to symmetry. The interested student who wishes to study this elegant device for formulating crystal symmetry may be expected to have the background necessary for really appreciating group theory by the time he reaches this point.

I am indebted to several sources for permission to use illustrations. Professor Clifford Frondel of Harvard University kindly permitted me to borrow Figs. 10, 39, 40, 41, 44, 79, 103, 106, 129, 130, 159, 160, 167, 168, 171, 172, and 173 of Chapter 10 from *Dana's System of Mineralogy*. Figures 9, 45, 46, 64, 65, 107, 108, 111, 114, 115, 116, 117, 124, 138, 139, 140, 141,

142, 143, 144, 145, 146, 147, 148, 149, 150, 151, 152, 163, and 164 of Chapter 10 are taken from *Dana's Textbook of Mineralogy,* and Figs. 16 and 17 of Chapter 11 are taken from Honess' *Etch Figures,* with the kind permission of John Wiley & Sons. I am indebted to Professor Cornelius Hurlbut of Harvard University for the use of Figs. 1, 3, and 4 of Chapter 11 from his revision of *Dana's Manual of Mineralogy,* and to Dr. H. E. Buckley for the use of Fig. 18 of Chapter 11. Dr. W. L. Bond supplied me with a sketch from which Fig. 9 of Chapter 11 was prepared. All other figures were drawn especially for this book. Mr. R. Ellis of Raytheon Manufacturing Co. was good enough to permit me to take photographs of his etched germanium spheres shown as Fig. 10 of Chapter 11. I am indebted to my colleague, Professor Avery Morton, for supplying modern equivalents for the names of organic compounds found in the older literature. Dr. Leonid V. Azaroff and Mrs. Sylvia Garvin kindly undertook the preparation of the index. Professors J. D. H. Donnay, I. Fankuchen, and E. M. Loebl each read a portion of the page proofs and made suggestions for corrections.

Finally, it is a pleasure to acknowledge the great debt I owe to two able assistants who took charge of putting different parts of the copy into final form. Mrs. Evelyn Gower started with my penciled draft and cheerfully saw it through three successively improved stages of typescript. Mr. Nobukazu Niizeki prepared most of the drawings from my rough penciled drafts and incidentally made many suggestions leading to improvement. It is certain that without the wholehearted help of these two assistants the book would have taken two years longer to produce.

M. J. BUERGER

February 1956

Contents

CHAPTER 8

CHAPTER 9

CHAPTER 10

CHAPTER 11

CHAPTER 12

CHAPTER 13

CHAPTER 14

CHAPTER 15

CHAPTER 16

CHAPTER 20

CHAPTER 21

CHAPTER 22

List of tables

CHAPTER 19

CHAPTER 21

CHAPTER 22

1 · The crystalline state and its relation to other states of matter

It is usual to regard matter as existing in three states, designated gaseous, liquid, and solid. With an increasing knowledge of the structure of matter it has become plain that a more rational subdivision of matter is into gaseous, liquid, and *crystalline* states. In order to appreciate the distinctive features of crystals, it is worthwhile to compare the crystalline state with the other states of matter.

The distinctive structural feature of a gas is that it is composed of particles (atoms or molecular groups of atoms) which are substantially independent of one another except for occasional collisions. According to Avogadro's law, a mole of gas contains 6.03×10^{23} molecules. Under standard conditions, a mole of gas occupies a volume of 22.4 liters. This is equal to 22.4×10^3 cc, or $(22.4 \times 10^3) \times 10^{24}$ Å^3.* Thus, the volume occupied by a molecule is

$$\frac{22.4 \times 10^{27}}{6.03 \times 10^{23}} = 37 \times 10^3 \text{ Å}^3.$$

This is equivalent to one molecule in a cube whose edge is $\sqrt[3]{37 \times 10^3} = 33$ Å. Since the diameter of a molecule of a simple gas is of the order of two or three Ångström units, it is evident that the space within a gas is very sparsely occupied. The molecules of the gas are in constant motion, owing to their temperature energy, and they course back and forth through their container, bouncing from its walls, and occasionally colliding and rebounding from one another. It is because of this very independence of the molecules from one another that gases can expand to an unlimited amount, and indeed can approximately obey the well-known perfect gas equation

$$pV = nRT.$$

This law can be derived as the expected behavior of a system of mutually independent particles which have a negligible volume compared with the volume, V, of their container. Thus, the salient characteristic of a gas is the near-independence of its particles and the consequent lack of influence of one particle on another.

In a liquid, the molecules are so close as to be in contact. For this reason the attraction of one molecule on its immediate neighbors is high. Indeed, the attraction is sufficiently great to hold neighboring molecules in contact so that,

* Å stands for Ångström unit. One Ångström unit is 10^{-8} cm.

when a liquid is poured, it maintains a constant volume. Yet the molecules do not have permanent holds on one another, because thermal agitation has a sufficiently high energy to frequently lift a molecule through the field of attraction of another. Therefore, a liquid is structurally a mass of molecules so close to one another that each attracts its neighbors strongly, yet not strongly enough that the bonds between molecules can be permanently maintained in the face of thermal agitation.

Suppose, in the model of a liquid just considered, that thermal agitation is reduced to a point where its energy is insufficient to separate a pair of molecules which become bonded together. At temperatures below this, bonds between neighboring molecules are permanently maintained, and the collection of molecules assumes a rigidity due to the permanent bridgework of bonds throughout the collection. While the arrangement of such a collection of molecules may be either random or ordered, an ordered arrangement is one of lesser energy and therefore tends to develop. This ordered arrangement is the *crystalline state*. This book is concerned with the geometrical nature of this order and some of its consequences.

From what has been said it is evident that the orderly arrangement of the molecules or atoms in crystals is a consequence of the dominance of the bonding of these units over other features of the aggregate. The order represents a state of low energy of the units with respect to this bonding. Thermal agitation tends to disturb the order, and when the temperature is high enough so that the average thermal energy of a molecule exceeds its bonding energy, the molecules escape from one another's influence, and the order is destroyed by melting.

2 · Repetition theory

One of the fundamental features of a pure chemical substance is that each molecule (or other unit) is a duplicate of all other molecules. From a geometrical point of view, each molecule is a copy, or *repetition*, of some arbitrarily chosen motif molecule of the mass.

When a motif is repeated systematically the result is a periodic pattern. The periodic repetition may extend in one, two, or three dimensions. A systematic study of patterns proves that there are only 2 types of purely one-dimensional patterns, 17 types of purely two-dimensional patterns, and 230 types of three-dimensional patterns. Since crystals are regions of matter composed of the same kind of molecule systematically repeated, these must be arranged in one of the 230 three-dimensional pattern types. The geometrical features of crystals are consequently determined by three-dimensional pattern theory. Any study of crystallography must therefore have pattern theory as a foundation.

Some of the geometrical aspects of crystallography can be appreciated, in anticipation, by informally examining patterns in two dimensions. It was stated above that there are 17 of these. This means that, if some general motif is selected, there are only 17 available ways of repeating it. Suppose that one selects a scalene triangle as an asymmetrical motif. The 17 possible ways of repeating it in two dimensions are shown in the illustration inside the covers of this book. That there are only these 17 ways will not be proved at this point. They are introduced here chiefly to illustrate the fundamental pattern characteristic of crystals. The labels of these patterns appear to be arbitrary, but they will turn out to be natural representations of the patterns as the theory of patterns is developed in this book.

It will benefit the student very much to become pattern-conscious from this point on. He is advised to study all two-dimensional patterns that come under his notice. Such patterns will be found in wallpaper, floor-tiling, textile weaves, necktie ornamentation, etc. All such patterns (provided they are truly two-dimensional) will be found to fall in one of the 17 categories mentioned above. They differ only in the motif selected for repetition. As the student begins his notice of plane patterns, many of their characteristics will be meaningless to him. As the study of this book proceeds, however, more and more of the characteristics of patterns will be recognized, until, finally, each one will come to be completely understood.

Crystals conform to a set of pattern types like those of the inside-cover illustrations, only there are more available types because crystals are three-dimensional. Given a molecule, or other motif group of atoms, however, only 230 types of patterns are available as repetitions of the motif group.

This book is largely devoted to finding these 230 types of space patterns by elementary means, to seeing what it is that limits them to this number, and to studying some of their characteristics, including resemblances and differences. *This is the primary objective of elementary crystallography.* Many of the intermediate results found in the process of deriving the 230 space patterns are useful in their own right. In the chapters that follow, attention is drawn to these intermediate results in crystallography and to their usefulness.

In this chapter some of the preliminary notions involved in repetition theory are discussed. This discussion is based on the fact that each possible pattern can be analyzed by considering what geometrical operations are necessary to repeat the motif molecule to become the numerous molecules of the crystal.

Geometrical operations required for repetition

Consider the repetition of some asymmetrical figure, such as a comma, Fig. 1. The geometrical problem involved in repetition can be appreciated in the following formulation: If one has a rubber stamp located so that it prints the comma at location *m* of Fig. 1*a*, what movement must be given to the stamp in order to place it so that it can print the comma at location *n* of Fig. 1*a*? The required movement can be analyzed into two parts. Figure 1*b* shows that the stamp must be translated from one location to the other by an amount *t*, and Fig. 1*c* shows that it must also be rotated through an angle α. Thus a combination of a translation and a rotation is sufficient to repeat a motif. (This is true in three dimensions as well as two dimensions.)

This conclusion has a somewhat restricted application, because any asymmetrical figure (such as a hand, or an appropriate molecule) can exist in both right-handed and left-handed varieties. These are said to be *enantiomorphous.* On the other hand, a pair of duplicate right-handed figures, such as the two commas of Fig. 1*a* (or a pair of duplicate left-handed figures), are said to be *congruent.* This means that if one of the congruent right-handed figures is placed over the other, they "run together." Figures which are thus related by either congruence or enantiomorphism are said to be *equivalent.*

If the specifications for drawing a right-handed figure are given, the information is sufficient for drawing the corresponding left-handed figure. Thus the left-handed figure can be regarded as a kind of repetition of the corresponding right-handed figure. Suppose, then, that a left-handed figure is to be repeated from a right-handed model, Fig. 2*a*. What geometrical operations are required? From Fig. 2*b*, *c*, and *d* it is evident that not only must the original figure be

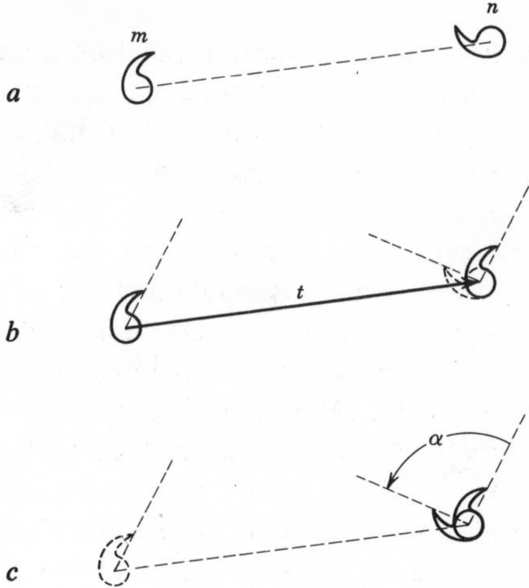

FIG. 1. Repetition of a congruent figure by a translation and a rotation.

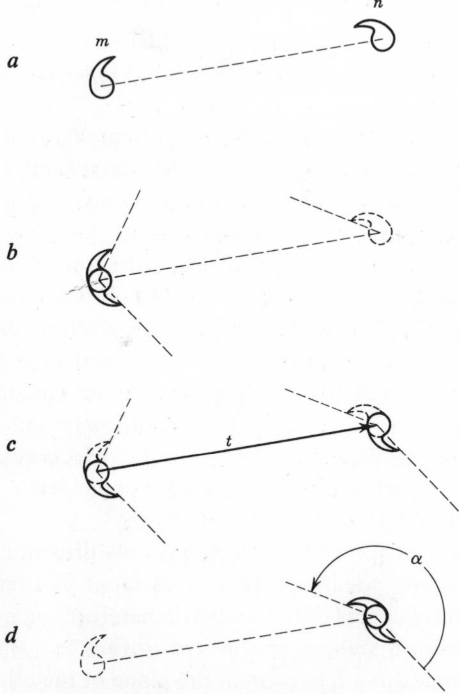

FIG. 2. Repetition of an enantiomorphous figure by a reflection, translation, and rotation.

displaced by translation and rotation but it must also be reflected to the left-handed equivalent figure. The geometrical operations of translation, rotation, and reflection are thus sufficient to repeat a left-handed figure from a right-handed figure (or the reverse) in two dimensions.

Nature of right and left

Consider an asymmetrical plane figure such as a comma, Fig. 3*a*. The figure can be specified by a list of the coordinates of its outline. If the same list is applied to a coordinate system in which the positive direction of the X axis

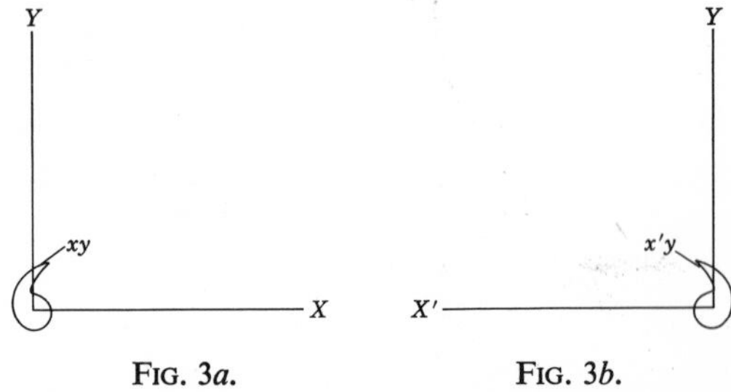

FIG. 3*a*. FIG. 3*b*.

is reversed, Fig. 3*b*, the left-handed equivalent figure develops instead of the original right-handed one in Fig. 3*a*. No movement of the figure in 3*b* can make it coincide with that of 3*a*. This is simply because no movement of the coordinate system $X'Y$ of Fig. 3*b* can make it coincide with the system XY of Fig. 3*a*. The total number of possibilities of reversal of the positive directions of the coordinate axes are outlined in Fig. 4. It is evident from a study of these that reversal of X to $\bar{X}$ corresponds to a reflection across Y, that a reversal of Y to $\bar{Y}$ corresponds to a reflection across X, while a reversal of both X and Y to $\bar{X}$ and $\bar{Y}$ corresponds to a 180° rotation about the origin. It can therefore be concluded that the reversal of one coordinate axis generates an enantiomorphous figure, whereas the reversal of two coordinate axes generates a congruent figure which can be brought into coincidence with the original figure by a rotation of 180°.

In three dimensions, reversals of the positive directions of one, two, or three coordinate axes are possible. This gives eight combinations as outlined in Fig. 5. The consequences of reversals are therefore somewhat more complicated for three dimensions, and are epitomized in Fig. 6: (1) A reversal of one axis, Fig. 6*b*, corresponds to a reflection in the plane of the other two. (2) A reversal of two axes, Fig. 6*c*, gives rise to a set of axes which can be brought back to the original set, XYZ, by a rotation of 180° about the unreversed axis. (3) A reversal of three axes, Fig. 6*d*, corresponds to an *inversion* of the three axes through the

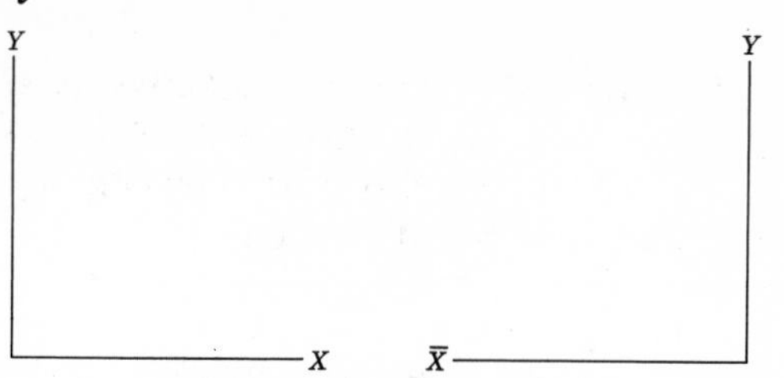

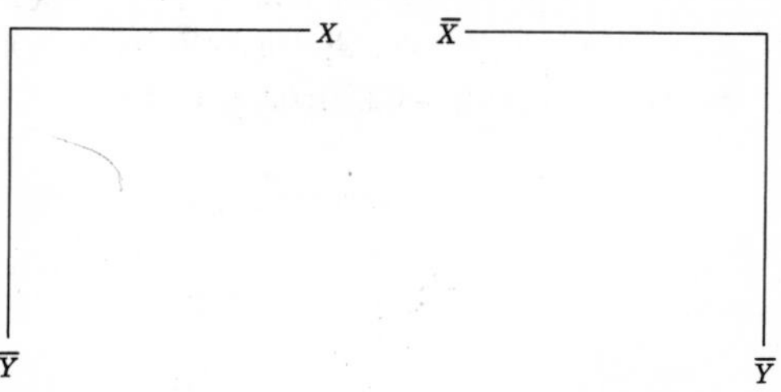

FIG. 4.

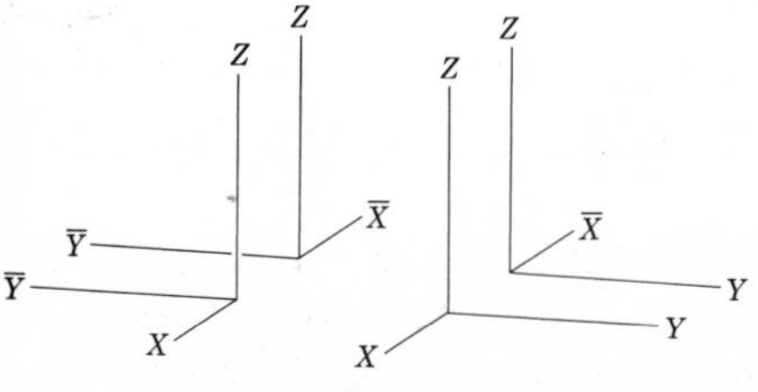

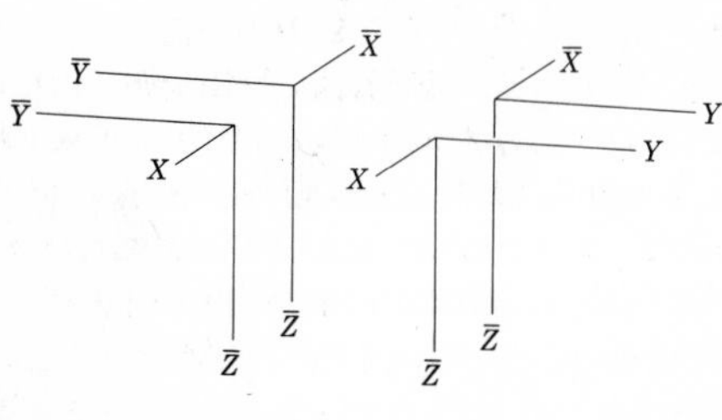

FIG. 5.

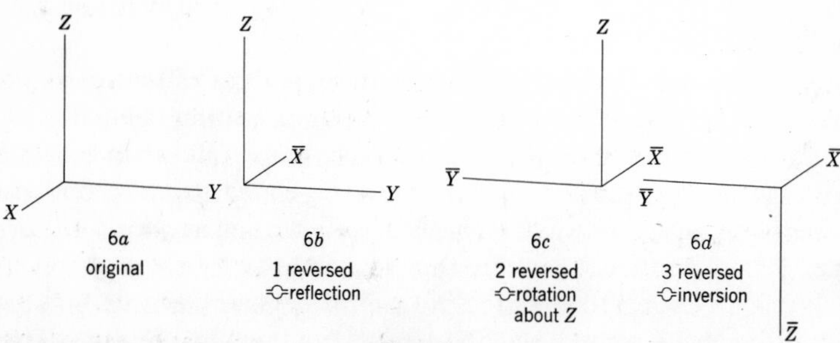

FIG. 6.

origin point. The axes of Fig. 6*c* can be brought into coincidence with those of Fig. 6*a* by a rotation of 180° about Z. The axes of Fig. 6*d* can be brought into coincidence with those of Fig. 6*b* by a rotation of 180° about $\bar{X}$. Thus Figs. 6*a* and 6*c* constitute one congruent set and Figs. 6*b* and 6*d* constitute another congruent set. These two sets cannot be rotated into each other in any way, and so are enantiomorphous. Thus, in three dimensions the enantiomorphic relation can be established either by a reflection or by an inversion.

Periodic repetitions

In a collection of like figures, the entire set can be reproduced from any one member by repetition. If the several repetition operations are not related to one another the result is a random aggregate. On the other hand, a special

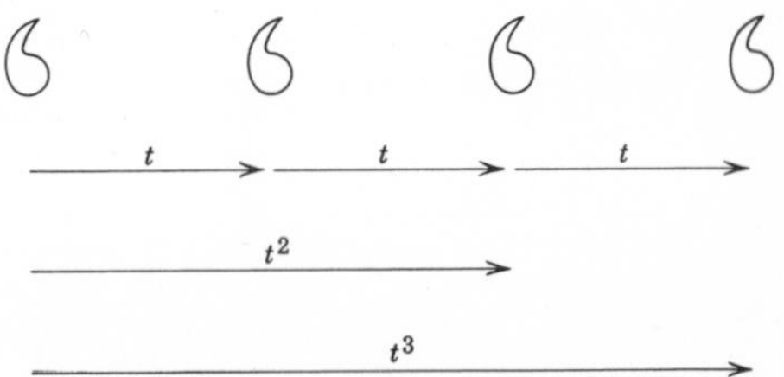

FIG. 7. Repetition by a periodically repeated translation, t.

kind of repetition can be generated by a continued application of the same operation. Thus, let the operation act on the first figure to produce the second figure, and let the same operation act on the second figure to produce a third, etc. In this case all the figures are related to the first by periodic compounding of the one operation. This results in a periodic array of figures. Such an array is recognized as an ordered array, and this order corresponds to the order observed in the arrangement of atoms in crystals.

Any kind of operation can be used as a generator of a periodic repetition. Figures 7, 8, 9, and 10, respectively, show periodic repetition generated by repeated application of a translation t, a rotation A_α, a reflection m, and of a combination of translation and reflection, the combination being designated g. Using Fig. 8 as an example, note that each figure is related to its immediate neighbors by the operation A. Each figure is related to its second neighbor by the operation repeated twice. This is usually written as a kind of "product" $A \cdot A$, i.e., A^2. Third neighbors are thus related by $A \cdot A \cdot A = A^3$, etc. Note that, if one figure is regarded as the progenitor of the others, its first neighbor is produced by A, its second neighbor by A^2, its third by A^3, etc. The set of

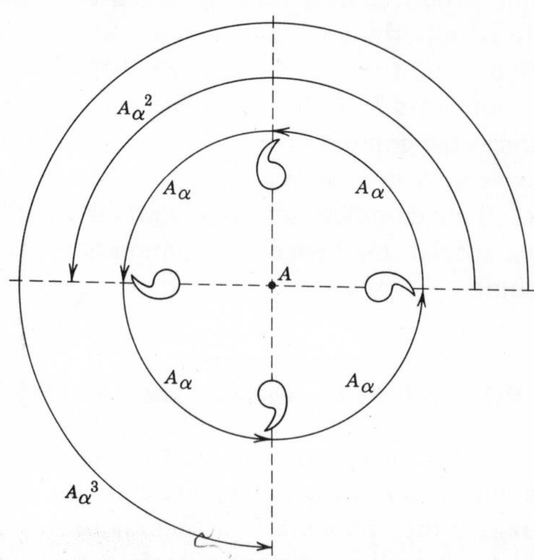

FIG. 8. Repetition by a periodically repeated rotation through angle α about axis *A*.

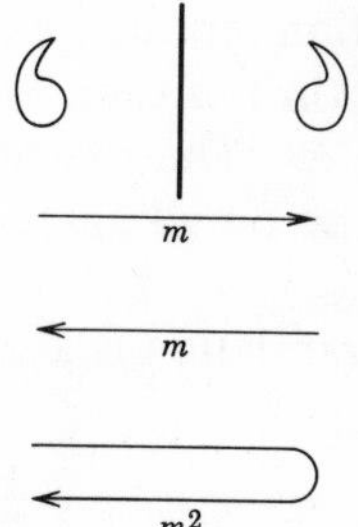

FIG. 9. Repetition by a periodically repeated reflection, *m*.

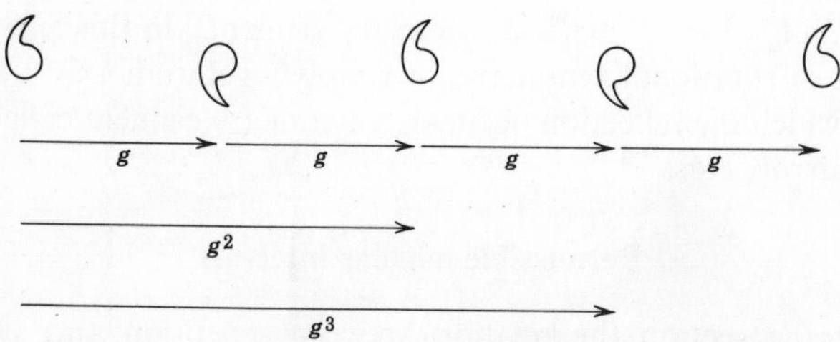

FIG. 10. Repetition by a periodically repeated translation-reflection, *g*.

repeated figures is thus produced from the original figure by the set of operations A, A^2, A^3, $\cdots$. It is important to have a label for the "operation" which produces the first figure from itself. This is called the *identical operation* and is designated 1 (or sometimes I or E). Thus the complete set of operations 1, A, A^2, A^3, $\cdots$ produces the complete set of figures from the first figure. There is a one-to-one correspondence between repeated figures and the operations that produce them. This complete set of operations is called a *group*. The word "group" has special mathematical connotations which will not be developed at this point.

Relation between repetition and symmetry

In a periodic repetition, such as in Fig. 8, the operation has been said to produce the second figure from the first, the third from the second, etc. A more general view is to regard the operation as acting on all space. In Fig. 8, then, the operation requires that all space (and therefore anything contained in it) be repeated at an angular interval α. The object is contained in space, so it is required to be repeated at an angular interval α as a second object. But the requirement of repeating all space at an angular interval α also requires that the second object be repeated again at an angular interval α to become a third object, etc. Thus, if an operation repeats space at an angular interval α, it is only consistent with a set of n (in this case, 4) symmetrically arranged objects separated by angular interval α. The operation is usually spoken of as a *symmetry operation*, since, acting on all space, it requires a symmetry of that space.

Note that the operation of translation is also a kind of symmetry operation.

Symmetry elements

The geometrical locus about which a group of repeating operations acts is called a *symmetry element*. Thus the line normal to the page about which operations A_α, A_α^2, $\cdots$ all act is a symmetry element; in this specific case it is called an axis of rotational symmetry, or simply a rotation axis. In Fig. 9, the plane across which the reflection occurs is a symmetry element called a reflection plane, or a mirror, etc.

Permissible angular intervals

In a foregoing section the relation between repetition and symmetry was discussed. A consequence of that discussion is that any angular repetition interval α is allowable provided that periodic repetition at this interval eventually superposes the repeated object on the original object. Suppose that n repetitions at angle α complete this cycle. It immediately follows that

$$n \cdot \alpha = 2\pi, \quad (1)$$

so that

$$\alpha = 2\pi/n. \quad (2)$$

Accordingly, the allowable angular-repetition interval is any aliquot part of 2π. Thus, to an angular-repetition interval α there correspond n repetitions per 2π. The symmetry element corresponding to this α is called an n-fold axis, since the axis is associated with an n-fold duplication of any motif. Evidently 1-fold, 2-fold, 3-fold, · · · axes are possible in angular repetition. The shorthand notations for these axes are simply the numerals 1, 2, 3, · · · , respectively.

Crystals and symmetry

Since crystals are orderly, periodic arrangements of atoms, it follows that the basic geometrical theory of crystals is fundamentally concerned with the operations of repetition and their combinations. The remainder of this book is largely concerned with a development and discussion of the symmetry properties of crystals. In the following chapters operations of repetitions are considered singly, and in combinations which prove to be useful in theoretical and practical crystallography.

Exercises

1. Set up a "right-handed" axial coordinate system XY in a plane. Locate points having coordinates 2, 1; 1, 3; and 5, 6. Construct a triangle by drawing lines between these points. Duplicate this exercise with a left-handed coordinate system and compare the triangles. Make a tracing of the triangle of the last drawing and try to superpose it on the triangle of the first drawing. Can you do this? Turn the tracing paper upside down and try to superpose it on the first drawing.

2. Repeat question 1, using points with coordinates 1, 1; 5, 1; and 3, 7. How do you explain the difference in the results obtained with the sets of coordinates given in questions 1 and 2?

3. Which patterns in the illustrations inside the covers have 2-fold axes? Which have 3-fold axes? Which have 4-fold axes? Which have 5-fold axes? Which have 6-fold axes? Which have 7-fold axes?

4. Which patterns in the illustrations inside the covers can be divided symmetrically by one or more mirror planes?

3 · The translation periodicity of crystals

In the Introduction it was pointed out that crystals are unique in being ordered matter, and in Chapter 2 a specific notion of the nature of order was given. A study of the kinds of order and their combination will form a large part of the discussion in this book, but there is one kind which is common to all crystals, that is, translational periodicity. Crystals have translational periodicity in three dimensions. Conversely, *a crystal may be defined as a region of matter within which the atoms are arranged in a three-dimensional translationally periodic pattern.* This translational periodicity has geometrical consequences which will receive initial attention in this chapter.

A digression is entered at this point to qualify the characteristic of translational periodicity in real crystals.

If the structure of a crystal is periodic when static, heat motion slightly disturbs the periodicity of the structure at any one instant. Since heat motion is extremely rapid, however, the structure is still periodic if it is considered over any appreciable interval of time. A crystal is thus statistically periodic when considered at any real temperature.

Instances are now recognized in which the entire pattern of a crystal is not periodic. In such instances the nonperiodic aspect of the structure is rendered so by extreme temperature motion of one or more kinds of atoms in the structure, or by a statistical situation which is the formal equivalent of it. For example, in crystals of the high-temperature form of AgI, the large iodine atoms form a periodic structure while the smaller silver atoms, under the influence of thermal energy, flow continuously through the interstitial channels between the iodine atoms. Statistically, over even a short period of time, this kind of pattern is triperiodic, and consequently it behaves geometrically in the same manner as a strictly periodic pattern. For this reason the designation "crystal" is extended to include even matter which is only statistically periodic in three dimensions.

Representation of translational periodicity by a lattice

The geometry consequent upon the translation periodicity of a pattern can be conveniently discussed if other features of the pattern are eliminated. Thus, Fig. 1*a* shows a section of a pattern which repeats at the translation interval, *t*. For purposes of studying the geometry of the repetition, rather than that of the motif which is repeated, the pattern can be represented by a row of points separated by interval *t*, Fig. 1*b*. Such a periodic sequence of points is called a *linear lattice* (or *row*). The points of a linear lattice may be regarded as generated by the repeated application of a translation, t, to some initial point. Any point may be taken as the initial point.

If a linear pattern having a repetition interval t_1 is itself periodically repeated by another translation t_2, as indicated in Fig. 2*a*, a plane pattern is generated. The repetitional aspects of the pattern can be abbreviated by a two-dimensional array of points called a *plane lattice* (or *net*), Fig. 2*b*.

FIG. 1*a*. Pattern produced by periodic repetition in one dimension and defined by translation, t.

FIG. 1*b*. One-dimensional lattice of pattern in Fig. 1*a*.

Finally, if a plane pattern having repetition intervals t_1 and t_2 is periodically repeated by a third noncoplanar translation t_3, a space pattern is generated, Fig. 3*a*. The geometrical characteristics of the pattern are conveniently represented by a three-dimensional collection of points known as a *space lattice*, Fig. 3*b*. When the term lattice is used without qualification, a space lattice is implied.

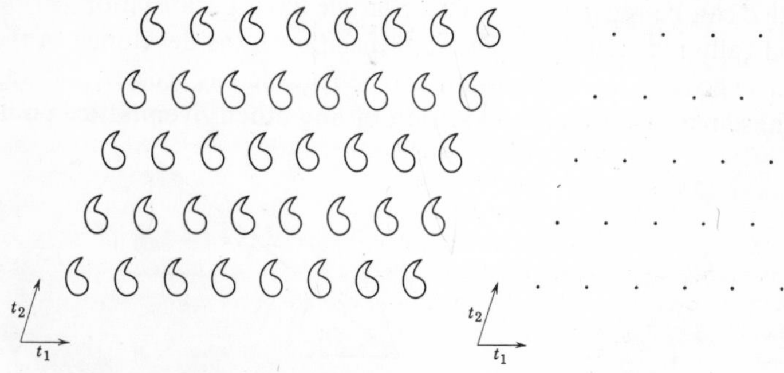

FIG. 2*a*. Pattern produced by periodic repetition in two dimension and defined by translations, t_1 and t_2.

FIG. 2*b*. Two-dimensional lattice of pattern in Fig. 2*a*.

A lattice is thus an epitome of the pattern of translational repetition. If any motif is imagined as placed so that a selected point falls on one of the points of the lattice, then the lattice implies that an identical, parallel motif unit appears in the neighborhood of each point, and specifically located so that each motif unit then has an identical point at a lattice point.

Except for the convenience of a particular problem, the lattice should not be thought of as having a definite origin in a crystal, any more than a periodic wave has a definite origin. Rather the lattice points of any row are separated from one another by phase differences of 2π, 4π, 6π, $\cdots$, $n(2\pi)$ of the cycle of repetition.

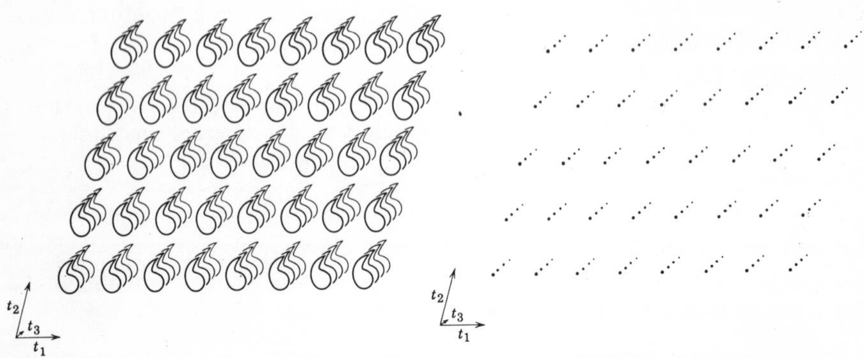

FIG. 3*a*. Pattern produced by periodic repetition in three dimensions and defined by translations t_1, t_2, and t_3.

FIG. 3*b*. Three-dimensional lattice of pattern in Fig. 3*a*.

Vector representation of a lattice

Any plane lattice can be regarded as a linear lattice having translation period t_1, Fig. 4*a*, periodically repeated by a second translation t_2, as developed in the previous section. The translations t_1 and t_2 can be regarded as vectors. If any lattice point is chosen as an origin, the location of any other given lattice point

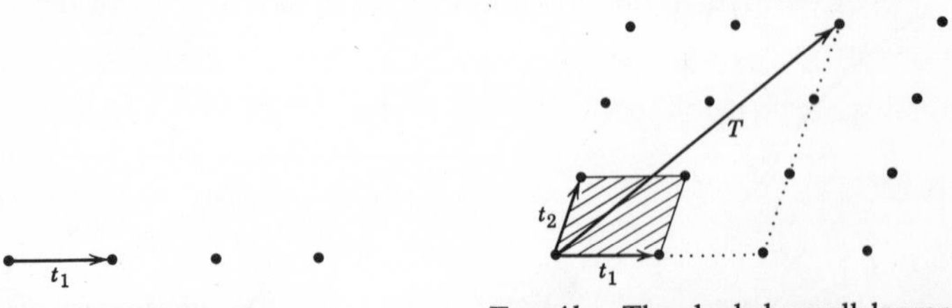

FIG. 4*a*.

FIG. 4*b*. The shaded parallelogram is a primitive cell.

can be defined with respect to this origin lattice point by a vector $\vec{T}$, Fig. 4*b*. Obviously $\vec{T}$ is a linear sum of vectors $\vec{t_1}$ and $\vec{t_2}$. For example, in Fig. 4*b*,

$$\vec{T} = 2\vec{t_1} + 3\vec{t_2}, \tag{1}$$

and, in general, for any lattice point

$$\vec{T} = u\vec{t_1} + v\vec{t_2}, \tag{2}$$

where u and v are integers. The more general relation for three dimensions is evidently

$$\vec{T} = u\vec{t_1} + v\vec{t_2} + w\vec{t_3}, \tag{3}$$

where u, v, and w are integers.

Let the symbol K stand for a collection. Then the complete set of vectors to all lattice points is

$$\begin{aligned} \mathbf{T} &= K\vec{T} \\ &= K\{u\vec{t_1} + v\vec{t_2} + w\vec{t_3}\} \qquad (u, v, w, \text{ integers}), \end{aligned} \tag{4}$$

Let $\cdot\vec{T}\cdot$ stand for the point at the end of vector $\vec{T}$. Then the point at the end of the vector (3) is $\cdot ut_1 + vt_2 + wt_3\cdot$. The collection of points constituting the space lattice Γ can then be represented as

$$\begin{aligned} \Gamma &= K\{\cdot\vec{T}\cdot\} \\ &= K\{\cdot u\vec{t_1} + v\vec{t_2} + w\vec{t_3}\cdot\} \qquad (u, v, w, \text{ integers}). \end{aligned} \tag{5}$$

Conjugate translations

If $\vec{t_1}$, $\vec{t_2}$, and $\vec{t_3}$ are chosen, the lattice is uniquely defined, according to (5). On the other hand, a given lattice does not uniquely fix a single set of translations t_1, t_2, and t_3. Fundamentally this is because a linear combination of t_1, t_2, and t_3 may be used to define another vector, say t_1'. Consider this feature in two dimension:

In Fig. 4*b* the vector $\vec{T}$ is specifically

(1) $$\vec{T} = 2\vec{t_1} + 3\vec{t_2}.$$

This relation implies that the plane lattice was regarded as a linear lattice having period t_1, repeated periodically at an interval t_2. But, since the original row having interval t_1 is infinite, the plane lattice can also be thought of as a periodic row of interval t_1, repeated periodically by a different translation t_2', Fig. 5. But $\vec{t_2}'$ can be defined as a linear combination of $\vec{t_1}$ and $\vec{t_2}$, specifically

$$\vec{t_2}' = -\vec{t_1} + \vec{t_2}. \tag{6}$$

This can be solved for the old t_2,

$$\vec{t_2} = \vec{t_1} + \vec{t_2}'. \tag{7}$$

If this value is substituted into (1), there results

$$\vec{T} = 2\vec{t_1} + 3\vec{t_2}$$

$$= 2\vec{t_1} + 3(\vec{t_1} + \vec{t_2}')$$

$$= 5\vec{t_1} + 3\vec{t_2}'. \tag{8}$$

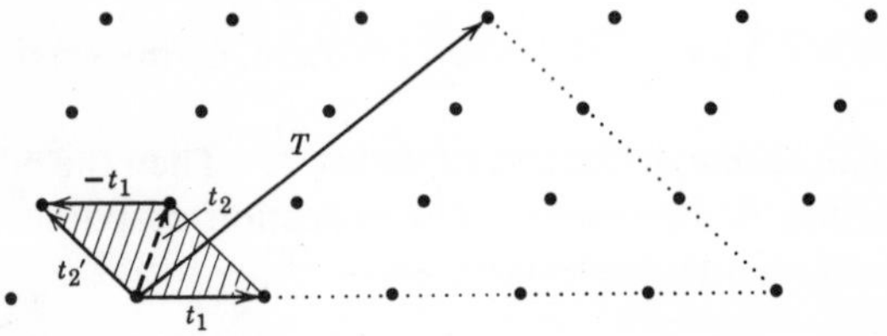

FIG. 5. The shaded parallelogram is a primitive cell.

Any of the infinite number of translations, t_2, which periodically repeats the row having interval t_1, can be chosen as a second translation. Furthermore, *any* of the infinite number of row directions of the lattice could have been used as the first row, and *any* translation which periodically repeats this row could have been chosen as second translation. Two such "paired" translations are called *conjugate translations.* Together they determine a parallelogram known as a *primitive cell.* A primitive cell is shaded in Fig. 4 and Fig. 5.

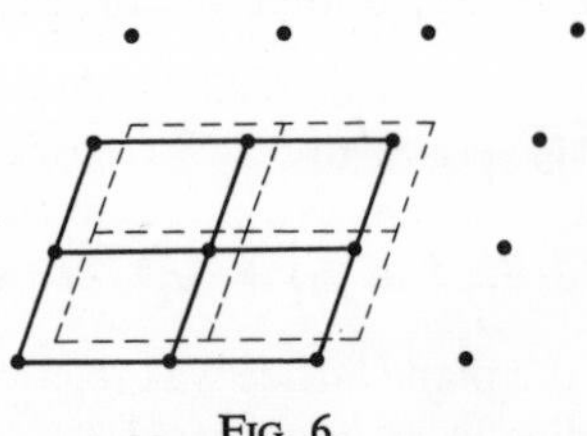

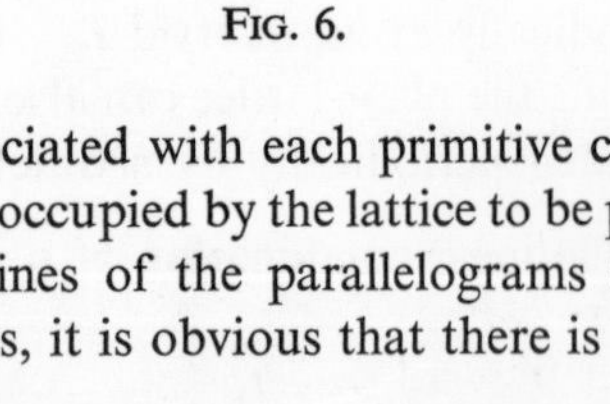

FIG. 6.

One lattice point is associated with each primitive cell. This can readily be seen by imagining the area occupied by the lattice to be partitioned into primitive cells, Fig. 6. If the outlines of the parallelograms are shifted slightly with respect to the lattice points, it is obvious that there is one lattice point in each cell.

Every primitive cell of a lattice has the same area. This is because the area is the product of the period of the first row, namely t_1, by the spacing between rows. The spacing is independent of the direction of t_2.

Nonprimitive cells

The cell outlined by two arbitrarily chosen vectors between lattice points is not necessarily a primitive cell, as is illustrated by the examples in Figs. 7*a* and 7*b*. The fundamental reason for this is that if the first row is taken as that row which has translation interval t_1, a second vector, $\vec{t_2}$, can be chosen so that it relates the original row to every second parallel row of the lattice, Fig. 7*a*, or to

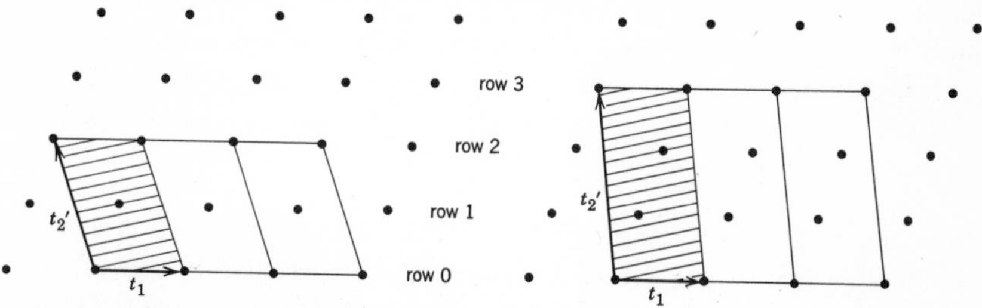

FIG. 7*a*. Translations defining a double cell.

FIG. 7*b*. Translations defining a triple cell.

every third row of the lattice, Fig. 7*b*, etc. These cells contain a total of several lattice points per cell; the count consists one lattice point for the lattice point at the corners of the cell, plus the additional lattice points in its interior. Such cells are called *multiple cells*. The translations in Fig. 7*a* outline a *double cell*; those of Fig. 7*b* outline a *triple cell*; etc.

It might be supposed that multiple cells are useless, and should be avoided. There are occasions, however, when they are very useful, especially to gain the advantages of orthogonality. This will be developed in Chapter 8. It is customary to select an appropriate cell, either primitive or multiple according to the requirements of the case, and call this the *unit cell* of the crystal.

The notions of this and the foregoing section can obviously be applied to three-dimensional lattices by the addition of one more translation.

Notations for the rational features of a crystal

Rational features. Those geometrical features of a crystal which are determined by lattice points are called *rational*. Thus, a lattice point (in respect to another lattice point) is a rational point; a row of lattice points is a rational line; and a plane of lattice points is a rational plane. All other features are *irrational*. It is important to have appropriate notations for referring to these rational features. These notations are developed in the following sections:

Notation for rational lines. If an origin point is chosen, then any other lattice point can be reached by a linear combination of the conjugate vectors:

$$\vec{T} = u\vec{t_1} + v\vec{t_2} + w\vec{t_3}. \tag{3}$$

Each such line $\vec{T}$ is determined by the two lattice points at the ends of the vector, and so is rational. This vector equation has the same form for all rational lines, and the only distinctive feature about a particular line is the set of coefficients *uvw*. Thus the three integers *uvw* are taken as the *indices* of the line defined by vector equation (3). To indicate that the sequence of three integers represents a line, they are placed between square brackets, thus: [*uvw*]. Particular examples are [124], [100], and [1$\bar{1}$1]. The bar over the integer in the last example indicates that it is negative; i.e., [1$\bar{1}$1] is a short, neat notation for [1, —1, 1].

Note that [222] defines the same line as [111]. For this reason it is customary to designate a line by the use of the three smallest permissible indices; i.e., if the three indices should contain a common factor, it is removed and the resulting set of integers without a common factor is given.

Notation for points. Since a vector from the origin lattice point defines the point at its end, the three integers that define the vector also define the point. It is currently customary to write these three numbers without parentheses or brackets. The reason for this is that one of the major uses of the notation for a point is to specify a point within a unit cell. Points within the cell necessarily have fractional coordinates, and a sequence of three fractions is not readily confused with the notations for a direction or a plane, which are sequences of three integers. When, however, one wishes to specify a rational point, i.e., a lattice point, then some definite notation is necessary. There existed a limited practice of enclosing them in a pair of double square brackets, to indicate that this set of three numbers refers to a point, thus : [[*uvw*]]. A preferable notation, used in this book, is to place them between dots, thus ·*uvw*·. This notation has advantages when symmetrical sets are to be designated.

Notation for rational planes. To derive a reasonable notation for rational planes, the well-known intercept form of the equation of a plane can be used.

Consider the analog of a plane in three dimensions, namely a line in two dimensions, Fig. 8*a*. If the line intercepts the coordinate axes *X* and *Y* at *A* units and *B* units respectively from the origin, then the equation of that line can be written

$$\frac{x}{A} + \frac{y}{B} = 1. \tag{9}$$

(If the student is unfamiliar with this he can readily verify that, when $y = 0$,

$x = A$; and when $x = 0$, $y = B$.) Similarly the equation of a plane in three dimensions, in terms of its intercepts A, B, and C, Fig. 8*b*, is

$$\frac{x}{A} + \frac{y}{B} + \frac{z}{C} = 1. \tag{10}$$

The numbers A, B, and C could be accepted as characteristics of the plane, and indeed this was done in the early days of crystallography. But there are advantages to manipulating (10) into another form.

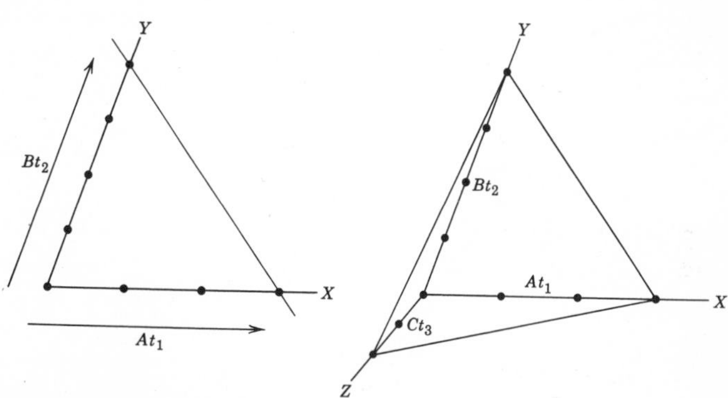

FIG. 8*a*. FIG. 8*b*.

A disadvantage of (10) is that the coefficients of x, y, and z are fractions. To convert them into integers, both sides can be multiplied by ABC, giving

$$\frac{ABC}{A}x + \frac{ABC}{B}y + \frac{ABC}{C}z = ABC \tag{11}$$

or

$$BCx + ACy + ABz = ABC. \tag{12}$$

The coefficients of (12) are now products of integers. For simplicity replace them by the integers*

$$\left.\begin{aligned} h &= BC, \\ k &= AC, \\ l &= AB, \end{aligned}\right\} \tag{13}$$

so that (12) has the simpler form

$$hx + ky + lz = ABC. \tag{14}$$

This is the equation of the *rational intercept plane*, i.e., of the particular plane whose intercepts are A, B, and C translations on the X, Y, and Z axes, respectively.*

* In order to display the general idea without unnecessary complication, it is assumed in this discussion that no pairs of the integers A, B, and C contain common factors. If they do, the situation is slightly more complicated; this complication is discussed in the next footnote. Cases in which A, B, or C are zero or infinity are also excluded.

The intercept plane does not, in itself, have very useful properties, nor is it easy to find from its equation. To transform (14) into something more useful, it is desirable at this point to introduce two auxiliary theorems, or *lemmae*:

Lemma 1. *There are ABC equally spaced, identical planes, from the origin to the rational intercept plane* (*provided that a common factor does not occur in any of the pairs AB, AC, or BC*).

To prove this, first consider the somewhat simplified problem in two dimensions, Figs. 8*a* and 9. There are A translation vectors of length t_1 along

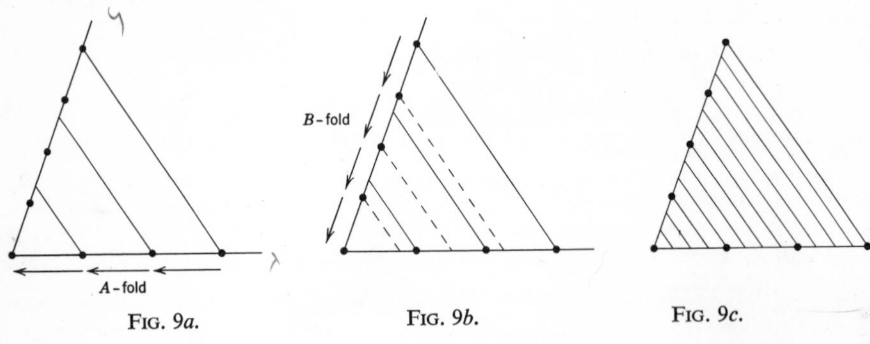

FIG. 9*a*. FIG. 9*b*. FIG. 9*c*.

the X axis from the origin to the intercept line. These A translations repeat the intercept line A times from the intercept plane to the origin, Fig. 9*a*. There are B translation vectors of length t_2 along the Y axis from the origin to the intercept line. These B translations repeat the intercept line B times from the intercept line to the origin, Fig. 9*b*. It similarly repeats B times each of the other A lines of Fig. 9*a*. (The truth of this last statement is not as obvious as the previous one. It will be appreciated if a careful sketch is made of Figs. 8*a*, 9*a*, and 9*b*, utilizing the B of the t_2 translations in *both* forward and reverse directions to operate on the other A lines of Fig. 9*a*.) Thus there are AB lines from the origin to the intercept line, Fig. 9*c*. If the reasoning is extended to three dimensions it then becomes evident that there are ABC planes from the origin to the intercept plane.* All these planes are identical since they are repetitions by translation of the plane through the origin point.

* (Do not read this footnote until after finishing this chapter.)

This is valid only so long as A, B, and C are each prime to one another. If any two of these, say AB, contain a common factor q, then the first line in the XY plane to have rational intercepts has intercepts A/q and B/q. There are therefore $(A/q)(B/q)$ lines from the origin to this rational-intercept line; there are q times as many lines from the origin to the line having intercepts A and B on X and Y, that is $(A/q)(B/q)q = AB/q$ lines. More generally, if

A and B contain the highest common factor q,
B and C ,, ,, ,, ,, ,, r,
C and A ,, ,, ,, ,, ,, s,

Lemma 2. The equation $ax + by + cz = m$ represents a plane m times as far from the origin as $ax + by + cz = 1$.

To see this, consider

$$ax + by + cz = m, \tag{15}$$

$$ax + by + cz = 1, \tag{16}$$

and let x, y, and z be zero in pairs in both equations. It is then plain that (15) is m times as far from the origin as (16).

Returning now to Lemma 1 and the equation (14), it is evident that (14) describes the ABCth plane from the origin. According to Lemma 2, the description of the first plane is

$$hx + ky + lz = 1. \tag{17}$$

This is the equation of the plane nearest to the origin. While (17) is specifically the equation of a particular plane, it is equivalent by translation to a whole stack of parallel, identical, equally spaced planes. The specific character of (17) for a particular plane is embodied in the coefficients h, k, and l. This set of three integers is called the *indices of the plane*. To indicate that a sequence of three integers represents a plane, they are placed in parentheses, thus: (hkl).

There is a simple interpretation of (hkl). To see this, recast (17) in intercept form, thus:

$$\frac{x}{1/h} + \frac{y}{1/k} + \frac{z}{1/l} = 1. \tag{18}$$

This is the intercept form of an equation of a plane whose intercepts are $1/h$, $1/k$, and $1/l$. *This signifies that the planes of the stack (hkl) divide the t_1 translation into h parts, the t_2 translation into k parts, and the t_3 translation into l parts.*

---

then there are ABC/qrs planes from the origin to the rational intercept plane. The more general version of Lemma 1 is then:

Lemma 1a. There are ABC/qrs equally spaced, identical planes from the origin to the rational intercept plane, where q is the HCF of A and B, r the HCF of B and C, and s the HCF of C and A.

Under these circumstances the sequence of equations from (11) to (14) becomes:

$$\frac{ABC/qrs}{A}x + \frac{ABC/qrs}{B}y + \frac{ABC/qrs}{C}z = \frac{ABC}{qrs}, \tag{11a}$$

$$\frac{BC}{qrs}x + \frac{AC}{qrs}y + \frac{AB}{qrs}z = \frac{ABC}{qrs}. \tag{12a}$$

Let

$$\left.\begin{aligned} h &= BC/qrs, \\ k &= AC/qrs, \\ l &= AB/qrs, \end{aligned}\right\} \tag{13a}$$

Then

$$hx + ky + lz = ABC/qrs. \tag{14a}$$

This is the equation of the plane having intercepts A, B, and C on X, Y, and Z. Since there are ABC/qrs planes from the origin to this plane, the equation of the first plane is

$$hx + ky + lz = 1. \tag{17a}$$

This theory has been developed for planes within a periodic pattern as repeated by a lattice. The notations are also applicable to, and used for, the designations of the surface planes of crystals, which are also "rational." This subject is further developed in Chapter 10.

Exercises

1. Using a piece of ordinary graph paper, locate the points having integral coordinates, thus defining a plane lattice. In this system of points draw lines between points which outline (*a*) a primitive cell, (*b*) a double cell, (*c*) a triple cell.

2. Using the plane lattice defined as in question 1, draw a square primitive cell. Maintaining a particular line for a base, and maintaining the same altitude, choose another side so that the cell so determined has the shape of a rhombus. Choose another side so that the cell so determined has the shape of a parallelogram. Are these primitive or multiple cells?

3. Using the plane lattice defined as in question 1, draw the directions [11], [13], [31], [10].

4. Using the plane lattice defined as in question 1, draw a line whose intercepts are $A = 2$, $B = 3$. Repeat this line by using the $+\vec{t}_1$, $-\vec{t}_1$, $+\vec{t}_2$, and $-\vec{t}_2$ translations successively several times (in other words, shift the lines in directions and amounts defined by these vectors, which are the edges of the square primitive cell of the plane lattice). When this has been done, a small area should be covered by a pattern of uniformly spaced lines. How many such lines are there from a cell origin to the line which makes intercepts $A = 2$ and $B = 3$ away from it? Compare the result with Lemma 1.

5. Carry out question 4 for $A = 3$, $B = 4$ and compare the result with Lemma 1.

6. Carry out question 4 for $A = 2$, $B = 4$, and compare the result with Lemma 1*a*.

7. Make a set of translation-equivalent dots representing a plane lattice. Pick any two noncollinear but nonconjugate translations. Draw the cell based upon these, and determine its multiplicity.

4 · The basic rotational symmetries of crystals

Possible rotational repetitions

Proper rotations. The discussion in the last part of Chapter 2 showed that periodic angular repetitions can be described by means of symmetry elements which are known as rotation axes. In the pure angular repetition, a right-handed object (say) is the original object, and all repeated objects are also right-handed. The rotational operation which repeats a congruent object from another object is termed a *proper rotation*, and the corresponding symmetry element is a *proper rotation axis*. The repetition of a point by some of the n-fold proper rotation axes is illustrated in Fig. 1.

Improper rotations. There exists, however, another kind of rotational repetition, namely one in which the enantiomorphous object (and indeed all enantiomorphous space) is repeated. The repetition operation is thus a combination of a rotation and a reversal of sense. From an initial right-handed object (for example) it repeats a left, a right, a left, · · · , so that neighboring objects are enantiomorphous, while alternate objects are congruent. The rotation concerned with this kind of repetition is called an *improper rotation* (in contrast to the pure, or proper, rotation), and the corresponding symmetry element is an *improper rotation axis*.

It was shown in Chapter 2 that three-dimensional enantiomorphous objects can be derived from one another either by a reflection or by an inversion. Accordingly, the alternating rotational repetition can be defined either in terms of a combination of a rotation and reflection or in terms of a combination of a rotation and an inversion. Symmetry axes corresponding to these possibilities are called *rotoreflection axes* and *rotoinversion axes* respectively. Rotoreflection axes are assigned the shorthand labels $\tilde{1}, \tilde{2}, \tilde{3}, \cdots$, i.e., $\tilde{n}$, while rotoinversion axes are assigned the labels $\bar{1}, \bar{2}, \bar{3}, \cdots$, i.e., $\bar{n}$. Figures 2 and 3 illustrate the way rotoreflection and rotoinversion axes repeat a point.

Since a reflection and an inversion are alternate ways of transforming an object into its enantiomorphous equivalent, it follows that the set of patterns of repetition of a point by rotoreflection (a few of which are shown in Fig. 2) is the same as the set of patterns of repetition of a point by rotoinversion (a few of which are shown in Fig. 3), although the arrangement and labeling of n are not necessarily the same. The correspondence between rotoreflection and rotoinversion axes is listed in Table 3 and will be discussed later.

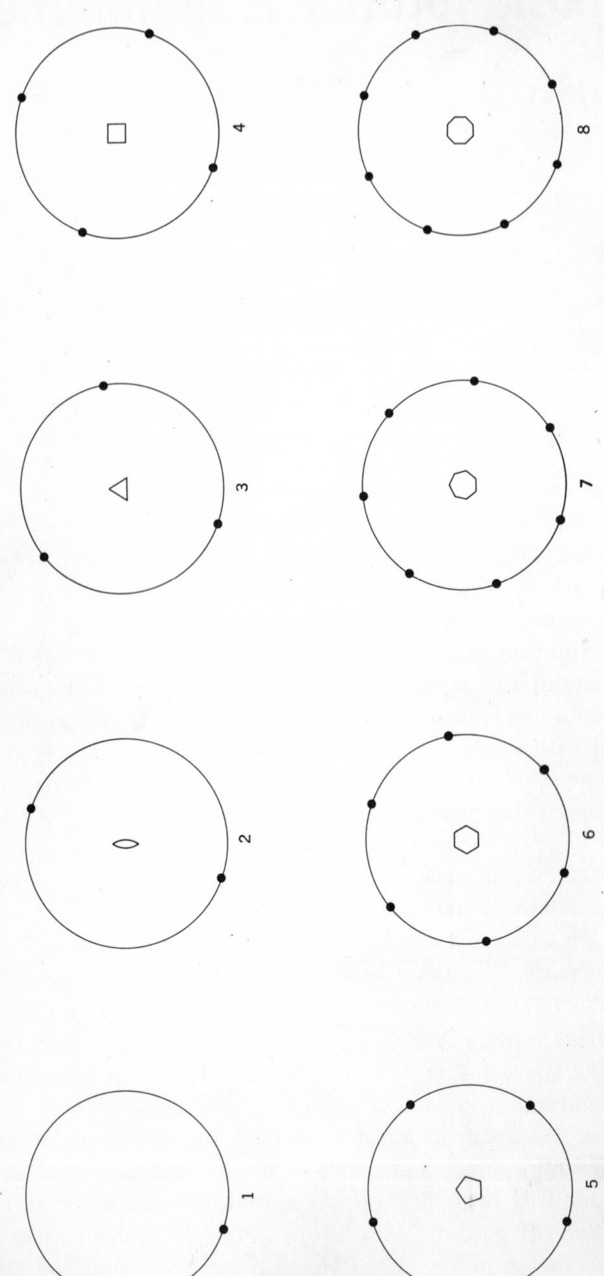

FIG. 1. Repetition produced by the operations of the proper rotation axes, *n*.

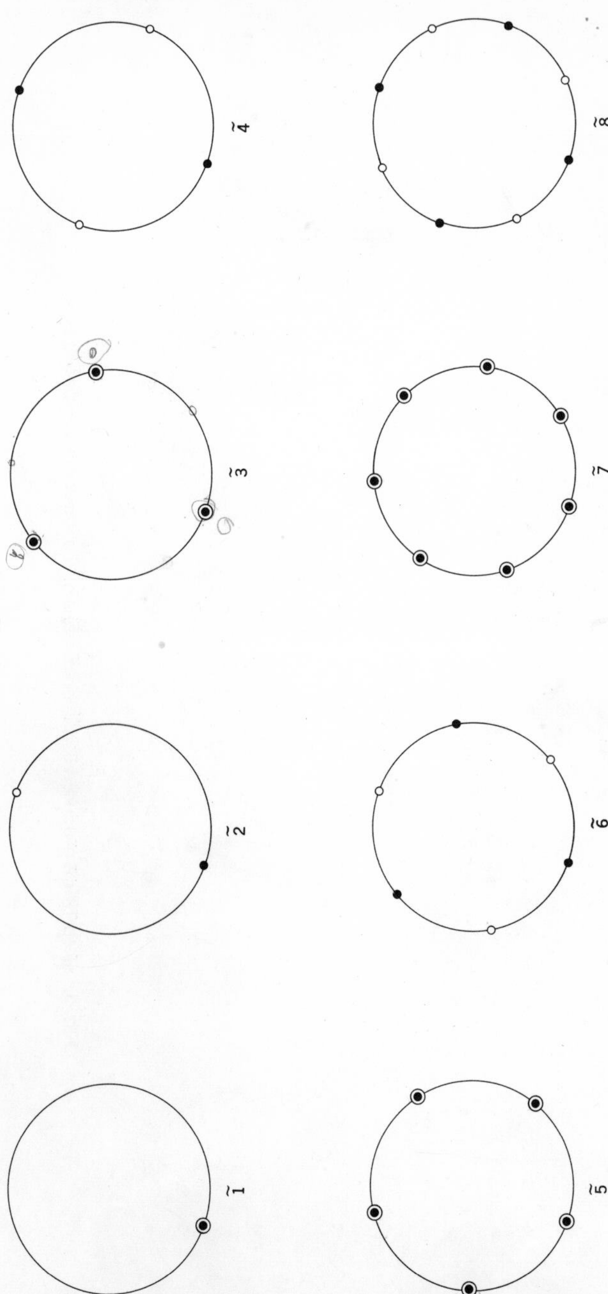

FIG. 2. Repetition produced by the operations of the improper rotation axes, $\tilde{n}$. Solid circles represent points above the plane of the paper: small open circles represent points below the plane of the paper.

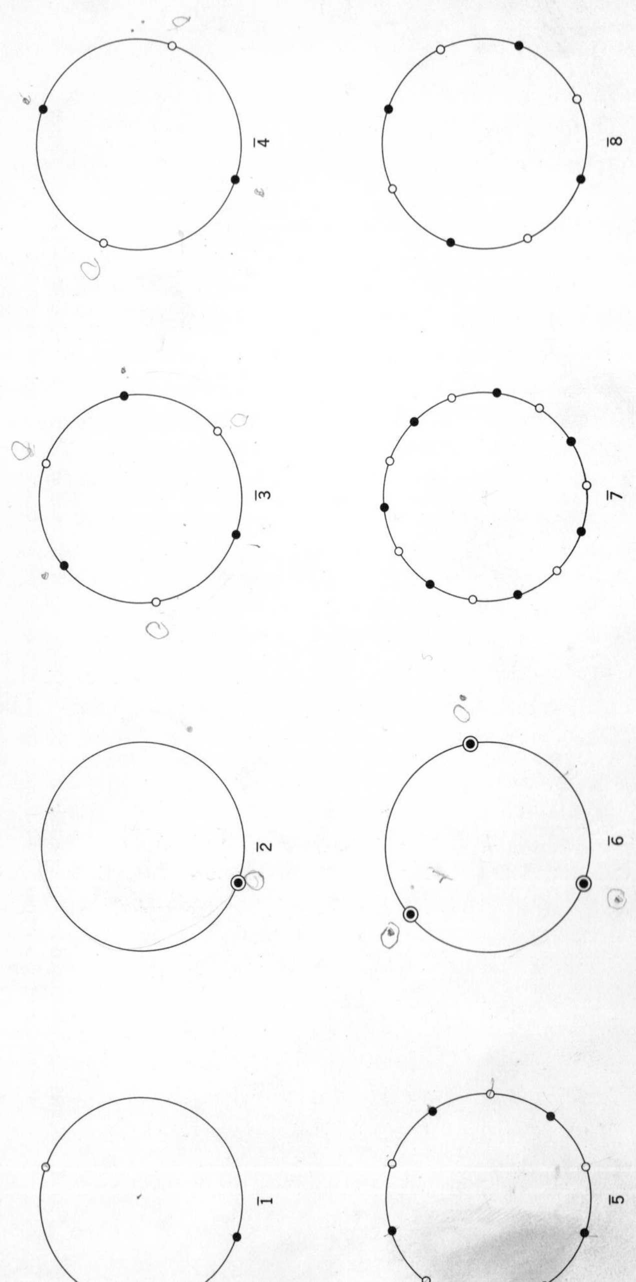

FIG. 3. Repetition produced by the operations of the improper rotation axes, $\bar{n}$.

Decomposition of improper rotation axes into other symmetry elements

Some improper rotations are unique whereas others can be decomposed into separate symmetry elements. The improper axes behave differently in this respect according as n is even or odd and according as $n/2$ is even or odd. This behavior is concerned with the placing of an enantiomorphous or a congruent point at angular separations of 2π and π from the original point.

First note that, when n is even, the cycle of repetitions is completed after the total angle of 2π has accumulated. But when n is odd, a total angle of 4π is required to complete the cycle. This can be readily appreciated for $\tilde{n}$, Fig. 2. For $\tilde{3}$, for example, 3 rotations of $2\pi/3$ bring the repeated point at the angular position of the initial point, but the repeated point is an enantiomorphous one. A second sequence of 2π is required to place a congruent point at the initial point.

Further discussion can be codified in three categories: (These are illustrated in Fig. 4. In these diagrams it is convenient to think of the solid circles as being above the plane of the paper and the open circles an equal distance below.)

***n* odd, i.e., $n = 4N \pm 1$** (where N is an integer). As pointed out above, when n is odd a sequence of 2π brings a point repeated by $\tilde{n}$ (upper left of Fig. 4) in reflecting position below the initial point. This reflection relation holds for all points. Thus $\tilde{n}$ behaves as if the pure rotation axis n had caused the angular repetition, and then a perpendicular mirror, m, had reflected all points. An n-fold axis and a perpendicular mirror is written $\frac{n}{m}$. Thus $\tilde{n} = \frac{n}{m}$.

The axis $\bar{n}$ can be compared with $\tilde{n}$ as follows: For every open circle in $\tilde{n}$ (Fig. 4, upper left), an open circle occurs on the opposite side of the axis (Fig. 4, lower left). Thus the general relation of points is shown in the left column of Fig. 4. Thus, while the solid and open circles are related by m in the upper part of Fig. 4, they are related by an inversion i in the lower part. Thus $\bar{n} = n \cdot i$.

***n* even, $n/2$ odd, i.e., $N = 4N + 2$.** In this case, since n is even, the cycle is complete after a rotation of 2π. The enantiomorphous points of $\tilde{n}$ are separated by an interval α. However, the congruent points are separated by an interval 2α so that they are related by a pure rotation period of $n/2$. Furthermore, since n is even, there is a point at π, but since $n/2$ is odd this point is enantiomorphous with the initial point. Thus every point has an opposite enantiomorphous point, i.e., a point related by an inversion. Therefore $\tilde{n} = \frac{n}{2} \cdot i$; i.e., the rotoinversion axis is equal to a pure rotation of half the order, combined with an inversion.

From the discussion of the last section it follows that $\tilde{n}$ has a mirror where $\bar{n}$ has an inversion, and vice versa. Therefore $\bar{n} = \dfrac{(n/2)}{m}$.

***n* even, *n*/2 even, i.e., *n* = 4*N*.** When $n = 4N$, a congruent point is repeated at an interval of π from the original point, as shown in the right column of Fig. 4.

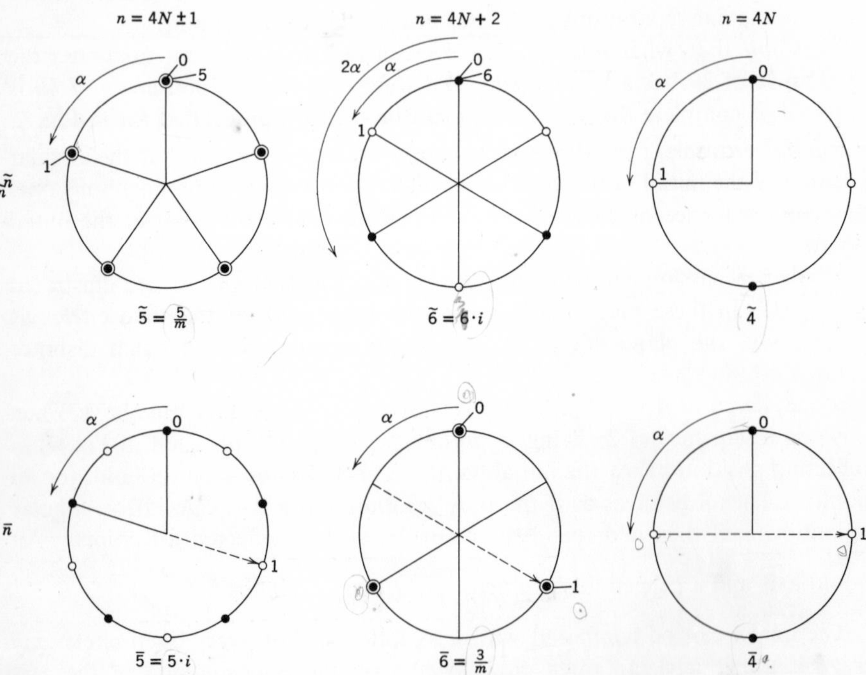

FIG. 4. Decomposition of improper rotation symmetries, and the relation between $\tilde{n}$ and $\bar{n}$ symmetries.

If this is not geometrically obvious, it can be proved as follows:

$$\alpha = \frac{2\pi}{n} = \frac{2\pi}{4N}. \tag{1}$$

$$\therefore \quad 2N\alpha = \pi.$$

That is, the angular repetition value of π is attained after $2N$ operations of interval α. Since $2N$ is an even number, the object repeated at π is congruent. Since neither the object at π nor that at 2π is enantiomorphous, the symmetry of neither $\tilde{n}$ nor $\bar{n}$ can be decomposed into elements involving i or m. Furthermore, for these values of n, $\tilde{n}$ and $\bar{n}$ are identical; i.e., the rotoreflection and rotoinversion axes have the same numerical label. This is because in each case the repeated sequence of points is an alternation of the same number of right- and left-handed points strung between the two points shown in the two cases of the right column of Fig. 4.

The decompositions of rotoreflection and rotoinversion axes are listed in Tables 1 and 2. The correspondence between rotoreflection and rotoinversion axes is shown in Table 3.

Table 1. The rotoreflection axes

	$n = 4N + 1$	$n = 4N + 2$	$n = 4N + 3$	$n = 4N$
Characteristics of n	i.e., n odd	i.e., $\begin{Bmatrix} n \text{ even} \\ \frac{n}{2} \text{ odd} \end{Bmatrix}$	i.e., n odd	i.e., $\begin{Bmatrix} n \text{ even} \\ \frac{n}{2} \text{ even} \end{Bmatrix}$
Decomposition of rotoreflection axes into other symmetry elements	$\tilde{1} = \frac{1}{m}$	$\tilde{2} = 1 \cdot \mathrm{i}$	$\tilde{3} = \frac{3}{m}$	$\tilde{4}$
	$\tilde{5} = \frac{5}{m}$	$\tilde{6} = 3 \cdot \mathrm{i}$	$\tilde{7} = \frac{7}{m}$	$\tilde{8}$
	$\tilde{9} = \frac{9}{m}$	$\widetilde{10} = 5 \cdot \mathrm{i}$	$\widetilde{11} = \frac{11}{m}$	$\widetilde{12}$
	$\widetilde{13} = \frac{13}{m}$	$\widetilde{14} = 7 \cdot \mathrm{i}$	$\widetilde{15} = \frac{15}{m}$	$\widetilde{16}$

Table 2. The rotoinversion axes

	$n = 4N + 1$	$n = 4N + 2$	$n = 4N + 3$	$n = 4N$
Characteristics of n	i.e., n odd	i.e., $\begin{Bmatrix} n \text{ even} \\ \frac{n}{2} \text{ odd} \end{Bmatrix}$	i.e., n odd	i.e., $\begin{Bmatrix} n \text{ even} \\ \frac{n}{2} \text{ even} \end{Bmatrix}$
Decomposition of rotoinversion axes into other symmetry elements	$\bar{1} = 1 \cdot i$	$\bar{2} = \frac{1}{m}$	$\bar{3} = 3 \cdot i$	$\bar{4}$
	$\bar{5} = 5 \cdot i$	$\bar{6} = \frac{3}{m}$	$\bar{7} = 7 \cdot i$	$\bar{8}$
	$\bar{9} = 9 \cdot i$	$\overline{10} = \frac{5}{m}$	$\overline{11} = 11 \cdot i$	$\overline{12}$
	$\overline{13} = 13 \cdot i$	$\overline{14} = \frac{7}{m}$	$\overline{15} = 15 \cdot i$	$\overline{16}$

Table 3. Correspondence between rotoreflection and rotoinversion axes

$n = 4N + 1$	$n = 4N + 2$	$n = 4N + 3$	$n = 4N$
i.e., n odd	i.e., $\begin{Bmatrix} n \text{ even} \\ \frac{n}{2} \text{ odd} \end{Bmatrix}$	i.e., n odd	i.e., $\begin{Bmatrix} n \text{ even} \\ \frac{n}{2} \text{ even} \end{Bmatrix}$
$\bar{1} = 1 \cdot i = \tilde{2}$	$\bar{2} = \frac{1}{m} = \tilde{1}$	$\bar{3} = 3 \cdot i = \tilde{6}$	$\bar{4} = \tilde{4}$
$\bar{5} = 5 \cdot i = \widetilde{10}$	$\bar{6} = \frac{3}{m} = \tilde{3}$	$\bar{7} = 7 \cdot i = \widetilde{14}$	$\bar{8} = \tilde{8}$
$\bar{9} = 9 \cdot i = \widetilde{18}$	$\overline{10} = \frac{5}{m} = \tilde{5}$	$\overline{11} = 11 \cdot i = \widetilde{22}$	$\overline{12} = \widetilde{12}$
$\overline{13} = 13 \cdot i = \widetilde{26}$	$\overline{14} = \frac{7}{m} = \tilde{7}$	$\overline{15} = 15 \cdot i = \widetilde{30}$	$\overline{16} = \widetilde{16}$

Operations of the first and second sorts. It is often convenient to refer to the general category of repetitional operations which cause a repetition of congruent objects only. Translations and pure rotations are operations of this kind. Such operations are called *operations of the first sort*. On the other hand the operations of rotoreflection, rotoinversion, reflections, and inversions fall into another category, namely operations which repeat an enantiomorphous object from an original object. These operations are called *operations of the second sort*.

In Chapter 12 two new composite operations, the screw and the glide-reflections, will be discovered. These belong to the operations of the first and second sort respectively.

The limitations of α set by translation periodicity

In the foregoing parts of this chapter the possible kinds of rotational symmetries have been discussed without any reference to their occurrence in crystals. When the rotational symmetry does occur in crystals, then severe restrictions on the value of α are imposed by the simultaneous occurrence of repetition by rotation and translation.

To understand this restriction, consider the interplay of a 4-fold axis and a translation, Fig. 5*a*. The 4-fold axis A requires the 4-fold repetition about itself of the translation. The translated axis A' also requires a set of translations at 90° to one another. Each of these translations, in turn, requires the repetition of a 4-fold axis at a distance t from another 4-fold axis. Now consider the two axes B and B'. These are derived by translation from the same axis A. Therefore B and B' are translation-equivalent, so that BB' is a translation. In this example BB' is exactly the same translation as the original $t = AA'$. If the same reasoning is applied to the interplay of a 3-fold axis and

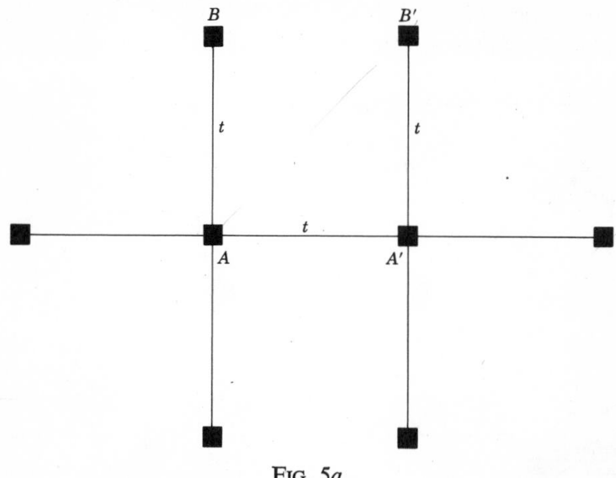

FIG. 5*a*.

a translation, Fig. 5*b*, one finds that $BB' = 2AA' = 2t$. In these two examples the interplay of a rotation and a translation produces new translations which are consistent with the original translation.

But this is not true for all rotation angles, α. For example, it is not true for

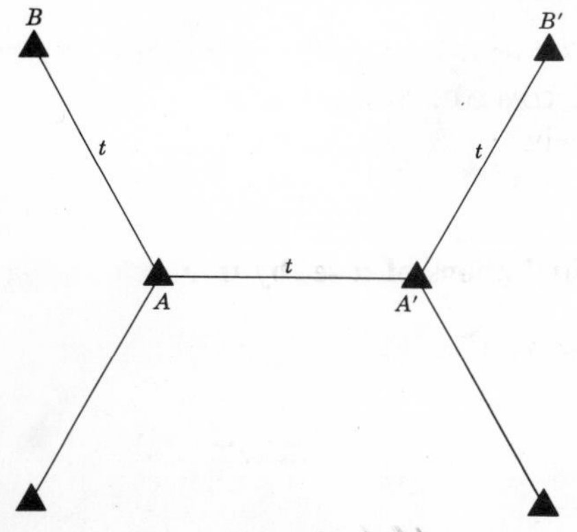

FIG. 5*b*.

a 5-fold axis, Fig. 5*c*. The 5-fold axis at A is required by translation t to be repeated at A'. Furthermore, the rotational symmetry of A requires the translation $AA' = t$ to be repeated at angular interval $\alpha = 2\pi/5 = 72°$ at AB, while the rotational symmetry of A' requires the translation $AA' = t$ to be repeated at $\alpha = 72°$ at $A'B'$. Since BA, AA', and $A'B'$ are all translations, BB'

is a translation, and it has the same direction as the original translation AA'. Yet the lengths of BB' and AA' are irrational with respect to one another. Thus BB' is a new translation t' in the same direction as t but inconsistent with it. This can also be expressed by stating that BB' violates the initial hypothesis that t is the shortest translation in that direction.

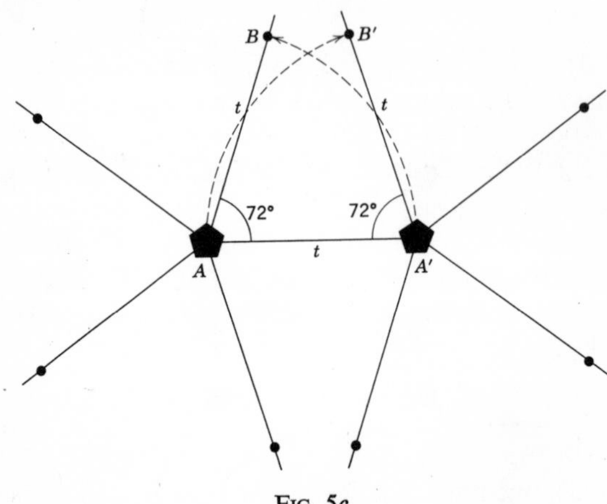

FIG. 5*c*.

In general, the only acceptable values of α are those that cause BB' in Fig. 6 to be an integral multiple of the original translation, t, in order to be consistent with it. Thus the translation involves the condition that

$$b = mt, \quad \text{where } m \text{ is an integer.} \tag{2}$$

But b is a simple function of α and t, Fig. 6:

$$b = t - 2t \cos \alpha. \tag{3}$$

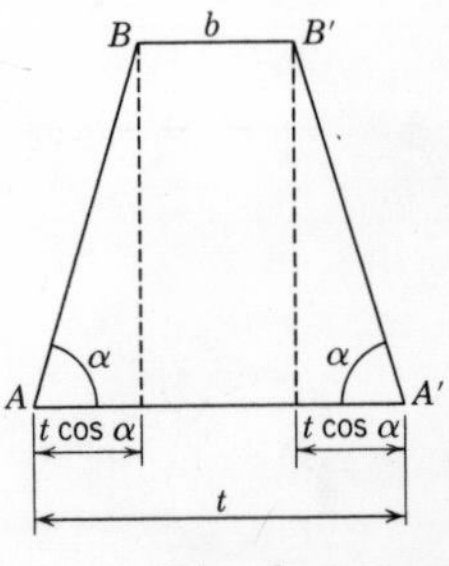

FIG. 6.

This can be compared with (2), giving

$$mt = t - 2t \cos \alpha,$$

so that

$$m = 1 - 2 \cos \alpha.$$

Consequently

$$2 \cos \alpha = 1 - m. \tag{4}$$

Since m is an integer, from (2), $1 - m$ is also an integer, say M, so that (4) can be simplified to

$$2 \cos \alpha = M \tag{5}$$

or

$$\cos \alpha = M/2. \tag{6}$$

Thus $\cos \alpha$ is restricted by translations to half-integral values. Only a few half-integers are values which the trigonometric function can have. The permitted values, and the corresponding values of α, n, and b, are listed in Table 4. The permissible values of b are illustrated in Fig. 7.

Table 4. Solutions of $M = 2 \cos \alpha$ for permissible periods of crystallographic axes

M	$\cos \alpha$	α	$n = \dfrac{2\pi}{\alpha}$	$b = t - 2t \cos \alpha$
-3	$-1\frac{1}{2}$	—	—	—
-2	-1	π	2	$3t$
-1	$-\frac{1}{2}$	$\frac{2\pi}{3}$	3	$2t$
0	0	$\frac{\pi}{2}$	4	t
1	$\frac{1}{2}$	$\frac{\pi}{3}$	6	0
2	1	0	$\infty \equiv 1$	$-t$
3	$1\frac{1}{2}$	—	—	—

Because of translation repetition, crystals can only have 1-*fold*, 2-*fold*, 3-*fold*, 4-*fold*, *and* 6-*fold axes* (these include 1, 2, 3, 4, 6, and also $\bar{1}$, $\bar{2}$, $\bar{3}$, $\bar{4}$, and $\bar{6}$ axes only). Another statement of this is that lattice nets can be consistent with symmetries 1, 2, 3, 4, 6, $\bar{1}$, $\bar{2}$, $\bar{3}$, $\bar{4}$, and $\bar{6}$ (or $\tilde{1}$, $\tilde{2}$, $\tilde{3}$, $\tilde{4}$, and $\tilde{6}$) only.

The symmetry axis discussed here is perpendicular to the lattice net, and it may require the net to assume a specialized shape, as shown in Fig. 8. The value $n = 1$ requires nothing special of the net. The value $n = 2$ requires each lattice point of the net to be symmetrical with respect to a 2-fold axis. Since all nets inherently have this property, nothing further is required of it. But $n = 4$ requires the net to be square, while $n = 3$ and $n = 6$ require the net to be as shown in Fig. 8, in which the points are on the vertices of nested equilateral triangles.

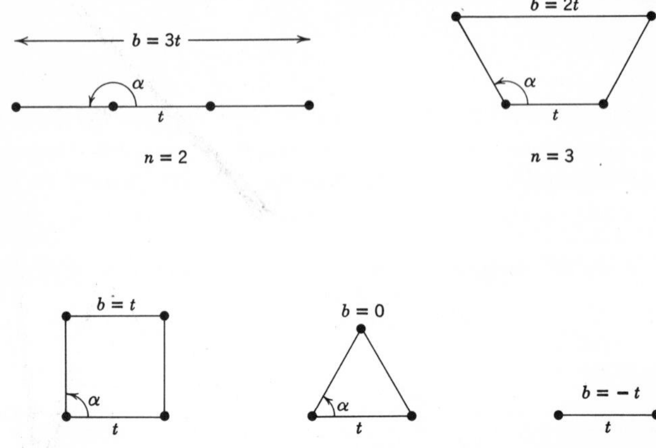

FIG. 7. Magnitudes of b in equation (2) for various crystallographic values of n.

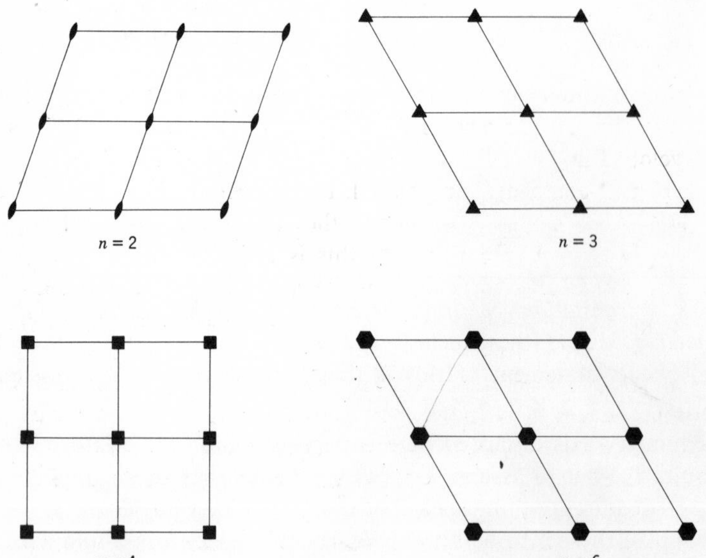

FIG. 8. Specialized plane nets for various crystallographic values of n.

Possibility of simultaneous rotational symmetries in different directions

A space lattice may be regarded as a stack of plane lattices. Thus a space lattice can only have symmetry axes with $n = 1, 2, 3, 4$, or 6, normal to a net. But one may discern nets in a space lattice parallel to many possible planes. Each such net plane could, conceivably, conform to the symmetry of a perpendicular n-fold axis. Thus a crystal could, conceivably, be symmetrical with respect

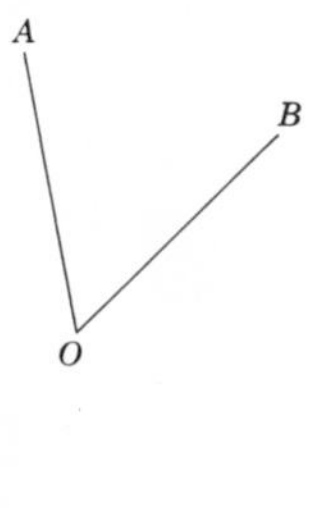

FIG. 9. Rotation axes A and B intersecting at O.

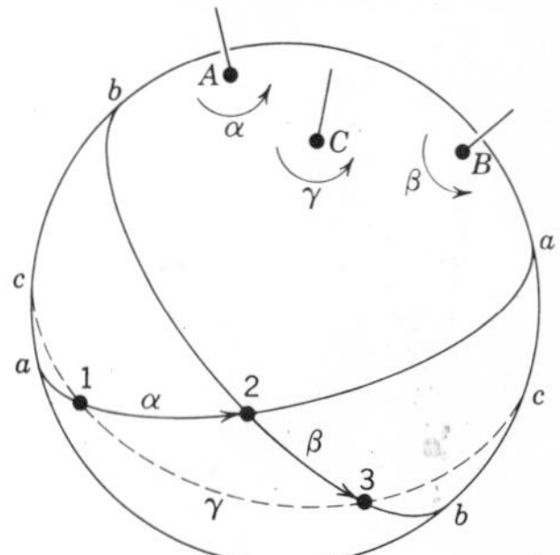

FIG. 10. The result of combining a rotation through angle α about A with a rotation through angle β about B.

to many different intersecting n-fold axes. But an interesting restriction again severely limits the angular relationships between intersecting n-fold axes. This will be developed in the following sections.

Combination of rotations. In general, two rotations about intersecting axes OA and OB, Fig. 9, cannot exist alone; they inevitably create a third rotation equivalent to the combination. That this is generally so can be grasped by considering the motion of a point on the surface of a sphere due to these rotations. Consider a fixed sphere, Fig. 10; let the two axes intersect at O, the center of the sphere. These axes pierce the surface of the sphere at points A and B respectively. The equator of axis A is aa, and the equator of B is bb. If objects on the surface of the sphere are caused to rotate by an angle α about A, a point on the equator, such as 1, moves along the equator through the arc α to point 2. If, next, objects on the surface of the sphere are caused to rotate through an angle β about B, point 2 moves along equator bb through arc β to point 3. (Note that test point 1 is deliberately chosen so that motion α would just bring it to equator bb.) Thus point 1 was moved by rotation A_α to 2 and by B_β to 3. But the two points 1 and 3 determine a great circle cc which is the equator of some pole C. It is obvious that the motion of 1 to 3 could also be achieved directly by a rotation through angle γ about C. Thus the combination of rotations A_α and B_β is equivalent to a single rotation C_γ. This can be written in the form of an operational equation

$$A_\alpha \cdot B_\beta = C_\gamma, \tag{7}$$

where the dot is read "followed by." This is similar to the simple vector addition equation

$$\vec{s} + \vec{t} = \vec{R}, \tag{8}$$

except that the sign of combination is a dot, not a +. The dot notation is commonly employed in analysis of motions. A more symmetrical interpretation of (8) is had by observing that the three vectors form a closed circuit. This can be written

$$\vec{s} + \vec{t} + (-\vec{R}) = 0. \tag{9}$$

A corresponding form of (7) is

$$A_\alpha \cdot B_\beta \cdot C_{-\gamma} = 1. \tag{10}$$

The symbol 1 of (10) corresponds to the symbol 0 of (9). It is the symbol of the "identical operation," or the operation of doing nothing. This was referred to earlier in Chapter 2. Equation (10) thus says that the combination of the three rotations is equivalent to no displacement. If the direction of γ which is accepted as positive is reversed, (10) takes the symmetrical form

$$A_\alpha \cdot B_\beta \cdot C_\gamma = 1. \tag{11}$$

It will appear that this holds provided that α, β, and γ are taken all clockwise or all counterclockwise.

Euler's construction. The construction suggested by the above demonstration has disadvantages when 2-fold axes are involved, since it requires arcs of $2\pi/2 \approx 180°$. An alternate construction, due to Euler, involves half-angles and is suitable for computation.

Let the two intersecting axes which cause rotations through angles α and β be OA and OB respectively. The two corresponding rotational operations can be called A_α and B_β (i.e., a rotation about A through angle α, and a rotation about B through angle β). Consider how these rotations move points on the surface of a sphere whose center is at O.

Euler's construction for these motions is illustrated in Fig. 11. The strategy of Euler's construction is to select for attention lines like AM which the rotational motion swings symmetrically from one side of the line AB (which joins the two axes) to the other. This requires that $MAB = M'AB = \alpha/2$.

Next, attention is directed to a line from B, namely BN, which the rotation B_β will swing symmetrically to the other side of AB, i.e., to BN'. This requires that $NBA = N'BA = \beta/2$. The intersection of AM' and BN is C', and the intersection of BN' and AM is C.

The combined motions of A_α and B_β have the following effect:

1: A_α brings C to C'.

2: B_β restores C' to C.

Thus, the combination of rotations A_α and B_β leaves C unmoved. Therefore, if there is a motion of points on the sphere due to A_α and B_β, it must be a

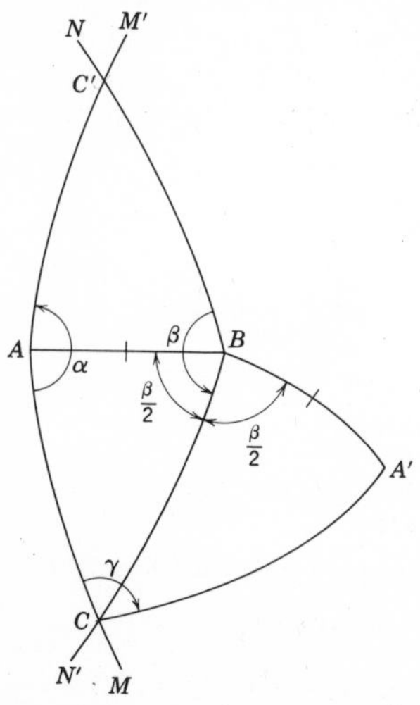

FIG. 11. Euler's construction for the combination of a rotation through angle α about A with a rotation through angle β about B.

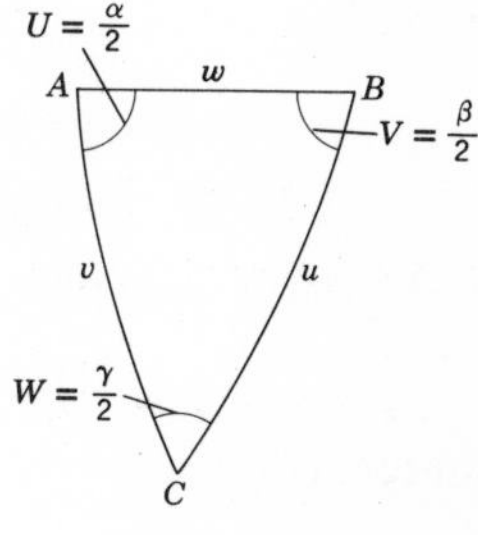

FIG. 12. Spherical triangle ABC for use in computations based upon Euler's construction.

rotation about an axis OC. The amount of the rotation can be readily measured by considering the total migration of a point at A:

1: A_α leaves A unmoved.

2: B_β moves A to A'.

Now, consider the spherical triangle $BA'C$.

$$\angle ABC = \angle A'BC = \beta/2.$$

$$AB = A'B.$$

$$\therefore \quad \triangle ABC = \triangle A'BC.$$

$$\therefore \quad \angle ACB = \angle A'CB.$$

Call this angle $\gamma/2$. Then the rotation about C carries A to A', i.e., through twice $\angle ACB$, or through angle γ. Equations (7), (10), and (11) are thus valid.

The advantage of Euler's construction is that it points out how the important angles can be computed. The important parts of Fig. 11 are redrawn in Fig. 12. One is evidently dealing with a spherical triangle whose angles are $U = \alpha/2$, $V = \beta/2$, and $W = \gamma/2$ and whose sides are the arcs u, v, and w. These quantities are related by the standard relations of spherical trigonometry. Specifically, the *law of cosines* provides that

$$\cos w = \cos u \cos v + \sin u \sin v \cos W. \tag{12}$$

This does not happen to be in a form which is immediately useful at this point, but it can be converted into a useful form by utilizing relations between the spherical triangle UVW and its polar triangle uvw. The relation between these is

$$\left.\begin{aligned} u &= 180° - U \qquad & U &= 180° - u \\ v &= 180° - V \qquad & V &= 180° - v \\ w &= 180° - W \qquad & W &= 180° - w \end{aligned}\right\}. \tag{13}$$

When the substitutions are made in (12), it can be transformed into the corresponding relation for the polar triangle, namely,

$$\begin{aligned} \cos(180° - W) = {} & \cos(180° - U)\cos(180° - V) \\ & + \sin(180° - U)\sin(180° - V)\cos(180° - w). \end{aligned} \tag{14}$$

This reduces to

$$-\cos W = \cos U \cos V - \sin U \sin V \cos w, \tag{15}$$

or

$$\cos W = -\cos U \cos V + \sin U \sin V \cos w. \tag{16}$$

Thus, the arc w can be found by solving (16) for w:

$$\cos w = \frac{\cos W + \cos U \cos V}{\sin U \sin V}. \tag{17}$$

Permissible intersection angles. In the general and noncrystallographic uses of the theory of combinations of rotations, any rotation α can be combined with any other rotation β at any intersection angle w. This combination implies a third rotation γ. The peculiar thing about the crystallographic application of the theory is that the only values of γ which are allowable are those permissible in crystals, namely 1-, 2-, 3-, 4-, and 6-fold rotations. This means that the intersection angles w are strictly limited to those which can be computed from (17) by letting U, V, and W be those corresponding to 1-, 2-, 3-, 4-, and 6-fold rotations.

Notation of combinations. It was evident from (10) that combinations of rotations are inextricably related in sets of three. The last section showed that in crystallographic applications these are restricted to the rotations of the crystallographic rotational symmetry operations. The three related rotations can then be designated by a set of three numbers used to designate the symmetry axes of the respective operations. Thus 234 signifies the set of three rotations corresponding to the 2-fold operation, the 3-fold operation, and the 4-fold operation.

Permissible combinations. In Table 5 the crystallographic values for substitution in (17) are tabulated. The values for the right of (17) for all crystallographic combinations are given in Table 6. It will be observed that not all

Table 5. Data for crystallographic solutions of

$$\cos w = \frac{\cos W + \cos U \cos V}{\sin U \sin V}$$

Axis at A, B, or C	Throw of axis, α, β, or γ	$U(=\alpha/2)$ $V(=\beta/2)$ or $W(=\gamma/2)$	cos U, V, W	sin U, V, W
1-fold	360°	180°	-1	0
2-fold	180°	90°	0	1
3-fold	120°	60°	$\frac{1}{2}$	$\frac{\sqrt{3}}{2}$
4-fold	90°	45°	$\frac{1}{\sqrt{2}}$	$\frac{1}{\sqrt{2}}$
6-fold	60°	30°	$\frac{\sqrt{3}}{2}$	$\frac{1}{2}$

results are possible values for a cosine. Such impossible solutions, of course, prohibit the corresponding crystallographic combinations which were assumed. A few combinations are trivial, specifically 236, 244, and 333. These combinations have $w = 0°$. In the case of 244 for example, this solution means that a half turn, followed by a quarter turn about the same axis, is the same as a quarter turn in the opposite direction. The permissible nontrivial combinations and their properties are listed in Table 7. This tabulation shows the angles of intersection of all axes. These have been computed by repeated application of relations like (17). In Tables 6 and 7 some curious angles occur. These are angles between some important directions in a cube. They can be expressed as angles between rational directions in the isometric crystal system and are identified in Table 8.

Table 6. Crystallographic solutions of

$$\cos w = \frac{\cos W + \cos U \cos V}{\sin U \sin V}$$

Combination	Form for first two rotations		$\cos w$	w
222	$\frac{\cos W + 0 \cdot 0}{1 \cdot 1}$	$\frac{0+0}{1}$	$=0$	90°
223		$\frac{\frac{1}{2}+0}{1}$	$=\frac{1}{2}$	60°
224		$\frac{\frac{1}{\sqrt{2}}+0}{1}$	$=\frac{1}{\sqrt{2}}$	45°
226		$\frac{\frac{\sqrt{3}}{2}+0}{1}$	$=\frac{\sqrt{3}}{2}$	30°
233	$\frac{\cos W + 0 \cdot \frac{1}{2}}{1 \cdot \frac{\sqrt{3}}{2}}$	$\frac{\frac{1}{2}+0}{\frac{\sqrt{3}}{2}}$	$=\frac{1}{\sqrt{3}}$	54° 44′
234		$\frac{\frac{1}{\sqrt{2}}+0}{\frac{\sqrt{3}}{2}}$	$=\frac{2}{\sqrt{6}}$	35° 16′
236		$\frac{\frac{\sqrt{3}}{2}+0}{\frac{\sqrt{3}}{2}}$	$=1$	0°

Table 6 (continued)

Combination	Form for first two rotations		cos w	w
244	$\dfrac{\cos W + 0\cdot\frac{1}{\sqrt{2}}}{1\cdot\frac{1}{\sqrt{2}}}$	$\dfrac{\frac{1}{\sqrt{2}}+0}{\frac{1}{\sqrt{2}}}$	$=1$	0°
246		$\dfrac{\frac{\sqrt{3}}{2}+0}{\frac{1}{\sqrt{2}}}$	$=\dfrac{\sqrt{6}}{2}>1$	—
266	$\dfrac{\cos W + 0\cdot\frac{\sqrt{3}}{2}}{1\cdot\frac{1}{2}}$	$\dfrac{\frac{\sqrt{3}}{2}+0}{\frac{1}{2}}$	$=\sqrt{3}>1$	—
333	$\dfrac{\cos W + \frac{1}{2}\cdot\frac{1}{2}}{\frac{\sqrt{3}}{2}\cdot\frac{\sqrt{3}}{2}}$	$\dfrac{\frac{1}{2}+\frac{1}{4}}{\frac{3}{4}}$	$=1$	0°
334		$\dfrac{\frac{1}{\sqrt{2}}+\frac{1}{4}}{\frac{3}{4}}$	$=\dfrac{2\sqrt{2}+1}{3}>1$	—
366		$\dfrac{\frac{\sqrt{3}}{2}+\frac{1}{4}}{\frac{3}{4}}$	$=\dfrac{2\sqrt{3}+1}{3}>1$	—
344	$\dfrac{\cos W + \frac{1}{2}\cdot\frac{1}{\sqrt{2}}}{\frac{\sqrt{3}}{2}\cdot\frac{1}{\sqrt{2}}}$	$\dfrac{\frac{1}{\sqrt{2}}+\frac{1}{2\sqrt{2}}}{\frac{\sqrt{3}}{2\sqrt{2}}}$	$=\dfrac{3}{\sqrt{3}}>1$	—
346		$\dfrac{\frac{\sqrt{3}}{2}+\frac{1}{2\sqrt{2}}}{\frac{\sqrt{3}}{2\sqrt{2}}}$	$=\dfrac{\sqrt{6}+1}{\sqrt{3}}>1$	—

Table 6 (continued)

Combination	Form for first two rotations		cos w	w
366	$\dfrac{\cos W + \frac{1}{2}\cdot\frac{\sqrt{3}}{2}}{\frac{\sqrt{3}}{2}\cdot\frac{1}{2}}$	$\dfrac{\frac{\sqrt{3}}{2}+\frac{1}{2}\cdot\frac{\sqrt{3}}{2}}{\frac{1}{2}\cdot\frac{\sqrt{3}}{4}}$	$=\dfrac{1+\frac{1}{2}}{\frac{1}{2}}=3$	—
444	$\dfrac{\cos W + \frac{1}{\sqrt{2}}\cdot\frac{1}{\sqrt{2}}}{\frac{1}{\sqrt{2}}\cdot\frac{1}{\sqrt{2}}}$ (444 and 446)	$\dfrac{\frac{1}{\sqrt{2}}+\frac{1}{2}}{\frac{1}{2}}$	$=\dfrac{2}{\sqrt{2}}+1>1$	—
446		$\dfrac{\frac{\sqrt{3}}{2}+\frac{1}{2}}{\frac{1}{2}}$	$=\sqrt{3}+1>1$	—
466	$\dfrac{\cos W + \frac{1}{\sqrt{2}}\cdot\frac{\sqrt{3}}{2}}{\frac{1}{\sqrt{2}}\ \frac{1}{2}}$	$\dfrac{\frac{\sqrt{3}}{2}+\frac{1}{\sqrt{2}}\cdot\frac{\sqrt{3}}{2}}{\frac{1}{\sqrt{2}}\cdot\frac{1}{2}}$	$=\sqrt{3}(\sqrt{2}-1)>1$	—
666	$\dfrac{\cos W + \frac{\sqrt{3}}{2}\cdot\frac{\sqrt{3}}{2}}{\frac{1}{2}\cdot\frac{1}{2}}$	$\dfrac{\frac{\sqrt{3}}{2}+\frac{\sqrt{3}}{2}\cdot\frac{\sqrt{3}}{2}}{\frac{1}{2}\cdot\frac{1}{2}}$	$=2\sqrt{3}+3>1$	—

Graphical descriptions of the results in Table 7 are given in Fig. 13. In each of the six sets of permissible combinations shown in Fig. 13, each operation axis is actually the location of a symmetry axis and requires an n-fold multiplication of each of the other symmetry axes. This results in a set of more than three symmetry axes, specifically a set of several axes, all of which are symmetrically placed with respect to the symmetry requirements of each of the other axes of the set. These six sets of permissible combinations of symmetry axes are shown in Fig. 14. *The rest of the crystallographic symmetry theory of crystals is restricted to conform to* 1-, 2-, 3-, 4-, *and* 6-*fold axes and to these six fundamental sets of their combinations.*

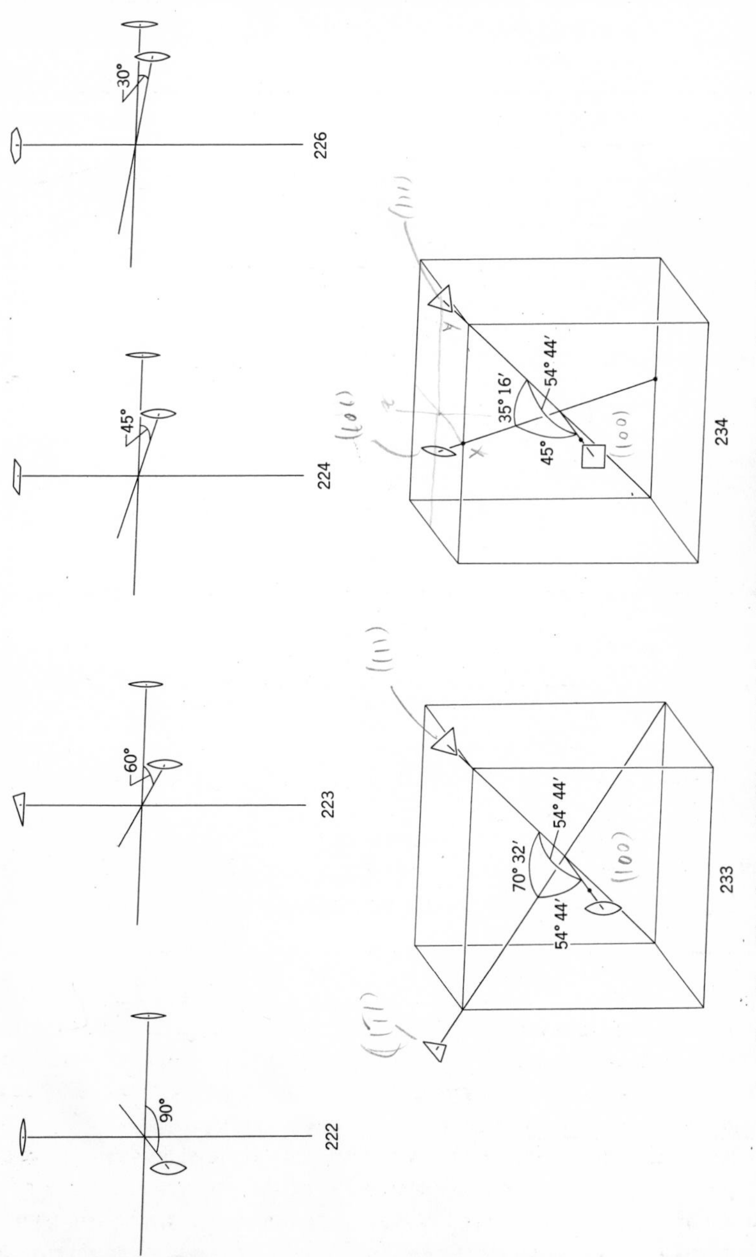

FIG. 13. The six permissible nontrivial crystallographic combinations of rotations.

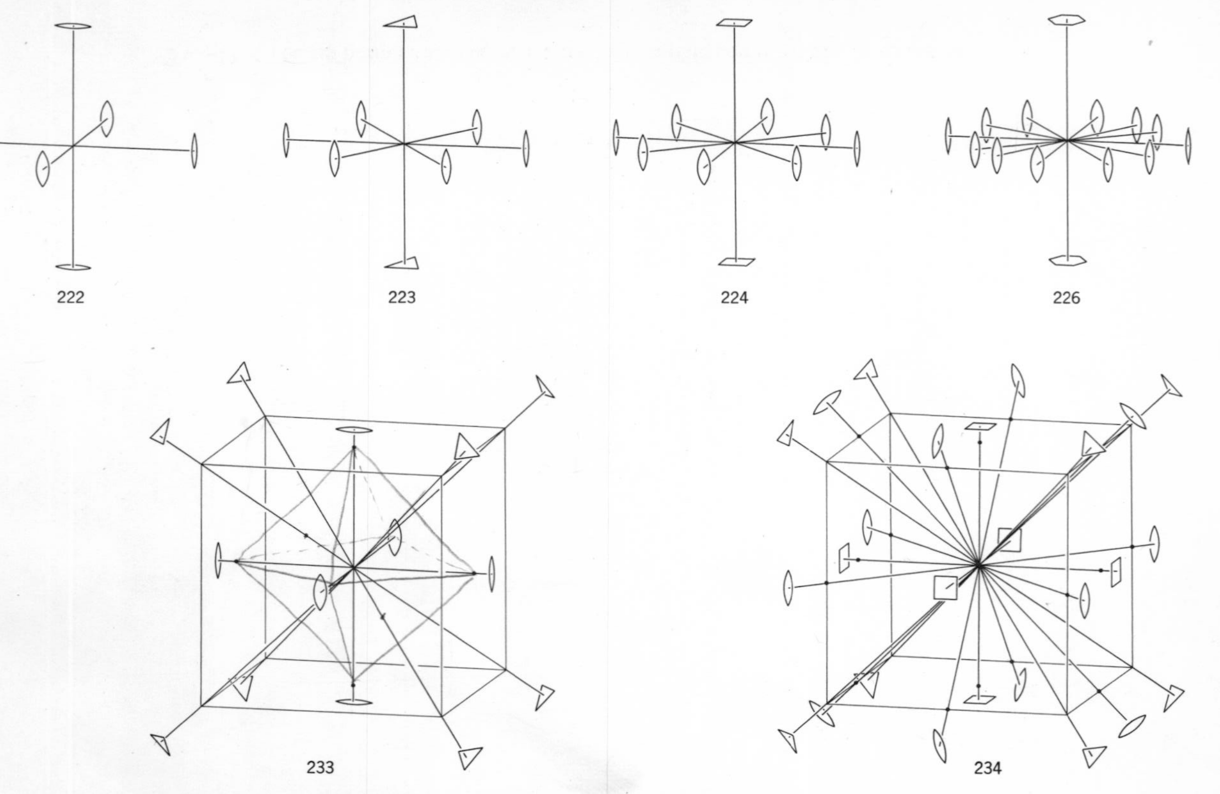

FIG. 14. The six crystallographic axial symmetries based upon the combinations in Fig. 13.

Table 7. Geometry of the permissible nontrivial combinations of rotations

Combinations	$2U = \alpha$	w	$2V = \beta$	u	$2W = \gamma$	v
222	180°	90°	180°	90°	180°	90°
223	180°	60°	180°	90°	120°	90°
224	180°	45°	180°	90°	90°	90°
226	180°	30°	180°	90°	60°	90°
233	180°	54° 44′	120°	70° 32′	120°	54° 44′
234	180°	35° 16′	120°	35° 16′	90°	45°

Table 8. Angles between certain rational directions in the isometric system

	[100]	[101]	[111]	[1$\bar{1}$1]
[100]		45°	54° 44′ 08″	54° 44′ 08″
[101]			35° 15′ 52″	35° 15′ 52″
[111]				70° 31′ 44″
[1$\bar{1}$1]				

Exercises

1. If possible, decompose the following improper rotation axes into simpler symmetry elements: $\bar{9}$, $\overline{12}$, $\overline{10}$, $\overline{20}$, $\overline{21}$, $\overline{25}$.
2. Show graphically that 7-fold axes are inconsistent with translations.
3. By using relation (17), ascertain whether the combination of axes 235 is possible.
4. By using relations like (17), find the angles between the noncrystallographic rotations of 2, 3, 5.
5. By using relation (17), ascertain whether the combination of axes 345 is possible.
6. Make a diagram showing the top view of a sphere for each combination of axes in Fig. 14.

5 · Derivation of the crystal classes

Importance of axial combinations

In Chapter 2 it was shown that any repetition can be produced by a combination of the geometrical motions of a rotation, a translation, and any operation producing the enantiomorphous figure. The last operation can be an improper rotation, for example. Consider, now, the particular kind of repetitions that can be produced if translations are omitted, that is, if only

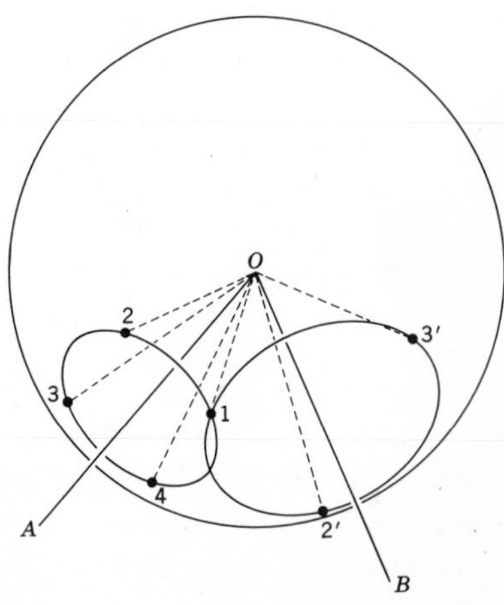

FIG. 1. The repetition of a point by two intersecting rotation axes.

proper and improper rotations are used. It can be readily shown (and will be shown in Chapter 13) that any two rotations about axes that do not intersect involve translations, and so such arrangements are excluded. The question can be reformulated, therefore, as follows: What is the nature of repetitions which can be produced by rotations (proper or improper) about intersecting axes?

Two such axes, A and B, are pictured in Fig. 1. If an arbitrary point, labeled 1 in Fig. 1, is introduced into this system, axis A repeats it to points 2, 3, and 4 (say), and axis B repeats it to 2′ and 3′ (say). It is obvious that all these points are equidistant from the intersection O of the several axes. The locus of points equidistant from a single point is the surface of a sphere. One answer to the question formulated above is, therefore, that rotations about intersecting axes produce repetitions such that a set of equivalent points is confined to the surface of a sphere.

These considerations need not be restricted to a single initial point, however. The repeated initial object may be a geometrical plane, for example. In this instance the collection of repeated planes constitutes a polyhedron whose faces are equidistant from the point of intersection of the several rotation axes. The polyhedron may, or may not, enclose space by itself. The rotation axes must, of course, repeat *any other* initial plane which is introduced into the system, producing another polyhedron of it. While all *equivalent planes* must be equidistant from the intersection of the rotation axes, *nonequivalent planes* (i.e., those belonging to sets repeated from different initial planes) need not have the same distances from the intersection of the rotation axes and, in general, do not lie at equal distances from it. If, for the present, each set of equivalent faces is called a simple polyhedron, then several sets of equivalent faces may be called a complex polyhedron.

In the discussion just given the notion of repetition was used. But in Chapter 2 it was shown that an axis of rotational repetition is also an axis of rotational symmetry. The possible sets of intersecting rotational axes are therefore the possible symmetries which polyhedra can have. This statement can be made stronger. Since all repetitions not involving translations can be produced by rotations, proper and improper, all symmetries not involving translations can be described by rotations, proper and improper. These are all the symmetries which polyhedra can have.

A useful answer to the question originally formulated can now be given as follows: *The permissible combinations of rotation axes, proper and improper, are the only possible symmetries of polyhedra.* These combinations thus constitute a set of categories for classifying symmetrical polyhedra.

The conclusions just given are perfectly general and are independent of the fact that only 1-, 2-, 3-, 4-, and 6-fold axes can occur in crystals. In Chapter 10 it will be pointed out that under appropriate circumstances crystals develop plane faces during growth. When this occurs they appear as polyhedra. Therefore intersecting rotation axes are appropriate for classifying crystals according to the symmetry of surface development they may display.

It is also true that combinations of rotation axes have a deeper significance in classification. The rotation angles of the axes, and the angles at which axes can combine, remain fixed whether the crystal pattern contains translations or not (this will be discussed at length in Chapter 13). Thus the axial combinations afford a very general framework which restricts the remainder of pattern theory.

Principles for discovering the permissible crystal symmetries

In the last chapter it was shown that a lattice can be consistent with an n-fold axis at right angles to one of its sets of plane lattices provided that n is 1, 2, 3, 4, or 6. Now, all lattices are inherently centrosymmetrical, and so the n-fold axis can be not only 1, 2, 3, 4, or 6, but also $\bar{1}$, $\bar{2}$, $\bar{3}$, $\bar{4}$, or $\bar{6}$. This can be stated another way: If a lattice is dimensionally specialized so that it is consistent with an axis n, it is also consistent with an axis $\bar{n}$. For example, a lattice whose cell has a square base is consistent with either an axis 4 or $\bar{4}$ normal to the square mesh. Furthermore, this lattice is consistent with a 4 axis and a $\bar{4}$ axis simultaneously.

The 32 crystal classes

A sufficient background has now been presented to permit deriving all the crystallographically permissible symmetries involving sets of axes all of which intersect in a common point. These sets are called the *crystallographic point groups.* There will prove to be 32 such groups. If the external form of a crystal is thought of as a solid polyhedral body, the external symmetry of every crystal must correspond to one of these 32 groups. It is therefore natural that crystals should be classified according to these 32 possible symmetries. For this reason the crystal kingdom is considered as being divided into 32 *crystal classes.* Thus, every crystal belongs to one of the 32 crystal classes. The practical method of determining what class a particular crystal belongs to is not discussed at this point but is reserved for Chapters 10 and 11.

In the last section it was pointed out that, if a net of a lattice is specialized so that the axis normal to the net can be n-fold, it is evident that the symmetry about that axis can be either n, $\bar{n}$, or both n and $\bar{n}$ simultaneously. Therefore all the axial symmetries can be derived by imposing these three alternatives (*a*) on each of the five possible individual symmetry axes and (*b*) on each of the six permissible combinations of intersecting sets of axes, but within the limitation that these combinations be consistent. This limitation is discussed in a following section.

Coincident rotation rotoinversion axes

In the last two sections it was noted that a lattice can be consistent with an axis n and an axis $\bar{n}$ simultaneously. This calls for an n-fold pure rotation axis coincident with an n-fold rotoinversion axis. This combination of n and $\bar{n}$ is written $\frac{n}{\bar{n}}$. These combinations can be reduced, partly with the help of Table

2, Chapter 4, to simpler symmetries. The reduction of such combinations, including noncrystallographic cases, is shown in Table 1 of this chapter. Table 2, Chapter 4, shows that, when $n = 4N \pm 2$, $\bar{n} = \frac{n/2}{m}$. When this is combined with a coincident n-fold pure rotation the combination becomes $\frac{n}{m}$. Table 2, Chapter 4, also shows that, when n is odd, $\bar{n} = n \cdot i$. In this case $\frac{n}{\bar{n}} = \frac{n}{n \cdot i}$. This is the same as $\bar{n}$, so that $\frac{n}{\bar{n}} = \bar{n}$. Finally, when $n = 4N$, $\frac{n}{\bar{n}} = \frac{n}{m}$.

Note that only those combinations in Table 1 are crystallographic possibilities for which $n = 1, 2, 3, 4$, or 6.

Table 1. Reduction of coincident rotation and rotoinversion symmetries

Characteristics of n	Reduction of $\frac{n}{\bar{n}}$	
$n = 4N + 1$; i.e., n odd	$\frac{1}{\bar{1}} = \frac{1}{1 \cdot i} = \bar{1}$	$\frac{5}{\bar{5}} = \frac{5}{5 \cdot i} = \bar{5}$
$n = 4N + 2$	$\frac{2}{\bar{2}} = \frac{2}{m}$	$\frac{6}{\bar{6}} = \frac{6}{3/m} = \frac{6}{m}$
$n = 4N - 1$; i.e., n odd	$\frac{3}{\bar{3}} = \frac{3}{3 \cdot i} = \bar{3}$	$\frac{7}{\bar{7}} = \frac{7}{7 \cdot i} = \bar{7}$
$n = 4N$	$\frac{4}{\bar{4}} = \frac{4}{m}$	$\frac{8}{\bar{8}} = \frac{8}{m}$

Permissible combinations of proper and improper rotations

In the last chapter it was demonstrated that a rotation about axis A, Fig. 2, followed by a rotation about axis B is equivalent to a rotation about a third axis, C. Thus the axes A, B, C are a connected set. Suppose that two of these are proper rotations, Fig. 3. Then A (say) repeats right-handed point 1 to become another right-handed point 2, and B repeats this to become right-handed point 3. Thus C, which is equivalent to the combination AB, repeats right-handed point 1 to become right-handed point 3. If R is taken to represent a right-handed point, this can be formulated as

$$A \text{ requires } 1R \rightarrow 2R,$$
$$B \text{ requires } 2R \rightarrow 3R,$$
$$\therefore \quad C \text{ requires } 1R \rightarrow 3R.$$

Since C does not produce an enantiomorphous repetition, it is a proper rotation. Let P stand for a proper rotation and I stand for an improper rotation. Then $AB = C$ has the character $PP = P$.

Next, let both A and B be improper rotations, Fig. 4. The repeating scheme is

$$A \text{ requires } 1R \rightarrow 2L,$$

$$B \text{ requires } 2L \rightarrow 3R,$$

$$\therefore \quad C \text{ requires } 1R \rightarrow 3R.$$

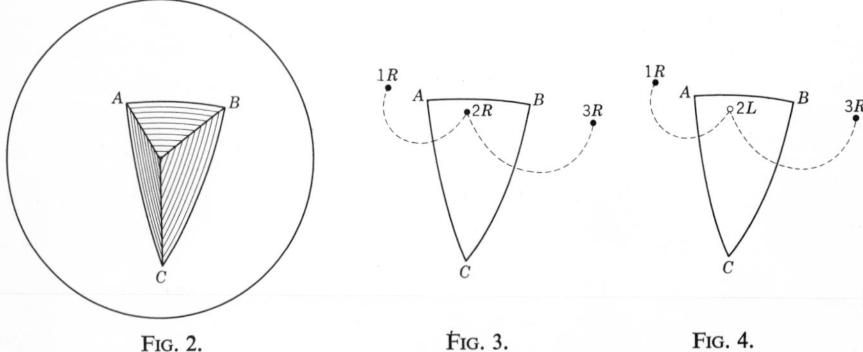

FIG. 2. FIG. 3. FIG. 4.

Thus C is a proper rotation. The characters of $AB = C$ are then $II = P$ Since

$$PP = P$$

$$\text{and} \quad II = P$$

it follows that sets of three related axes ABC must have one of two character combinations, either PPP or IIP. The order of terms is inconsequential. Thus

$$\left.\begin{array}{l} IIP, \\ IPI, \\ PII, \end{array}\right\} \text{are all permissible sets}$$

$$\text{as well as} \quad PPP.$$

But note that III is impossible.

Derivation of the crystal classes

The monaxial classes. Consider first the axial symmetries consisting of a single n-fold axis. This axis can be proper, improper, or both proper and improper at the same time; i.e., for each value of n there exist the symmetries n, $\bar{n}$, $n \cdot \bar{n}$. The symbol for an axis n coincident with an axis $\bar{n}$ is customarily written as the fraction $\frac{n}{\bar{n}}$. Note that in this fraction the numerator is the symbol for the proper axis, and the denominator is the symbol for the improper axis, if both are present. Thus the monaxial classes are n, $\bar{n}$, $\frac{n}{\bar{n}}$. These are enumerated in Table 2. This table also indicates some of the more customary labels for these classes.

Table 2. The monaxial crystal classes

n	Crystal classes		
	Proper rotation only	Improper rotation only	Combination of proper and improper axes
1	1	$\bar{1}$	$\left(\frac{1}{\bar{1}} = \bar{1}\right)$
2	2	$\bar{2} = m$	$\frac{2}{\bar{2}} = \frac{2}{m}$
3	3	$\bar{3}$	$\left(\frac{3}{\bar{3}} = \bar{3}\right)$
4	4	$\bar{4}$	$\frac{4}{\bar{4}} = \frac{4}{m}$
6	6	$\bar{6} = \frac{3}{m}$	$\frac{6}{\bar{6}} = \frac{6}{m}$
Total number of classes	5	5	3 = 13

The polyaxial symmetry combinations. The scheme just used can be extended to the six combinations of three intersecting axes, subject to the restriction that the fundamental axes must conform to *PPP* or *IIP*. For each of the six axial sets, there is only one *PPP* combination; these are given in the second column of Table 3.

Table 3. The polyaxial classes conforming to *PPP* or *P I I*

Combination	Crystal classes			
	Proper combinations *PPP*	Permissible improper combinations: *P I I*	*I P I* if distinct	*I I P* if distinct
222	222	$2\bar{2}\bar{2} = 2mm$		
322	322	$3\bar{2}(\bar{2}) = 3m(m)$, called $3m$	$\bar{3}2\bar{2} = \bar{3}2m$	
422	422	$4\bar{2}\bar{2} = 4mm$	$\bar{4}2\bar{2} = \bar{4}2m$	
622	622	$6\bar{2}\bar{2} = 6mm$	$\left(\bar{6}2\bar{2} \to \frac{3}{m}2\frac{1}{m} \to \frac{3}{m}\frac{2}{i}\frac{2}{m} \to \frac{6}{m}\frac{2}{m}\frac{2}{m}\right)$	
332	332	—	—	$\left(\bar{3}\bar{3}2 \to \frac{3}{i}\frac{3}{i}2 \to \frac{3}{i}\frac{3}{i}\frac{2}{m} \to \bar{3}\bar{3}\frac{2}{m}\right.$, called $\left.\frac{2}{m}\bar{3}\right)$
432	432	$\left(4\bar{3}\bar{2} \to 4\frac{3}{i}\frac{1}{m} \to \frac{4}{m}\frac{3}{i}\frac{2}{m} \to \frac{4}{m}\bar{3}\frac{2}{m}\right)$	$\bar{4}3\bar{2} = \bar{4}3m$	$\left(\bar{4}\bar{3}\bar{2} \to \bar{4}\frac{3}{i}\frac{1}{m} \to \frac{\bar{4}}{m}\frac{3}{i}\frac{2}{m} \to \frac{4}{m}\bar{3}\frac{2}{m}\right)$
Total number of classes	6		7	= 13

In the *IIP* combinations the proper axis can in general be assigned to any of the three axes of the set. In the event that two of the three are symmetrically equivalent, as the two 3-fold axes in 332, obviously these must always be the same; i.e., if the first 3 is *I*, so is the second. Furthermore, in classes like 422, *IPI* and *IIP* involve only an interchange of the proper character from one 2-fold axis to the other. These are the same by a rotation about the other axis, so that combinations like $\bar{n}2\bar{2}$ and $\bar{n}\bar{2}2$ are not distinct. The permissible combinations of *IIP* are set down in the last three columns of Table 3.

In three cases, the combinations develop into more complicated combinations, best treated in the next section. These combinations are placed in parentheses since they really belong in the more complicated category of Table 4. The developments, in each case, involve the symmetry element $\bar{1} = i$, which combines with other symmetries present (in a manner discussed in the next chapter) to create additional symmetry elements. An outline of how this occurs is contained in the parentheses.

Table 4. The polyaxial classes conforming to both proper and improper combinations

Axial combination	Crystal classes formed by proper-improper combination
222	$\frac{2\,2\,2}{\bar{2}\,\bar{2}\,\bar{2}} = \frac{2}{m}\frac{2}{m}\frac{2}{m}$
322	$\frac{3\,2\,2}{\bar{3}\,\bar{2}\,\bar{2}} = \bar{3}\frac{2}{m}\frac{2}{m}$ (called $\bar{3}\frac{2}{m}$)
422	$\frac{4\,2\,2}{\bar{4}\,\bar{2}\,\bar{2}} = \frac{4}{m}\frac{2}{m}\frac{2}{m}$
622	$\frac{6\,2\,2}{\bar{6}\,\bar{2}\,\bar{2}} = \frac{6}{m}\frac{2}{m}\frac{2}{m}$
332	$\frac{3\,3\,2}{\bar{3}\,\bar{3}\,\bar{2}} = \bar{3}\,\bar{3}\frac{2}{m}$ (called $\frac{2}{m}\bar{3}$)
432	$\frac{4\,3\,2}{\bar{4}\,\bar{3}\,\bar{2}} = \frac{4}{m}\bar{3}\frac{2}{m}$
Number of classes	6

In the same way that the same lattice can be simultaneously consistent with symmetry n, $\bar{n}$, or $n/\bar{n}$, so a lattice can be consistent with the proper combination $n_1n_2n_3$, the improper combination $n_1\bar{n}_2\bar{n}_3$, or simultaneously with both. In other words, the corresponding proper and improper combinations of Table 3 can be combined to give new composite symmetries.

When such a combination is made, an important simplification occurs. If $n_1n_2n_3$ is combined with $n_1\bar{n}_2\bar{n}_3$ (i.e., *PII*), the combination can be tentatively written

$$\begin{pmatrix} n_1 \\ n_1 \end{pmatrix} \begin{pmatrix} n_2 \\ \bar{n}_2 \end{pmatrix} \begin{pmatrix} n_3 \\ \bar{n}_3 \end{pmatrix}. \tag{1}$$

Here the two numbers within each pair of parentheses are coincident axes. The lattice is simultaneously consistent with all these axes. This means that the lattice must be consistent with pairs of axes selected from any two of the three places of (1). Of course, the third axis must be consistent with this combination, which implies it must conform to the characteristics *IIP*. But this cannot be true for combinations like

$$(\quad)(\bar{n}_2)(n_3)$$

unless the first position also contains $\bar{n}_1$. This requires that (1) is not complete unless each position contains both n and $\bar{n}$. Thus the only permissible complete combinations must have the form

$$\frac{n_1}{\bar{n}_1}\frac{n_2}{\bar{n}_2}\frac{n_3}{\bar{n}_3}. \tag{2}$$

The six possibilities are shown in Table 4.

This chapter presents merely a systematic derivation of the crystal classes without discussing the symmetries of these classes in any detail. In the next chapter the details of the symmetries are followed more closely.

The total number of classes derived in this chapter is as follows:

The monaxial classes	$5 + 5 + 3 = 13$
The polyaxial classes conforming to *PPP* or *PII*	$6 + 7 = 13$
The polyaxial classes conforming to *PPP* + *III*	6
	32

Exercises

1. On page 50 it is stated that combination *III* is impossible. Why?
2. Derive the symmetry classes based upon the noncrystallographic axial combination 235.
3. Derive the symmetry classes based upon the noncrystallographic axes and axial combinations 5, 7, 8, 225, 227, 228.

6 · Combinations of symmetry operations involving reflections and inversions

In the derivation of the 32 crystal classes it was convenient to make use of axial symmetries only. But in discussing the axial symmetries in Chapter 4 it was shown that (except for $n = 4N$) an improper axis can be decomposed into either a proper axis and a perpendicular reflection plane or a proper axis and an inversion center. This implies that the crystal classes can also be described in terms of the proper axes only plus reflection planes and inversion centers, and without reference to improper axes except when $n = 4$. This description of crystal symmetry is more readily appreciated than the description involving improper axes, and it lends itself well to generalization for space-group theory.

To work with descriptions of symmetry involving mirrors and inversion centers, it is necessary to understand how the operations of these symmetry elements combine with the axial operations and with each other. These combinations are discussed in the following sections.

Fundamental combinations

Two reflections. The combination of two mirrors is illustrated in Fig. 1. Let the two mirrors, m_1 and m_2, be normal to the paper and intersect in a line A which is normal to the paper. Let the angle between the two mirrors be μ, and let the original point be $1R$. The symbol R is used to designate a right-handed point, and L is used for a left-handed point. Then

$$\left.\begin{aligned} m_1 &\text{ repeats } 1R \text{ to become } 2L, \\ \text{and} \quad m_2 &\text{ repeats } 2L \text{ to become } 3R. \end{aligned}\right\} \tag{1}$$

Thus m_1 and m_2 together repeat $1R$ to become $3R$. Because of the geometry of reflection, the distances

$$A \text{ to } 1R = A \text{ to } 2L = A \text{ to } 3R, \tag{2}$$

$$\left.\begin{aligned} \text{and} \quad \varphi_1 &= \varphi_2, \\ \psi_1 &= \psi_2. \end{aligned}\right\} \tag{3}$$

$$\text{Also} \quad \varphi_2 + \psi_1 = \mu. \tag{4}$$

Since the distances A to $1R = A$ to $3R$, the repetition from $1R$ to $3R$ is a rotation about A. The amount of the rotation is $\varphi_1 + \varphi_2 + \psi_1 + \psi_2$. According to (3) and (4), this is

$$2\varphi + 2\psi = 2\mu. \tag{5}$$

That is, two mirrors at an angle μ together produce a rotation of 2μ. One can therefore describe the combination of two mirrors as

$$\underset{\mu}{\underbrace{m_1 \cdot m_2}} = A_{2\mu}. \tag{6}$$

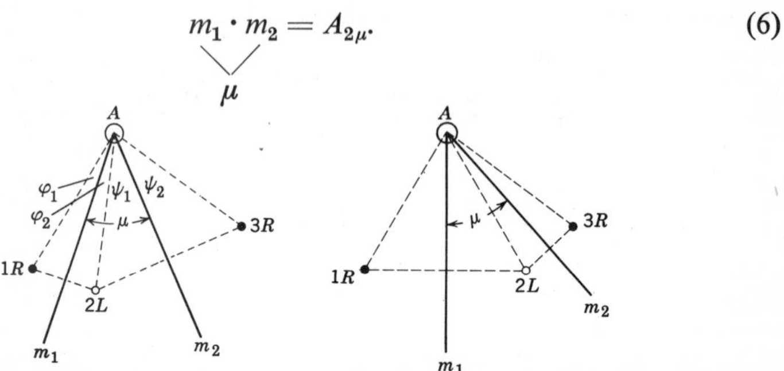

FIG. 1. Combination of two reflections by mirrors intersecting at angle μ.

FIG. 2. Demonstration that the orientation of the mirror pair in Fig. 1 does not affect the resulting combination.

In the crystallographic application, A is a symmetry axis of angular period α, so that $\alpha = 2\mu$. In this case (6) can also be written

$$\underset{\alpha/2}{\underbrace{m_1 \cdot m_2}} = A_{\alpha}. \tag{7}$$

It is important to note that the three operations of (6) and (7) are connected in such a way that, if any two are given, the third follows. For example, if, instead of combining the operations of m_1 and m_2, one combines the operations of A_α and m_2, then m_1 appears because

$$\left.\begin{aligned} &A_\alpha \text{ repeats } 1R \text{ to become } 3R,\\ &m_2 \text{ repeats } 3R \text{ to become } 2L.\end{aligned}\right\} \tag{8}$$

Therefore, the combination

$$A_\alpha \cdot m_2 \text{ repeats } 1R \text{ to become } 2L, \tag{9}$$

and, according to (1), this is exactly the function of m_1. Consequently an equally valid relation is

$$A_\alpha \cdot m_2 = m_{1,\alpha/2}. \tag{10}$$

A compact way of expressing all this is to note that m_1, followed by m_2, followed by A_α in reversed sense, is a sequence of operations which restores the original point to itself. This can be expressed as

$$\underbrace{m_1 \cdot m_2}_{\alpha/2} \cdot A_{-\alpha} = 1. \quad (11)$$

As mentioned in another place (pages 10 and 36), the symbol 1 signifies no change from the original condition. The interpretation of equation (11) is therefore that the reflection operation m_1, followed by reflection operation m_2, followed by the reverse rotation $A_{-\alpha}$, leaves everything in space unmoved.

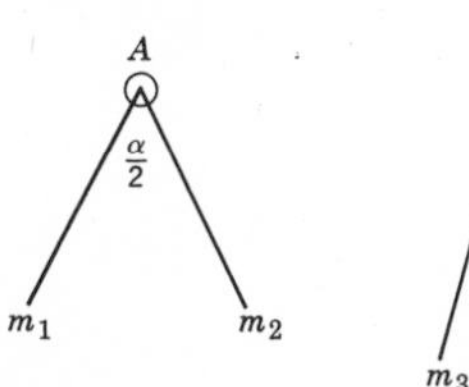

FIG. 3.

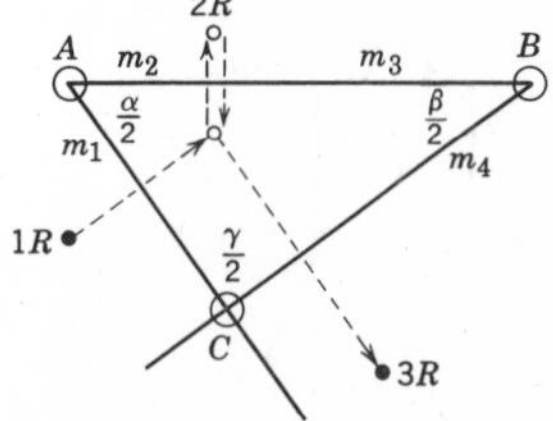

FIG. 4. Alternative demonstration of Euler's construction using intersecting mirrors.

Three reflections. For the purposes of this section it should be observed that, provided the angle between the two mirrors in Fig. 1 is fixed, the locations of $1R$ and $3R$ are unaffected by the orientation of the pair of mirrors. Thus the mirror pair can be rotated about the intersection to a different orientation, Fig. 2, and, provided that the dihedral angle, μ, is not changed, $1R$ and $3R$ remain unmoved. (Note, however, that $2L$ *is* a function of the position of m_1 and m_2.) Accordingly, if m_1 and m_2 are thought of as acting *only in combination*, they can be substituted for $A_{2\mu}$ for the purposes of solving a problem.

Now, consider two pairs of mirrors, Fig. 3, namely m_1 and m_2, intersecting in A at an angle $\alpha/2$, and m_3 and m_4 intersecting in B at an angle $\beta/2$. Since the effect of a mirror pair is independent of orientation, reorient the pairs so that m_2 and m_3 coincide as in Fig. 4. Then $m_1 \cdot m_2$ causes $1R \rightarrow 2R$ and $m_3 \cdot m_4$ causes $2R \rightarrow 3R$. The net effect of the four mirrors is to cause $1R \rightarrow 3R$. But this is exactly what would be caused by the pair $m_1 \cdot m_4$ intersecting in C at an angle $\gamma/2$. The combination can be written as follows:

$$(m_1 \cdot m_2) \cdot (m_3 \cdot m_4) = (m_1 \cdot m_4). \quad (12)$$

Formally, this is because the effects of m_2 and m_3 in (12) and in Fig. 4 nullify one another, leaving only $m_1 \cdot m_4$ acting at an angle $\gamma/2$.

Now, if relations like (7) are substituted for the pairs in parentheses in (12), specifically

$$\left.\begin{aligned}(m_1 \cdot m_2) &= A_\alpha,\\ (m_3 \cdot m_4) &= B_\beta,\\ (m_1 \cdot m_4) &= C_{-\gamma},\end{aligned}\right\} \tag{13}$$

there results

$$A_\alpha \cdot B_\beta = C_{-\gamma}. \tag{14}$$

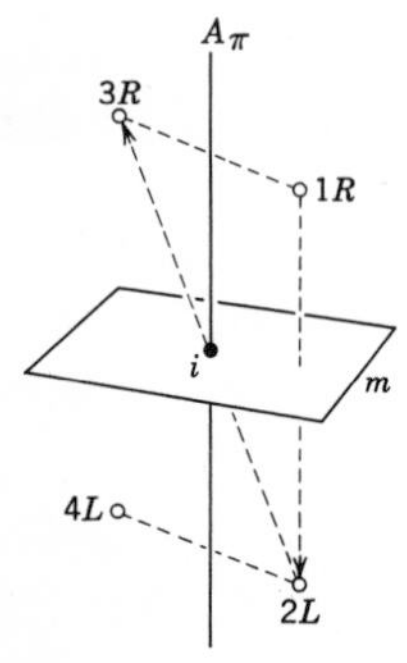

FIG. 5. Demonstration that $m \cdot i = A_\pi$.

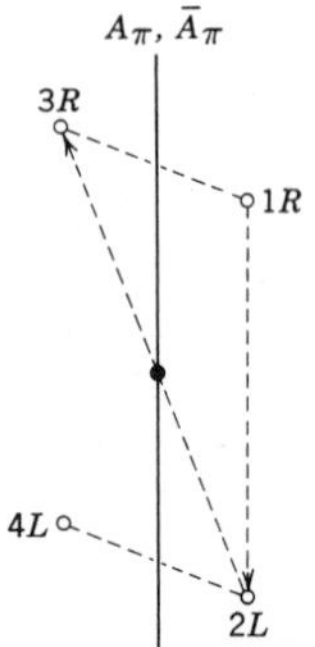

FIG. 6. Alternative demonstration of relation in Fig. 5.

This is exactly the same as (10) of Chapter 4. It can be rewritten so that α, β, and γ have the same rotational sense, as follows:

$$A_\alpha \cdot B_\beta \cdot C_\gamma = 1. \tag{15}$$

which is the same as (11) of Chapter 4. This is an alternative demonstration of Euler's construction.

Reflection and inversion. The combination of a reflection and inversion are illustrated in Fig. 5. If one starts with a mirror, m, containing an inversion center, i, then these act on an arbitrary point, $1R$, as follows:

$$\left.\begin{aligned}&m \text{ repeats } 1R \text{ to become } 2L,\\ &i \text{ repeats } 2L \text{ to become } 3R.\end{aligned}\right\} \tag{16}$$

The first and last points, $1R$ and $3R$, are related by the 2-fold axis A_π. An alternative proof, in which this conclusion is more obvious, is to use, instead of m, the same operation expressed as $\bar{2}$, and instead of i the same operation expressed as $\bar{1}$, Fig. 6. This is a combination of two improper rotations about the same axis, and can be written

$$\bar{2} \cdot \bar{1} = 2. \tag{17}$$

$$\text{Thus} \qquad m \cdot i = A_\pi, \tag{18}$$

$$\text{or} \quad m \cdot i \cdot A_\pi = 1. \tag{19}$$

Summary of relations. The following two relations which have been demonstrated will be of use in subsequent discussions:

(*a*) (11) $\underbrace{m_1 \cdot m_2}_{\alpha/2} \cdot A_{-\alpha} = 1.$

Important variants of this are

(7) $\underbrace{m_1 \cdot m_2}_{\alpha/2} = A_\alpha.$

(10) $A_\alpha \cdot m_2 = m_{1,\alpha/2}.$

(*b*) (19) $m \cdot i \cdot A_\pi = 1.$

Important variants of this are

$$m \cdot i = A_\pi. \tag{20}$$

$$m \cdot A_\pi = i. \tag{21}$$

$$i \cdot A_\pi = m. \tag{22}$$

Alternative derivation of the crystal classes

The combination relations just discussed, together with some relations given in Chapter 4, constitute tools for a somewhat different derivation of the crystal classes. This alternative derivation is essentially the classical method.

Principles of derivation. The alternative method of derivation differs from that used in Chapter 5 only in the method of allowing for enantiomorphous repetition. In both methods one starts with the 11 sets of pure rotation axes, namely 1, 2, 3, 4, 6, 222, 322, 422, 622, 332, and 432. These are the 11 ways of repeating congruent objects about a point.

It is convenient, now, to adopt a classical nomenclature. An operation which repeats an original object to become a congruent object is called an *operation of the first sort*; an operation which repeats an original object to become the enantiomorphous object is called an *operation of the second sort*. The way the operations of repetition fall into these two categories is shown in Table 1. Note that the only kinds of operations of the first sort applicable to point-group symmetries are rotations.

The 11 axial groups involve only operations of the first sort. It was shown in Chapter 5 that the rest of the symmetry classes can be derived by adding to these groups appropriate rotoinversions (or equivalent rotoreflections). But, except when $n = 4$, any rotoinversion is equivalent to a rotation with an inversion or reflection. The rest of the symmetry classes (except for $\bar{4}$) can therefore be derived by starting with the 11 axial groups and adding to each of them an inversion center or a reflection in a permissible orientation. From the decomposition of a rotoinversion axis, it follows that a permissible orientation is normal to a permissible location of an even-fold axis. *These are all either perpendicular or parallel to the "principal" axis.*

Table 1. Classification of symmetry operations

	Operations of first sort	Operations of the second sort
Operations occurring in point groups	Rotations	Reflections Inversions Rotoreflections Rotoinversions
Additional operations occurring in space groups	Translations Translation-rotations (i.e., screws)	Translation-reflections (i.e., glides)

The Schoenflies notation. These possibilities are neatly represented by the symbols of Schoenflies. Schoenflies treated the crystallographic symmetries as mathematical "groups" of operations. A group containing only an operation and its powers is called a *cyclic group*. For example, the operations of a 4-fold axis are the rotations 1, $\pi/2$, π, $3\pi/2$. These are all "powers"* of the fundamental rotation $\pi/2$, specifically the powers 0, 1, 2, and 3. These operations form a cyclical group. The symbol for a cyclical group corresponding to a rotation axis of order n is C_n. The crystallographic symmetries involving a single rotation axis are therefore C_1, C_2, C_3, C_4, and C_6.

The axial groups containing more than one axis are obviously not cyclical since they contain operations other than powers of one rotation. These remaining axial groups are of two general kinds. One kind combines a set of 2-fold axes at right angles to a chief axis of order n. Because of their 2-fold axes these are called *dihedral groups*, symbolized by D_n. A second kind consists of the several sets of axes oriented along rational directions of a cube. These are designated the *octahedral group*, O (corresponding to 432), and the *tetrahedral group*, T (corresponding to 332 or "23"), since these symmetries are the axial symmetries of the octahedron and tetrahedron respectively.

* See the section "Periodic repetitions," page 8, Chapter 2.

In this symbolism, the 11 axial symmetries are represented by C_1, C_2, C_3, C_4, C_6, D_2, D_3, D_4, D_6, O, and T. All except one of the groups of the second sort can be found by adding inversion centers and reflection planes to these. The addition of an inversion center is symbolized by adding an "i" to the subscript.* The addition of a "vertical" plane (parallel to the chief symmetry axis) is symbolized by adding v to the subscript, a "horizontal" plane by adding h to the subscript, and "diagonal" planes ("vertical" planes between the 2-fold axes of the dihedral groups) by adding d to the subscript.

Derivation of the crystal classes. The derivation of the crystal classes by the alternative method is outlined in Table 2. The distribution of symmetry elements in these symmetries is illustrated in Fig. 7. These diagrams are drawn in such a way that the point in which these symmetry elements intersect is at the center of a sphere. The outline of the sphere is shown as seen from the "top."† This outline is lightly dotted unless there is an equatorial reflection plane, in which case it is shown as a heavy line. The symmetry elements are drawn as they would appear outcropping on the surface of the sphere, except that the symbols are conventional not necessarily drawn in perspective. A small circle is added at the center if the symmetry collection includes an inversion center.

In the upper part of Table 2 are listed the 11 axial groups C_n, D_n, T, and O. The rest of the table contains crystal classes of the second sort.

The first subdivision of the groups of the second sort contains the one class $S_4 \Leftrightarrow \bar{4}$. Note that this symmetry consists of a single rotoinversion axis $\bar{4}$, which is the only crystallographic axis of the second sort which cannot be described by adding an inversion center, or perpendicular plane, to an axis of the first sort. No combinations of $\bar{4}$ with other axes need be considered, for all combinations of $\bar{4}$ with other axes require another improper axis, according to the IIP rule, none of which has order 4 according to Table 7, Chapter 4. Since this other improper axis is not $\bar{4}$, it can always be decomposed into a proper axis plus a mirror or inversion center. An inversion center or perpendicular mirror transforms $\bar{4}$ into $4/m$. The possibility of a mirror parallel to $\bar{4}$ is included in the category D_{nd}, at the bottom of Table 2.

In the next division planes and centers are systematically added to the C_n groups. In the upper line a plane is added normal to the axis. Since the axis is regarded as "vertical," the plane is "horizontal," and the groups can be represented by adding a horizontal plane, h, to a group C_n, i.e., $(C_n)^h$. The customary designation is C_{nh}, except where $n = 1$, which Schoenflies designated as C_s. The s stands for *Spiegel* (German: mirror). If the axis is even-fold, then (21) applies, and the symmetry collection accordingly contains an inversion

* In the original Schoenflies' symbols such additions were added as a superscript.

† This is therefore an orthographic projection, not the customary stereographic projection; i.e., it is exactly the way the sphere looks from a distance.

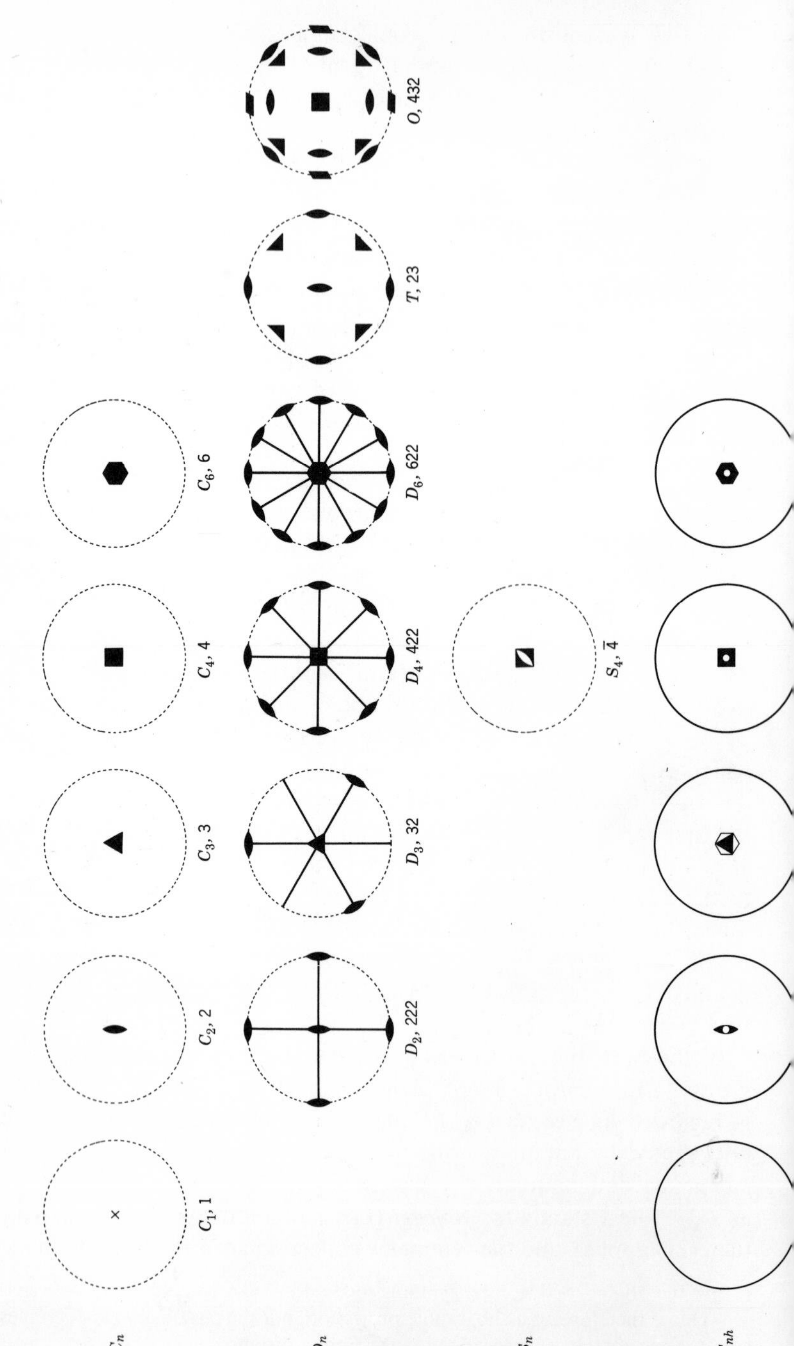
C_n
D_n
S_n
C_{nh}
C_1, 1
C_2, 2
C_3, 3
C_4, 4
C_6, 6
D_2, 222
D_3, 32
D_4, 422
D_6, 622
T, 23
O, 432
S_4, $\bar{4}$

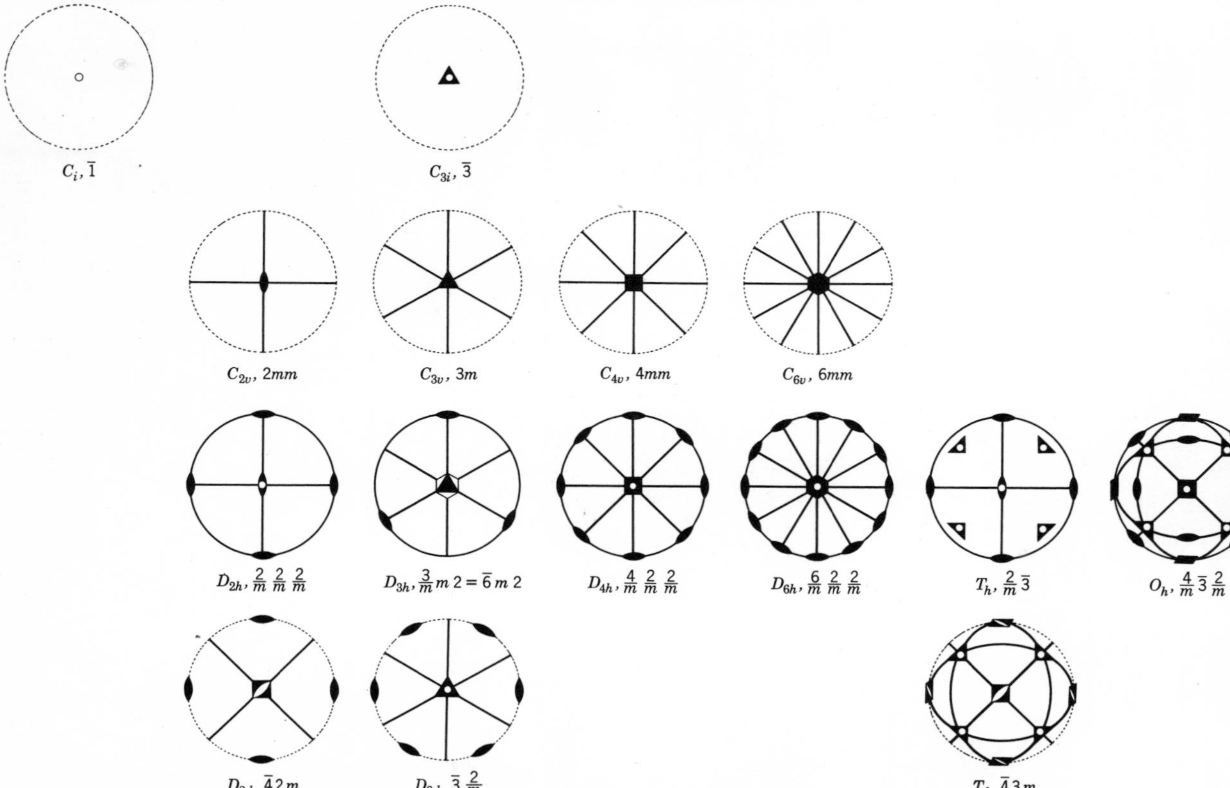

FIG. 7. Derivation of the 32 crystal classes.

Table 2. The 32 crystal classes

Type of group	Classes							Number of classes
C_n	C_1 1	C_2 2	C_3 3	C_4 4	C_6 6			5
D_n and cubic		D_2 222	D_3 32	D_4 422	D_6 622	T 332 (23)	O 432	6 11
S_n				S_4 $\bar{4}$				1
C_{nh}	C_s m	(*i*) C_{2h} $\frac{2}{m}$	C_{3h} $\frac{3}{m} = \bar{6}$	(*i*) C_{4h} $\frac{4}{m}$	(*i*) C_{6h} $\frac{6}{m}$			5
C_{ni}	(*i*) C_i $\bar{1}$		(*i*) C_{3i} $\bar{3}$					2
C_{nv}		C_{2v} $2mm$	C_{3v} $3m$	C_{4v} $4mm$	C_{6v} $6mm$			4
D_{nh} and cubic		(*i*) D_{2h} $\frac{2}{m}\frac{2}{m}\frac{2}{m}$	D_{3h} $\bar{6}m2$	(*i*) D_{4h} $\frac{4}{m}\frac{2}{m}\frac{2}{m}$	(*i*) D_{6h} $\frac{6}{m}\frac{2}{m}\frac{2}{m}$	(*i*) T_h $\frac{2}{m}\bar{3}$	(*i*) O_h $\frac{4}{m}\bar{3}\frac{2}{m}$	6
D_{nd} and cubic		D_{2d} $\bar{4}2m$	(*i*) D_{3d} $\bar{3}\frac{2}{m}$			T_d $\bar{4}3m$		3 21 32

center, which is indicated in Table 2 by placing the designation (*i*) above the Schoenflies symbol.

When n is even, the symmetry collections of C_{nh} contain a center, so that no group different from those already derived can be found by adding an inversion center to C_n. In other words the symmetries C_{ni} are the same as C_{nh} when n is even. When n is odd, however, C_{nh} contains no inversion center, and so the C_{ni} symmetries are new. The only crystallographic cases where n is odd are $n = 1$ and $n = 3$. These two new groups are listed in the next line.

There remains only the possibility of adding "vertical" planes to C_n. These could be designated $(C_n)^v$, but are now customarily designated C_{nv}. Note that, if a single plane is placed so that it contains the axis, the n-fold axis makes n planes out of it, each separated by an angle α with its nearest neighbor. To each of these planes (10) applies; that is, the fundamental rotation, α, of the axis, combined with the reflection, requires another mirror at an angular distance of $\alpha/2$ from the original mirror. This means that halfway between the n planes repeated by the axis, a second set of n more planes is interleaved. When n is odd (the only crystallographic case is $n = 3$) the "back" part of the original set of planes coincides with the "front" part of the new, interleaving planes. It is for this reason that, in the international notation, whereas C_{2v} is designated $2mm$, C_{3v} is designated $3m$ and not $3mm$, since the two sets of planes are not distinct.

The permissible ways of adding horizontal planes, vertical planes, and inversion centers to the C_n group are now exhausted. Note that each of the symmetry elements of the second sort which have been added (or produced by the addition) has the effect of transforming the original axis into itself. This means that the new group is truly based upon the original axis of the first sort, and no new axes of the first sort have been introduced. If they had been introduced, the only permissible ones would have been such as to produce a D_n, T, or O group, and these are still to be considered as bases for groups of the second sort.

In the next section, operations of the second sort are added to the D_n, T, and O groups. If a "horizontal" plane is added, the D_{nh}, T_h and O_h groups result. In each of these the "horizontal" plane and "horizontal" 2-fold (even-fold in the case of group O) axes combine according to (10) to require another mirror at an angle of $\pi/2$ from the "horizontal" plane. This is accordingly a "vertical" plane. Therefore no new groups would result if a "vertical" plane were added to the D_n, T, or O groups. Note that, when n is even, (21) requires the group to have an inversion center. The only crystallographic case for $n =$ odd is D_{3h}, which accordingly lacks an inversion center. Therefore one new group can be obtained by adding an inversion center to D_n, specifically $(D_3)^i$. But this is identical with D_{3d}, to be considered as part of the next category.

The addition of a horizontal plane throws the D_n, T, and O axial sets into coincidence with themselves. There is only one other general way to cause this kind of self-coincidence, and this is to add a "vertical" plane *between* pairs of similar 2-fold axes in D_n and T groups. (A "diagonal" plane between 2-fold axes already exists in O_h. A vertical plane between the "horizontal" 4 and 2 axes of O would not throw the set of axes into coincidence with itself.)

This possibility has interesting limitations. Since m is equivalent to a perpendicular $\bar{2}$ axis, this amounts to combining a $\bar{2}$ axis with a 2 axis. According to Table 7, Chapter 4, these can be combined at angles $\gamma = 180°, 120°, 90°$, and $60°$ for combinations 222, 223, 224, and 226 respectively. But one of the 2-fold axes is 2 and the other is $\bar{2}$. Therefore, according to the *P I I* rule of Chapter 5, the "chief" axis must be improper, giving $2\bar{2}\bar{2}$, $2\bar{2}\bar{3}$, $2\bar{2}\bar{4}$, and $2\bar{2}\bar{6}$ as possibilities. Returning to Table 2, the D_{nd} groups would have the $\bar{2}$ axes halfway between the 2 axes of the D_n group. In Table 3 are listed the characteristics of D_{nd} and

Table 3. Some characteristics of D_{nd} and T_d groups

n	D_{nd}	Angle between nearest axes 2	Angle between axis 2 and nearest axis $\bar{2} = m$	Required vertical axis
1	D_{1d}	180°	90°	$\bar{2}$
2	D_{2d}	90	45	$\bar{4}$
3	D_{3d}	60	30	$\bar{6}$
4	D_{4d}	45	$22\frac{1}{2}$	$\bar{8}$
6	D_{6d}	30	15	$\overline{12}$
2	T_d	90	45	$\bar{4}$

T_d groups which are consequences of this. Note that 8 and 12 axes would arise for D_{4d} and D_{6d} groups. Since n cannot be 8 or 12 for crystallographic groups, these need not be considered as possible crystal classes. Furthermore, D_{1d} is just another description of a 2-fold axis at right angles to a mirror, and so is equivalent to C_{2h}. Thus, the only new crystallographic D_{nd} groups are D_{2d}, D_{3d}, and T_d. Note that, according to the last column of Table 3, which is a consequence of the *P I I* rule, the chief axes are rotoinversion axes. Only D_{3d} has n odd, and therefore this alone, according to Table 2, Chapter 4, has an inversion center.

Correspondence between Schoenflies and international symbols. In this alternative derivation of the crystal classes the natural designations are the Schoenflies symbols. The correspondence between the Schoenflies symbols and the currently used international symbols is shown in Table 4. Both symbols are included in Table 2 and Fig. 7.

Table 4. Correspondence between Schoenflies notation and international notation

Crystal system	Schoenflies notation	International symbol	Crystal system	Schoenflies notation	International symbol
Triclinic	C_1	1	Hexagonal	C_3	3
	C_i	$\bar{1}$		D_3	32
				C_{3i}	$\bar{3}$
	C_2	2		C_{3v}	$3m$
Monoclinic	C_s	m		D_{3d}	$\bar{3}\,\frac{2}{m}$ $(\bar{3}m)$
	C_{2h}	$\frac{2}{m}$		C_{3h}	$\bar{6}$
				D_{3h}	$\bar{6}m2$
Orthorhombic	D_2	222		C_6	6
	C_{2v}	$2mm$		D_6	622
	D_{2h}	$\frac{2}{m}\frac{2}{m}\frac{2}{m}$		C_{6v}	$6mm$
				C_{6h}	$\frac{6}{m}$
Tetragonal	C_4	4		D_{6h}	$\frac{6}{m}\frac{2}{m}\frac{2}{m}$ $(6/mmm)$
	D_4	422			
	S_4	$\bar{4}$	Isometric	T	23
	C_{4h}	$\frac{4}{m}$		O	432
	C_{4v}	$4mm$		T_h	$\frac{2}{m}\bar{3}$ $(m3)$
	D_{2d}	$\bar{4}2m$		T_d	$\bar{4}3m$
	D_{4h}	$\frac{4}{m}\frac{2}{m}\frac{2}{m}$ $(4/mmm)$		O_h	$\frac{4}{m}\bar{3}\frac{2}{m}$ $(m3m)$

Exercises

1. Prove that the combination of two parallel reflections is a translation. (Hint: Start with two mirrors at a small finite angle, let the point of intersection recede to infinity while the angle between mirrors reduces to zero, but permit a small distance to remain between the two mirrors.)

2. Solve (6) for μ for the noncrystallographic axes 7, 8, 9, and 10.

3. Set up an orthogonal coordinate system XYZ with a 2-fold axis along Z and the mirror in the plane XY. Choose an arbitrary point P having coordinates xyz. Derive the coordinates of the points equivalent to P by the symmetry operation. Demonstrate that this proves (19).

4. Using the methods of this chapter, derive the symmetry classes based upon the noncrystallographic axes 7, 8, 9, 10.

5. Using the methods of this chapter, derive the symmetry classes based upon the noncrystallographic combination of axes 235.

7 · The symmetrical plane lattices

So far, only those groups of operations have been considered that repeat an object about a fixed point. Since the "object" is any and all objects, this is equivalent to referring to groups of operations that repeat all space about a point and yet leave the point unmoved. The fact that a point is left unmoved by these groups of operations gives rise to the designation *point* groups.

More general kinds of repetition involve not only rotations, reflections, and inversions, but translations as well. In Chapter 3, translations were considered by themselves. But obviously it is possible for an object to be repeated by translations and also by rotations, to form a more complex, extended pattern. The group of operations containing translations does not leave a point unmoved. In a sense, however, it leaves space unmoved, for a translation requires a duplication of space at periodic intervals. A complete consideration of all combinations of translations with all kinds of rotations yields complex symmetry groups which leave space unmoved (in this sense), and these are accordingly called *space groups*. Before dealing with such complex symmetry collections, it is first necessary to know how rotations interact with translations.

The consequence of combining a rotation with a translation is far-reaching and, indeed, underlies all space-group theory. In this chapter, however, only the consequences of combining a translation with the kinds of rotation that transform a plane into itself are considered. These are obviously rotations about axes perpendicular to, or parallel to, the plane. (A rotation parallel to a plane evidently affects the points on the plane in the same way as a reflection across a mirror perpendicular to the plane and intersecting the plane in the line of the rotation axis.)

The crystallographic plane point groups

Periodic translations in a plane are consistent with five axial symmetries, according to Chapter 4. These are the symmetries 1, 2, 3, 4, and 6, Fig. 1. In Chapter 1 it was shown that the only operation in a plane which transforms an object into the enantiomorphous object is a reflection. For this reason all symmetries concerned with an alternating repetition of left and right can be found by adding to each of the possible rotation axes a parallel reflection plane. The n-fold axis repeats this mirror to n mirrors, separated by angular intervals

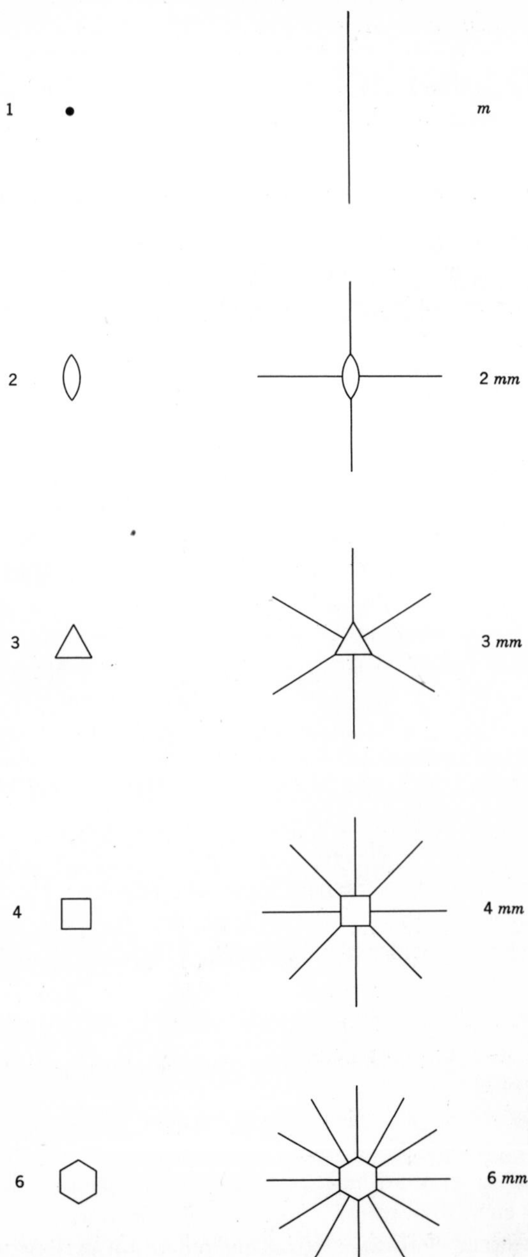

FIG. 1. The ten crystallographic point groups in a plane.

α. Relation (10) of Chapter 6 requires a second set of mirrors interleaved between this first set, at an angular interval $\alpha/2$. When n is odd, these two sets coincide.

The five axial groups and the five further groups of the second sort which correspond to crystallographic symmetries in a plane are illustrated in Fig. 1.

Combination of a rotation and a perpendicular translation

Now consider the operation of a rotation about an axis A through an angle α, followed by a translation t perpendicular to A, Fig. 2. As in Euler's construction, this combination is readily analyzed by a consideration of how

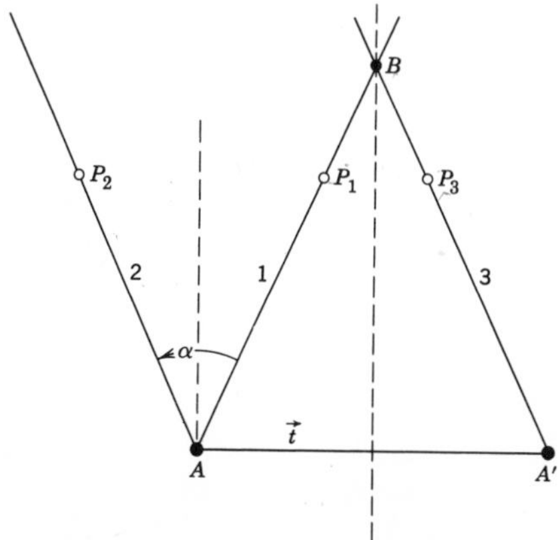

FIG. 2. Combination of a rotation, A_α, with a translation $t_\perp$.

space is moved about by these operations, attention being fixed on a special line. This strategic line, labeled 1 in Fig. 2, is one which, when rotated about A through α, places the initial line, 1, and the rotated line, 2, symmetrically on either side of the perpendicular to the translation, t, through A. The operation A_α brings 1 to 2, and the translation brings 2 to 3, Fig. 2. The initial and final positions of the lines are 1 and 3. Obviously, at their intersection, point B, the line has not moved. The net motion of the line is therefore equivalent to a rotation about B. Naturally, this rotation applies to all points on the line. For example,

$$\begin{aligned} &A_\alpha \text{ causes } P_1 \to P_2, \\ \text{then, } &t \text{ causes } P_2 \to P_3, \\ \therefore\ &A_\alpha \cdot t \text{ causes } P_1 \to P_3, \end{aligned}$$

which is a rotation through angle ABA' about B. It is evident that this angle is α, in the same sense (counterclockwise in the example) as P_1AP_2. Furthermore, since the line is embedded in space, and since the operations A_α and t act on all space, it is evident that all space must also be rotated about B by this combination of operations. As a result of this discussion, it can be said that *a rotation about an axis A through an angle α, followed by a translation perpendicular to the axis, is equivalent to a rotation through the same angle α, in the same sense, but about an axis B situated on the perpendicular bisector of AA′ and at a distance (AA′/2) cot $\alpha/2$ from AA′.* This can be expressed analytically as

$$A_\alpha \cdot t_\perp = B_\alpha. \tag{1}$$

Combination of the rotation axes with a plane lattice

General principles. The results of the last section can be applied to combining the several rotations of an n-fold axis with the translations of a plane lattice

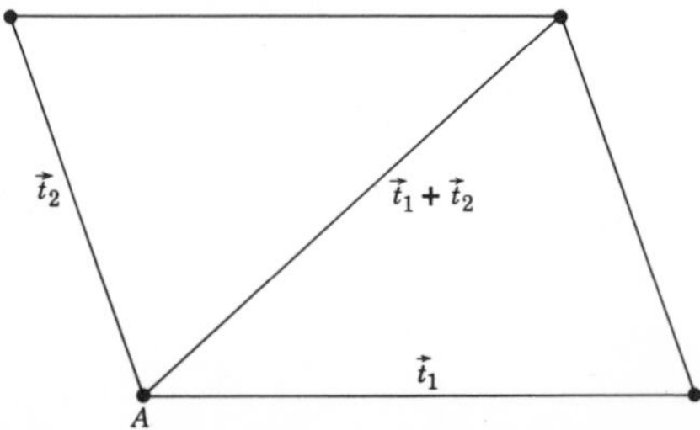

FIG. 3. The nonequivalent translations of a plane cell to be combined with rotations of axis A.

whose plane is perpendicular to the axis. In forming the combination, two principles should be observed:

In the first place, a rotation axis implies, in general, several related rotations. Thus, if the symmetry axis is n-fold, the smallest rotation is $\alpha = 2\pi/n$. The rotation axis then implies the rotations α, 2α, 3α, $\cdots$, $n\alpha$, where $n\alpha = 2\pi$. *Each* of these rotations is to be combined with the translation.

In the second place, each rotation must be combined with the various translations of the plane lattice. Actually, it is sufficient to consider only the translations $\vec{t}_1$, $\vec{t}_2$, and $\vec{t}_1 + \vec{t}_2$, because these terminate in the primitive cell, Fig. 3.

2-fold axis. The 2-fold axis implies the operations 1 and A_π. The operation 1 is trivial and can be neglected. The operation A_π is concerned with a rotation of π about A, Fig. 4. Thus (1) becomes $A_\pi \cdot t = B_\pi$. The location of B is on the perpendicular bisector of AA' and at such a location of this bisector that $ABA' = \pi$, Fig. 5. This places B on AA' halfway between A and A'. This combination of A_π must be made for each of the translations $\vec{t}_1$, $\vec{t}_2$, and $\vec{t}_1 + \vec{t}_2$, Fig. 6. Thus, as a consequence of A_π and the translations of the lattice, the additional operations of rotations through π occur at points B, C, and D. Therefore, a plane lattice consistent with a perpendicular 2-fold rotation axis has 4 nonequivalent* 2-fold rotation axes in each of its primitive cells, Fig. 7.

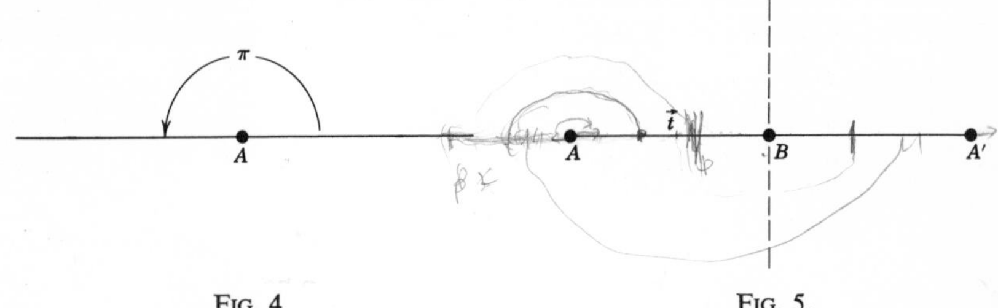

FIG. 4. FIG. 5.

One occurs at the cell corners, one occurs at the cell centers, and the third and fourth occur at the centers of the two cell edges.

3-fold axis. If a plane lattice is consistent with a 3-fold axis, then its translations $\vec{t}_1$ and $\vec{t}_2$ are carried into one another by the 3-fold axis at A, Fig. 8,

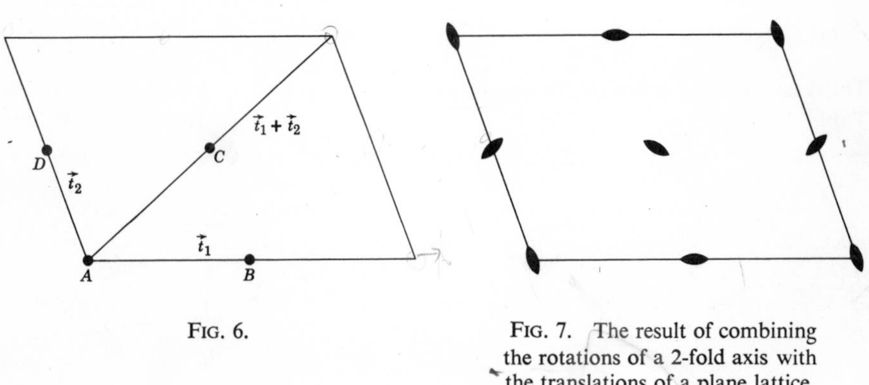

FIG. 6.

FIG. 7. The result of combining the rotations of a 2-fold axis with the translations of a plane lattice.

* Two symmetry elements are *equivalent* if an operation of some other symmetry element carries one of them into the other. For example, the alternate 2-fold axes of $D_4 = 422$ are equivalent (see Fig. 7, Chapter 6). On the other hand, two symmetry elements are *nonequivalent* if no operation of any other symmetry element carries one of them into the other. For example, the neighboring 2-fold axes of $D_4 = 422$ are nonequivalent.

and so are equivalent. In this case it is only necessary to combine the rotations at A with $\vec{t}_1$ and $\vec{t}_1 + \vec{t}_2$, since any result obtained by combining A with $\vec{t}_2$ would be equivalent to that obtained by combining A with $\vec{t}_1$.

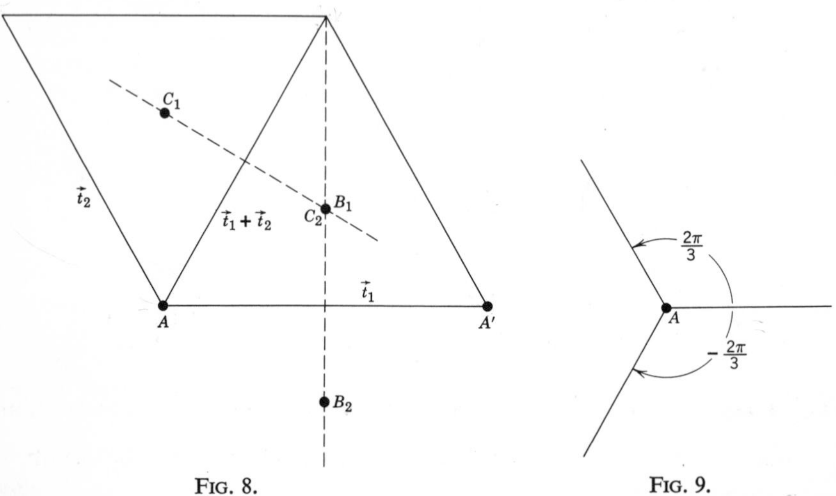

FIG. 8. FIG. 9.

The operations at A are rotations of 1, $2\pi/3$, and $4\pi/3$, ($\Leftrightarrow -2\pi/3$), Fig. 9. The results of combining these rotations with $\vec{t}_1$ and $\vec{t}_1 + \vec{t}_2$ are shown in Table 1. Since $B_1 = C_2$ and $B_2 \Leftrightarrow C_1$ by the 3-fold axis at A, it is evident

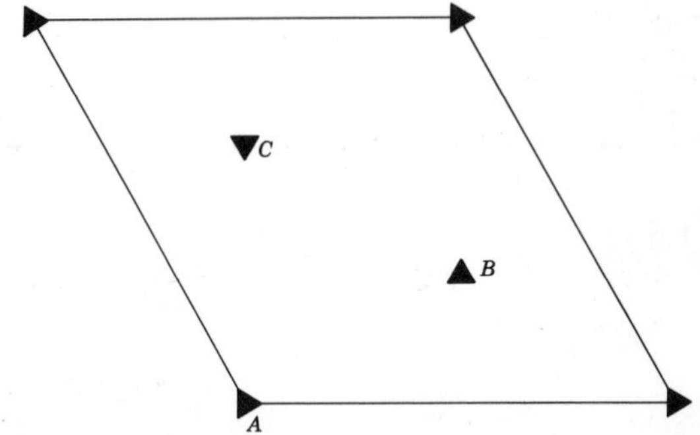

FIG. 10. The result of combining the rotations of a 3-fold axis with the translations of a plane lattice.

that the rotations 1, $2\pi/3$, and $-2\pi/3$ ($\Leftrightarrow 4\pi/3$) exist at B_1 and C_1. Since these are the three operations of a 3-fold axis, it is evident that three non-equivalent 3-fold axes are located in the cell at A, B_1, and C_1 as shown in Figs. 8 and 10.

Table 1. The rotations resulting from combining the operations of a 3-fold axis with the nonequivalent translations of the cell

Rotations at A	Translations	
	$\vec{t_1}$	$\vec{t_1} + \vec{t_2}$
1	1	1
$\frac{2\pi}{3}$	$\frac{2\pi}{3}$ at B_1	$\frac{2\pi}{3}$ at C_1
$-\frac{2\pi}{3}$	$-\frac{2\pi}{3}$ at B_2 ($\Bumpeq C_1$)	$-\frac{2\pi}{3}$ at C_2 ($= B_1$)

4-fold axis. If a plane lattice is consistent with a 4-fold axis its translations $\vec{t_1}$ and $\vec{t_2}$ are equivalent. It is therefore only necessary to combine the operations

Table 2. The rotations resulting from combining the operations of a 4-fold axis with the nonequivalent translations of the cell

Rotations at A	Translations	
	$\vec{t_1}$	$\vec{t_1} + \vec{t_2}$
1	1	1
$\frac{\pi}{2}$	$\frac{\pi}{2}$ at B_1	$\frac{\pi}{2}$ at C_1 ($\Bumpeq A$)
π	π at B_2	π at C_2 ($= B_1$)
$-\frac{\pi}{2}$	$-\frac{\pi}{2}$ at B_3 ($\Bumpeq B_1$)	$-\frac{\pi}{2}$ at C_3 ($\Bumpeq A$)

of the 4-fold axis with $\vec{t_1}$ and $\vec{t_1} + \vec{t_2}$. The operations of the 4-fold axis are rotations of 1, $\pi/2$, π, and $3\pi/2$ ($= -\pi/2$), Fig. 11. The combinations of these operations with the translations are shown in Table 2 and Fig. 12. It is evident that at B_1 there occur rotations of 1, $\pi/2$, π, and $-\pi/2$. Since these are the operations of a 4-fold axis, it is evident that a 4-fold axis occurs at B_1. This axis is not equivalent to the original 4-fold axis at A. Furthermore, at B_2 there occur the rotations 1 and π, which are the operations of a 2-fold axis. Therefore

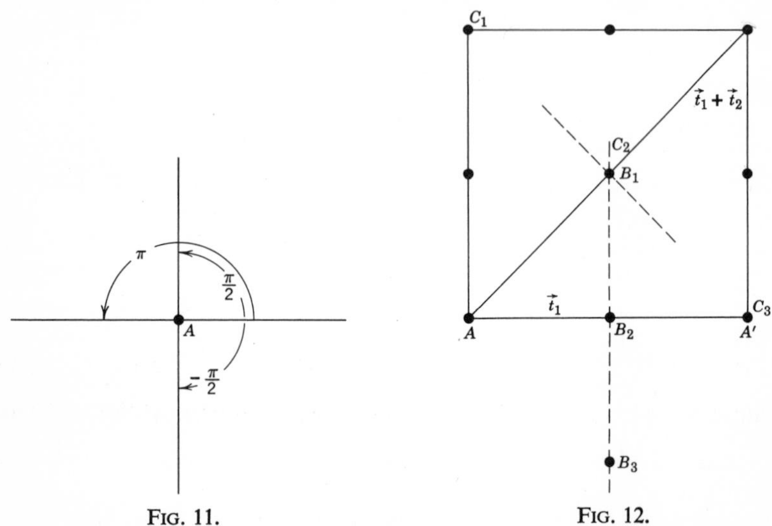

FIG. 11.

FIG. 12.

a 2-fold axis occurs at B_2. (The further operations at C_1 and C_3, shown in Table 2, already exist at A as a part of the original 4-fold axis.) The distribution of symmetry elements in the primitive cell of a lattice consistent with a 4-fold axis is consequently as shown in Fig. 13.

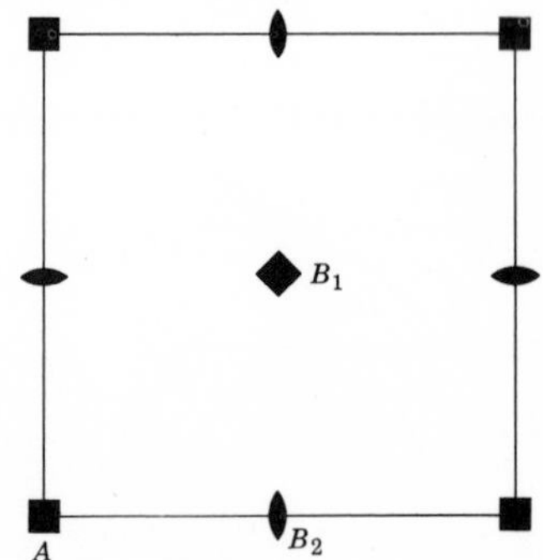

FIG. 13. The result of combining the rotations of a 4-fold axis with the translations of a plane lattice.

6-fold axis. If a plane lattice is consistent with a 6-fold axis, then $\vec{t}_1 \Leftrightarrow \vec{t}_1 + \vec{t}_2 \Leftrightarrow \vec{t}_2$. Thus it is only necessary to consider combinations of $\vec{t}_1$ with the rotations of the 6-fold axis. This axis implies the rotations of 1, $\pi/3$, $2\pi/3$, π, $4\pi/3$, and $5\pi/3$. In terms of rotations of π or less, this list of rotations can be

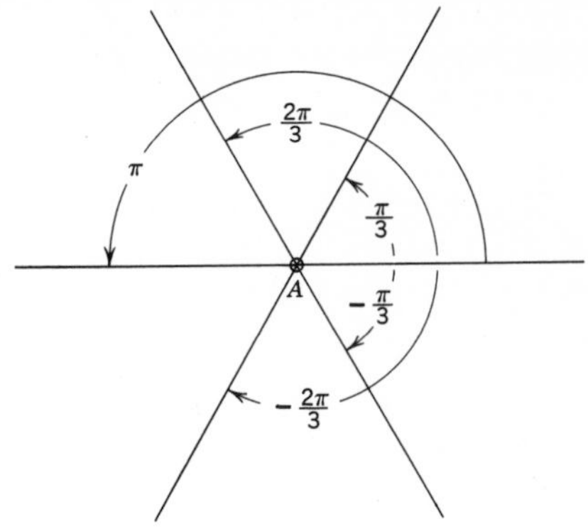

Fig. 14.

restated as 1, $\pi/3$, $2\pi/3$, π, $-2\pi/3$, and $-\pi/3$ (Fig. 14). The combinations of these rotations with $\vec{t_1}$ are listed in Table 3 and illustrated in Fig. 15. At B_2

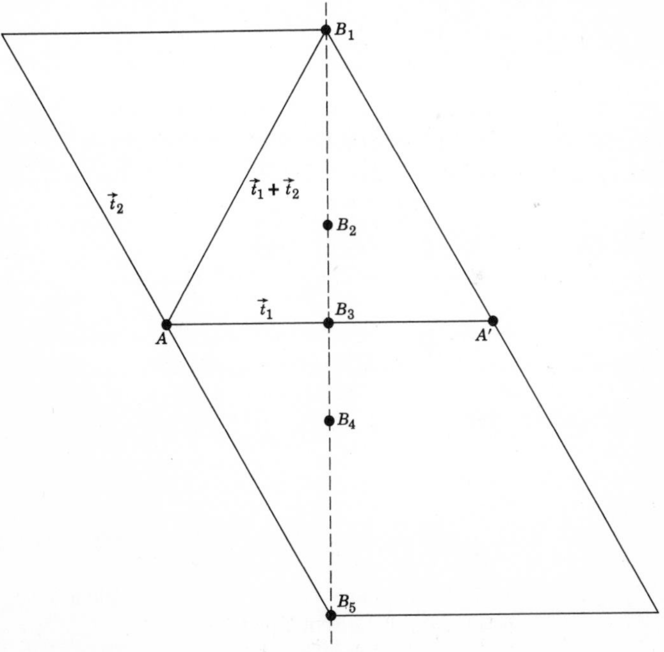

Fig. 15.

or its equivalent there occur rotations of 1, $2\pi/3$, and $-2\pi/3$. These are the operations of a 3-fold axis, which must therefore arise at B_2. At B_3 there occur

Table 3. The rotations resulting from combining the operations of a 6-fold axis with the nonequivalent translations of the cell

Rotations at A	Translation t_1
1	1
$\frac{\pi}{3}$	$\frac{\pi}{3}$ at B_1 ($\Leftrightarrow A$)
$\frac{2\pi}{3}$	$\frac{2\pi}{3}$ at B_2
π	π at B_3
$-\frac{2\pi}{3}$	$-\frac{2\pi}{3}$ at B_4 ($\Leftrightarrow B_2$)
$-\frac{\pi}{3}$	$-\frac{\pi}{3}$ at B_5 ($\Leftrightarrow A$)

rotations of 1 and π. These are the operations of a 2-fold axis, which must therefore arise at B_3. (The further rotations of $\pm\pi/3$ at B_1 and B_5 are already operations occurring in the original 6-fold axis at A and equivalent positions.)

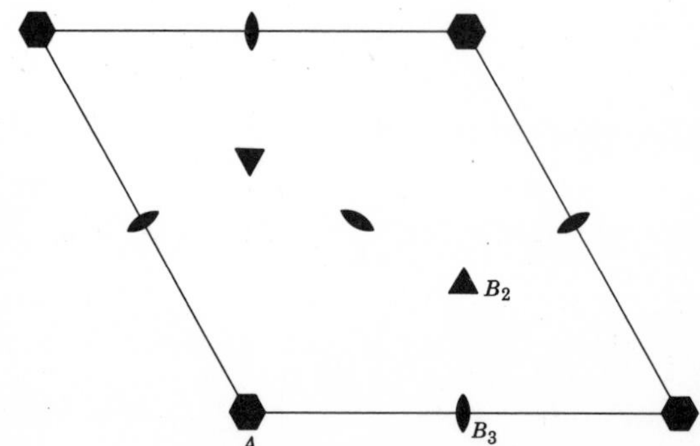

FIG. 16. The result of combining the rotations of a 6-fold axis with the translations of a plane lattice.

The complete distribution of symmetry elements in the cell is found by operating with the 6-fold axis at A, Fig. 15, on the symmetry elements found at B_2 and B_3. The resulting symmetry distribution is shown in Fig. 16.

Some results of combining axes and plane lattices

The number of nonequivalent axes per cell. The discussion just given of the combination of axial symmetry with lattice translations shows that, in general, there are several nonequivalent axes of the same kind per cell. The number of nonequivalent axes for each kind of axis is listed in Table 4. The tabulation can be compared with Fig. 24.

Table 4. The numbers and locations of nonequivalent axes

Axis	Number of nonequivalent axes per cell	Coordinates of axes, in fractions of translations t_1 and t_2
2	4	$0\,0$, $\frac{1}{2}\frac{1}{2}$, $\frac{1}{2}0$, $0\frac{1}{2}$
3	3	$0\,0$, $\frac{2}{3}\frac{1}{3}$, $\frac{1}{3}\frac{2}{3}$
4	2	$0\,0$, $\frac{1}{2}\frac{1}{2}$
6	1	$0\,0$

Lattice types consistent with plane symmetries of the first sort. The discussion also shows that there are a limited number of cell shapes, or lattice types, required for the five permissible axial symmetries. A perfectly general parallelogram-shaped mesh serves for a pattern based on 1-fold axes. It also serves for the 2-fold axial symmetry. A 120°-rhombus-shaped mesh serves for both 3-fold and 6-fold axes, and a square mesh is required for a 4-fold axis. Thus only three kinds of lattice types are required for the five purely rotational symmetries.

Lattice types consistent with plane symmetries of the second sort

In the foregoing sections the distributions of symmetry in plane lattices consistent with the plane symmetries 1, 2, 3, 4, and 6 were derived. It is possible to systematically derive the distributions of symmetry in plane lattices consistent with the symmetries m, $2mm$, $3m$, $4mm$, and $6mm$. The immediate purposes will be achieved, however, if merely the specialized shapes of the meshes of the plane lattices are derived. For this purpose, the following lemma is convenient:

Lemma: For $n > 2$, the shape of a plane lattice consistent with pure axial symmetry n is also consistent with corresponding symmetry nmm containing reflection planes m.

This is because, when $n > 2$, any lattice translation is repeated by the rotations of the axis to three or more noncollinear translations. The set of shortest equivalent translations determine the mesh of the lattice, which in this case must have the shape of a regular polygon. These regular polygons are already symmetrical with respect to mirrors normal to the plane of the net.

Thus, only when $n = 1$ and $n = 2$ can new lattice types arise due to reflections in planes normal to the plane lattice. These two cases are inherently the

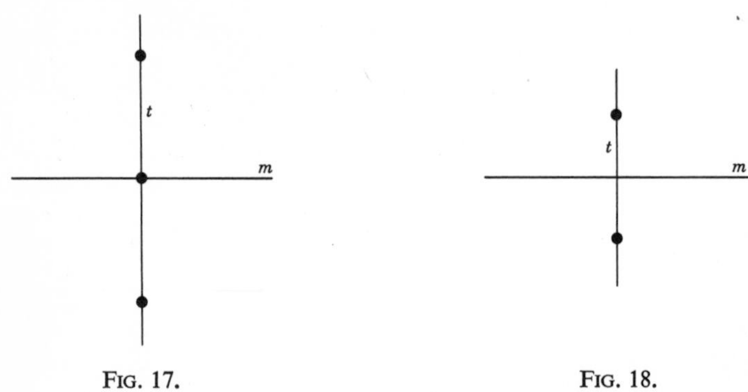

FIG. 17. FIG. 18.

same. This is because, so far as mesh *shape* is concerned, even in a completely general mesh, to each translation $\vec{t_1}$ there exists the reverse translation $-\vec{t_1}$. Thus the distribution of lattice points is inherently 2-fold about each plane-lattice point.

Therefore new plane-lattice mesh types can only be found by causing a general lattice type to be consistent either with symmetry *m* (or 2*mm*). The types of lattices consistent with symmetry *m* can be readily derived as follows:

Consider a point (not on the mirror) and its reflection. These two points determine a row. This row is necessarily normal to the mirror. Let the period along the row be *t*. The points on the row are only consistent with the reflection if a point lies on the mirror, Fig. 17, or if the mirror occurs halfway between points, Fig. 18.

Now consider a pair of adjacent lattice rows (both normal to the mirror). Both can be as in Fig. 17, both can be as in Fig. 18, or one can be as in Fig. 17 and the other as in Fig. 18. These combinations are shown in Figs. 19, 20, and 21, respectively. Note that the points of Figs. 19 and 20 determine a net with a rectangular mesh, whereas the points of Fig. 21 determine a net with a rhombus or diamond mesh. It is evident that the rectangular net has reflection planes in both the places shown in Figs. 19 and 20. The distribution of mirror planes in the rectangular lattice and the diamond lattice is as shown in Figs. 22 and 23.

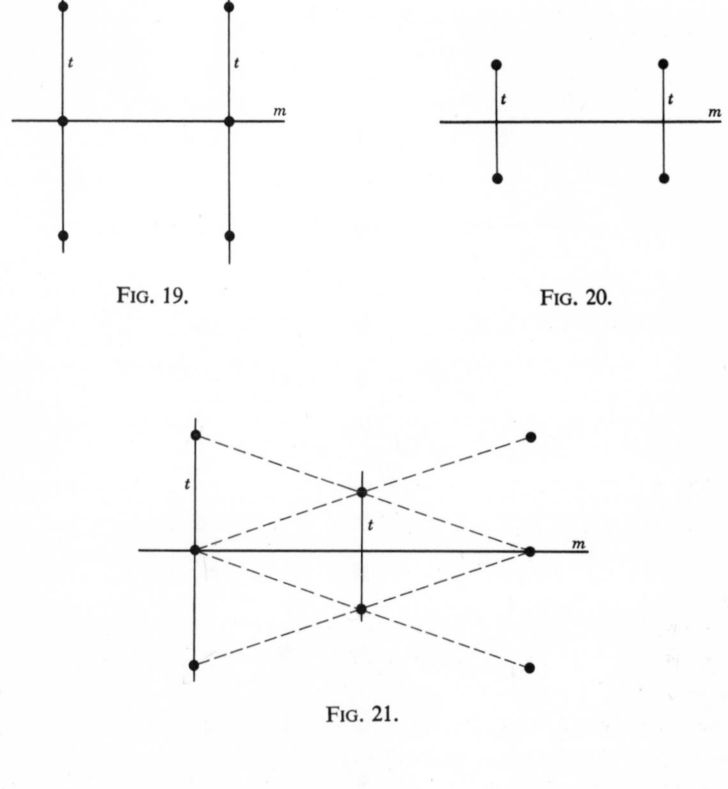

FIG. 19.

FIG. 20.

FIG. 21.

FIG. 22 and FIG. 23. The two plane lattices consistent with symmetry *m* or 2*mm*. The heavy lines are mirrors.

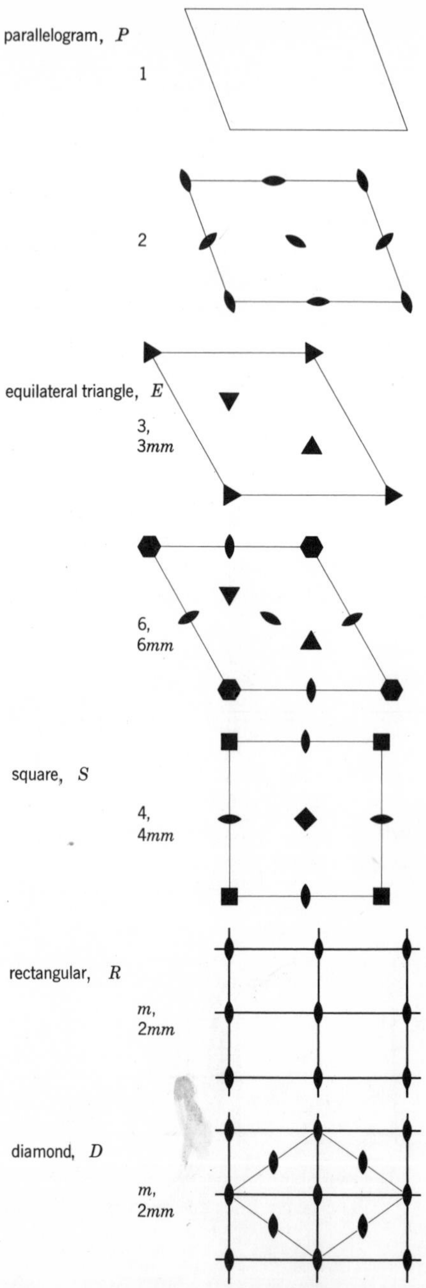

FIG. 24. The distribution of rotation axes and mirrors in the five plane lattice types.

The five plane lattices

In Fig. 24 are assembled the distributions of symmetry in the plane lattices consistent with the plane symmetries 1, 2, 3, 4, 6, and 2*mm*. It will be observed that there are five distinct lattice types or mesh shapes. These are also listed in Table 5, together with the plane symmetries consistent with each lattice type.

Table 5. The plane-lattice types consistent with the 10 plane point groups

Mesh shape	Symbol	Consistent with plane symmetries
Parallelogram	*P*	1, 2
120°-rhombus	*E*	3, 3*m*, 6, 6*mm*
Square	*S*	4, 4*mm*
Rectangle	*R*	*m*, 2*mm*
Diamond (rhombus)	*D*	*m*, 2*mm*

Exercises

1. Derive the noncrystallographic plane point groups having *n* up to 15.

8 · The symmetrical space-lattice types

In the last chapter it was shown that the several point groups in a plane require certain specializations of the translations in the plane. As a consequence there are five symmetrical plane lattices. In the same way, the several three-dimensional point groups require certain specializations of the translations in three-dimensional space. These symmetrical space lattices are derived in this chapter.

Principles of derivation

Resolution of a space lattice into a sequence of plane lattices. In Chapter 3 it was shown that translational repetition in three dimensions can be described as the periodic repetition of a two-dimensional pattern by a third translation. Accordingly, a three-dimensional lattice can be described as the periodic repetition of a two-dimensional lattice by a third translation. Thus, it is convenient to think of a three-dimensional lattice as a stack of two-dimensional lattices. Let each two-dimensional lattice in the stack be called a *level*. The translations in a level are described by the conjugate translations $\vec{t_1}$ and $\vec{t_2}$. Neighboring levels are related by the translation $\vec{t_3}$. When the plane-lattice type and $\vec{t_3}$ have been selected, the space lattice is determined. An alternate statement is that, if the plane-lattice type is chosen, and the relative positions of a pair of neighboring levels are selected, the space lattice is determined. It is convenient to think of the relative positions of the zero level (the level containing the origin, and corresponding to the "ground floor") and the first level, in this connection.

General procedure. A stack of plane lattices consistent with an n-fold axis, can evidently be devised by starting with a plane lattice type which has an n-fold axis location (Fig. 24, Chapter 7). The axis and plane lattice are mutually consistent if the axis is placed normal to the plane lattice and intersecting the plane of the lattice at the n-fold axial location. This constitutes the selection and placing of the zero level of the space lattice. The next level must be an identical lattice in parallel position with the zero level. In general, however, there are alternative locations for the axis on that level. This follows from

Fig. 24 and Table 4 of Chapter 7. In most cases this feature makes it possible to fit more than one type of space lattice to the same symmetry.

The relative placement of the zero and first levels can be described by giving the components of $\vec{t_3}$ in terms of fractions, x and y, of the vectors $\vec{t_1}$ and $\vec{t_2}$ respectively, plus a distance parameter z normal to the plane of the plane lattice. This parameter is the distance between the plane lattice levels of the stack. This system is used in the second last column of Table 1. For example, the notation in the third line for t_3 is $\frac{1}{2}\ \frac{1}{2}\ z$. This means that the components of $\vec{t_3}$ on $\vec{t_1}$, $\vec{t_2}$, and the normal to the plane of t_1 and t_2, are respectively $\frac{1}{2}t_1$, $\frac{1}{2}t_2$, z. A definite number (instead of z) for the last component indicates that the length of a unit along the normal is equal to a definite part of the particular length of the unit used along vectors t_1 and t_2. This notation occurs only in the last three entries of Table 1, and will be explained when it arises.

Symmetries to be considered. For many purposes it is desirable to distinguish between symmetries which include the operation of an inversion from those which do not. If the operation of inversion is present, the collection of symmetry elements includes a symmetry center (center of inversion); otherwise it does not. The adjective *centric* (or *centrosymmetrical*) means that the symmetry collection includes an inversion center, whereas the adjective *acentric* (or *noncentrosymmetrical*) means that it does not.

For every translational repetition represented by a vector $\vec{t}$, there exists the reverse repetition, represented by the reverse vector $-\vec{t}$. Therefore space lattices are inherently centric. Thus, whether a crystal class does or does not contain a symmetry center, the lattice types consistent with it do contain symmetry centers. Therefore, only those crystal classes need be considered that are obtained by adding a symmetry center (if not already present) to the 32 crystal classes. This results in 11 symmetries, which are the 11 centric crystal classes. The condensation of symmetries that results from adding a symmetry center to each of the crystal classes is shown in the first two columns of Table 1.

The lemma given in Chapter 7 showed that, when n is greater than 2, the same lattice type results whether the crystal class has "vertical" planes or not. This allows a further reduction in the number of symmetries which need to be considered. The reduction is shown in the second and third columns of Table 1.

Designation of space-lattice types

In the derivation that follows it will develop that, in general, each symmetry is consistent with more than one lattice type. It would be possible to accept as coordinate axes the translations of the primitive cell of each lattice type so

Table 1. Derivation of the space-lattice types

Crystal class characteristics			Plane-lattice sequence		Designation of space lattice
Crystal class	Representative centrosymmetrical class	Dimensional symmetry of lattice	Plane-lattice type	t_3	
$1,\ \bar{1}$	$\bar{1}$	$\bar{1}$	P	$x\ y\ z$	$1P$
$2,\ m,\ \frac{2}{m}$	$\frac{2}{m}$	$\frac{2}{m}$	P	$0\ 0\ z$	$2P$
			P	$\frac{1}{2}\ \frac{1}{2}\ z$	$2I$
$2\,2\,2$; $2\,m\,m$; $\frac{2}{m}\frac{2}{m}\frac{2}{m}$	$\frac{2}{m}\frac{2}{m}\frac{2}{m}$	$\frac{2}{m}\frac{2}{m}\frac{2}{m}$	R	$0\ 0\ z$	$222P$
			R	$\frac{1}{2}\ \frac{1}{2}\ z$	$222I$
			R	$0\ \frac{1}{2}\ z$	$\{222A$
			D	$0\ 0\ z$	$222C\}$
			D	$\frac{1}{2}\ \frac{1}{2}\ z$	$222F$
$4,\ \bar{4},\ \frac{4}{m}$	$\frac{4}{m}$	$\frac{4}{m}\frac{2}{m}\frac{2}{m}$	S	$0\ 0\ z$	$4P$
$422,\ 4\,m\,m$, $\bar{4}2m$, $\frac{4}{m}\frac{2}{m}\frac{2}{m}$	$\frac{4}{m}\frac{2}{m}\frac{2}{m}$		S	$\frac{1}{2}\ \frac{1}{2}\ z$	$4I$
$3,\ \bar{3}$	$\bar{3}$	$\bar{3}\frac{2}{m}$	E	$\frac{1}{2}\ \frac{2}{3}\ z$	$3R$
$32,\ 3m,\ \bar{3}\frac{2}{m}$	$\bar{3}\frac{2}{m}$		E	$0\ 0\ z$	$\{3P$
$6,\ \bar{6},\ \frac{6}{m}$; $622,\ 6\,m\,m$; $\bar{6}m2,\ \frac{6}{m}\frac{2}{m}\frac{2}{m}$	$\frac{6}{m}$; $\frac{6}{m}\frac{2}{m}\frac{2}{m}$	$\frac{6}{m}\frac{2}{m}\frac{2}{m}$	E	$0\ 0\ z$	$3P\}$
$23,\ \frac{2}{m}\bar{3}$	$\frac{2}{m}\bar{3}$	$\frac{4}{m}\bar{3}\frac{2}{m}$	S	$0\ 0\ 1$	$23P$
$432,\ \bar{4}\,3\,m$			S	$\frac{1}{2}\ \frac{1}{2}\ 1$	$23I$
$\frac{4}{m}\bar{3}\frac{2}{m}$	$\frac{4}{m}\bar{3}\frac{2}{m}$		S	$0\ \frac{\sqrt{2}}{2}\ \frac{\sqrt{2}}{2}$	$23F$

derived. But, if this were done, then, wherever $\vec{t}_3$ does not coincide with the symmetry axis as in Fig. 3*a*, the unit cell and the coordinate system have a lesser symmetry than the crystal class. This unsymmetrical kind of cell and axial system has disadvantages. The advantages of symmetry of the coordinate system can be retained if a nonprimitive cell is chosen as shown in the full lines of Fig. 3*b*. When this is done the "unit" cell has lattice points in its interior, or on one or more of its faces, as well as at its corners. Nonprimitive cells are also chosen to gain the advantages of orthogonal axes. These various cells will be derived in the subsequent sections. Their designations and properties are listed in advance in Table 2.

Table 2. Designations of the general space-lattice types

Symbol	Name	Locations of additional points	Total number of lattice points per cell
P	primitive	—	1
I	body-centered	center of cell	2
A	*A*-centered	center of *A*, or (100) face	2
B	*B*-centered	center of *B*, or (010) face	2
C	*C*-centered	center of *C*, or (001) face	2
F	face-centered	centers of *A*, *B*, and *C* faces	4
R	rhombohedral	at $\frac{1}{3}\frac{2}{3}\frac{1}{3}$ and $\frac{2}{3}\frac{1}{3}\frac{2}{3}$, i.e., two points along the long body diagonal of cell	3

The designations *P*, *C*, *I*, etc., take care of the general nature of the lattice, in particular the multiplicity of the cell. A more complete designation can be given by prefixing to this designation the symbol of one of the crystal classes with which the lattice is consistent. The simplest prefix is that of the least symmetrical class. Such designations are used in the last column of Table 1.

Derivation of the space-lattice types

Table 1 outlines the derivations of the symmetrical space lattices. Some details of the derivations are discussed under the appropriate symmetry in the following sections. The symmetries that need be considered are only those listed in the third column of Table 1. In most cases, however, it is simpler to require the lattice stacks to be consistent with the crystal class of least symmetry listed in the first column which is embraced by this "shape symmetry" rather than to deal with the full "shape symmetry" itself.

Symmetry 1. A 1-fold axis places no restriction on the perpendicular plane lattice. Consequently a general parallelogram plane lattice is consistent with this symmetry, Fig. 24, Chapter 7. Nor is there any symmetry restriction on $\vec{t}_3$, Fig. 1*a*. Consequently the primitive cell of the lattice is a general parallelepiped, Fig. 1*b*.

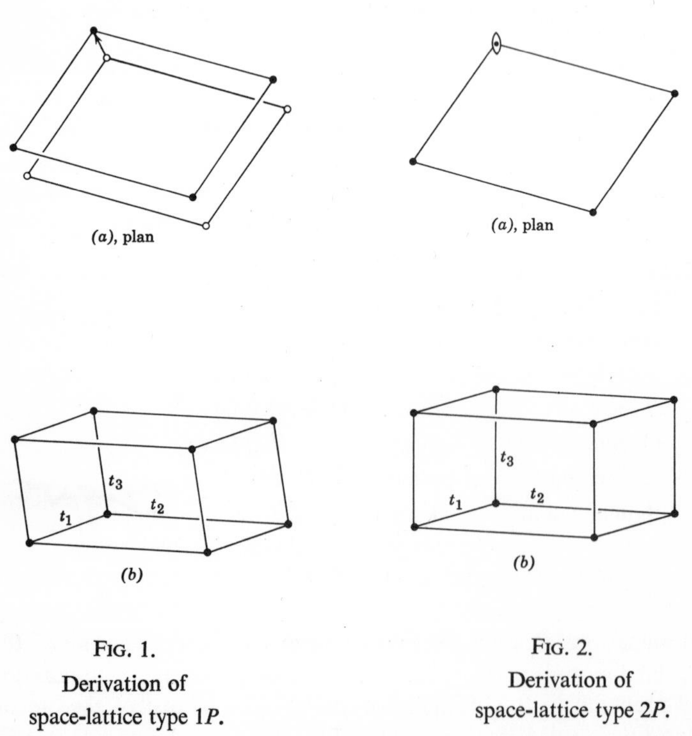

FIG. 1. Derivation of space-lattice type 1*P*.

FIG. 2. Derivation of space-lattice type 2*P*.

Symmetry 2. Figure 24 of Chapter 7 shows that a parallelogram plane lattice is consistent with a 2-fold axis. There are four different places where a 2-fold axis can be placed in the lattice, Table 4, Chapter 7. If one of these is chosen for the 2-fold axis location of the zero level, and the same location is chosen for its location in the next level, a primitive lattice results, Fig. 2. Alternatively, different locations can be used for the axis on adjacent levels. There are only three possible displacement vectors, $\vec{t}_3$, other than $0\ 0\ z$, however. These are $\frac{1}{2}\ \frac{1}{2}\ z$, $\frac{1}{2}\ 0\ z$, and $0\ \frac{1}{2}\ z$. The first of these is shown in Fig. 3*a*. Figure 3*b* shows that a *body-centered cell* can be chosen in this lattice for which a new $\vec{t_3}'$ can be normal to the plane lattices, and consequently parallel to the 2-fold axis.

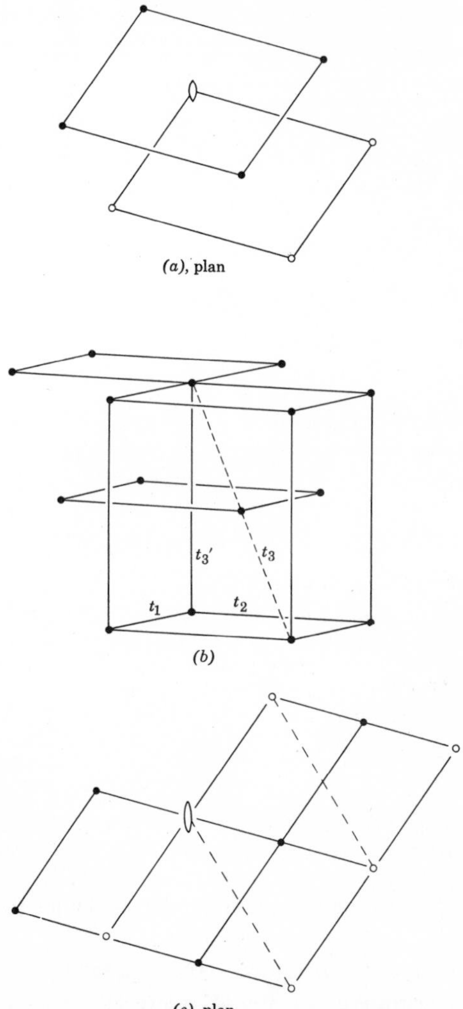

FIG. 3. (*a*) and (*b*). Derivation of space-lattice type 2*I*.
(*c*) Equivalence of lattice type 2*A* and 2*I*.

If $\vec{t_3}$ is chosen as $\frac{1}{2}\,0\,z$ or $0\,\frac{1}{2}\,z$, Fig. 3*c* results. But these both determine lattices which can be described as body-centered if the alternative cell shown by the broken lines in Fig. 3*c* is adopted.

The only distinct lattice types consistent with symmetry 2 are consequently the P and I types. These can be specifically designated $2P$ and $2I$ respectively.

Symmetry 222. It is convenient to substitute the symmetry $2mm$ ($\simeq 2\bar{2}\bar{2}$) for 222 in this derivation. This is because in the last chapter the plane-lattice types consistent with $2mm$ were derived (see Table 5 and Fig. 24 of Chapter 7). There are two plane lattices consistent with this symmetry, rectangular and diamond.

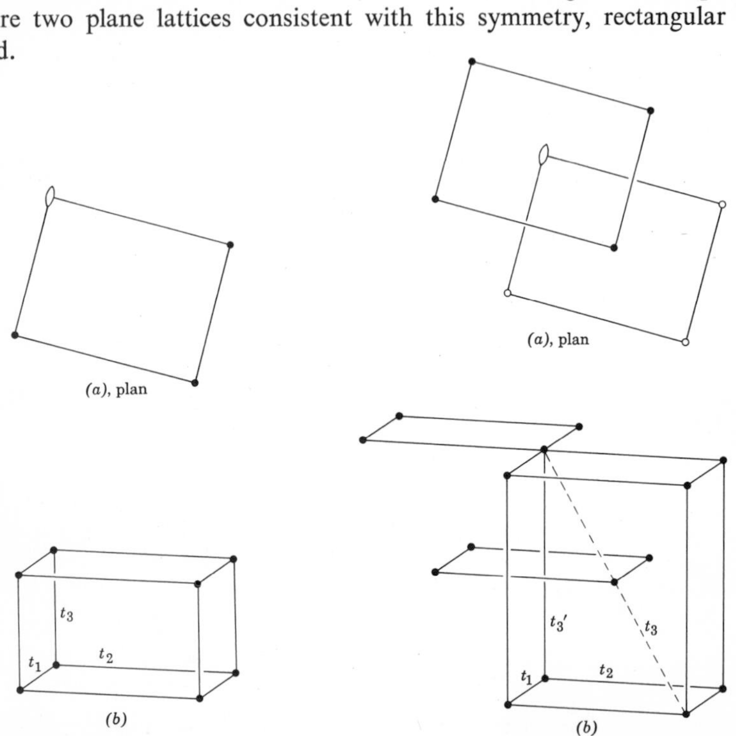

FIG. 4. Derivation of space-lattice type $222P$.

FIG. 5. Derivation of space-lattice type $222I$.

First consider the rectangular plane lattice. The locations having symmetry $2mm$ are $0\,0$, $\frac{1}{2}\,\frac{1}{2}$, $\frac{1}{2}\,0$, and $0\,\frac{1}{2}$ (see Fig. 24 and Table 4, Chapter 7). The possible displacement vectors are therefore $0\,0\,z$, $\frac{1}{2}\,\frac{1}{2}\,z$, $0\,\frac{1}{2}\,z$, and $\frac{1}{2}\,0\,z$. The first of these defines a primitive cell, Fig. 4. The second defines a different lattice, Fig. 5*a*, for which a body-centered orthogonal cell can be chosen, Fig. 5*b*. The third possibility, Fig. 6*a*, defines a lattice from which an orthogonal A-centered* cell can be chosen, Fig. 6*b*. The fourth possibility is essentially equivalent to the third, but the cell is *B-centered.** This is not a lattice type

* A-centered means that there is a lattice point in the center of the A face, which is (100). Similarly, B-centered means that there is a lattice point in the center of the B face, or (010), and C-centered means that there is a lattice point in the center of the C face, or (001).

different from an *A*-centered cell since a rotation of 90° about the new $\vec{t_3}'$ vector transforms one into the other.

Next consider the diamond plane lattice. The locations of symmetry *2mm* are 0 0 and $\frac{1}{2}\,\frac{1}{2}$ (Fig. 24 and Table 4, Chapter 7). This permits two possibilities for $\vec{t_3}$, namely $0\,0\,z$ and $\frac{1}{2}\,\frac{1}{2}\,z$. The first possibility, Fig. 7, defines a primitive lattice with a diamond base. A more convenient cell is the alternative

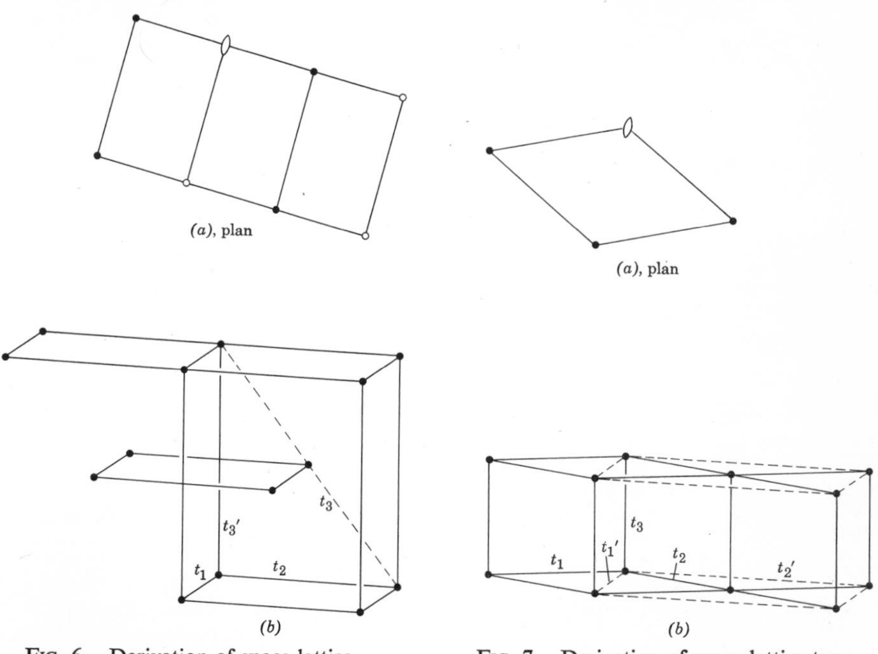

FIG. 6. Derivation of space-lattice type 222*A*.

FIG. 7. Derivation of space-lattice type 222*C* (equivalent to 222*A*).

*C-centered** cell shown in Fig. 7*b*. This is not a lattice type different from the *A*-centered cell since one can be derived from the other by a rotation of 90° about the new $\vec{t_1}'$. The second possibility is shown in Fig. 8. The primitive cell is very difficult to deal with, and it is customary to choose a new cell with orthogonal edges. This is a *face-centered* cell† with multiplicity 4.

This discussion shows that there are four general lattice types consistent with symmetry 222, specifically *P*, *I*, *F*, and *C* (≎ *A* ≎ *B*). For this symmetry these are identified as 222*P*, 222*I*, 222*F*, and 222*C*.

Symmetry 4. Figure 24 of Chapter 7 shows that only one plane lattice is consistent with a 4-fold rotation axis. Table 4 of Chapter 7 shows that there are two locations for the 4-fold axis, namely at 0 0, and $\frac{1}{2}\,\frac{1}{2}$. This permits $\vec{t_3}$ to have the two possible values $0\,0\,z$ and $\frac{1}{2}\,\frac{1}{2}\,z$. The first defines an orthogonal

* See footnote on page 90.

† In a face-centered cell, each of the *A*, *B*, and *C* faces is centered.

primitive cell, Fig. 9; the second defines an oblique primitive cell, Fig. 10. To gain the advantages of orthogonality, this second alternative lattice is referred to a body-centered cell, Fig. 10*b*.

A body-centered cell is a double cell, Table 2. The second alternative could also be referred to a face-centered cell, Fig. 10*c*. But, according to Table 2, this is a quadruple cell, and is accordingly not used, except for special purposes.

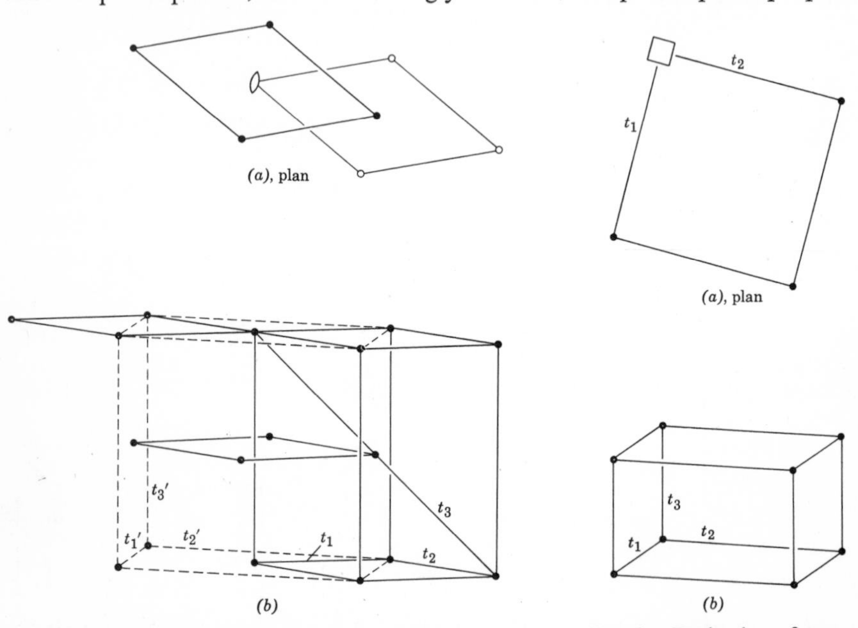

FIG. 8. Derivation of space-lattice type 222*F*.

FIG. 9. Derivation of space-lattice type 4*P*.

There are therefore only two distinct lattice types consistent with symmetry 4, namely *P* and *I*. For this symmetry they are identified as 4*P* and 4*I*.

Symmetry 3. Table 5 and Fig. 24 of Chapter 7 show that the equilateral plane lattice is consistent with a 3-fold axis, and Table 4 of Chapter 7 shows that there are three locations for 3-fold axes, which for present purposes may be taken as 0 0, $\frac{2}{3}\,\frac{1}{3}$, $\frac{1}{3}\,\frac{2}{3}$. (Note that 0 0 $\Leftrightarrow$ 1 0 $\Leftrightarrow$ 0 1.) These lie along the long diagonal of the cell. This permits the following displacement vectors, $\vec{t}_3$: 0 0 z, $\frac{2}{3}\,\frac{1}{3}\,z$, $\frac{1}{3}\,\frac{2}{3}\,z$, $\bar{\frac{2}{3}}\,\bar{\frac{1}{3}}\,z$, and $\bar{\frac{1}{3}}\,\bar{\frac{2}{3}}\,z$. Since $\frac{1}{3} \Leftrightarrow -\frac{2}{3}$, only the first three are distinct possibilities. The first possibility defines a primitive cell, Fig. 11. The second two are shown in Figs. 12*a* and *b* and in Figs. 12*c* and *d*, respectively. These two possibilities are the same and can be transformed into one another by a rotation of 180° about the normal to the plane lattices; therefore only one will be discussed. It is customary to refer this lattice to one of two different kinds of cells. One of these is a prism which has a base outlined by the original $\vec{t}_1$ and $\vec{t}_2$ of the original primitive equilateral lattice, an altitude normal to it, and three levels high. This cell is a triple one. Alternatively, a *rhomobohedral*

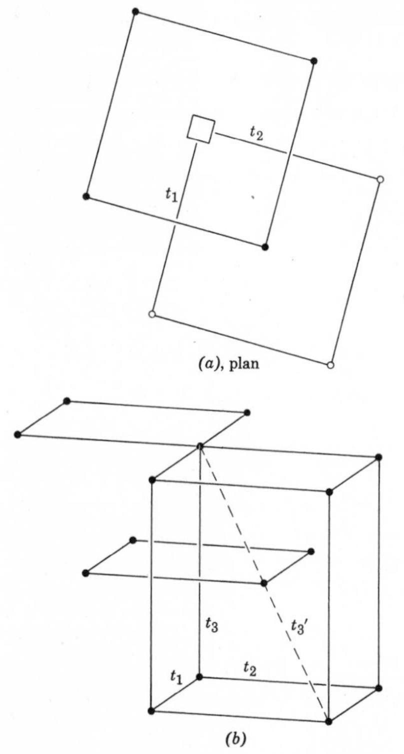

(c)

FIG. 10. Derivation of space-lattice type 4*I*.

FIG. 10*c*. Equivalence of space-lattice types 4*I* and 4*F*.

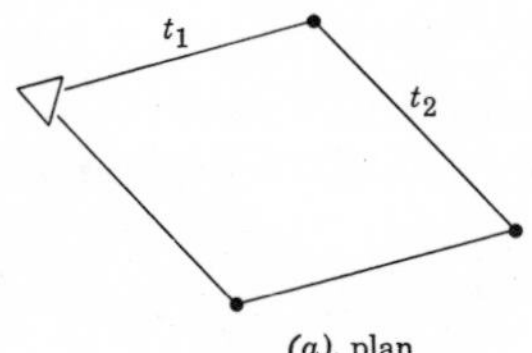

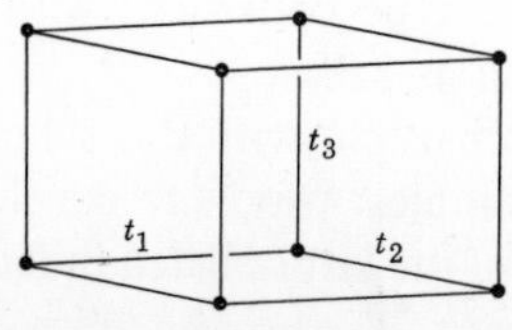

FIG. 11. Derivation of space-lattice type 3*P*.

cell can be defined by taking $\vec{t_3}$ and two other edges symmetrical with it with respect to the 3-fold axis. The rhombohedral cell is primitive but is little used except in special cases because its axes are nonorthogonal.

There are therefore only two distinct lattice types consistent with symmetry 3, namely P and R. For this symmetry they are identified as $3P$ and $3R$.

Symmetry 6. Figure 24 and Table 5 of Chapter 7 show that only one plane-lattice type is consistent with a perpendicular 6-fold axis, namely the equilateral

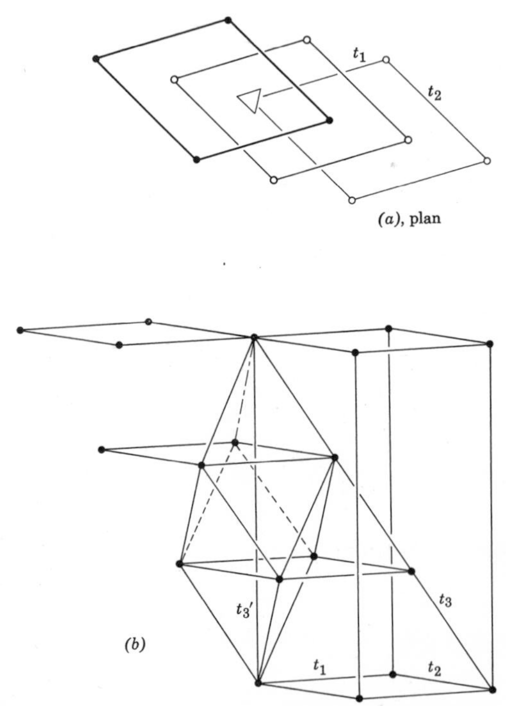

FIG. 12. Derivation of space-lattice type $3R$.

lattice. Figure 24 and Table 4 of Chapter 7 show that there is only one location for a 6-fold axis, namely at 0 0. There is thus only one possible kind of $\vec{t_3}$, namely 0 0 z. This defines the same lattice as shown in Fig. 11.

Thus there is only one lattice type consistent with symmetry 6, namely P. For this symmetry it is identified as $3P$.

Symmetry 23. The lattices consistent with this symmetry can be investigated in several ways. Perhaps the simplest way is to consider the lattices consistent with the dimensional symmetry of the lattice listed in the third column of Table 1, namely the symmetry $\frac{4}{m}\bar{3}\frac{2}{m}$. The lattices can be determined by finding plane-lattice stacks consistent with the 4-fold axis and the parallel reflection planes of 4*mm*, and then requiring these to be consistent with the 3-fold axis as well. The space lattices consistent with the 4-fold axes have already been considered and are shown in Figs. 9*b*, 10*b*, and 10*c*. To see how these can be made consistent with the 3-fold axis requires a little further consideration:

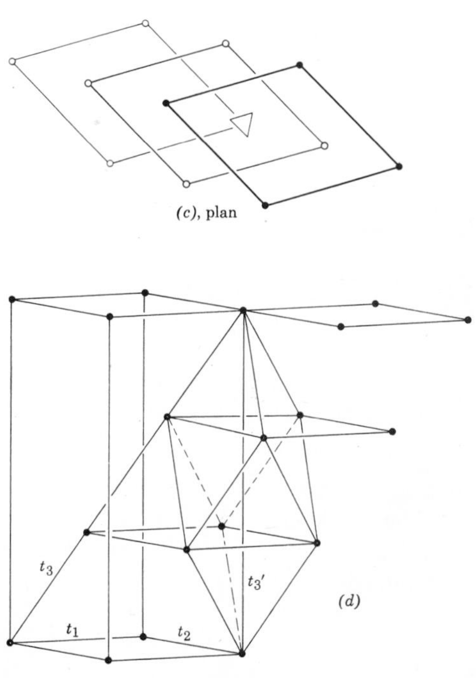

FIG. 12 continued.

The shape symmetry of the lattice must be $\frac{4}{m}\bar{3}\frac{2}{m}$. This is shown in Fig. 7, Chapter 6. It will be observed that the symmetry about the 4-fold axis is 4*mm*. This has two nonequivalent sets of orthogonal mirrors. The locations of symmetry 4*mm* in the square plane lattice are shown in Fig. 13. There are two alternative ways of placing the square with respect to the 3-fold axis. These correspond to placing either one set of mirrors or the other through the 3-fold axis, as shown in Figs. 14 and 15. Call these settings (*a*) and (*b*) respectively.

These two alternatives must be compounded with the two alternatives for $\vec{t}_3$, namely $00z$ and $\frac{1}{2}\frac{1}{2}z$. This appears to offer four possibilities. But these four possibilities must be consistent with the 3-fold axis. These produce lattice types according to the following combinations:

$$(a),\quad 00z \rightarrow P,$$
$$(a),\quad \tfrac{1}{2}\tfrac{1}{2}z \rightarrow I,$$
$$(b),\quad 00z \rightarrow C,$$
$$(b),\quad \tfrac{1}{2}\tfrac{1}{2}z \rightarrow F.$$

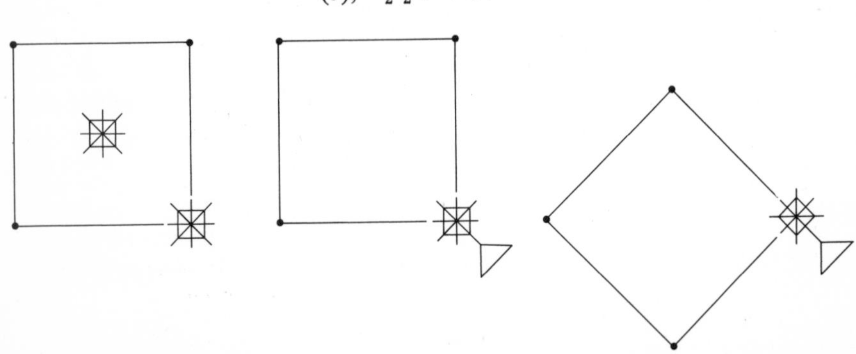

FIG. 13. Locations of symmetry $4mm$ in the square plane lattice.

FIG. 14 and FIG. 15. The two ways of orienting the square plane lattice with respect to a 3-fold axis of the isometric crystal classes.

If, now, the 3-fold axis acts on these, P, I, and F remain unchanged, but C transforms into F. The 3-fold axis also specializes z as shown in Table 1. Accordingly, symmetry 23 permits only P, I, and F lattice types. For this symmetry they are identified as $23P$, $23I$, and $23F$.

Alternative discussion of symmetry 23. An alternative derivation is as follows: Consider how the 3-fold axis repeats one plane lattice in each of the two orientations of Figs. 14 and 15. This is shown in Figs. 16 and 18. The possibility in Fig. 16 has $\vec{t}_3 = [001]$; this is a lattice with a cube-shaped primitive cell. The possibility in Fig. 18 has translations $\vec{t}_3 = \frac{1}{2}\frac{1}{2}\frac{\sqrt{2}}{2}$, where the components are based on $t_1 =$ unity. (Note that the third component is the perpendicular distance between the upper and middle levels of points in Fig. 18.) Thus this possibility has a kind of $\vec{t}_3$ specified as $\frac{1}{2}\frac{1}{2}z$. The only condition imposed upon the lattice so far is that it be simultaneously consistent with $4mm$ and 3. It still remains to apply the two conditions that $\vec{t}_3$ may be either $00z$ or $\frac{1}{2}\frac{1}{2}z$.

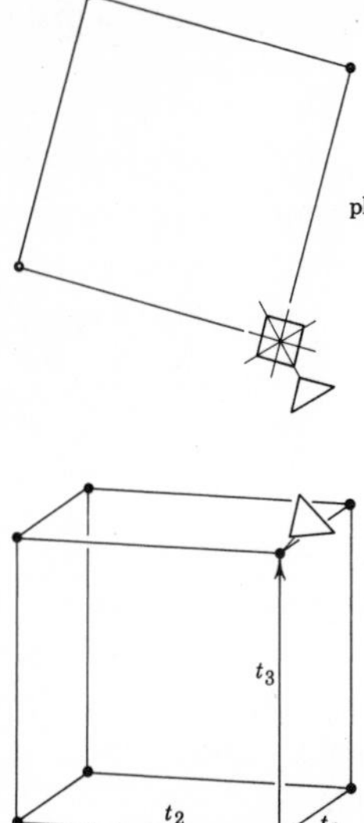

FIG. 16. Derivation of space-lattice type 23*P*.

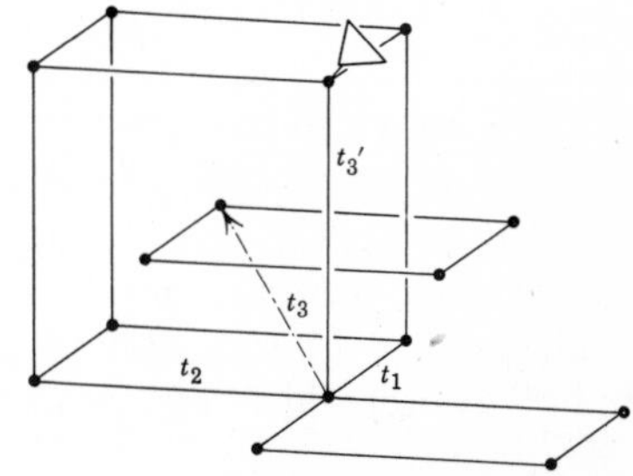

FIG. 17. Derivation of space-lattice type 23*I*.

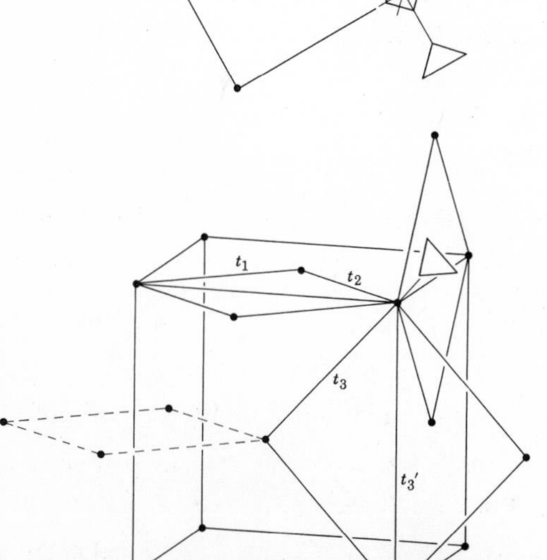

FIG. 18. Derivation of space-lattice type 23*F*.

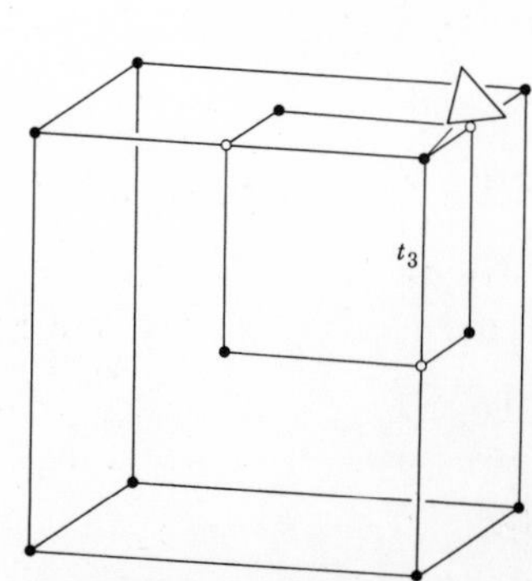

FIG. 19. Alternative derivation of space-lattice type 23*P*.

If t_3 is required to have the form $0\,0\,z$, then it must be of such a distance z that the new point (open circle in Fig. 19) produced by repeating the original points (solid circles of Fig. 19) is such as to make them a consistent set of translations. The only solution is the primitive cubic cell of Fig. 19 having half the edge of the cube of Fig. 18. This lattice type is the same as that in Fig. 16.

The remaining possibility is to impose a new translation of the form $\frac{1}{2}\,\frac{1}{2}\,z$ on the possibility of Fig. 15. This results in Fig. 17, a new lattice type, the body-centered cube.

The 14 space lattices

The foregoing considerations have discovered 14 symmetrically specialized kinds of lattices, namely those listed in the last column of Table 1. These are the so-called 14 Bravais space lattices, named after the crystallographer who first showed that there are just 14 specialized lattices. Another investigator, Frankenheim, had already derived the symmetrical space lattices, but had counted 15, two of which later proved to be duplicates.

Exercises

1. In Fig. 7 of Chapter 6, which classes are centric and which are acentric?
2. Can symmetry 1 have a *C* lattice?
3. Can symmetry 4 have a *C* lattice?

9 · The coordinate systems of crystallography

Crystallography is concerned with the geometry of arrangements of atoms in crystals, and the various consequences of such arrangements. Whenever aspects of this geometry are to be expressed in analytical form, an appropriate coordinate system must be chosen. Although almost any arbitrary coordinate system could be used, the results appear simple only when the coordinate system chosen is one that is natural to the problem.

There are many examples of the simplification which results in adopting a natural coordinate system. For example, the equation of a parabola referred to arbitrary axes X and Y has the form

$$ax^2 + bxy + cy^2 + dx + cy + f = 0.$$

But, if the parabola is referred to a pair of orthogonal axes, X and Y, placed so that the origin is located at the vertex of the parabola and Y is directed along the symmetry axis of the parabola, the equation of this curve then has the much simpler form

$$y = ax^2.$$

This example illustrates the value of choosing axes whose symmetry is consistent with the symmetry of the geometry to be represented.

Another familiar example is afforded by the street system of a city. In giving directions for reaching a certain place, one could say "go 1320 feet east then 528 feet north." But a simpler and more natural statement is "go 3 blocks east and 2 blocks north." In general, city streets are not laid out so that the blocks are equal in both directions. (In this example there are 12 blocks to the mile east and west, which gives the block a length of 440 feet this way, whereas there are 20 blocks to a mile north and south, making the block 264 feet long this way.) *It is therefore unnatural to use equal arbitrary units along streets and avenues.* The natural coordinate system to use in the city is one based upon its natural units, the city blocks, even if these units are unequal along streets and avenues. This example has a close analogy in crystals.

The six symmetrical cells

The simplest analytical expressions are obtained when the coordinate axes are also axes of high symmetry. Accordingly, the most appropriate reference axes for crystals are its symmetry axes. From another point of view, the most

Table 1. The crystal systems

Crystal classes	Lattice type	Cell type	Name of crystal system	Description of coordinate system
1, $\bar{1}$	$1P$	$1P$	triclinic	$a \neq b \neq c$ $\alpha \neq \beta \neq \gamma$
2, m, $\frac{2}{m}$	$2P$, $2I$	$2P$	monoclinic	$a \neq b \neq c$ $\alpha = \gamma = 90°$
222, $2mm$, $\frac{2}{m}\frac{2}{m}\frac{2}{m}$	$222P$, $222I$	$222P$	orthorhombic	$a \neq b \neq c$ $\alpha = \beta = \gamma = 90°$
4, $\bar{4}$, $\frac{4}{m}$; 422, $4mm$, $\bar{4}2m$, $\frac{4}{m}\frac{2}{m}\frac{2}{m}$	$4P$, $4I$	$4P$	tetragonal	$a_1 = a_2 \neq c$ $\alpha = \beta = \gamma = 90°$
3, $\bar{3}$; 32, $3m$, $\bar{3}\frac{2}{m}$	$3P$, $3R$	$3P$	hexagonal	$a_1 = a_2 = a_3 \neq c$ $\beta_1 = \beta_2 = \beta_3 = 90°$ $\gamma = 120°$
6, $\bar{6}$, $\frac{6}{m}$, 622, $6mm$, $\bar{6}m2$, $\frac{6}{m}\frac{2}{m}\frac{2}{m}$	$3P$			
23, $\frac{2}{m}\bar{3}$; 432, $\bar{4}3m$, $\frac{4}{m}\bar{3}\frac{2}{m}$	$23P$, $23I$ $23F$	$23P$	cubic (isometric)	$a_1 = a_2 = a_3$ $\alpha = \beta = \gamma = 90°$

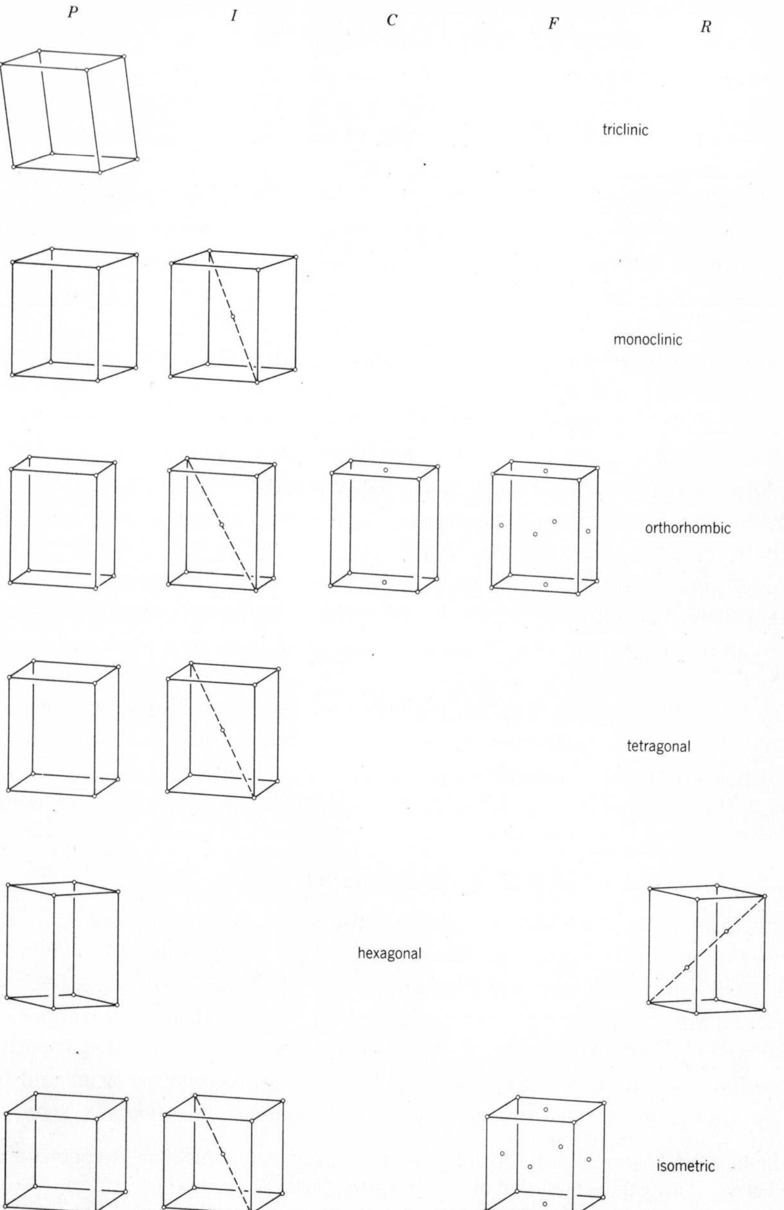

FIG. 1. The six crystal systems and their included space-lattice types.

natural reference system is based upon the translations of a primitive cell of the crystal. Unfortunately, these translations do not always coincide with the symmetry axes. But when a translation does not coincide with a symmetry axis, there are always n equivalent translations symmetrically disposed with respect to the symmetry axis. The vector sum of these n equivalent translations is another translation of the lattice which does coincide with the symmetry axis. To gain the advantages of symmetry, such a complex symmetrical translation is always* chosen as one of the coordinate axes rather than the simpler unsymmetrical one. Whenever this is done, the unit cell is nonprimitive. It is for this reason that lattices with simple translations not corresponding to symmetry axes are customarily represented by nonprimitive cells.

If the nonprimitivity of a cell is disregarded, the tabulation of lattice types shown in Table 1 of Chapter 8 shows that there are only six types of symmetrical cells. The edges of these cells form the natural coordinate systems of crystals. The coordinate axes are customarily referred to as *crystallographic axes*.

It will be observed that each of the six coordinate systems can be used to represent several related crystal classes. Conversely, several related symmetries can be referred to the same coordinate system. Such a group of classes is said to constitute a *crystal system*. Accordingly, there are six crystal systems. These axial systems are so important in crystallography that each one is given a name. The names, properties, and symmetries included in each system are listed in Table 1.

The left column of Fig. 1 shows the cells and their axes adopted in each of the six crystal systems. These are simply the six symmetrical primitive cells. In the other columns are shown the symmetrical nonprimitive cells of other space-lattice types which are represented by the cell and axes of the first column.

Labeling and orientation of axes

The three vectors chosen for axes of the unit cell are labeled a, b, and c unless the particular symmetry causes any of them to be equivalent. When this occurs the equivalent axes are labeled a_1, a_2, and, if necessary, a_3. The angles between pairs of axes are labeled α (between b and c), β (between c and a), and γ (between a and b), Fig. 2. In crystal drawings it is customary to orient c vertically, b approximately left and right, and a approximately front and back.

Crystallographers customarily use a *right-handed coordinate system*†. In

* Some crystallographers who do not appreciate this advantage make an exception for 3-fold symmetry. This will be discussed on a subsequent page.

† An easy way to remember the arrangement of axes in right-handed and left-handed coordinate systems is as follows: If the coordinate system is regarded as a screw, then turning $+X$ toward $+Y$ causes the screw to advance toward $+Z$. If the coordinate system is right-handed, the rotation and advance are similar to a right-handed screw; if left-handed they are as in a left-handed screw.

standard drawings, the axes are positive as follows: a toward the observer, b toward the right, and c above, Fig. 2. The set of six lines representing the positive and negative ends of the three axes is called the *axial cross*.

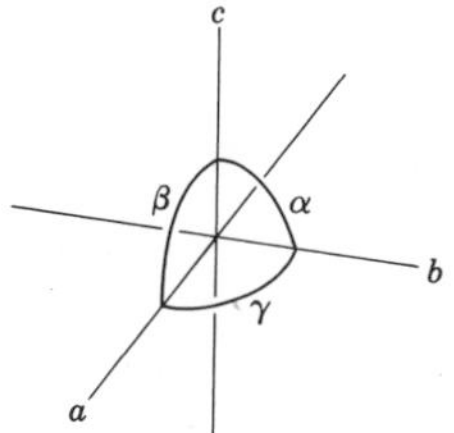

FIG. 2. The axial cross of the general coordinate system.

Peculiarities of the crystal systems

Cubic (isometric) system. All classes having four 3-fold axes can be referred to a cell having the shape of a cube. The axes are therefore the three cube edges. Since this system has three equivalent orthogonal axes, it is the usual Cartesian coordinate system customarily used in analytical geometry, except that in analytical geometry the system is customarily left-handed whereas it is right-handed in crystallography. Because of the equivalence of the three reference axes they are usually designated a_1, a_2, and a_3 instead of a, b, and c. Note that the axes have the directions of cube edges. They correspond to the 4-fold symmetry axes (proper or improper) in the crystal, if present, otherwise to the 2-fold axes.

Tetragonal system. All crystal classes having a 4 or $\bar{4}$ axis can be referred to a cell having the shape of a square prism. The c axis is the 4 or $\bar{4}$ axis of the crystal class. The other two axes lie in a plane at right angles to the 4 or $\bar{4}$ axis and are equivalent to each other because of the 4-fold axis. They are consequently at right angles to one another. Since they are equivalent they are usually designated a_1 and a_2 instead of a and b. If the crystal cell is known, as a result of an x-ray diffraction study, then the a_1 and a_2 axes are easily fixed as the shortest translations in the net at right angles to the 4 or $\bar{4}$ axis. In classes containing one set of 2 or $\bar{2}$ axis at right angles to the 4 or $\bar{4}$ axis, this set coincides with either the a axes or the cell diagonals. In some classes there are two sets of 2-fold axes. One of these coincides with the cell edges and the other with the cell diagonal, Fig. 3. The correct choice is, by definition, the set of 2-fold axes which coincide with the edges of the smaller cell. The alternative choice defines a double C-centered cell, Fig. 3, or a quadruple F-centered cell.

Hexagonal system. All crystal classes having a single 3, $\bar{3}$, 6, or $\bar{6}$ axis can be referred to a cell which is one-third of a hexagonal prism, Fig. 4. The c axis is the 3, $\bar{3}$, 6, or $\bar{6}$ axis of the crystal class. The other two axes lie in a plane at right angles to the 3- or 6-fold axis and are equivalent to one another by the $2\pi/3$ rotation of the axis. They therefore make an angle of 120° with one another, Fig. 4. Since they are equivalent they are usually designated a_1 and a_2 instead of a and b. If the crystal cell is known as a result of an x-ray diffraction study, then the a_1 and a_2 axes are readily chosen as the shortest

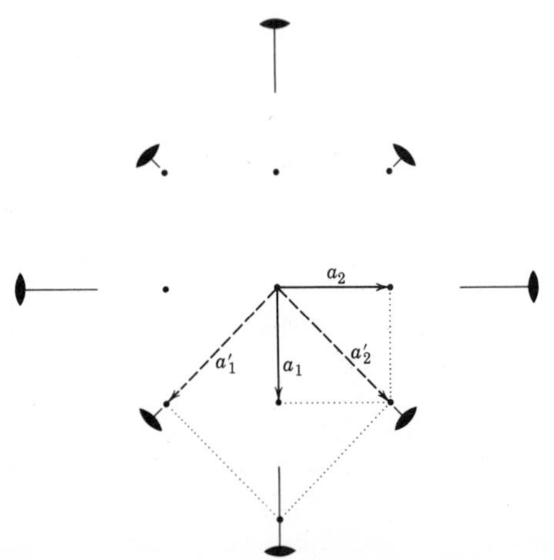

FIG. 3. Alternative cells in the tetragonal system.

translations in the net normal to the 3- or 6-fold axis. In the classes that contain one set of 2 or $\bar{2}$ axes at right angles to the 3- or 6-fold axis, this set coincides with either the a axes or the cell diagonals In some classes there are two sets of 2-fold axes. In this case the correct set cannot be fixed by symmetry alone, and an ambiguity occurs unless the shortest translation can be found by x-ray diffraction measurements.

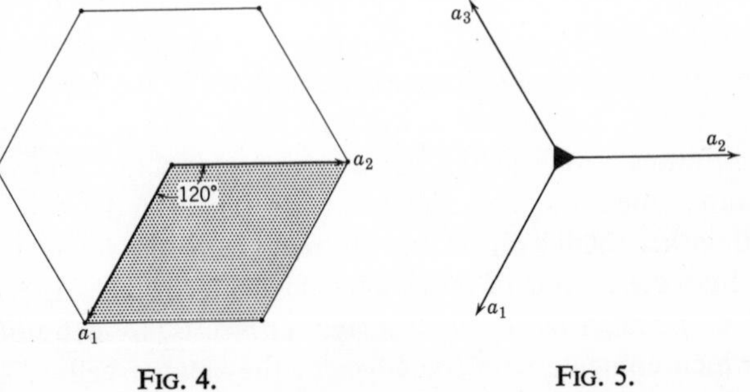

FIG. 4. FIG. 5.

There is a peculiarity in the hexagonal system which is not encountered in other systems. The $2\pi/3$ rotation of the 3- or 6-fold axis not only repeats an a_1 axis to become an equivalent a_2 axis, Fig. 4, but it repeats it again to become a third axis, called a_3, Fig. 5. If this third axis is ignored, then, in general, the indices of planes equivalent by the 3-fold axis display no obvious relationship. On the other hand, if the third a axis is somehow included in the indices, then equivalent planes display an obviously 3-fold relationship. For this reason the three coplanar axes a_1, a_2, and a_3 (as well as c) are customarily used in the hexagonal system.

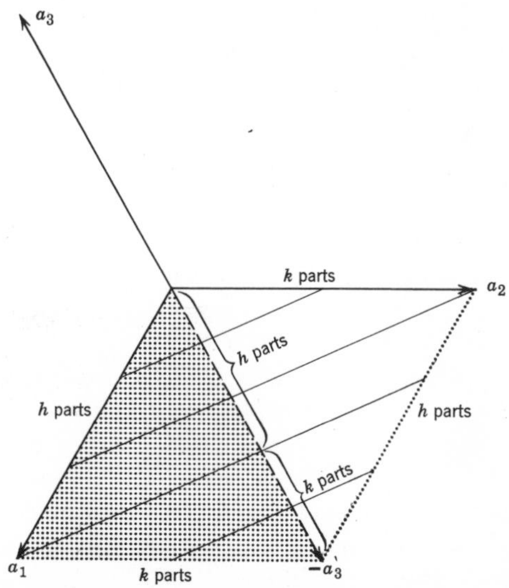

FIG. 6. Demonstration that $h + k = -i$.

Obviously only two coordinate axes are sufficient to fix a point in a plane. Therefore coordinates with respect to the third a axis must be related to the coordinates with respect to the other two. The relationship between the indices of a plane for the three axes is very simple indeed. Consider a plane which would be designated (hkl) if only the two axes a_1 and a_2 were used. The set of planes of this index divides the a_1 axis in h parts and the a_2 axis in k parts, Fig. 6. The question is, into how many parts does the set of planes divide the a_3 axis? If one builds a parallelogram on the edges of a_1 and a_2, Fig. 6, then the negative end of the a_3 axis is the diagonal of this parallelogram. The four sides of the parallelogram are divided by the set of planes into h, k, h, and k parts respectively. The two sides of the shaded half of the parallelogram project along the planes to the diagonal. Thus the number of the parts along a_1 plus the number of parts along the adjacent side of the shaded half is the total number of parts into which the diagonal is divided. Let this number be i parts. Ignoring the sign of i for the moment, it is evident that

$$|i| = h + k. \tag{1}$$

Now, considering the sign of i, it is evident that if the planes intercept the positive ends of a_1 and a_2, as shown in Fig. 6, they must intercept the negative end of a_3. Thus, if the indices corresponding to intercepts on a_1 and a_2 are positive, the indices with respect to a_3 must be negative. If proper signs are attributed to the quantities in (1), they must be

$$\left.\begin{aligned} -i &= h + k \\ \text{or} \qquad i &= -(h + k). \end{aligned}\right\} \tag{2}$$

A symmetrical form of this is evidently

$$h + k + i = 0. \tag{3}$$

That is, the sum of the indices with respect to the a_1, a_2, and a_3 axes must be zero.

The four axes, a_1, a_2, a_3, and c, for the hexagonal crystals are known as *hexagonal axes*, or Bravais-Miller axes, and the four indices ($hkil$) are known as *hexagonal indices*, or Bravais-Miller indices, to distinguish them from a variant which will be discussed in the next section. When one uses Bravais-Miller indices but wishes to omit the i index, for some reason, the omission is indicated by a dot, thus ($hk{\cdot}l$).

Rhombohedral axes. Some crystallographers use *rhombohedral* (Miller) axes rather than hexagonal (Bravais-Miller) axes for crystals which can be referred to a rhombohedral lattice, $3R$. These are the classes 3, $\bar{3}$, 32, $3m$, and $\bar{3}\,\frac{2}{m}$ (see Table 1). The relation of rhombohedral axes to hexagonal axes was shown in Fig. 12*b* of Chapter 8.

Rhombohedral axes have the advantage of corresponding to a primitive cell. This is an advantage provided that the crystal actually has a rhombohedral lattice. But Table 1 of Chapter 8 shows that the classes which may have a rhombohedral lattice may alternately have a primitive hexagonal lattice. Knowing the mere symmetry of a crystal does not, therefore, determine whether its cell is rhombohedral or hexagonal. To use rhombohedral axes on a crystal which *may* turn out to have a rhombohedral cell, but which *eventually* turns out to have a hexagonal cell, results in confusion. Furthermore, to refer one crystal of a class to rhombohedral axes, and another to hexagonal axes, because the lattice types are R and P respectively, also leads to confusion. For this reason the use of rhombohedral axes is to be discouraged.

The orthorhombic system. The crystal classes which have three orthogonal 2-fold axes, either proper or improper (i.e., 222, $2\bar{2}\bar{2} = 2mm$, and $\frac{2}{m}\frac{2}{m}\frac{2}{m}$), can be referred to a cell which has the shape of a rectangular parallelepiped (the same shape as a brick). The edges of the cell are the coordinate axes, and they correspond with the 2-fold axes of the crystal classes. The three axes can therefore be fixed unambiguously by symmetry. Which shall be labeled *a*, which *b*, and which *c*, is not determined by symmetry, except that in the class $2mm$ the axis 2 is unique. It is usually chosen as the *c* axis.

It is customary to assign the labels *a*, *b*, and *c* to the three axes of the cell according to a convention. The convention is based upon the relative lengths of the edges of the cell. The axes *b* and *a* are uniformly chosen so that their lengths are $b > a$, There is a divergence of opinion as to how the length of *c* shall be related to *a* and *b*. Some crystallographers use the rule $c > b > a$; others use $b > a > c$. In the first case *c* is the longest axis, in the second case it is the shortest. The reason some crystallographers prefer *c* as the shortest axis is that crystals ordinarily grow so that they are elongated parallel to the shortest translation, and the choice of *c* (vertical) for the shortest translation causes the crystal to look like a vertical column. When the crystal is drawn in conventional position the column looks more column-like when elongated parallel to *c* than when elongated parallel to *a*.

The monoclinic system. The crystal classes having a single 2-fold axis, either proper or improper (i.e., classes 2, *m*, and $2/m$), can be referred to a cell having the shape of a right prism with a parallelogram base. This implies one axis normal to the plane of the other two, which are inclined to one another. Two different conventional choices of labels for the axes are in use. In the *first setting*, the rule adopted is consistent with the rule for crystals with a unique 3-fold, 4-fold, or 6-fold axis. Specifically, the unique 2-fold axis is labeled *c*, and the *a* and *b* are chosen normal to *c* and inclined to one another by the angle γ. In the *second setting*, the rule is inconsistent with other rules: *b* is taken as the unique 2-fold axis, while *a* and *c* are chosen normal to *b* and inclined to one another by the angle β.

The axes *a* and *b* in the first setting (or *a* and *c* in the second) are not fixed by symmetry. They are simply a pair of conjugate translations in the net normal to the 2-fold axis. It is a standard convention to select the two smallest translations in this net. When this is done the resulting cell is called the *reduced cell*. Of these two translations, the shorter is selected as *a*, the longer as *b*. (Some crystallographers using the second setting, which has *a* and *c* normal to the 2-fold axis, prefer $a > c$. This has the effect of orienting the crystal so that the crystal growth shape has *c* longer than *a*. But *b* may be longer or shorter than either *a* or *c*.)

The triclinic system. The crystal classes 1 and $\bar{1}$ can be referred to a perfectly general parallelepiped cell. The edges of the cell are taken as the three crystallographic axes *a*, *b*, and *c*. The interaxial angles are designated α (between *b* and *c*), β (between *c* and *a*), and γ (between *a* and *b*). There are an infinite number of ways of selecting this cell since it is not fixed by symmetry. One kind of cell, however, is unique, namely the one which has as edges the three shortest translations of the lattice. This is called the *reduced cell.** It is a uniform convention that the axes of a crystal are based upon the edges of the reduced cell.

There are numerous ways of assigning the labels, a, b, and c to the three edges of the reduced triclinic cell. Let one corner of the cell be selected as the origin, and let three edges meeting in this corner be labeled X, Y, and Z. The *axial cross* of the coordinate system comprises three positive and three negative

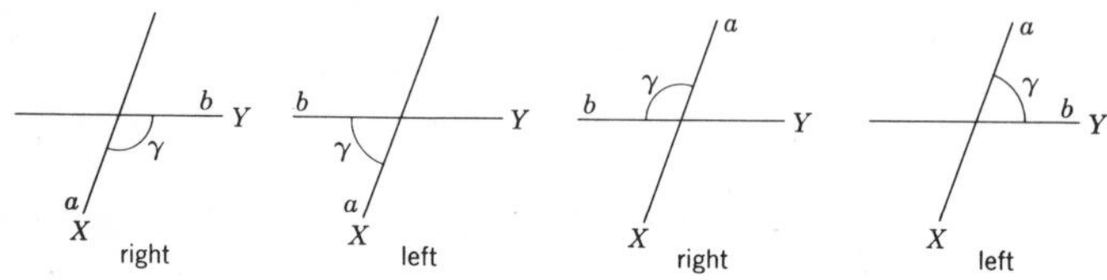

FIG. 7. The four ways of assigning labels a and b to the axes X and Y.

lines, X, $-X$, Y, $-Y$, Z, and $-Z$. The label $+a$ can be assigned to any of the six lines. This also fixes the opposite line as $-a$. Then the label $+b$ can be assigned to any of the remaining four lines. This also fixes the opposite line as $-b$. Up to this point there are $6 \times 4 = 24$ possibilities of assigning the labels a and b to the axes. There remain two lines to be assigned the label $+c$. Now, if only right-handed coordinate systems are permitted, this can be assigned to only one line, giving a total of 24 possibilities of assigning a, b, and c. But if both right- and left-handed coordinate systems are permitted there are two different possibilities of assigning $+c$, giving $6 \times 4 \times 2 = 48$ possible ways of labeling the axes.

To reduce this large number of conceivable ways of labeling the axes, crystallographers have adopted conventions of labeling based on the dimensions of the axes, as in the case of orthorhombic crystals. Some crystallographers use the convention $c > b > a$. Another group of crystallographers prefers the convention $b > a > c$ for reasons mentioned in the discussion of the orthorhombic system.

But, even when c, b, and a have been assigned to lines of specific length of the axial cross, there still remains the ambiguity due to which end of each line shall be positive. There are two ways of assigning $+a$, two ways of assigning $+b$, and two ways of assigning $+c$, making $2 \times 2 \times 2 = 8$ ways, of which four are left-handed and four are right-handed. Consider the four ways of assigning $+a$ and $+b$ to a pair of axes, X and Y, Fig. 7. In two ways γ is acute, and in two ways it is obtuse. If c is positive above the plane of the paper, then in two ways

* A different "reduced cell," has been defined by Delaunay. See last reference on p. 119.

the coordinate system is right-handed, and in two ways left-handed, as labeled. Evidently a further convention can be based upon the acute or obtuse character of the interaxial angles.

Now consider the possibilities for the third axis. This can be studied with the aid of Fig. 8, which shows the case $X \wedge Y$ acute. It is convenient to think of the plane of a and b as occupying the equatorial plane of a sphere; then $+c$ can pierce the upper hemisphere in points like Z_1, Z_2, Z_3, and Z_4, Fig. 8. Assume a general axial cross $XYZ\,\bar{X}\bar{Y}\bar{Z}$. The axes X and Y can be crossed in only one general way, namely in such a way that alternate interaxial angles are acute and obtuse. On the other hand, the axis Z can be added to this cross in two

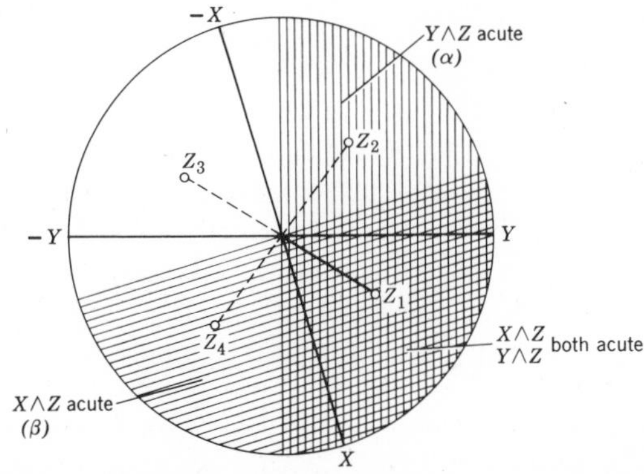

FIG. 8. Derivation of the two kinds of triclinic crystals.

different ways: The projection of the ends of Z on the plane of XY can lie in either an acute or an obtuse angle, Fig. 8. In terms of acute or obtuse interaxial angles $X \wedge Z$ and $Y \wedge Z$ this can be more precisely defined as follows: Referring to Fig. 8, the zone on the $+X$ side of the perpendicular to X is shaded. If the projection of Z lies in this zone, $X \wedge Z$ is acute. Similarly the zone on the $+Y$ side of the perpendicular to Y is shaded. If the projection of Z lies in this zone, $Y \wedge Z$ is acute.

Let Z_1 lie in the zone for which $X \wedge Z$ is acute and also in the zone for which $Y \wedge Z$ is acute, and let Z_2 lie in the zone for which $X \wedge Z$ is acute and also in the zone for which $Y \wedge Z$ is obtuse. Furthermore, let Z_3 lie opposite Z_1, and Z_4 opposite Z_2, with respect to the origin. Then

$$\left.\begin{aligned} &XYZ_1 \text{ rotated } 180^\circ = \bar{X}\bar{Y}Z_3, \\ \text{and} \qquad &XYZ_2 \text{ rotated } 180^\circ = \bar{X}\bar{Y}Z_4. \end{aligned}\right\} \tag{4}$$

Therefore the acute-obtuse combinations on the right of (4) are the same as those on the left of (4), and so need not be separately considered. This means that there are two kinds of triclinic crystals, epitomized by axial systems like XYZ_1 and XYZ_2. If the two kinds of triclinic crystals are called type I and type II, respectively, they are (for the moment) characterized by angles as follows:

$$\text{type I: } XYZ_1 \begin{cases} \alpha \text{ acute,} \\ \beta \text{ acute,} \\ \gamma \text{ acute;} \end{cases}$$
$$\text{type II: } XYZ_2 \begin{cases} \alpha \text{ acute,} \\ \beta \text{ obtuse,} \\ \gamma \text{ acute.} \end{cases} \quad (5)$$

It is possible to describe any triclinic crystal by different combinations of acute and obtuse angles. These are different *representations* of the same crystal. For example, if a is changed from $+X$ to $-X$, the character of β and γ changes from acute to obtuse, or vice versa. In a similar way any reassignment of axes causes a change in α, β, or γ, according as the sign combination of YZ, XZ, or XY changes. With this tool, all representations of the two types in (5) can be deduced analytically. The possible arrangements of a, b, and c and the angle characters they define are listed in Table 2. In this table an acute angle is indicated by a positive cosine and an obtuse angle by a negative cosine.

Table 2 shows that for each type of crystal there are four representations for right-handed axes and four equivalent representations on left-handed axes. None of the representations of type I crystal correspond to any of type II crystal, which confirms the separate character of the two types. These representatives are graphically illustrated in Fig. 9. Note that corresponding R and L representations are opposite one another and related by the symmetry center of the cell shape.

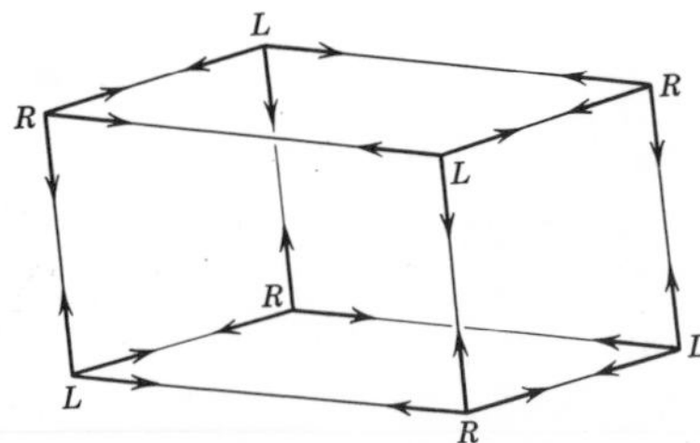

FIG. 9. Relation of the eight representations of a triclinic crystal to each other.

Now, consider the four kinds of representations of a particular triclinic crystal. Three of these representations treat the interaxial angles differently, that is, by mixed acute-obtuse assignment. But one representation treats all three angles equally. The equal-treatment representation of type I crystals is all-acute; the equal-treatment representation of type II crystals is all-obtuse. They may be called *normal representations*. Normal representations should always be used for triclinic crystals.

Table 2. Possible sets of interaxial angles in the triclinic system

Type I crystal

Orientation	cos $\alpha\ \beta\ \gamma$	Type of coordinate system	Designation of representation	
$abc = XYZ_1$	$+ + +$	R	$1R$	normal
$abc = \bar{X}YZ_1$	$+ - -$	L		$3L$
$abc = \bar{X}\bar{Y}Z_1$	$- - +$	R	$2R$	
$abc = X\bar{Y}Z_1$	$- + -$	L		$4L$
$abc = \bar{X}Y\bar{Z}_1$	$+ + +$	L		$1L$ normal
$abc = X\bar{Y}\bar{Z}_1$	$+ - -$	R	$3R$	
$abc = XY\bar{Z}_1$	$- - +$	L		$2L$
$abc = \bar{X}Y\bar{Z}_1$	$- + -$	R	$4R$	

Type II crystal

Orientation	cos $\alpha\ \beta\ \gamma$	Type of coordinate system	Designation of representation	
$abc = XYZ_2$	$+ - +$	R	$1R$	
$abc = \bar{X}YZ_2$	$+ + -$	L		$3L$
$abc = \bar{X}\bar{Y}Z_2$	$- + +$	R	$2R$	
$abc = X\bar{Y}Z_2$	$- - -$	L		$4L$ normal
$abc = \bar{X}Y\bar{Z}_2$	$+ - +$	L		$1L$
$abc = X\bar{Y}\bar{Z}_2$	$+ + -$	R	$3R$	
$abc = XY\bar{Z}_2$	$- + +$	L		$2L$
$abc = \bar{X}Y\bar{Z}_2$	$- - -$	R	$4R$	normal

Exercises

1. Draw a plan of the a_1, a_2, and a_3 axes of the hexagonal system. Draw an arbitrary line (representing the trace of an arbitrary plane $(hkil)$ on the plane of the axes a_1, a_2, and a_3) intercepting a_1 and a_2 on their positive ends. Making use of similar triangles, prove that $h + k = -i$.

2. A cell is said to have the dimensions

$$a = 1$$
$$b = \sqrt{2}, \qquad \beta = 135°$$
$$c = 1$$

Is this a reduced cell? Why?

3. A monoclinic lattice is described by a cell having the following dimensions:

$$a = 10$$
$$b = 11, \qquad \beta = 125°$$
$$c = 12$$

Find the reduced cell corresponding to this.

10 · Crystal forms

Isogonal relations between space groups and point groups

In Chapter 2 it was seen that crystals are bodies of matter characterized by periodic repetitions of some motif unit. All possible periodic repetitions can be carried out by rotations (proper and improper) and translations. The most general sort of repetitional operation is a combination of a rotation (proper or improper) and a translation. Such operations and their combinations will be considered systematically in Chapter 13. At this point only enough need be anticipated to properly understand crystal forms.

An operation consisting of a rotation (proper or improper) and an operation consisting of a combination of the same rotation with a translation are said to be *isogonal*, since the same angular repetition is involved in both cases. The combinations of rotations are limited to certain angles. These combinations determine the 32 point groups. The combinations of rotation-translations are limited to the same angles as their corresponding isogonal rotations. The permissible combinations of the possible translation-rotations determine the 230 *space groups*. The larger number of space groups than point groups is caused by the fact that the permissible rotations can usually be combined with more than one set of translations. Thus the angular relations characterizing one point group ordinarily occur in a number of different space groups. Each symmetry element of each space group of this set is isogonal with the corresponding symmetry element of the point group. Each space group of the set is accordingly said to be isogonal with the particular point group.

Repetition by space group and point group

Now consider the repetition of a plane (*hkl*) by the operations of a space group, as compared with its repetition by the operations of the isogonal point group, Figs. 1 and 2. To illustrate the principle, let the space group consist of the operations of an axis $A_{\alpha,\tau}$ of rotation-translation, as well as the translation operations of the lattice. The lattice translations produce from plane (*hkl*) a *stack* of parallel planes, as discussed in Chapter 3. The axis $A_{\alpha,\tau}$ then repeats this stack of planes to become a set of stacks related by an angular interval α and at the same time displaced by a translation, τ, as illustrated in Fig. 1.

(The value of τ may, or may not, be zero.) In the isogonal point group, Fig. 2, the operation of the isogonal axis A_α merely produces a set of individual planes separated by angular interval α. In both the point-group and space-group cases, the normals to the planes OP, OP' occupy the same locations, and, of course, the planes have the same slopes.

More generally, suppose that the number of space-group symmetry operations per cell is n. These operations require that any stack of planes with general

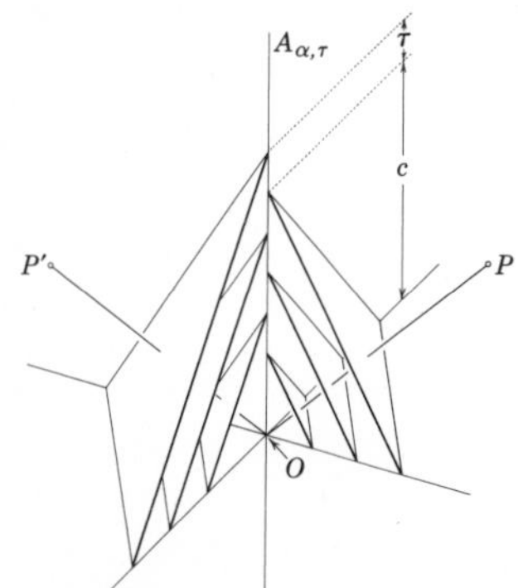

FIG. 1. Repetition of a stack of planes (*hkl*) by a translation-rotation, $A_{\alpha,\tau}$.

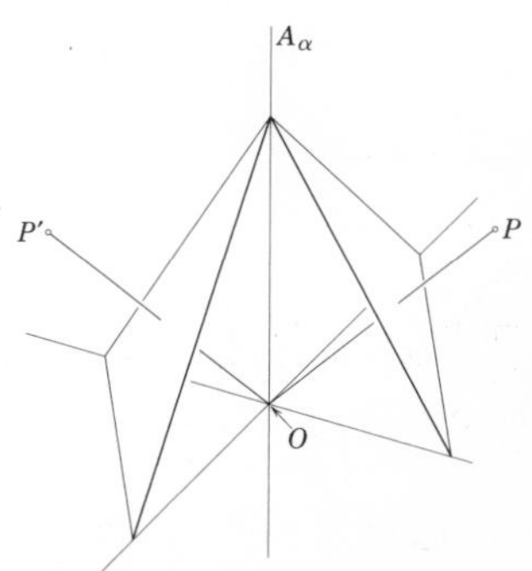

FIG. 2. Repetition of a plane (*hkl*) by a rotation, A_α.

indices (*hkl*) be a part of a symmetrical set of n stacks of planes related to (*hkl*) by the n symmetry operations. (In the event that the planes (*hkl*) occupy a specialized location with respect to the symmetry elements, the number of stacks of planes in the symmetrical set is a submultiple of n, as discussed in a later section.) It is desirable to have a designation for a complete symmetrical set of stacks of planes. If one stack of planes of the set is designated (*hkl*) the symmetrical set is designated ((*hkl*)). In other words, the symbol ((*hkl*)) means all the stacks of planes equivalent by symmetry to the specific stack of planes (*hkl*).

Similarly, suppose that the number of symmetry operations in the isogonal point group is n. These operations require that any plane of general indices (*hkl*) be a part of a set of n symmetrically equivalent planes (unless the plane occupies a special position with respect to the symmetry elements, when the symmetrical set is a submultiple of n). The symmetrical set in this case is called a *form* and is usually designated {*hkl*}. The word *form* does not mean "shape" but has the purely technical meaning just mentioned.

The convention of using parentheses about the indices of single plane, and braces about the indices of the corresponding symmetrical set of planes, is an awkward one which resembles the inflection of an irregular verb. A more rational convention is to indicate the symmetrical set by doubling the sign for the individual. This convention can be used not only for rational planes but for rational directions and points as well. These would appear as follows:

	individual	symmetrical set
plane	(*hkl*)	((*hkl*))
line	[*uvw*]	[[*uvw*]]
point	·*uvw*·	:*uvw*:

The older signs are

plane	(*hkl*)	{*hkl*}
line	[*uvw*]	⟨*uvw*⟩*
point	[[*uvw*]]	—

The external surfaces of crystals

Under favorable circumstances the growth of a crystal takes place in such a way that it maintains an external surface consisting of plane *faces*. Each face is parallel to a stack of rational planes of the lattice. Although the lattice has an infinite number of stacks of rational planes, only a few having simple indices are represented in the external surface of the crystal by faces.†

These are the facts of *crystal morphology*. The reasons for them are concerned with the physics of crystal growth and are therefore beyond the scope of this discussion. These facts, however, can be readily combined with symmetry theory to give interesting and useful results:

According to the theory discussed in the foregoing sections of this chapter, the symmetry operations of the space group relate the individual stacks of planes of the symmetrical set ((*hkl*)). The fact that these planes are equivalent by symmetry also requires that they be equivalent in every chemical and physical way. They must therefore behave identically during growth provided that growth takes place in a symmetrical environment. This implies that, if one plane of the set ((*hkl*)) attains a certain external development during the growth process, all the other planes of the set will attain the same development. If the planes of Fig. 1 are equivalent by space-group symmetry, then a corresponding form of equivalent faces, Fig. 2, appears in the crystal morphology. Consequently the crystal morphology must conform to the angular components of the space-group symmetry operations, the translation components being suppressed. This implies that the symmetry of the external morphology of a

* This sign is used by some metallurgists. Unfortunately the signs ⟨ ⟩ also mean "the average value of," and in addition are used in inequality relations.

† Which of the planes having simple indices actually develop during growth depends on the rate of growth, the nature of the environment, such as temperature and impurity content of the precipitating medium, and also on the nature of the crystal itself.

crystal is exactly that of the point group isogonal with its space group. Therefore it is possible to assign a crystal to a point group on the basis of its morphology. It is this relation of the symmetry of the morphology to the detailed symmetry of the repetition that causes point-group symmetry to be so important in crystallography.

Crystal morphology

The foregoing discussion makes it plain that, under favorable circumstances, a crystal which has grown unhindered displays a morphology consisting of plane faces. The entire morphology is consistent with the symmetry of the point group isogonal with its space group. This morphology consists of one or more crystal forms. In general the different forms should have unequal areas and are then said to have unequal development. It should be emphasized again that the relative development of the several forms on a particular crystal not only is dependent upon the crystal itself but also may vary from crystal to crystal of the same species, depending upon the conditions that prevailed during its growth. The details of form control are not discussed here since they belong to the subject matter of the physics of crystal growth.

The general, nontechnical description of the appearance of the morphology of a crystal is known as its *habit*. For example, crystals may have habits which can be described as *platy*, *tabular*, *equidimensional*, *columnar*, *prismatic*, *long prismatic*, *acicular* (needle-like), *cubo-octahedral*, etc. The various habits result from the relative development of the individual crystal forms present.

The symmetry of the morphology may depart from the true point-group symmetry if the crystal has a nonsymmetrical environment during its growth. For example, alum crystals commonly have an octahedral habit and should ideally display an equal development of all eight faces of the octahedron in order to be consistent with the point-group symmetry of alum, $\frac{4}{m}\bar{3}\frac{2}{m}$. But if an alum crystal grows at the bottom of a beaker it is usually found to be flattened parallel to one pair of octahedral faces. This results from the fact that the convection currents which feed the crystal with supersaturated solutions are not as symmetrical as the structure of the crystal itself. On the other hand, crystals grown in free space tend to be ideally symmetrical. For example, quartz crystals of quartz-porphyry rock are usually symmetrical hexagonal bipyramids. These crystals were grown freely suspended in the liquid magma before it became solid rock.

Form theory

A simple way of investigating the possible crystal forms is to consider in what way the normals to the various planes (hkl) are repeated by the symmetry elements of the point group. A simple case of this was illustrated in Fig. 2. A convenient way of visualizing this for the more complicated symmetries is to think of the symmetry elements as intersecting at the center of a sphere. The symmetry elements are then represented by their intersections with the surface of the sphere. For example, the symmetry $\frac{2}{m}\frac{2}{m}\frac{2}{m}$ in this representation is shown in Fig. 3.

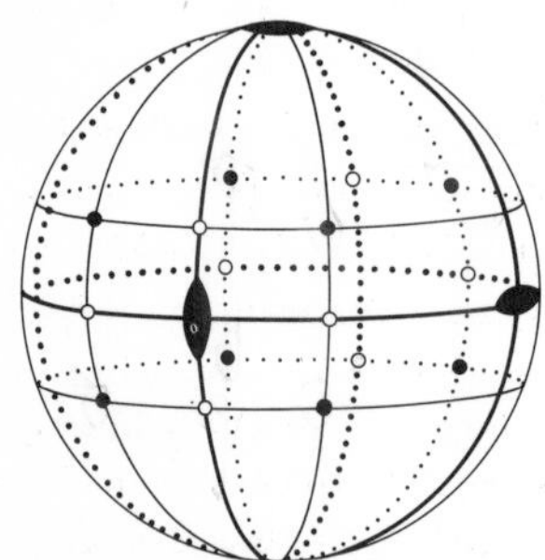

FIG. 3. Repetition of points on the surface of a sphere by symmetry $\frac{2}{m}\frac{2}{m}\frac{2}{m}$. Small black circles indicate points in general position, and small open circles indicate points in two different special positions.

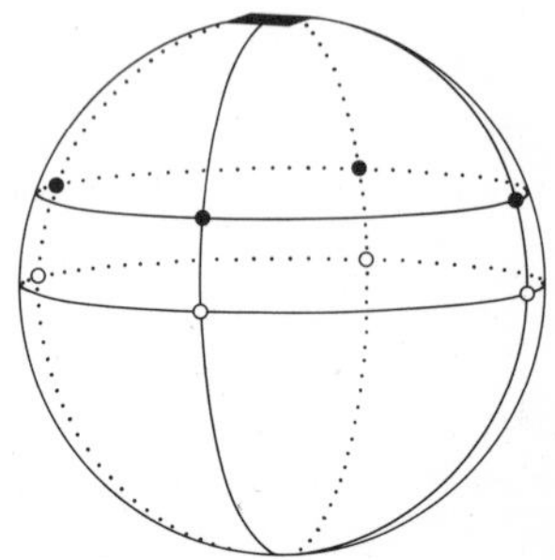

FIG. 4. Repetition of points on the surface of a sphere by symmetry 4. Small black circles indicate points in general position, and small open circles indicate points in special position.

In this representation the normal to a plane (*hkl*) is a point. In Fig. 3, it is evident that the symmetry operations require eight points provided (*hkl*) occupies a general position. These correspond to the eight faces of the form ((*hkl*)). On the other hand, if the location of (*hkl*) is specialized so as to occupy a symmetry plane as shown in Fig. 3, then pairs of the eight points coalesce on the symmetry plane, and the form has merely four planes. If the location of the point is further specialized so as to lie on the intersections of two symmetry planes, sets of four of the eight points of the general form coalesce so that the eight points become only two points. These three diverse ways of placing (*hkl*) with respect to the symmetry elements determine three diverse kinds of forms which receive names according to their geometrical appearances.

The form corresponding to a location of the motif point in the most general position with respect to the symmetry elements is called the *general form* of the class.

In the foregoing discussion it was evident that there exist certain *special forms* which correspond to placing a motif point in some specialized location with respect to the symmetry elements. Each has a symmetry equal to or higher than that of the general form. There are a total of 16 such special forms, most of which appear in several classes. The special forms can be found by moving the motif point for the general position to a specialized position. Such specialized positions include each of the symmetry elements, positions located between symmetry elements, and the locus on a plane normal to a rotation axis. This last specialized locus can be used to illustrate the notion of special forms. Consider the set of points on the sphere having general locations and consistent with an n-fold axis, Fig. 4. The n-fold axis requires n such points. These points determine n face normals inclined (in general) to the n-fold axis. These correspond to a pyramid of n faces. But, if the points are moved onto the equator of the n-fold axis, the face normals lie in a plane (Fig. 4) and determine a degeneration of the pyramid, namely a prism of n faces all parallel to the n-fold axis. This form, taken by itself, has a symmetry plane normal to the n-fold axis. Accordingly, if the original point is moved onto the plane normal to the axis, the form displays a symmetry plane exactly as if there were a symmetry plane in the point group. In the systematic discussion of forms which is given later in this chapter, such special planes which are not true symmetry planes are shown in broken lines.

It is convenient to distinguish those crystal classes which are as symmetrical as the distribution of points in their lattice. These are the seven classes listed in the third column of Table 1, Chapter 8. These classes are called *holosymmetric.* All other classes utilizing the same lattice are called *merosymmetric.*

In the holosymmetric classes there tend to be seven forms, of which one is the general form and six others are special forms. The reason for this is that the symmetry planes or other special position planes partition the sphere into a series of equivalent triangles. The triangle is bordered by three symmetry planes and has three vertices, all of which are special positions. The six special positions and one general one determine seven forms, except in the monoclinic system, when the triangle degenerates into a hemisphere, and in the triclinic system, where it is absent altogether.

There prove to be 48 different crystal forms. Some forms enclose space; others do not. They are called *closed forms* and *open forms*, respectively. An actual crystal may display only one form provided it is a closed form. An open form can exist only in combination with one or more open forms which together enclose space, or in combination with closed forms, with or without other open forms. Ordinarily a crystal displays several forms. Whatever the form combination, at least four non-parallel faces are required to enclose space.

Enantiomorphism

Twenty-one point groups contain one or more operations of the second sort. The other eleven point groups contain no operations of the second sort. These are the point groups containing pure rotation axes only, specifically 1, 2, 3, 4, 6, 222, 32, 422, 622, 23, and 432. If a point having particular but general coordinates is placed in any of these symmetries, the pattern of points resulting from the repetition of this motif point by the symmetry elements is different according as a right-handed or left-handed coordinate system is used. The two arrangements of points are *enantiomorphous*; that is, they are related to one another as mirror images (or inversions). On the other hand, if a point having general coordinates is placed in a point group having one or more operations of the second sort, the patterns of points which result with a right- or left-handed coordinate system are exactly the same. This is because any operation of the second sort requires that the pattern itself be composed of equivalent right- and left-handed aspects. In this case the pattern contains parts which are already enantiomorphous. A reflection of such a pattern in a mirror reproduces the same pattern.

For this general reason a pattern of atoms occurring in any of the axial point groups 1, 2, 3, 4, 6, 222, 32, 422, 622, 23, or 432 has both right-handed and left-handed possibilities. Crystals belonging to classes having any of these eleven symmetries, accordingly, may occur in right- and left-handed structural varieties which are called *enantiomorphs*. Naturally, enantiomorphous crystals have enantiomorphous form developments whenever the nature of this development is not so specialized that right- and left-handed developments are not distinguishable. For example, a prism occurring on a right-handed crystal is the same as a prism occurring on a left-handed crystal. However, when a prism is combined with general forms it is usually possible to distinguish right- *versus* left-handed developments.

Systematic discussion of forms

The remainder of this chapter is devoted to a systematic listing of the forms occurring in the various crystal systems and in the specific crystal classes. The forms contained in a given crystal system are characteristic of it, except that the pedion and pinacoid of the triclinic system are also found in all other crystal systems save the isometric, and except that the prism occurs in both monoclinic and orthorhombic systems. For this reason the several forms occurring in each crystal system (except the triclinic, where the forms are trivial) are first tabulated together. Their specific distributions among the classes of the system are then shown in Tables 1–7.

In each class, the way a motif point is repeated by the symmetry operations is shown by a sphere diagram. In a separate diagram there is also shown the special positions which the motif point can occupy to give rise to special forms. In these diagrams a broken line indicates the locations of special positions which are not symmetry elements, for example planes (which are not reflection planes) normal to rotation axes.

For each of the 32 possible symmetries a listing is given of some actual representatives of that crystal class. Mineral representatives, other inorganic representatives, and organic representatives are separately listed. These lists are not exhaustive, although an attempt has been made to give as many representatives as possible of the classes for which comparatively few representatives are known. These lists have been compiled largely from the following sources:

Charles Palache, Harry Berman, and Clifford Frondel, *The system of mineralogy of James Dwight Dana and Edward Salisbury Dana*, Vols. I (1944) and II (1951) (John Wiley, New York).

Paul Groth, *Elemente der physikalischen und chemischen Krystallographie* (R. Oldenbourg, Munich and Berlin, 1921.)

J. D. H. Donnay and Werner Nowacki, *Crystal data*, Geological Society of America Memoir 60 (1954), especially pp. 7–83.

The triclinic system

The forms occurring in the triclinic system are listed in Table 1.

Table 1. Forms occurring in the triclinic system

Indices	Classes	
	1	$\bar{1}$
hkl	pedion	pinacoid

Class 1. The repetition of a motif point by the symmetry of this class is illustrated in Fig. 5. Since there are no symmetry elements, any face in this

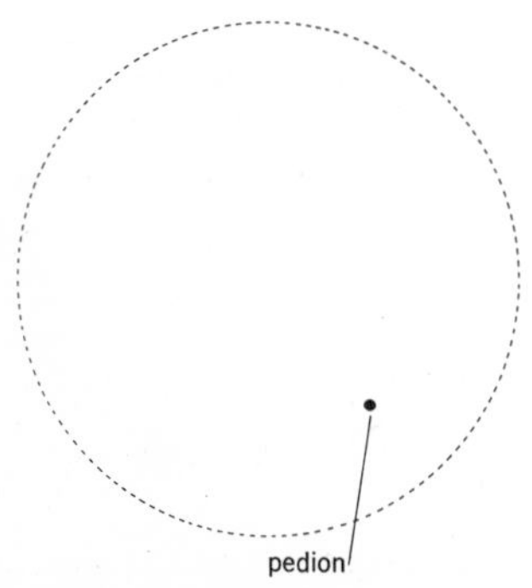

FIG. 5. Repetition of a point by symmetry 1. In diagrams like this, the dotted circle is the outline of a sphere. Solid dots are points on the upper hemisphere while open dots are points on the lower hemisphere.

class is also a form. This form is known as a *pedion*, from the Greek word for "plain." Since the symmetry does not contain an operation of the second sort, crystals of this class can occur in right- and left-handed varieties whose form developments are enantiomorphous.

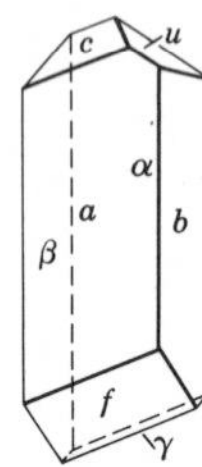

FIG. 6. Example of form development in class 1: strontium acid tartrate tetrahydrate, $SrH_2(C_4H_4O_6)_2 \cdot 4H_2O$.

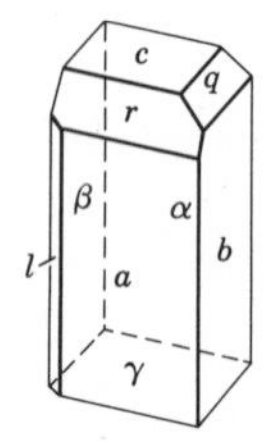

FIG. 7. Example of form development in class 1; *d*-ethyldiamine cobalt chlorotartrate, $C_4H_4O_6ClCo(N_2H_4C_2H_4)_3$.

Mineral representatives

parahilgardite, $Ca_8B_{18}Cl_4 \cdot 4H_2O$

Other inorganic representatives

$CaS_2O_3 \cdot$ 6H2O

Organic representatives

strontium acid tartrate tetrahydrate, $SrH_2(C_4H_4O_6)_2 \cdot 4H_2O$, Fig. 6
rubidium ferrocyanide dihydrate, $Rb_4Fe(CN)_6 \cdot 2H_2O$
d-ethyldiamine cobalt chlorotartrate, $C_4H_4O_6ClCo(N_2H_4C_2H_4)_3$, Fig. 7

Class $\bar{1}$. The symmetry of this class and its repetition of a motif point are shown in Fig. 8. Since the only symmetry element is a symmetry center, every face is accompanied by a centrosymmetrical (and therefore parallel)

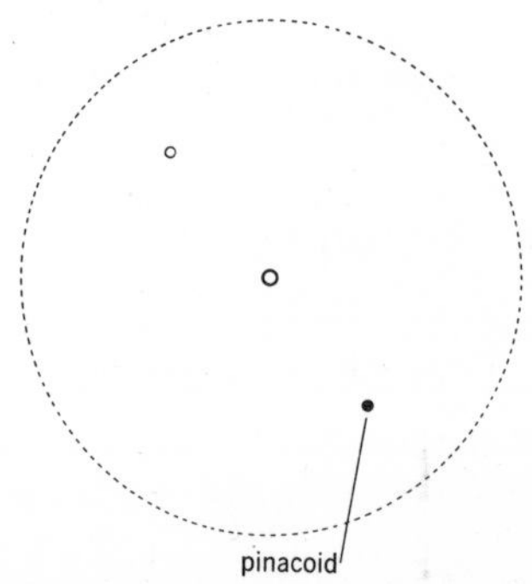

FIG. 8. Repetition of a point by symmetry $\bar{1}$. Small heavy circle indicates an inversion center at the center of the sphere.

opposite face. The two faces constitute the only forms of the class, known as a *pinacoid*, from the Greek word for "board."

Mineral representatives

amblygonite, $LiAlFPO_4$
turquois, $CuAl_6(PO_4)_4 \cdot 4H_2O$
kyanite, Al_2SiO_5
albite, $NaAlSi_3O_8$ (and other plagioclase feldspars)
rhodonite, $MnSiO_3$, Fig. 9.

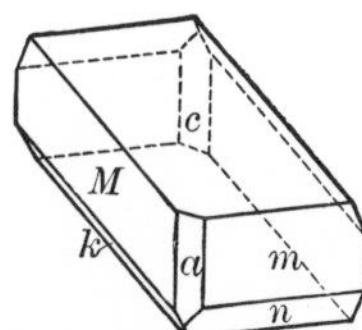

FIG. 9. Example of form development in class $\bar{1}$; rhodonite, $MnSiO_3$.

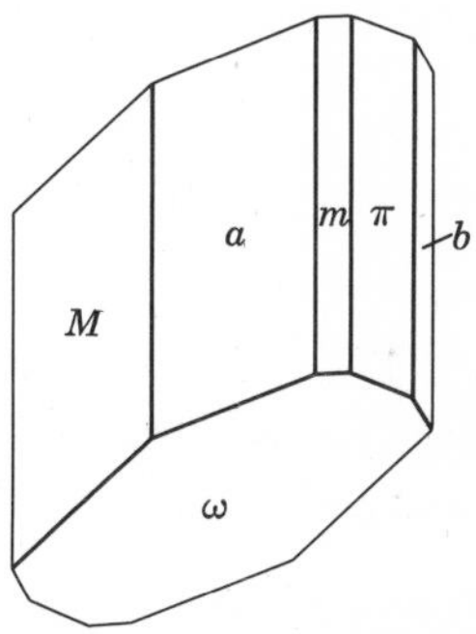

FIG. 10. Example of form development in class $\bar{1}$; $CuSO_4 \cdot 5H_2O$.

Other inorganic representatives

$B(OH)_3$
$CuSO_4 \cdot 5H_2O$, Fig. 10
$K_2S_2O_8$
$Bi(NO_3)_2 \cdot 9H_2O$
$Ce(NO_3)_2 \cdot 6H_2O$

Organic representatives

yttrium acetate tetrahydrate, $Y(C_2H_3O_2) \cdot 4H_2O$
malonic acid, $CH_2(CO_2H)_2$
p-bromonitrobenzene, $C_6H_4Br(NO_2)$
3,4,5-trichloronitrobenzene, $C_6H_2Cl_3(NO_2)$

The monoclinic system

The forms occurring in the monoclinic system are listed in Table 2. The forms not already encountered in the less symmetrical triclinic system are

the *sphenoid*, after the Greek for "axe," Fig. 11,
the *dome*, after the Greek for "roof," Fig. 12,
the *rhombic prism*, Fig. 13.

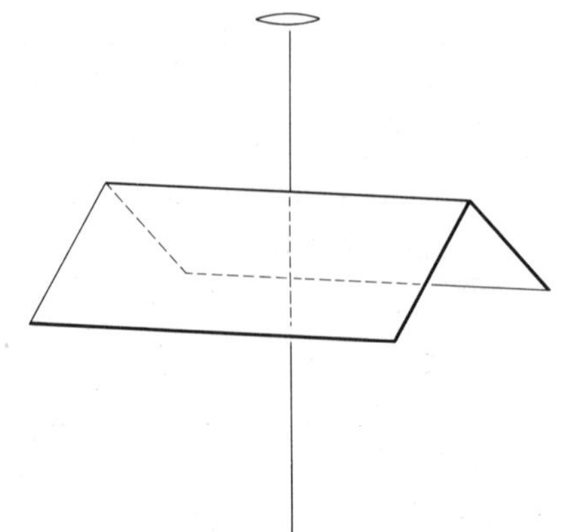

FIG. 11. Sphenoid.

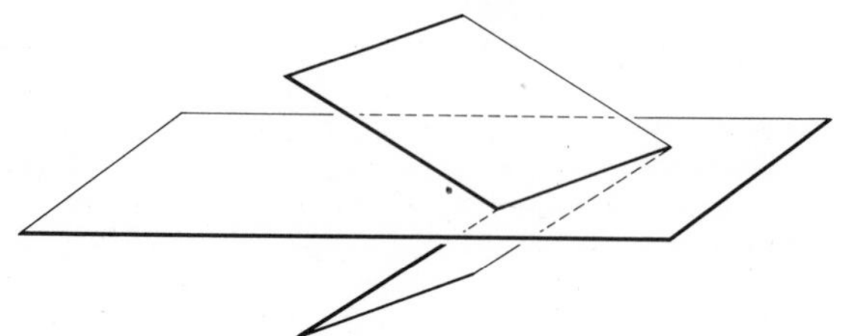

FIG. 12. Dome.

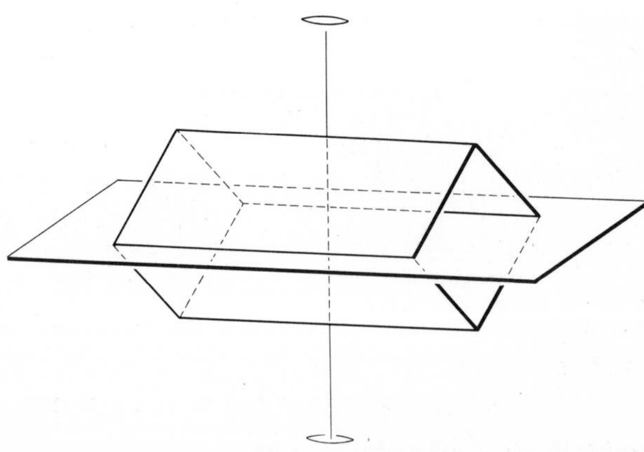

FIG. 13. Prism.

All forms are open forms and can consequently occur only in appropriate combination with each other.

The sphenoid and dome are geometrically indistinguishable. If they are counted as the same form there are only 47 crystal forms instead of 48. The faces of a sphenoid are related by a rotation; those of the dome are related by a reflection. For this reason many crystallographers prefer to make a distinction between them even though, if present without other accompanying forms, as, for example, a part of a broken crystal, they could not be distinguished by appearance alone.

Table 2. Forms occurring in the monoclinic system

First setting, $c = 2$

Indices	Classes		
	2	m	$\frac{2}{m}$
hkl	sphenoid	dome	prism
*hk*0	pinacoid	pedion	pinacoid
001	pedion	pinacoid	pinacoid

Second setting, $b = 2$

Indices	Classes		
	2	m	$\frac{2}{m}$
hkl	sphenoid	dome	prism
*h*0*l*	pinacoid	pedion	pinacoid
010	pedion	pinacoid	pinacoid

Class 2. The symmetry of this class and its repetition of a motif point are shown in Fig. 14. Special positions are shown in Fig. 15. Since this class lacks symmetry elements of the second sort, crystals belonging to it can occur in right- and left-handed varieties whose form developments are enantiomorphous.

Mineral representatives

pickeringite, $MgSO_4 \cdot Al_2(SO_4)_3 \cdot 22H_2O$
halotrichite, $FeAl_2(SO_4)_2 \cdot 22H_2O$, and other members of the group

Other inorganic representatives

$LiSO_4 \cdot H_2O$

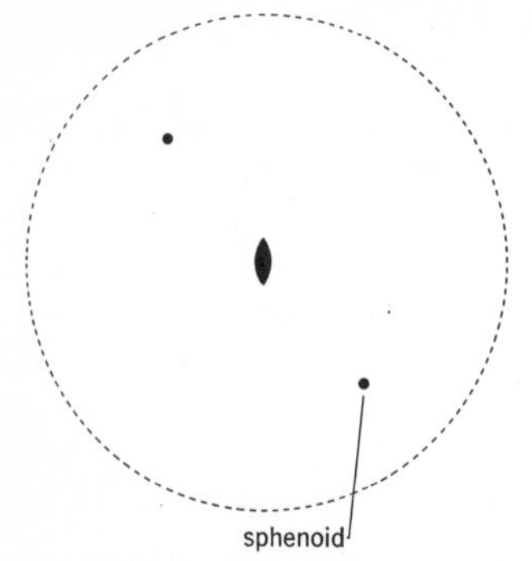

FIG. 14. Repetition of a point in the general position by symmetry 2.

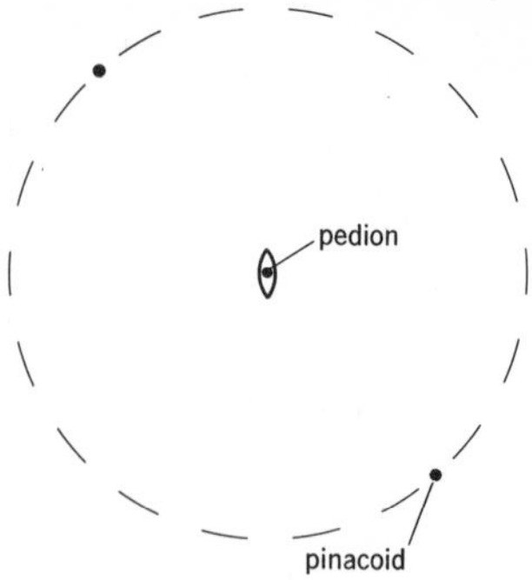

FIG. 15. Special positions of symmetry 2.

Organic representatives

sucrose, $C_{12}H_{22}O_{11}$, Fig. 16
lactose monohydrate, $C_{12}H_{22}O_{11} \cdot H_2O$, Fig. 17
tartaric acid, $H_2C_4H_4O_6$, Figs. 18 and 19
fichtelite, $C_{18}H_{32}$
d–α-chlorocamphor, $C_{10}H_{15}OCl$
r-cocaine, $C_{17}H_{21}O_4N$
strychnine nitrate, $C_{21}H_{22}O_2N_2 \cdot HNO_3$

Class *m*. The symmetry of this class and its repetition of a motif point are shown in Fig. 20. Special positions are shown in Fig. 21.

Mineral representatives

hilgardite, $Ca_8B_{18}O_{33}Cl_4 \cdot 4H_2O$, Fig. 22
tilasite, $CaMg(AsO_4)F$
trigonite, $MnPb_3H(AsO_3)_3$, Fig. 23
scolecite, $CaAl_2Si_3O_{10} \cdot 3H_2O$
clinohedrite, $H_2CaZnSiO_5$

Other inorganic representatives

KNO_2
$K_2S_4O_6$
$CuSO_4 \cdot 3H_2O$
Na_2SiO_3

Organic representatives

norpinic acid, $C_8H_{12}O_4$
2,4,6-tribromobenzonitrile, $C_6H_2Br_3(CN)$

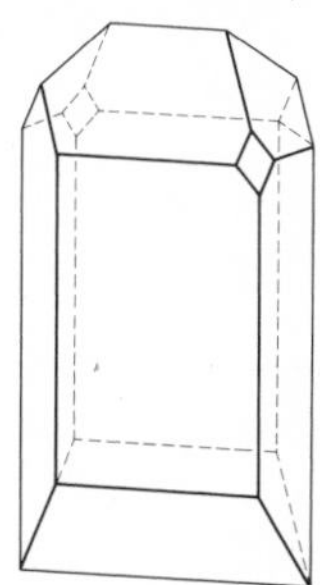

FIG. 16. Example of form development in class 2: sucrose, $C_{12}H_{22}O_{11}$.

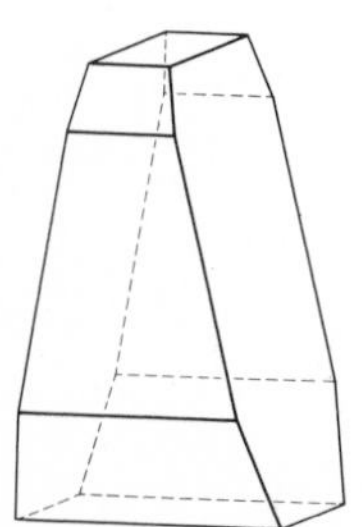

FIG. 17. Example of form development in class 2: lactose monohydrate, $C_{12}H_{22}O_{11} \cdot H_2O$.

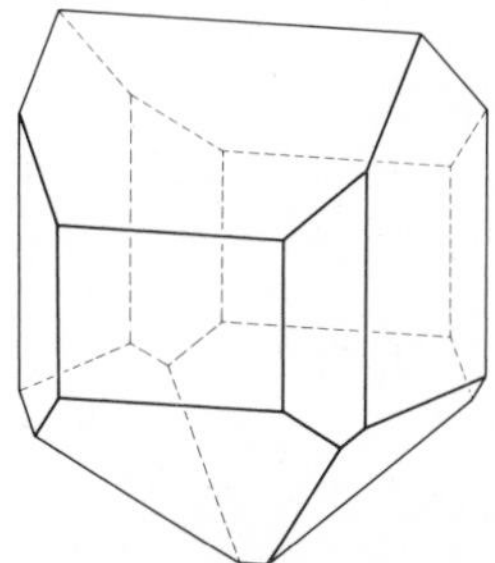

FIG. 18 and FIG. 19. Examples of enantiomorphous form development in class 2: left tartaric acid, $H_2C_4H_4O_6$ (Fig. 18); and right tartaric acid (Fig. 19).

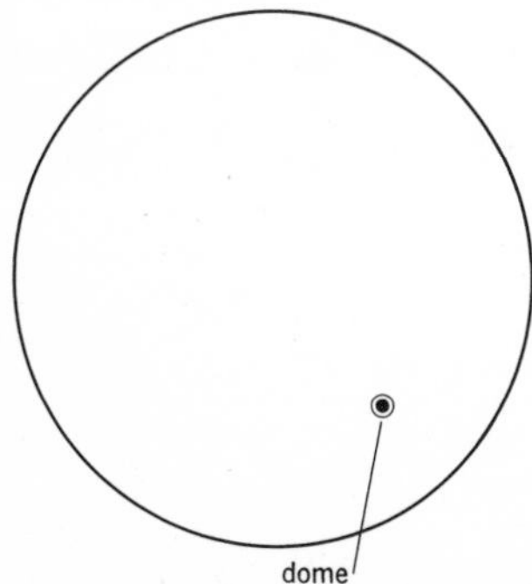

FIG. 20. Repetition of a point in the general position by symmetry *m*.

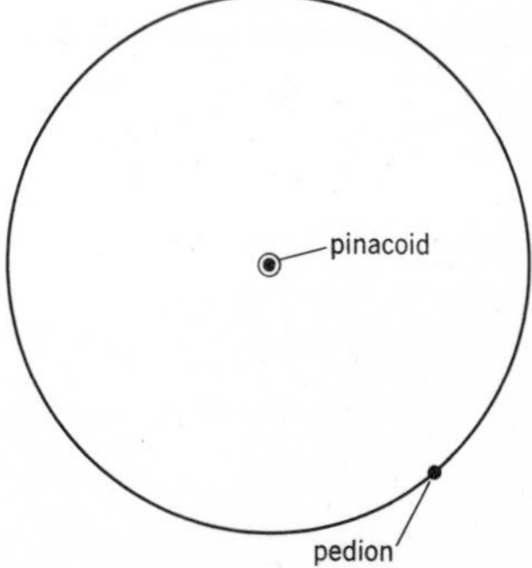

FIG. 21. Special positions of symmetry *m*.

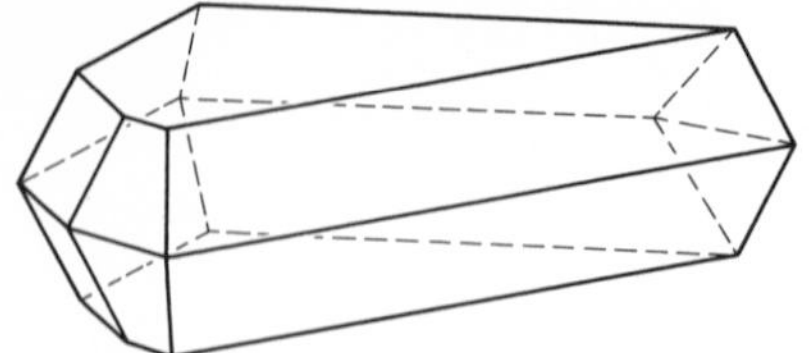

FIG. 22. Example of form development in class m: hilgardite, $Ca_8B_{18}O_{33}Cl_4 \cdot 4H_2O$.

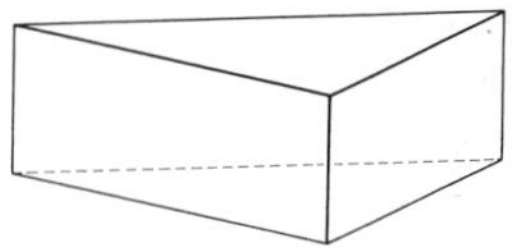

FIG. 23. Example of form development in class m: trigonite, $MnPb_3H(AsO_3)_3$.

Class $\frac{2}{m}$. The symmetry elements of this class and repetition of a motif point are shown in Fig. 24. Special positions are shown in Fig. 25. There are abundant crystal representations of this symmetry.

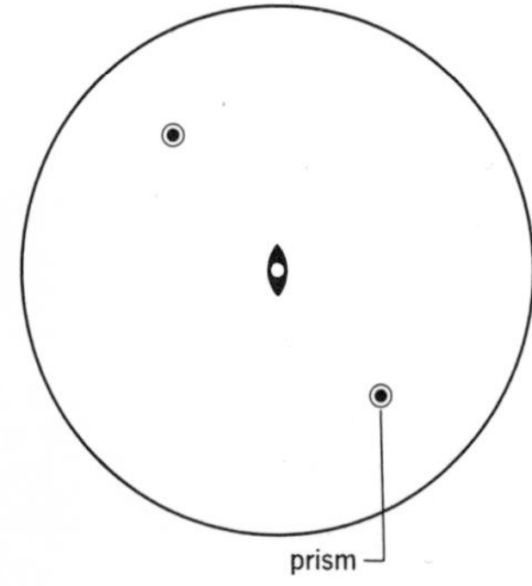

FIG. 24. Repetition of a point in the general position by symmetry $\frac{2}{m}$.

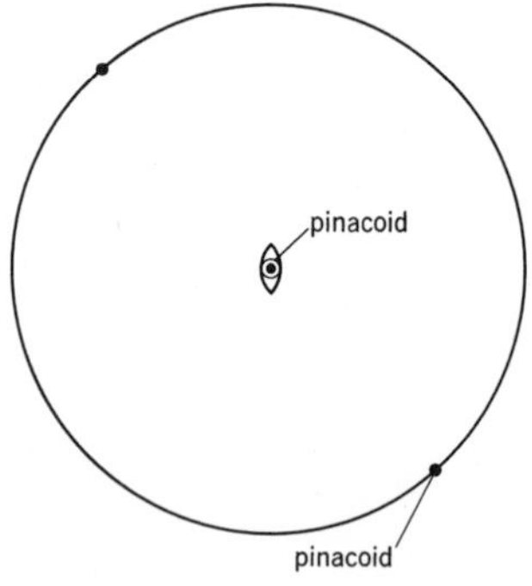

FIG. 25. Special positions of symmetry $\frac{2}{m}$.

Mineral representatives

realgar, As_4S_4
orpiment, As_2S_3
cryolite, Na_3AlF_6
borax, $Na_2B_4O_7 \cdot 10H_2O$
malachite, $Cu_2(OH)_2CO_3$
azurite, $Cu_3(OH)_2(CO_3)_2$
gypsum, $CaSO_4 \cdot 2H_2O$
monazite, $(Ce,La,Y,Th)PO_4$
epidote, $HCa_2(Al,Fe)Al_2Si_3O_{13}$
titanite, $CaTiSiO_5$
datolite, $CaBSiO_4(OH)$
diopside, $CaMg(SiO_3)_2$, and other pyroxenes
tremolite, $Ca_2MgSi_8O_{22}(OH)_2$
orthoclase, $KAlSi_3O_8$,

Other inorganic representatives

high-sulfur
$BaCl_2 \cdot 2H_2O$
$KClO_3$
$NaHCO_3$
$MgSO_4 \cdot 6H_2O$
$FeSO_4 \cdot 7H_2O$, Fig. 26
$BaS_2O_6 \cdot 2H_2O$, Fig. 27

Organic representatives

naphthalene, $C_{10}H_8$
anthracene, $C_{14}H_{10}$
piperine, $C_{17}H_{19}O_3N$
oxalic acid dihydrate, $H_2C_2O_4 \cdot 2H_2O$
salicyclic acid, $C_6H_4(OH)CO_2H$
sodium acetate trihydrate, $NaC_2H_3O_2 \cdot 3H_2O$

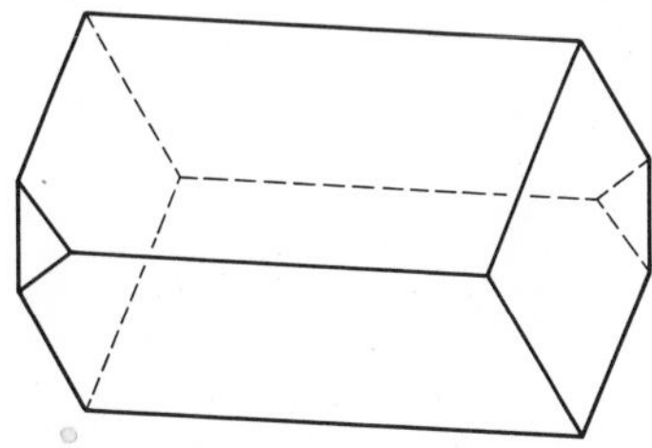

FIG. 26. Example of form development in class $\frac{2}{m}$: $FeSO_4 \cdot 7H_2O$.

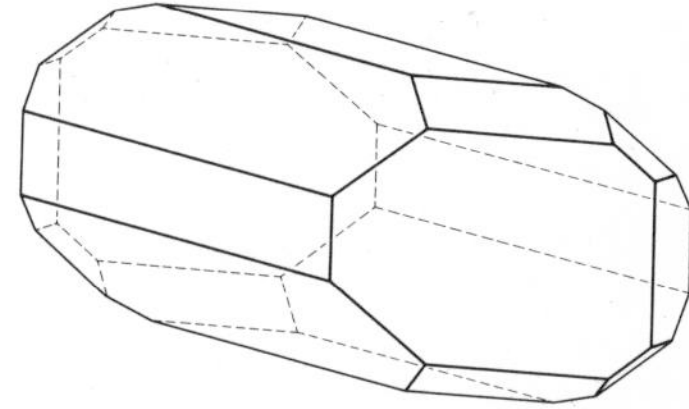

FIG. 27. Example of form development in class $\frac{2}{m}$: $BaS_2O_6 \cdot 2H_2O$.

The orthorhombic system

The forms occurring in the orthorhombic system are listed in Table 3. The additional forms not encountered in the less symmetrical triclinic and monoclinic systems are

the *rhombic bisphenoid*, Fig. 28
the *rhombic pyramid*, Fig. 29
the *rhombic bipyramid*, Fig. 30

It will be observed that prisms can occur which have their several faces parallel to either the *a*, *b*, or *c* axes. When need arises, the prisms can be distinguished by designating them *a* prisms, *b* prisms, and *c* prisms, respectively. The domes can be distinguished in the same manner. In a similar way the

Table 3. Forms occurring in the orthorhombic system

Indices	Classes 222	*mm*2	$\frac{2}{m}\frac{2}{m}\frac{2}{m}$
hkl	bisphenoid	pyramid	bipyramid
*hk*0	*c* prism	*c* prism	*c* prism
0*kl*	*a* prism	*a* dome	*a* prism
*h*0*l*	*b* prism	*b* dome	*b* prism
100	*A* pinacoid	*A* pinacoid	*A* pinacoid
010	*B* pinacoid	*B* pinacoid	*B* pinacoid
001	*C* pinacoid	*C* pedion	*C* pinacoid

different pinacoids are distinguishable as the *A* pinacoid, i.e., parallel to the *A* or (100) face of the unit cell, the *B* pinacoid, and the *C* pinacoid.

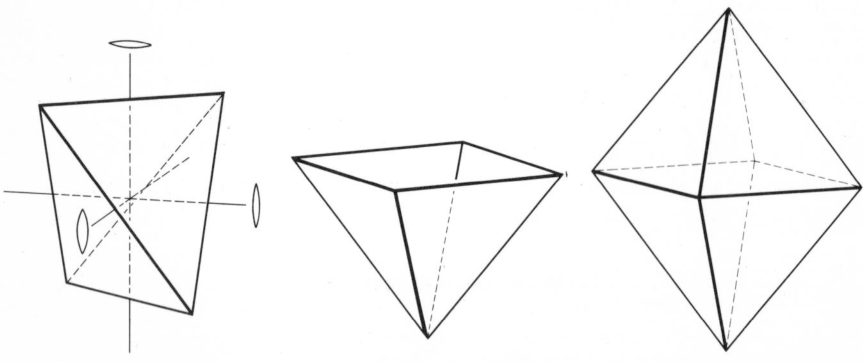

FIG. 28. Bisphenoid. FIG. 29. Pyramid. FIG. 30. Bipyramid.

Class 222. The symmetry elements of this class and their repetition of a motif point are shown in Fig. 31. Special positions are shown in Fig. 32. Since the point group contains no operations of the second sort, crystals having this symmetry can occur in right- and left-handed varieties whose form developments are enantiomorphous.

This class is richly represented by sulfates, phosphates, arsenates, and by crystals of organic compounds.

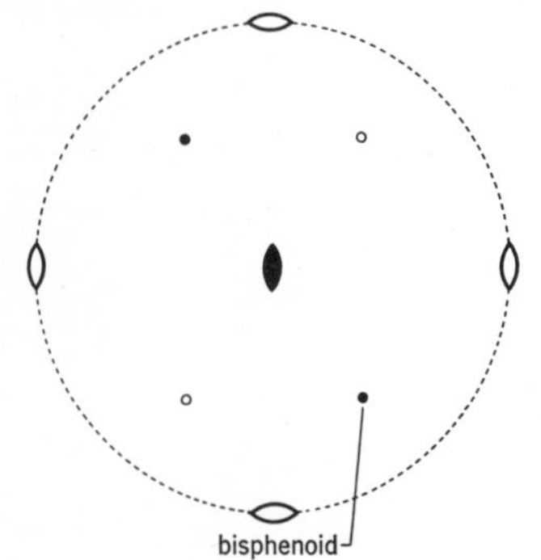

FIG. 31. Repetition of a point in the general position by symmetry 222.

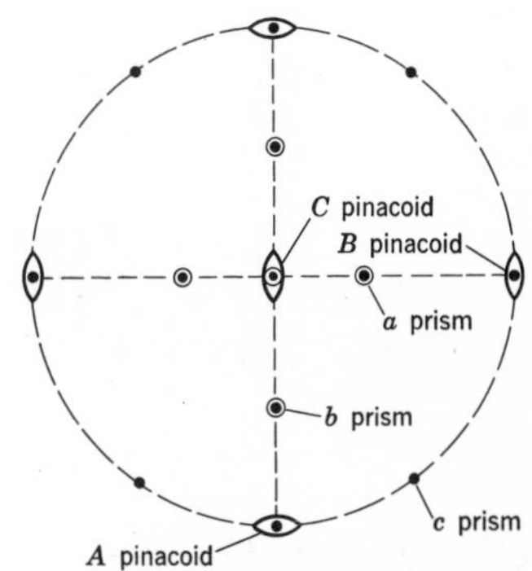

FIG. 32. Special positions of symmetry 222.

Mineral representatives

chalcomenite, $CuSeO_3 \cdot 2H_2O$
epsomite, $MgSO_4 \cdot 7H_2O$, Figs. 33 and 34
goslarite, $ZnSO_4 \cdot 7H_2O$
morenosite, $NiSO_4 \cdot 7H_2O$
olivenite, $Cu_2(OH)AsO_4$
austinite, $CaZn(AsO_4)OH$
frondelite, $(Mn,Fe)Fe_4(PO_4)_3(OH)_5$
euchroite, $Cu,AsO_4(OH) \cdot 3H_2O$
sterrettite, $Al_6(PO_4)_4 \cdot 5H_2O$
conichalcite, $CaCu(AsO_4)OH$

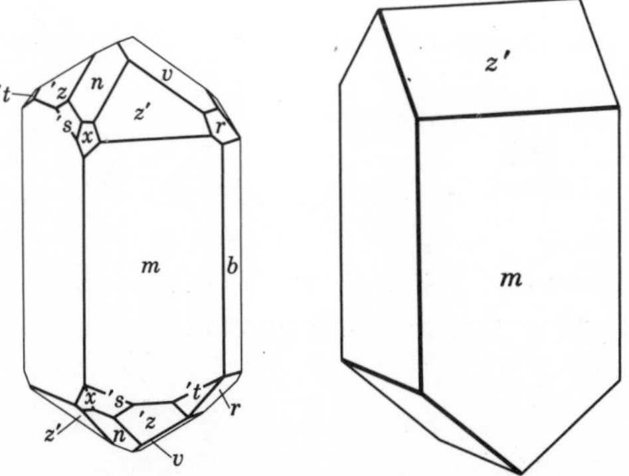

FIG. 33 and FIG. 34. Examples of form development in class 222: $MgSO_4 \cdot 7H_2O$.

Other inorganic representatives

$AgNO_3$
$Na_2PO_4 \cdot 2H_2O$
$KH_2PO_4 \cdot 2H_2O$, etc.

Organic representatives

tartar emetic, $K(SbO)(C_4H_4O_6)$
Rochelle salt, $KNa(C_4H_4O_6) \cdot 4H_2O$
strontium formate, $Sr(HCOO)_2$
barium formate, $Ba(HCOO)_2$, Figs. 35 and 36
strontium formate dihydrate, $Sr(HCOO)_2 \cdot 2H_2O$
N-bromosuccinimide, $(CH_2CO)_2NBr$
diglycine hydrobromide, $C_4H_{11}BrN_2O_4$
terramycin hydrochloride, $C_{22}H_{24}N_2O_9 \cdot HCl$

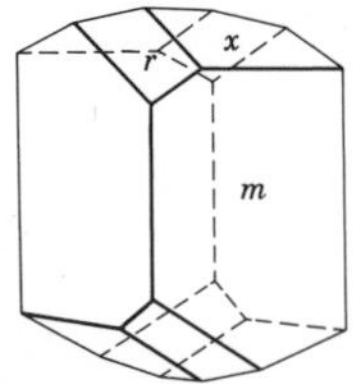

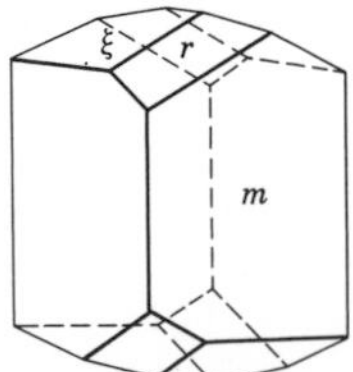

FIG. 35 and FIG. 36. Examples of enantiomorphous form development in class 222; left barium formate, $Ba(HCOO)_2$ (Fig. 35) and right barium formate (Fig. 36).

Class *mm*2. The symmetry elements of this class and their repetition of a motif point are shown in Fig. 37. Special positions are shown in Fig. 38. It is customary to orient crystals belonging to this class so that the unique 2-fold axis is *c*.

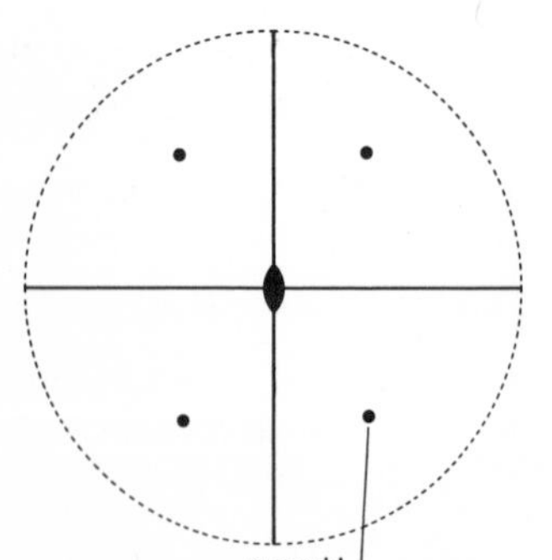

FIG. 37. Repetition of a point in the general position by symmetry *mm*2.

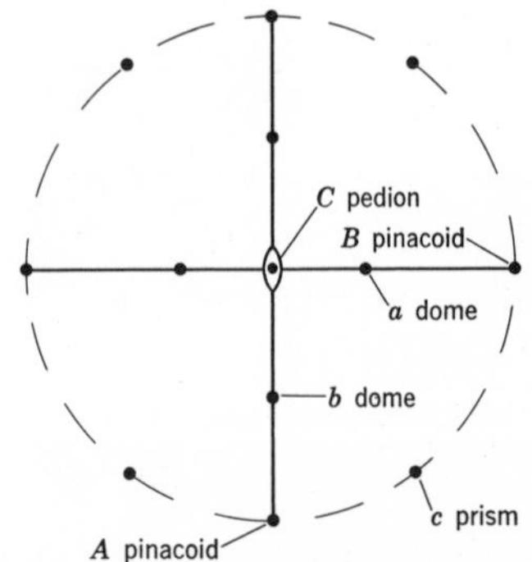

FIG. 38. Special positions of symmetry *mm*2.

Mineral representatives

shortite, $Na_2Ca_2(CO_3)_3$, Fig. 39
pirssonite, $Na_2Ca(CO_3)_2 \cdot 2H_2O$, Fig. 40
struvite, $Mg(NH_4)PO_4 \cdot 6H_2O$, Fig. 41
bertrandite, $Be_4(OH)Si_2O_7$
hemimorphite, $Zn_4(OH)_2Si_2O_7 \cdot H_2O$
natrolite, $NaAl_2Si_3O_{10} \cdot 2H_2O$
eddingtonite, $BaAl_2Si_3O_{10} \cdot 2H_2O$

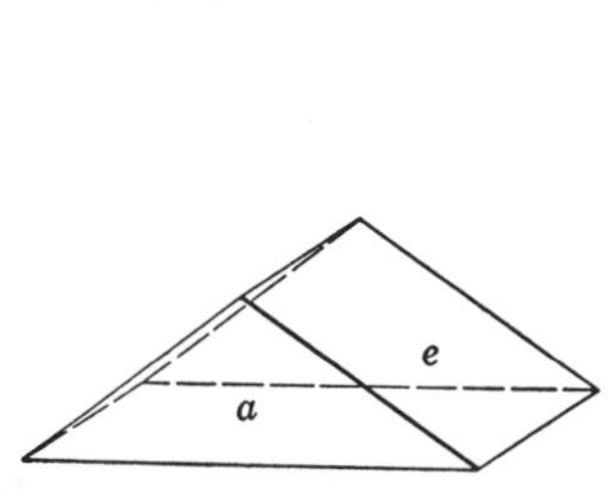

FIG. 39. Example of form development in class *mm*2: shortite, $Na_2Ca_2(CO_3)_3$.

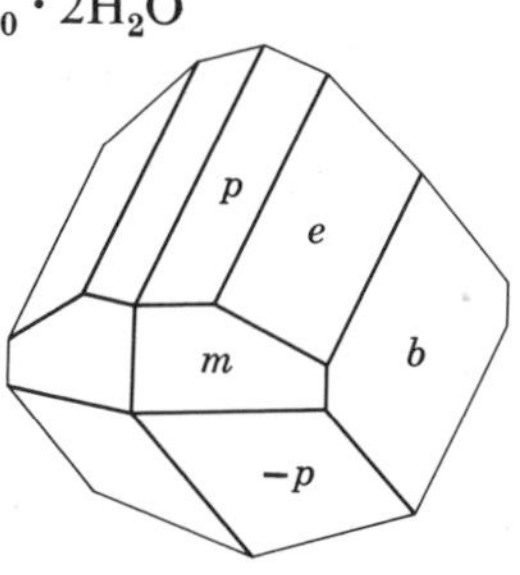

FIG. 40. Example of form development in class *mm*2: pirssonite, $Na_2Ca(CO_3)_2 \cdot 2H_2O$.

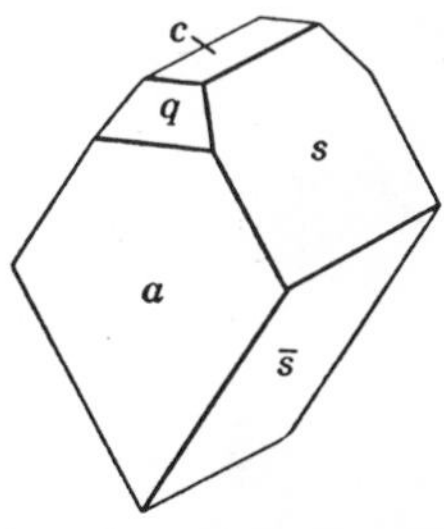

FIG. 41. Example of form development in class *mm*2; struvite, $Mg(NH_4)PO_4 \cdot 6H_2O$.

Other inorganic representatives

$Sr(ClO_3)_2$
$KMgPO_4 \cdot 6H_2O$

Organic representatives

bismuth thiocyanate, $Bi(CNS)_3$
triphenylmethane, $CH(C_6H_5)_3$
picric acid, $C_6H_2(NO_2)_3OH$
resorcinol, $C_6H_4(OH)_2$

Class $\frac{2}{m}\frac{2}{m}\frac{2}{m}$. The symmetry elements of this class and their repetition of a motif unit are shown in Fig. 42. Special positions are shown in Fig. 43. This symmetry has abundant crystal representatives, especially among minerals.

Mineral representatives

sulfur, Fig. 44
marcasite, FeS_2
löllingite, $FeAs_2$
stibnite, Sb_2S_3
brookite, TiO_2
barite, $BaSO_4$
olivine, Mg_2SiO_4, Fig. 45
staurolite, $HFeAl_5Si_2O_{13}$, Fig. 46

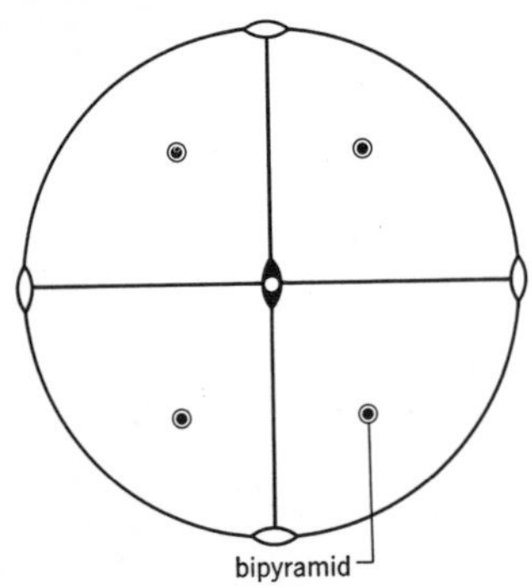

FIG. 42. Repetition of a point in the general position by symmetry $\frac{2}{m}\frac{2}{m}\frac{2}{m}$.

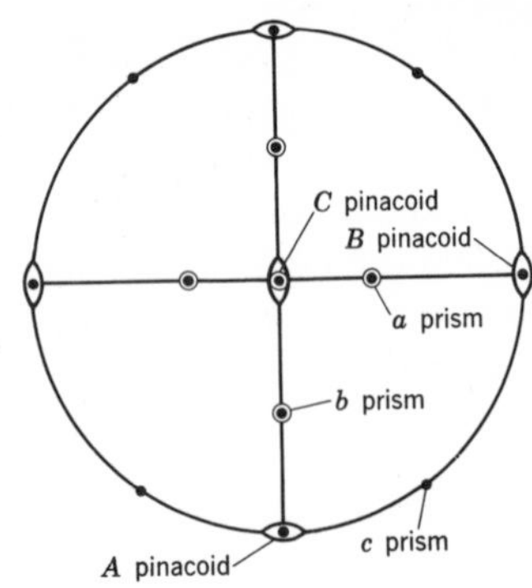

Fig. 43. Special positions of symmetry $\frac{2}{m}\frac{2}{m}\frac{2}{m}$.

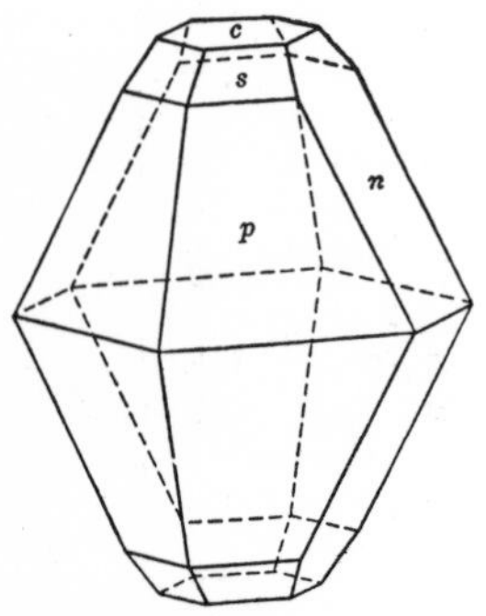

FIG. 44. Example of form development in class $\frac{2}{m}\frac{2}{m}\frac{2}{m}$: sulfur.

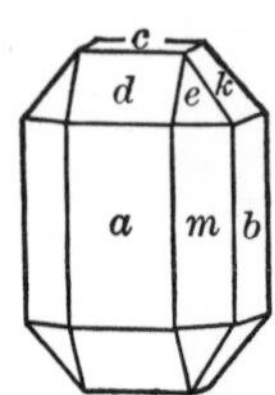

FIG. 45. Example of form development in class $\frac{2}{m}\frac{2}{m}\frac{2}{m}$: olivine, Mg_2SiO_4.

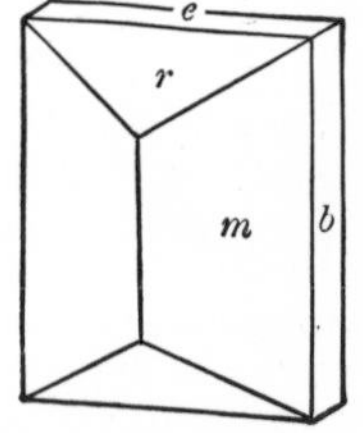

FIG. 46. Example of form development in class $\frac{2}{m}\frac{2}{m}\frac{2}{m}$: staurolite, $HFeAl_5Si_2O_{13}$.

Other inorganic representatives

I
$PtCl_2$
$HgCl_2$
$KClO_4$

Organic representatives

diammine zinc chloride, $ZnCl_2 \cdot 2NH_3$
oxalic acid, $(COOH)_2$
acetic acid, CH_3CO_2H
acetamid, CH_3CONH_2

Table 4. Forms occurring in the tetragonal system

Indices	Classes						
	4	$\bar{4}$	$\frac{4}{m}$	422	$4mm$	$\bar{4}2m$	$\frac{4}{m}\frac{2}{m}\frac{2}{m}$
hkl	tetragonal pyramid	tetragonal bisphenoid	tetragonal bipyramid	tetragonal trapezohedron	ditetragonal pyramid	tetragonal scalenohedron	ditetragonal bipyramid
hhl	,,	,,	,,	tetragonal bipyramid	tetragonal pyramid	tetragonal bisphenoid	tetragonal bipyramid
*h*0*l*	,,	,,	,,	,,	,,	tetragonal bipyramid	,,
*hk*0	tetragonal prism	tetragonal prism	tetragonal prism	ditetragonal prism	ditetragonal prism	ditetragonal prism	ditetragonal prism
110	,,	,,	,,	tetragonal prism	tetragonal prism	tetragonal prism	tetragonal prism
100	,,	,,	,,	,,	,,	,,	,,
001	pedion	pinacoid	pinacoid	pinacoid	pedion	pinacoid	pinacoid

The tetragonal system

The forms occurring in the tetragonal system are listed in Table 4. The forms not encountered in less symmetrical systems are

pyramidal forms

tetragonal pyramid, Fig. 47
tetragonal bisphenoid, Fig. 48
tetragonal bipyramid, Fig. 49
tetragonal trapezohedron (i.e., a polyhedron whose faces are trapeziums), Fig. 50
tetragonal scalenohedron (i.e., a polyhedron whose faces are scalene triangles), Fig. 51
ditetragonal pyramid, Fig. 52
ditetragonal bipyramid, Fig. 53

prismatic forms

tetragonal prism, Fig. 54
ditetragonal prism, Fig. 55

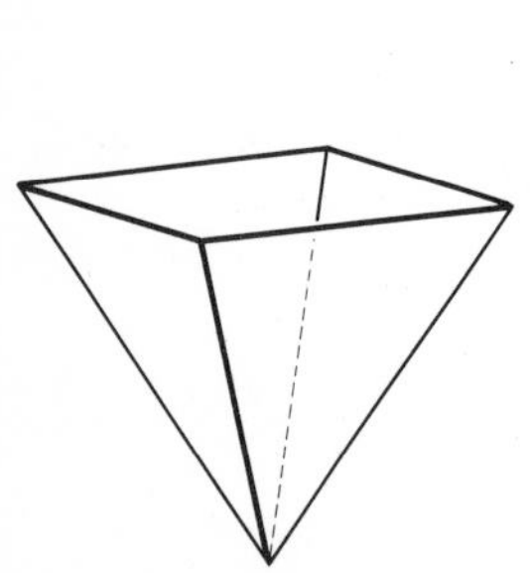

FIG. 47.
Tetragonal pyramid.

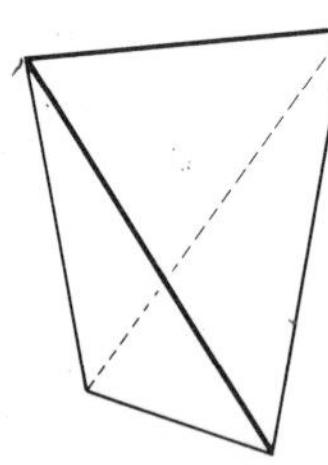

FIG. 48.
Tetragonal bisphenoid.

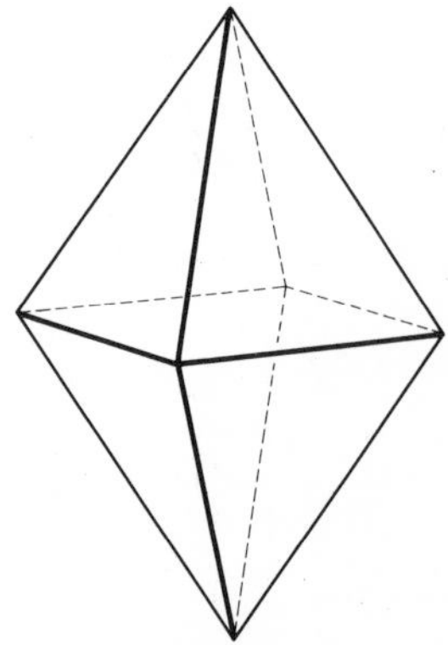

FIG. 49.
Tetragonal bipyramid.

The a_1 and a_2 coordinate axes are always taken parallel to a set of 2 or $\bar{2}$ axes, if present. In some point groups this gives two possible choices of locations for the a axes. If the lattice has been investigated, as by x-ray diffraction, the shortest translations in the plane perpendicular to the 4-fold axis are chosen as the directions of the a axes.

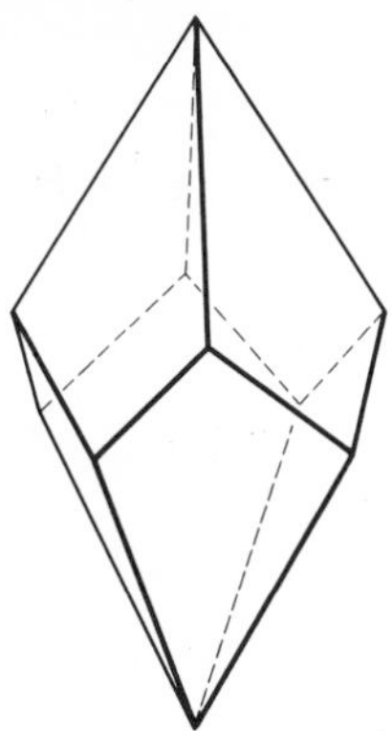

FIG. 50. Tetragonal trapezohedron.

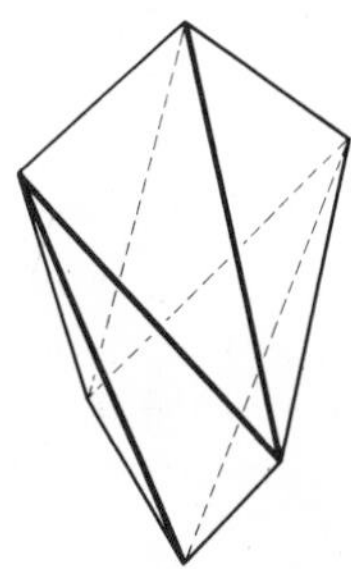

FIG. 51. Tetragonal scalenohedron.

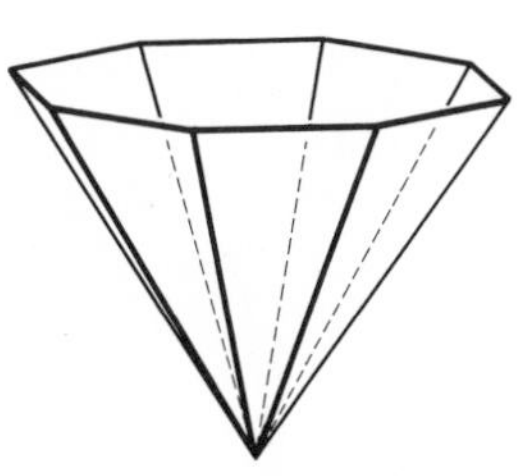

FIG. 52. Ditetragonal pyramid.

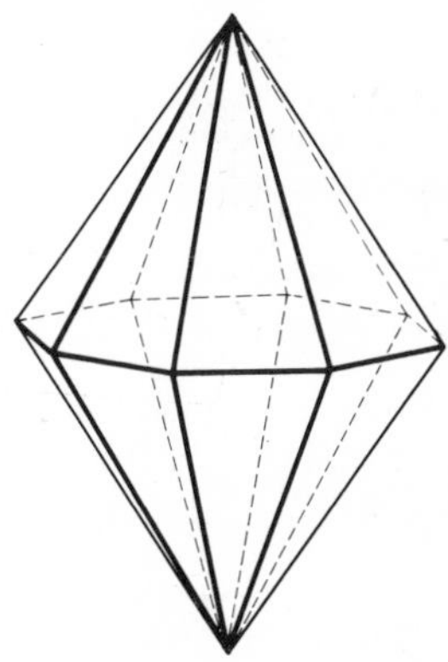

FIG. 53. Ditetragonal bipyramid.

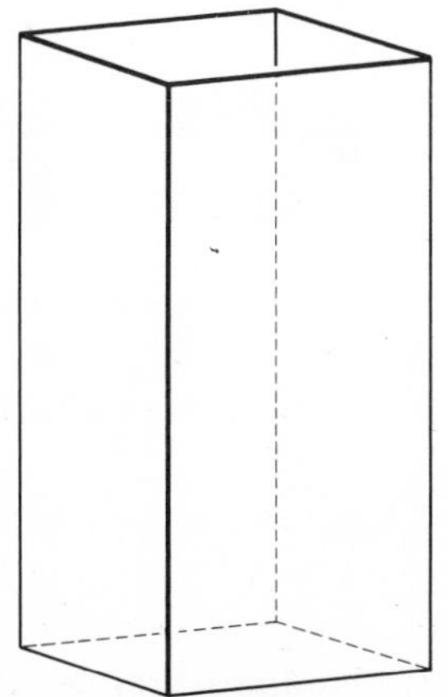

FIG. 54. Tetragonal prism.

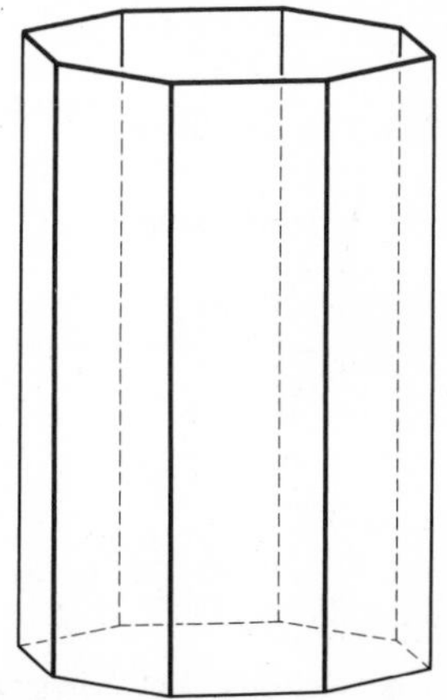

FIG. 55. Ditetragonal prism.

Class 4. Figure 56 shows the symmetry of this class and its repetition of a motif point. Special positions are shown in Fig. 57. Since the symmetry does not contain an operation of the second sort, right- and left-handed variations can occur in crystals of this class, their form developments being enantiomorphic.

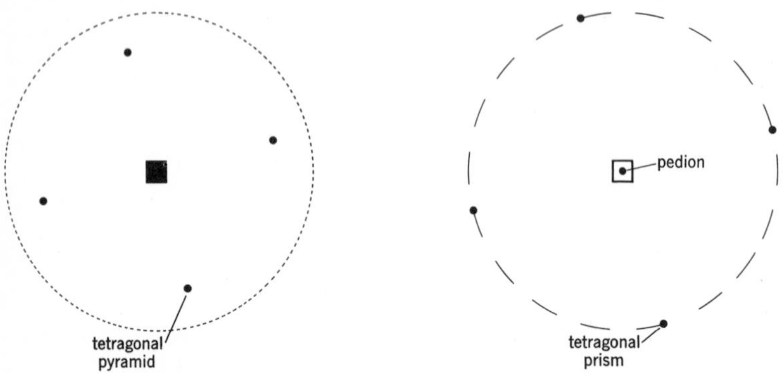

FIG. 56. Repetition of a point in the general position by symmetry 4.

FIG. 57. Special positions of symmetry 4.

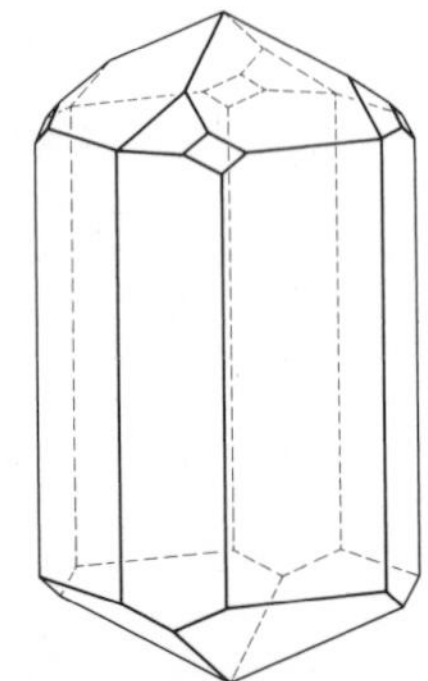

FIG. 58. Example of form development in class 4: barium antimonyl tartrate monohydrate, $Ba(SbO)_2(C_4H_4O_6)_2 \cdot H_2O$.

Mineral representatives

none known

Other inorganic representatives

none known

Organic representatives

barium antimonyl tartrate monohydrate, $Ba(SbO)_2(C_4H_4O_6)_2 \cdot H_2O$, Fig. 58
metaldehyde, $(CH_3CHO)_4$
pleopsidic acid, $C_{17}H_{28}O_4$

Class $\bar{4}$. Figure 59 shows the symmetry of the class and its repetition of a motif point. Special positions are shown in Fig. 60.

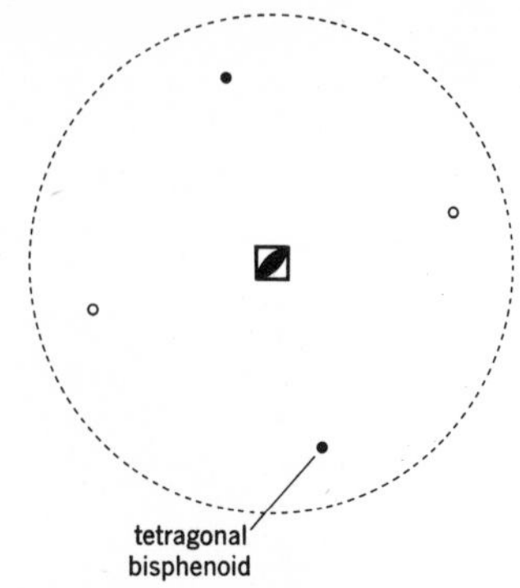

FIG. 59. Repetition of a point in the general position by symmetry $\bar{4}$.

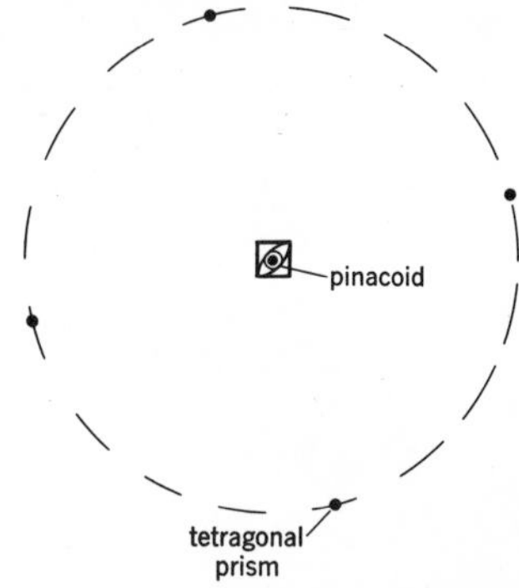

FIG. 60. Special positions of symmetry $\bar{4}$.

Mineral representatives

cahnite, $CaB(OH)_4AsO_4$, Fig. 61

Other inorganic representatives

BPO_4
$BAsO_4$

Organic representatives

pentaerythritol, $C(CH_2OH)_4$

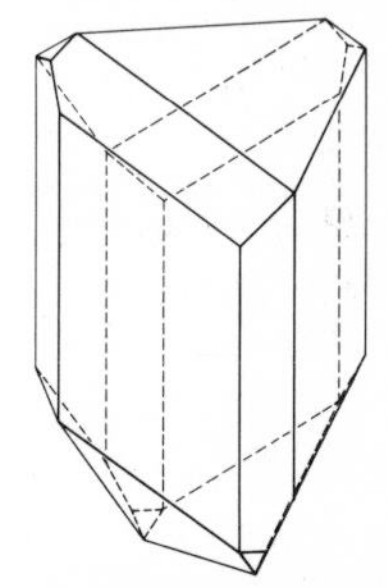

FIG. 61. Example of form development in class $\bar{4}$: cahnite, $CaB(OH)_4AsO_4$.

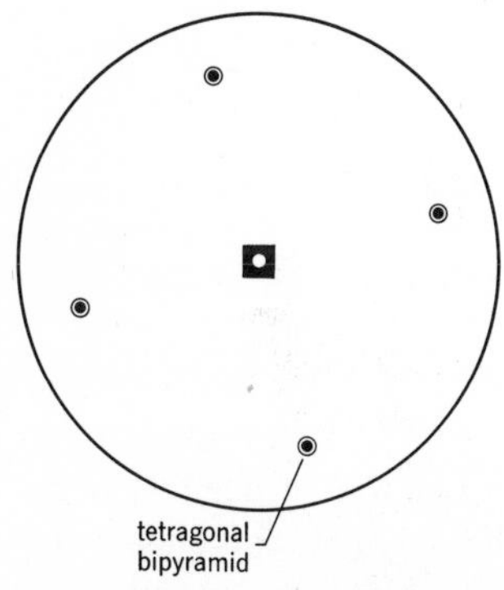

FIG. 62. Repetition of a point in the general position by symmetry $\frac{4}{m}$.

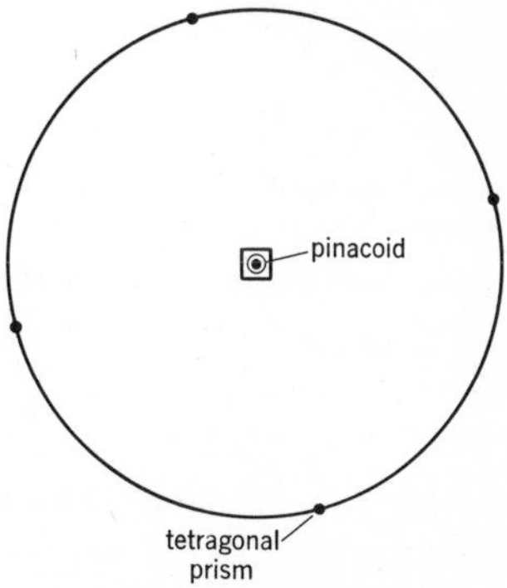

FIG. 63. Special positions of symmetry $\frac{4}{m}$.

Class $\frac{4}{m}$. Figure 62 shows the symmetry of the class and its repetition of a motif point. Special positions are shown in Fig. 63.

Mineral representatives

fergusonite, (Y,Er) (Cb,Ta,Ti)O_4
scheelite, $CaWO_4$, Fig. 64
wolfenite, $PbMoO_4$
powellite, $CaMoO_4$
pinnoite, $Mg(BO_2)_2 \cdot 3H_2O$
scapolite, $Na_4Al_3Si_9O_{24}Cl$ (variety meionite), Fig. 65

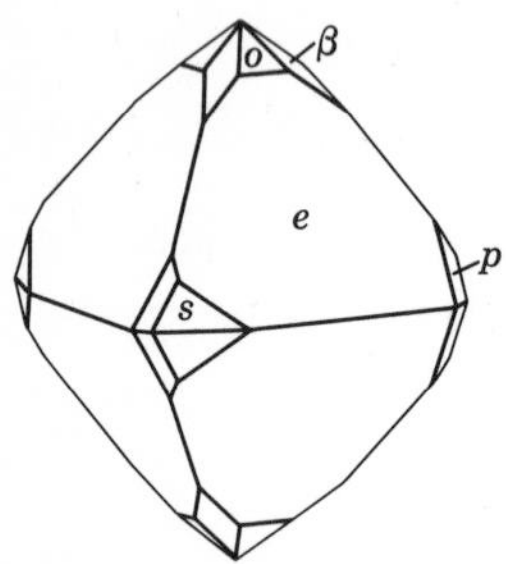

FIG. 64. Example of form development in class $\frac{4}{m}$: scheelite, $CaWO_4$.

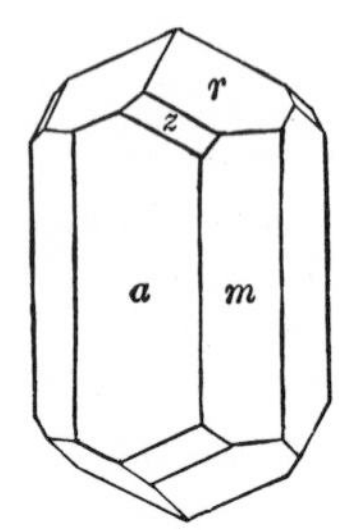

FIG. 65. Example of form development in class $\frac{4}{m}$: meionite, $Na_4Al_3Si_9O_{24}Cl$.

Other inorganic representatives

$NaIO_4$
KIO_4

Organic representatives

i-erythritol, $C_4H_{10}O_4$
phloroglucinol diethylether, $C_6H_3(OH)(OC_2H_5)_2$
p-bromophenol, $C_6H_4Br(OH)$
o-toluenesulfonamide, $C_6H_4(CH_3)SO_2NH_2$
lupinine nitrate, $C_{10}H_{19}ON \cdot HNO_3$

Class 422. The symmetry of this class and its repetition of a motif point are shown in Fig. 66. Special positions are shown in Fig. 67. Since this symmetry contains no operation of the second sort, crystals belonging to this class can occur in right- and left-handed varieties where form developments are enantiomorphic.

Mineral representatives

phosgenite, $Pb_2CO_3Cl_2$

Other inorganic representatives

$NiSO_4 \cdot 6H_2O$

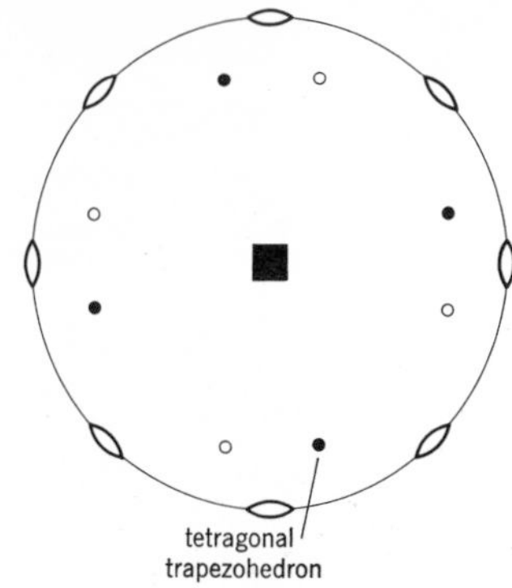

FIG. 66. Repetition of a point in the general position by symmetry 422.

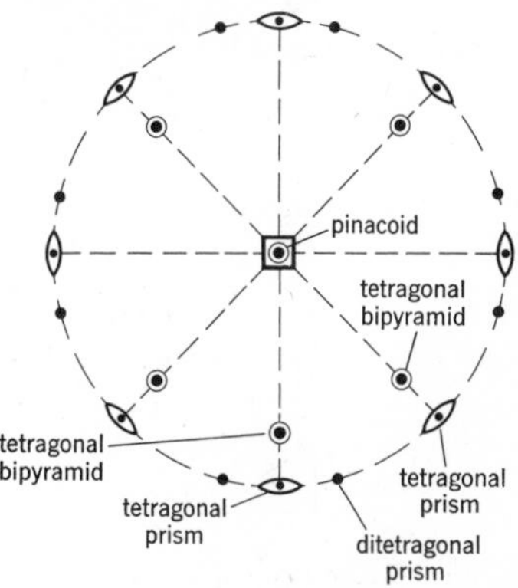

FIG. 67. Special positions of symmetry 422.

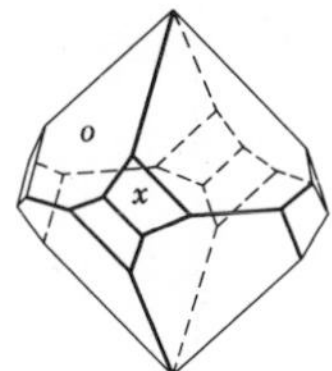

FIG. 68. Example of form development in class 422: monopotassium trichloracetate, $Cl_3CCO_2K \cdot Cl_3CCO_2H$.

Organic representatives

methyl ammonium iodide, $NH_3(CH_3)I$
guanadine carbonate, $2CNH(NH_2)_2 \cdot H_2CO_3$
ethylene diamine sulfate, $C_2H_4(NH_2)_2 \cdot H_2SO_4$
ammonium uranyl acetate, $NH_4UO_2(CH_3COO)_3$
monopotassium trichloracetate, $Cl_3CCO_2K \cdot Cl_3CCO_2H$, Fig. 68
benzenesulfonyl trisulfide $(C_6H_5SO_2)_2S_3$
diacetylphenolphthalein, $(C_6H_4)_3C_2O_2(C_2H_3O)_2$
zinc dimalate dihydrate, $Zn(C_4H_5O_5)_2 \cdot 2H_2O$

Class 4*mm*. The symmetry of this class and its repetition of a motif point are shown in Fig. 69. Special positions are shown in Fig. 70.

Mineral representatives

diaboleite, $Pb_2Cu(OH)_4Cl_2$

Other inorganic representatives

$AgF \cdot H_2O$

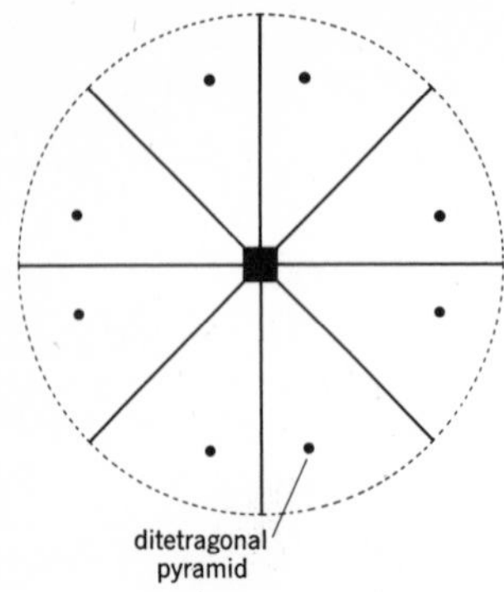

FIG. 69. Repetition of a point in the general position by symmetry 4*mm*.

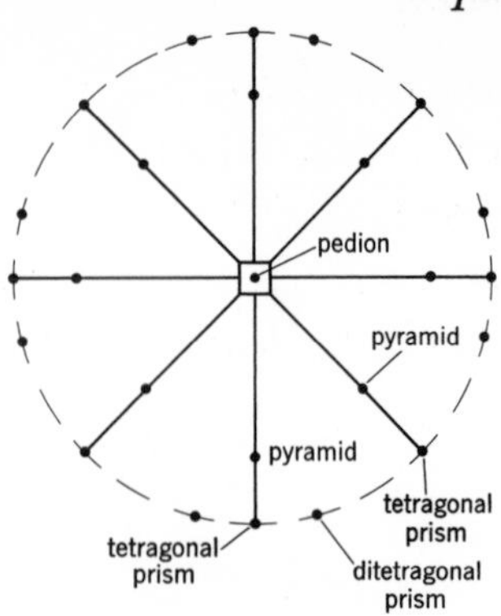

FIG. 70. Special positions of symmetry 4*mm*.

Organic representatives

auro dibenzylsulfinchloride, $AuS(CH_2C_6H_5)_2Cl$, Fig. 71

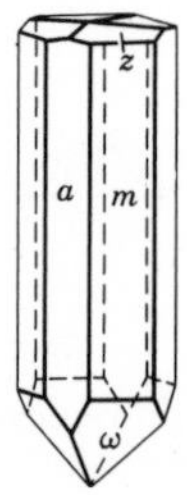

FIG. 71. Example of form development in class 4*mm*: aurodibenzylsulfinchloride, $AuS(CH_2C_6H_5)_2Cl$.

Class $\bar{4}2m$. The symmetry of this class and its repetition of a motif point are shown in Fig. 72. Special positions are shown in Fig. 73.

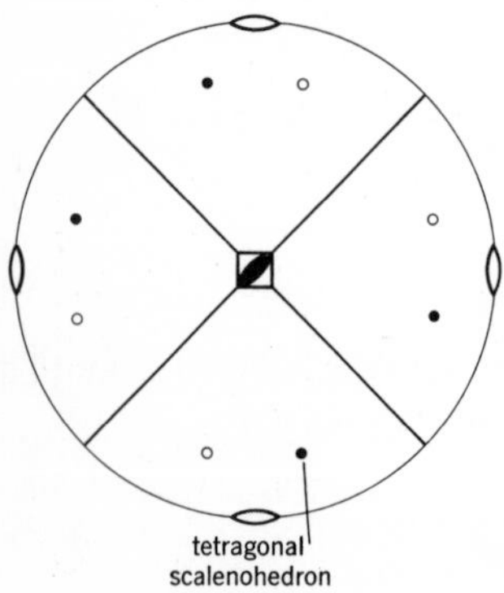

FIG. 72. Repetition of a point in the general position by symmetry $\bar{4}2m$.

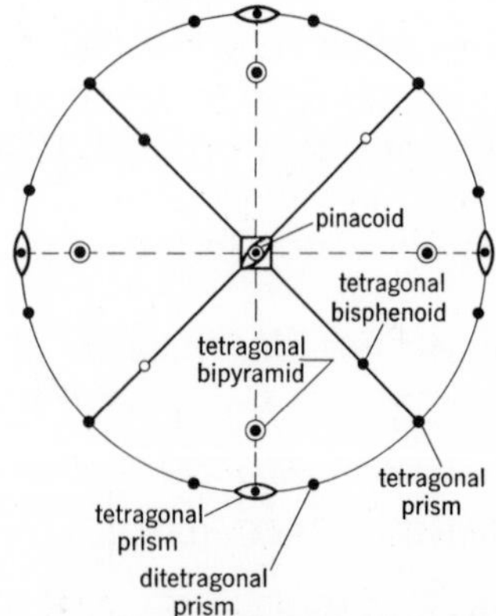

FIG. 73. Special positions of symmetry $\bar{4}2m$.

Mineral representatives

chalcopyrite, $CuFeS_2$, Figs. 74 and 75
stannite, Cu_2FeSnS_4

Other inorganic representatives

KH_2PO_4, and many similar components

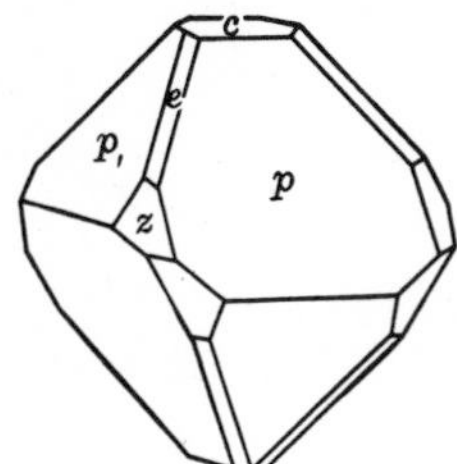

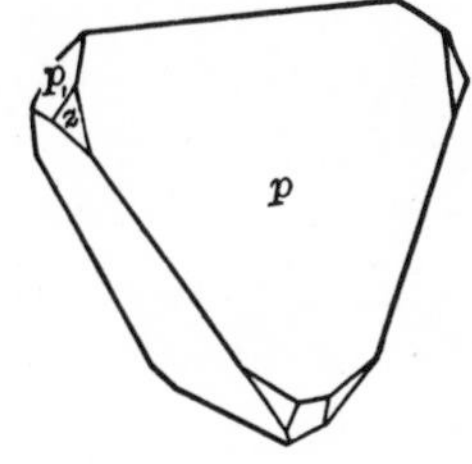

FIG. 74 and FIG. 75. Examples of form development in class $\bar{4}2m$: chalcopyrite, $CuFeS_2$.

Organic representatives

mercuric cyanide, $Hg(CN)_2$, Fig. 76
tetraethylammonium iodide, $N(C_2H_5)_4I$
urea, $CO(NH_2)_2$
barium copper cesium thiocyanate, $BaCu_2Cs_3(CNS)_8$
barium silver cesium thiocyanate, $BaAg_2Cs_3(CNS)_8$

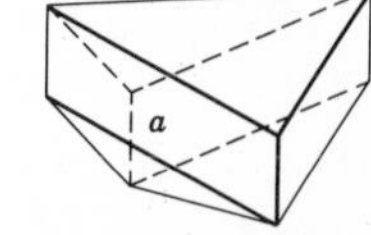

FIG. 76. Example of form development in class $\bar{4}2m$: mercuric cyanide, $Hg(CN)_2$.

Class $\frac{4}{m}\frac{2}{m}\frac{2}{m}$. The symmetry of this class and its repetition of a motif unit are shown in Fig. 77. Special positions are shown in Fig. 78.

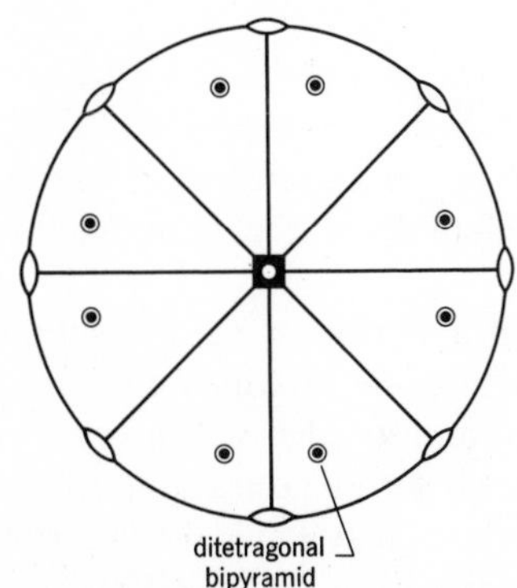

FIG. 77. Repetition of a point in the general position by symmetry $\frac{4}{m}\frac{2}{m}\frac{2}{m}$.

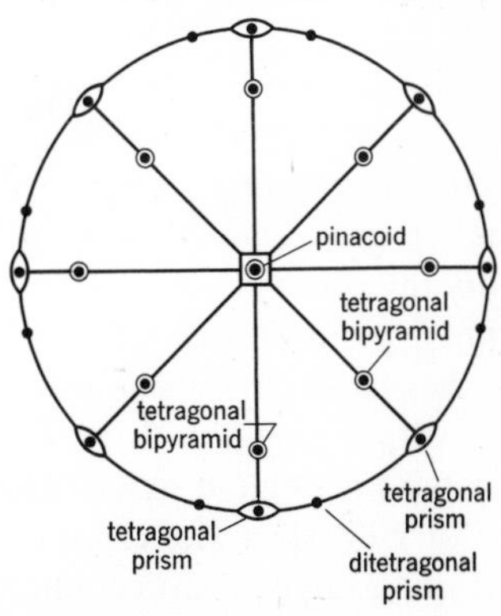

FIG. 78. Special positions of symmetry $\frac{4}{m}\frac{2}{m}\frac{2}{m}$.

Mineral representatives

rutile, TiO_2, Fig. 79
anatase, TiO_2
hausmannite, $MnMn_2O_4$
zircon, $ZrSiO_4$, Fig. 80
vesuvianite, $Ca_{10}Al_4(Mg,Fe)_2Si_9O_{34}(OH)_4$
teepleite, $Na_2B_2O_4 \cdot 2NaCl \cdot 4H_2O$
bandylite, $CuB_2O_4 \cdot CuCl_2 \cdot 4H_2O$

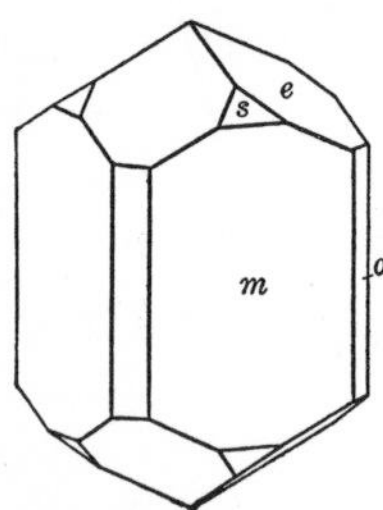

FIG. 79. Example of form development in class $\frac{4}{m}\frac{2}{m}\frac{2}{m}$: rutile, TiO_2.

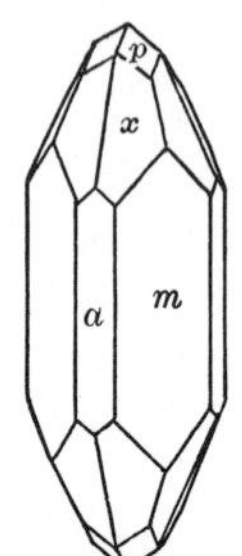

FIG. 80. Example of form development in class $\frac{4}{m}\frac{2}{m}\frac{2}{m}$: zircon, $ZrSiO_4$.

Other inorganic representatives

HgCl
$CoH_2PO_2 \cdot 6H_2O$

Organic representatives

tetramethylammonium iodide $N(CH_3)_4I$

The hexagonal system

Crystals containing a single 3, $\bar{3}$, 6, or $\bar{6}$ axis can all be referred to a hexagonal system of axes. More point groups are referable to the hexagonal system than to any other crystal system.

From a point of view of form development a somewhat natural subdivision of the hexagonal system is into two subsystems, one of which contains those classes with a single 3, $\bar{3}$, or $\bar{6}$ (= $3/m$) axis, and another which contains the classes with a single 6 axis. This subdivision is an unnatural one from other points of view since the classes with 3 and $\bar{3}$ axes may have either a rhombohedral or hexagonal lattice whereas the classes with 6 or $\bar{6}$ (= $3/m$) axes may have only a hexagonal lattice. Since this subdivision is a more fundamental one, it is observed here. The forms occurring in these subdivisions are tabulated in Tables 5 and 6 respectively.

The a_1, a_2, and a_3 coordinate axes are always taken as parallel to the 2 or $\bar{2}$ (i.e., $\perp m$) axes, if present. In some point groups this gives two possible choices of location for the *a* axes. If the lattice has been investigated, as by x-ray diffraction, the shortest translations in the plane perpendicular to the 3- or 6-fold axis are chosen as the direction of the *a* axes.

The forms occurring in the entire hexagonal system and not encountered in less symmetrical systems are as follows:

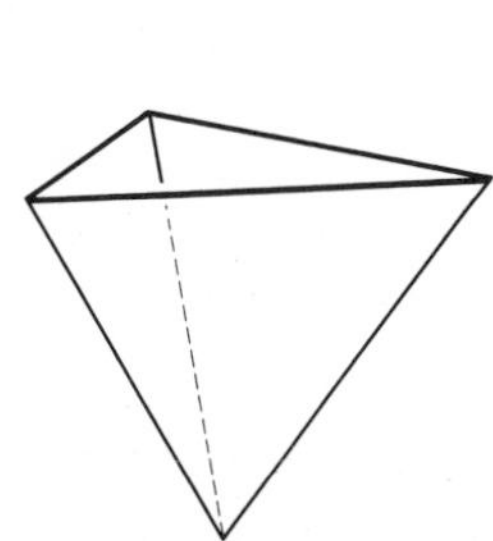

FIG. 81. Trigonal pyramid.

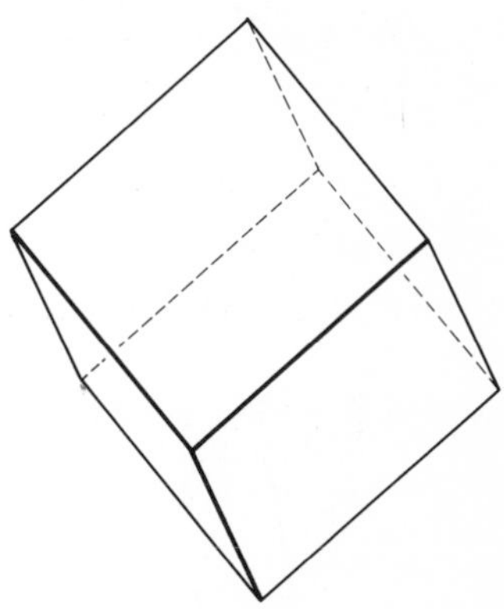

FIG. 82. Rhombohedron.

pyramidal forms

trigonal pyramid,	Fig. 81
rhombohedron	Fig. 82
(i.e., a polyhedron whose faces are rhombuses)	
trigonal trapezohedron	Fig. 83
ditrigonal pyramid	Fig. 84
hexagonal scalenohedron	Fig. 85
hexagonal pyramid	Fig. 86
hexagonal bipyramid	Fig. 87
trigonal bipyramid	Fig. 88
hexagonal trapezohedron	Fig. 89
dihexagonal pyramid	Fig. 90
ditrigonal bipyramid	Fig. 91
dihexagonal bipyramid	Fig. 92

prismatic forms

trigonal prism	Fig. 93
hexagonal prism	Fig. 94
ditrigonal prism	Fig. 95
dihexagonal prism	Fig. 96

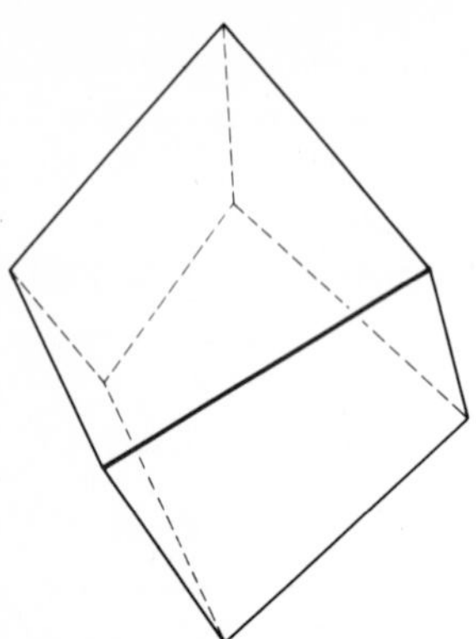

FIG. 83. Trigonal trapezohedron.

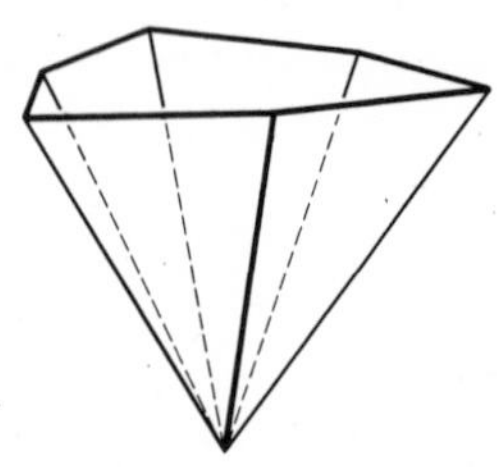

FIG. 84. Ditrigonal pyramid.

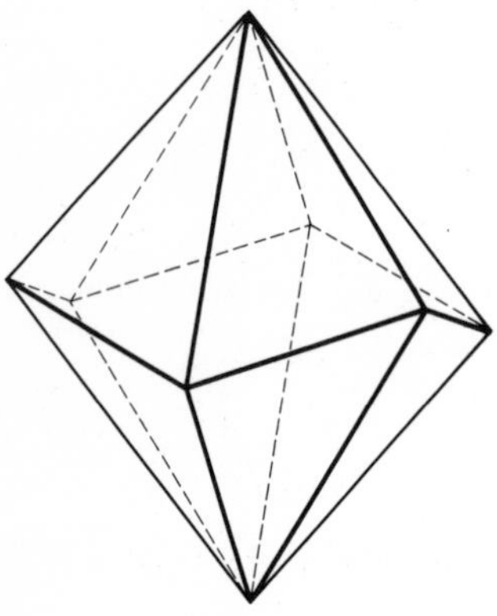

FIG. 85. Hexagonal scalenohedron.

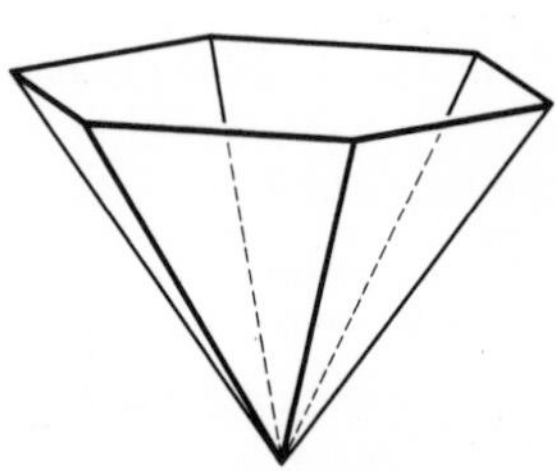

FIG. 86. Hexagonal pyramid.

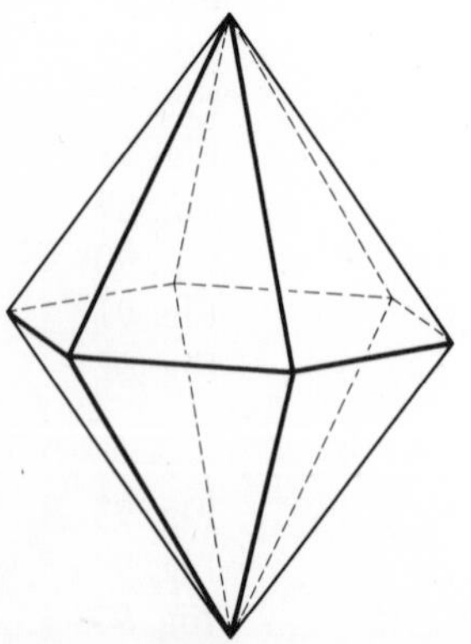

FIG. 87. Hexagonal bipyramid.

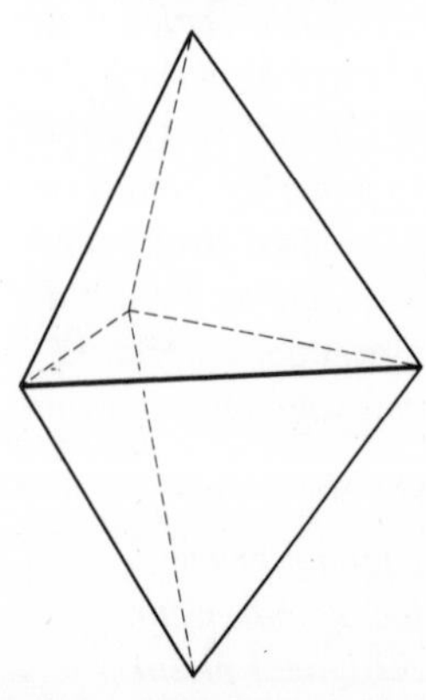

FIG. 88. Trigonal bipyramid.

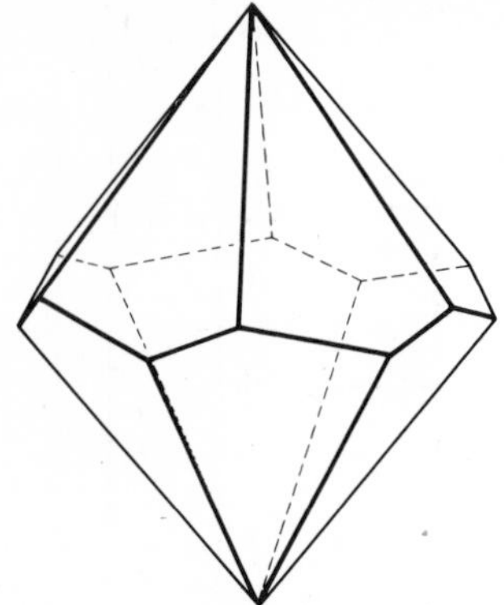

FIG. 89. Hexagonal trapezohedron.

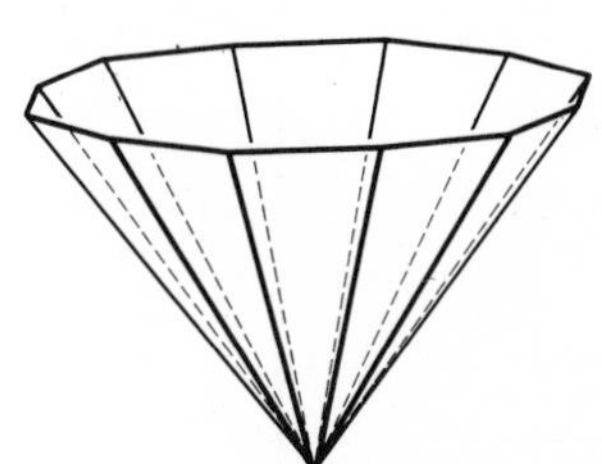

FIG. 90. Dihexagonal pyramid.

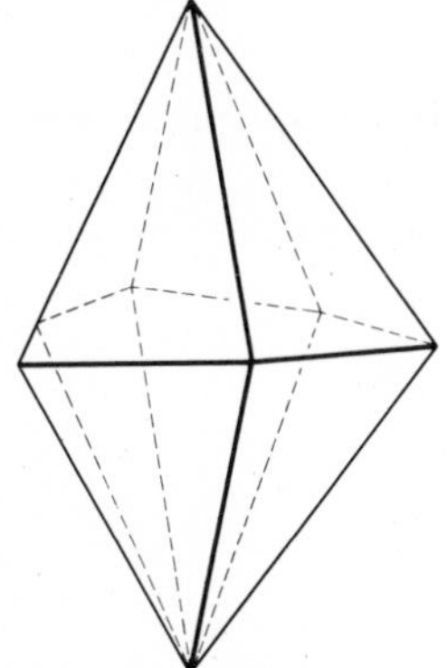

FIG. 91. Ditrigonal bipyramid.

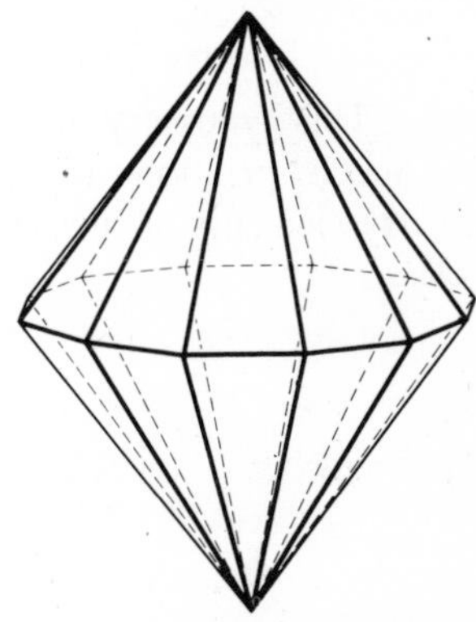

FIG. 92. Dihexagonal bipyramid.

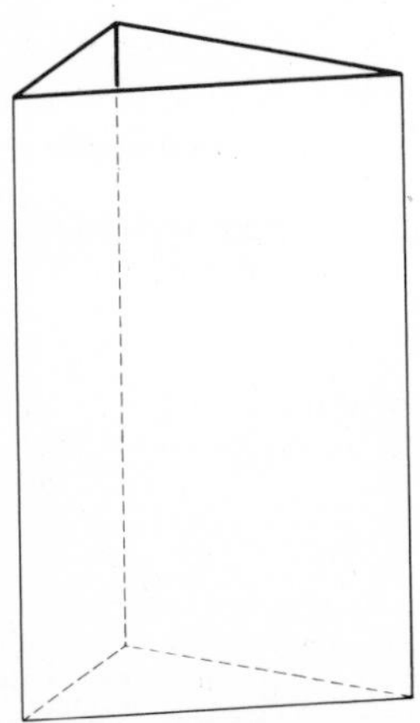

FIG. 93. Trigonal prism.

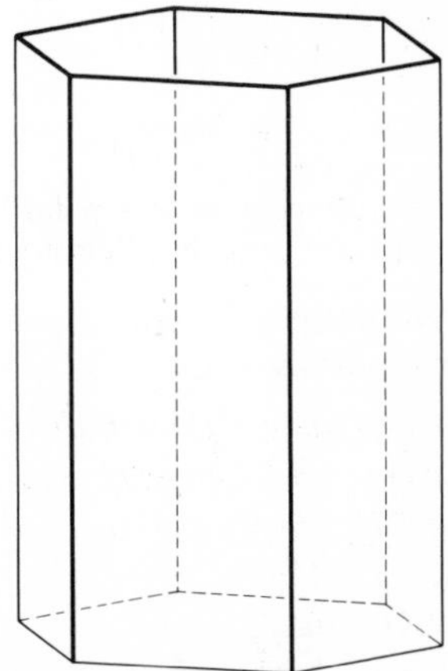

FIG. 94. Hexagonal prism.

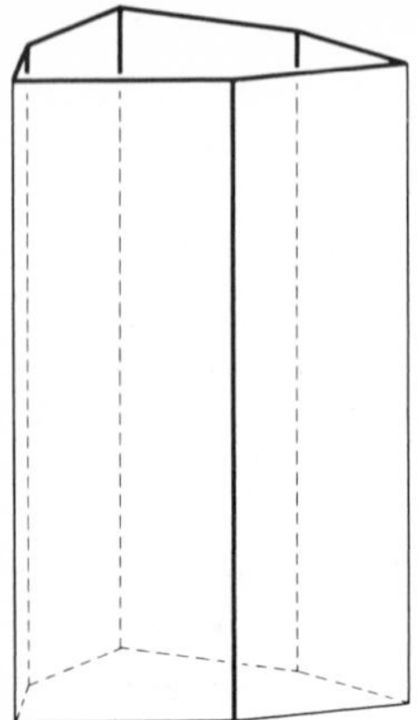

FIG. 95. Ditrigonal prism.

FIG. 96. Dihexagonal prism.

Class 3. This symmetry and the way it repeats a motif point are shown in Fig. 97. Special positions are shown in Fig. 98. Since the symmetry contains no symmetry elements of the second sort, enantiomorphous crystals can occur in this class.

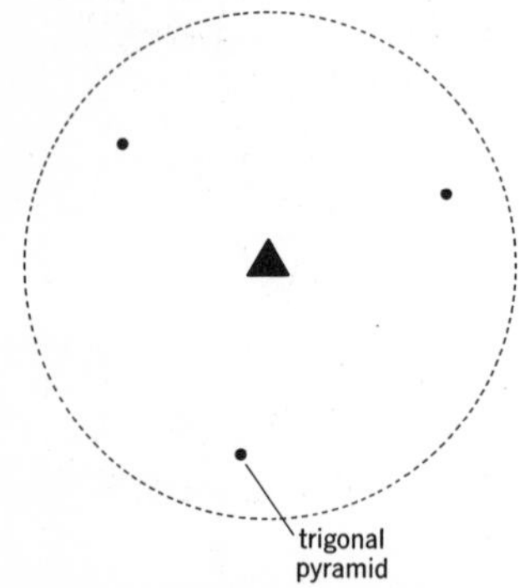

FIG. 97. Repetition of a point in the general position by symmetry 3.

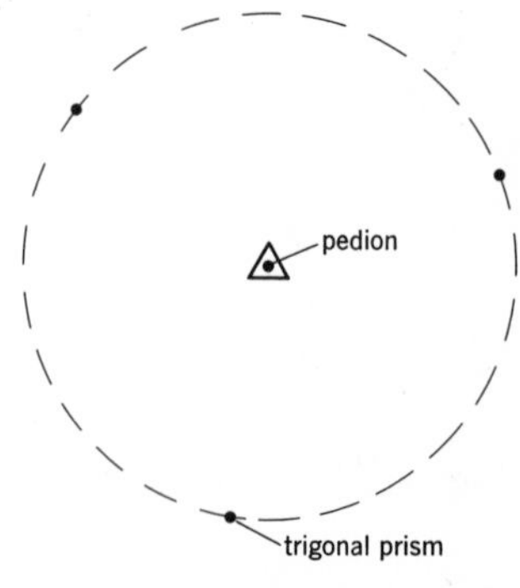

FIG. 98. Special positions of symmetry 3.

Mineral representatives

not certainly known (possibly gratonite, $Pb_9As_4S_{15}$)

Other inorganic representatives

$NaIO_4 \cdot 3H_2O$, Fig. 99
$MgSO_3 \cdot 6H_2O$
$NiSO_3 \cdot 6H_2O$
$CoSO_3 \cdot 6H_2O$

Organic representatives

(apparently none is known)

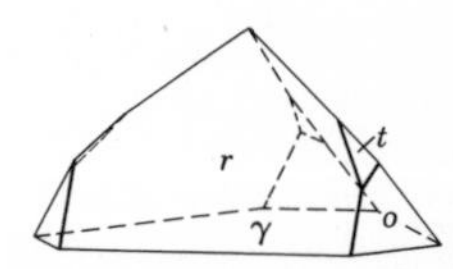

FIG. 99. Example of form development in class 3: $NaIO_4 \cdot 3H_2O$.

Table 5. Forms occurring in the classes of the hexagonal system having a 3 or $\bar{3}$ axis

Indices	Classes				
	3	$\bar{3}$	32	$3m$	$\bar{3}\,\frac{2}{m}$
$hkil$	trigonal pyramid	rhombohedron	trigonal trapezohedron	ditrigonal pyramid	hexagonal scalenohedron
$h0\bar{h}l$	,,	,,	rhombohedron	trigonal pyramid	rhombohedron
$hh\overline{2h}l$	,,	,,	trigonal bipyramid	hexagonal pyramid	hexagonal bipyramid
$hki0$	trigonal prism	hexagonal prism	ditrigonal prism	ditrigonal prism	dihexagonal prism
$10\bar{1}0$	,,	,,	hexagonal prism	trigonal prism	hexagonal prism
$11\bar{2}0$	,,	,,	trigonal prism	hexagonal prism	,,
0001	pedion	pinacoid	pinacoid	pedion	pinacoid

Table 6. Forms occurring in the classes of the hexagonal system having a 6 or $\bar{6}$ axis

Indices	Classes						
	6	$\bar{6}\ (=\frac{3}{m})$	$\frac{6}{m}$	622	$6mm$	$\bar{6}m2\ (=\frac{3}{m}m2)$	$\frac{6}{m}\frac{2}{m}\frac{2}{m}$
$hkil$	hexagonal pyramid	trigonal bipyramid	hexagonal bipyramid	hexagonal trapezohedron	dihexagonal pyramid	ditrigonal bipyramid	dihexagonal bipyramid
$h0\bar{h}l$	,,	,,	,,	hexagonal bipyramid	hexagonal pyramid	trigonal bipyramid	hexagonal bipyramid
$hh\overline{2h}l$	,,	,,	,,	,,	,,	hexagonal bipyramid	,,
$hki0$	hexagonal prism	trigonal prism	hexagonal prism	dihexagonal prism	dihexagonal prism	ditrigonal prism	dihexagonal prism
$10\bar{1}0$	,,	,,	,,	hexagonal prism	hexagonal prism	hexagonal prism	hexagonal prism
$11\bar{2}0$	,,	,,	,,	,,	,,	trigonal prism	,,
0001	pedion	pinacoid	pinacoid	pinacoid	pedion	pinacoid	pinacoid

Class $\bar{3}$. The symmetry of this class and its repetition of a motif point are shown in Fig. 100. Special positions are shown in Fig. 101.

Mineral representatives

ilmenite, $FeTiO_3$, Fig. 102
dolomite, $CaMg(CO_3)_2$, Fig. 103
nordenskioldine, $CaSn(BO_3)_2$
paracoquimbite, $Fe(SO_4)_3 \cdot 9H_2O$
willemite, Zn_2SiO_4
phenakite, Be_2SiO_4
(possibly dioptase, CuH_2SiO_4)

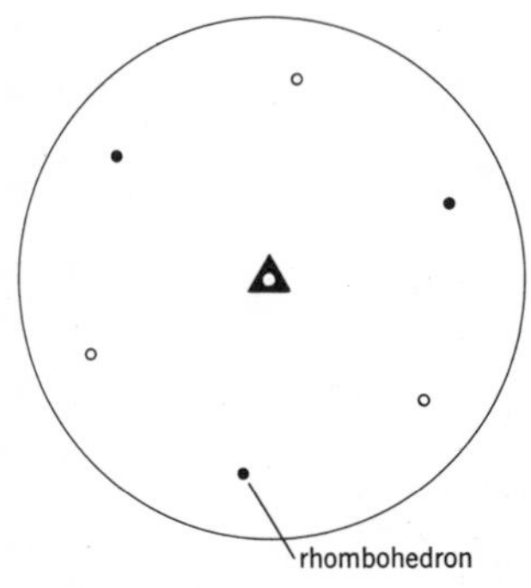

FIG. 100. Repetition of a point in the general position by symmetry $\bar{3}$.

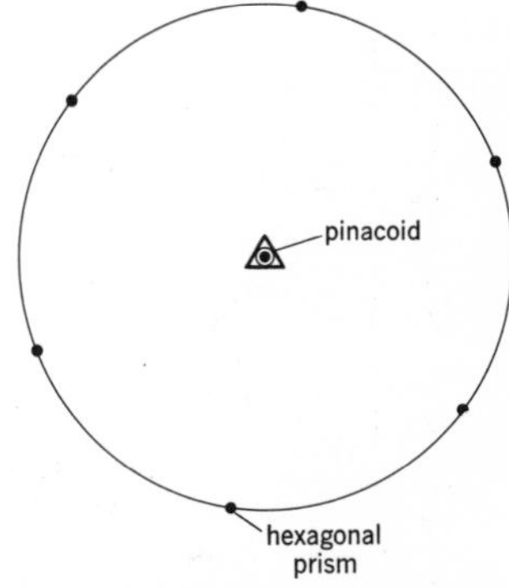

FIG. 101. Special positions of symmetry $\bar{3}$.

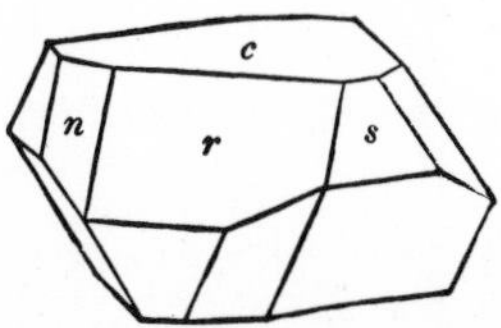

FIG. 102. Example of form development in class $\bar{3}$: ilmenite, $FeTiO_3$.

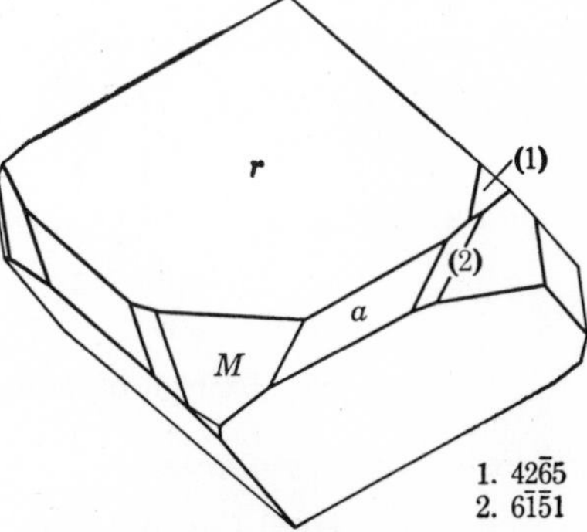

FIG. 103. Example of form development in class $\bar{3}$: dolomite, $CaMg(CO_3)_2$.

Other inorganic representatives

Na_2SO_3
$(NH_4)_2H_3IO_6$
Li_2BeF_4
Li_2MoO_4
Li_2WO_4

Organic representatives

(apparently none is known)

Class 32. The symmetry of this class and its repetition of a motif point are shown in Fig. 104. Special positions are shown in Fig. 105. Since the symmetry contains no symmetry elements of the second sort, enantiomorphous crystals can occur in this class.

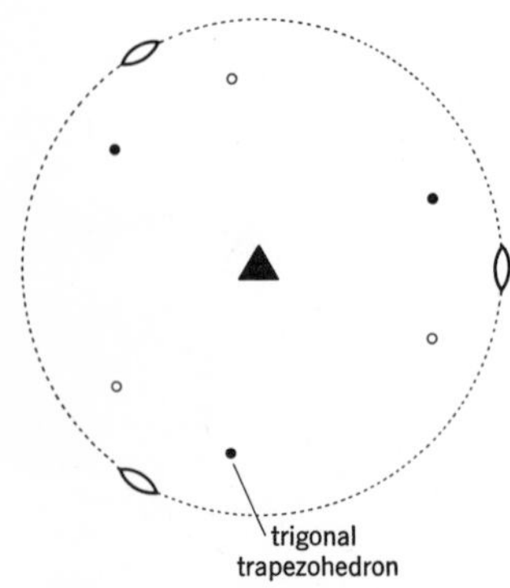

Fig. 104. Repetition of a point in the general position by symmetry 32.

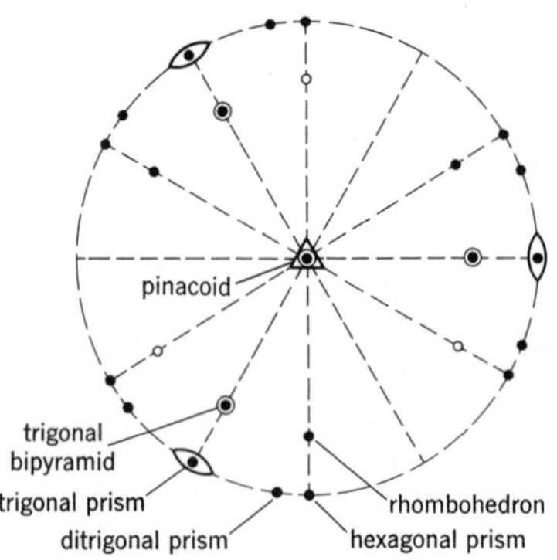

Fig. 105. Special positions of symmetry 32.

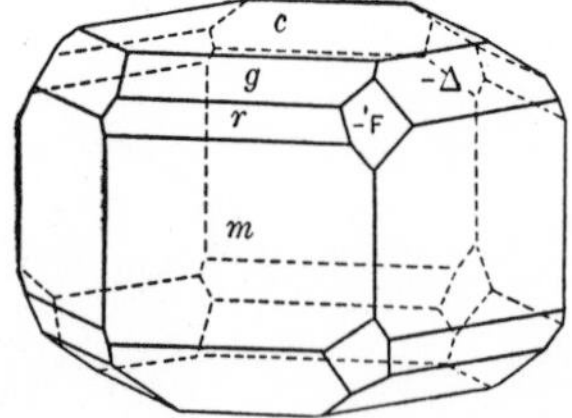

Fig. 106. Example of form development in class 32: cinnabar, HgS.

Mineral representatives

cinnabar, HgS, Fig. 106
low quartz, SiO_2, Figs. 107 and 108
berlinite, $AlPO_4$

Other inorganic representatives

Se, Te
$K_2S_2O_6$
$Rb_2S_2O_6$
$PbS_2O_6 \cdot 4H_2O$

Organic representatives

rubidium tartrate, $RbC_4H_4O_6$
potassium cobalt oxalate monohydrate, $K_3Co(C_2O_4)_3 \cdot H_2O$
potassium rhodium oxalate monohydrate, $K_3Rh(C_2O_4)_3 \cdot H_2O$
d-camphor, $C_{10}H_{16}O$
l-maticocamphor, $C_{12}H_{20}O$
benzil, $(C_6H_5CO)_2$
guaiacol, $C_6H_4(OH)(OCH_3)$

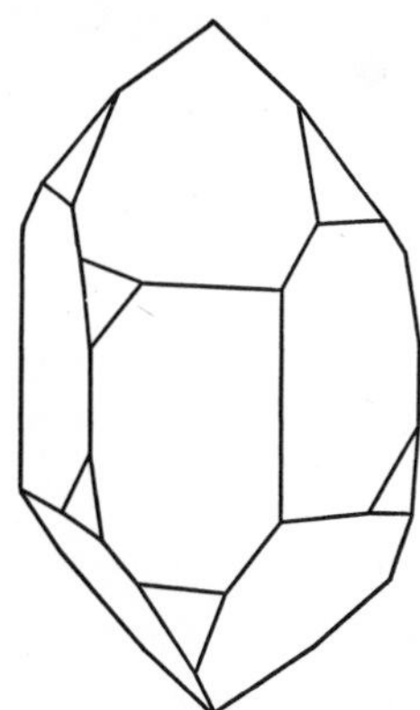

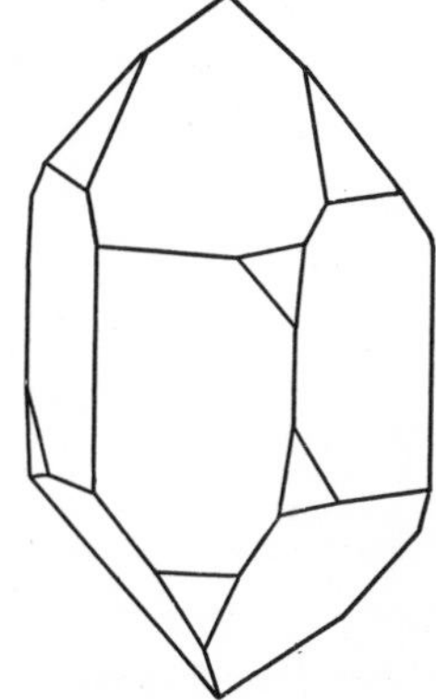

FIG. 107 and FIG. 108. Examples of enantiomorphous form development in class 32: left quartz, SiO_2 (Fig. 107) and right quartz (Fig. 108).

Class 3*m*. The symmetry of this class and its repetition of a motif point are shown in Fig. 109. Special positions are shown in Fig. 110.

Mineral representatives

pyrargyrite, Ag_3SbS_3
proustite, Ag_3AsS_3
alunite, $KAl_3(SO_4)_2(OH)_6$ (and alunite family)
spangolite, $Cu_6AlSO_4(OH)_{12}Cl \cdot 3H_2O$
deltaite, $Cu(Al_2Ca)(PO_4)_2(OH) \cdot H_2O$
tourmaline, $NaMg_3B_3Al_6Si_6O_{27}(OH)_4$, Fig. 111

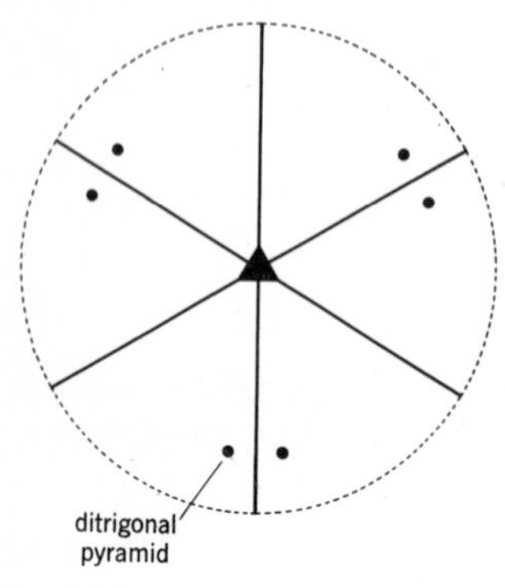

FIG. 109. Repetition of a point in the general position by symmetry $3m$.

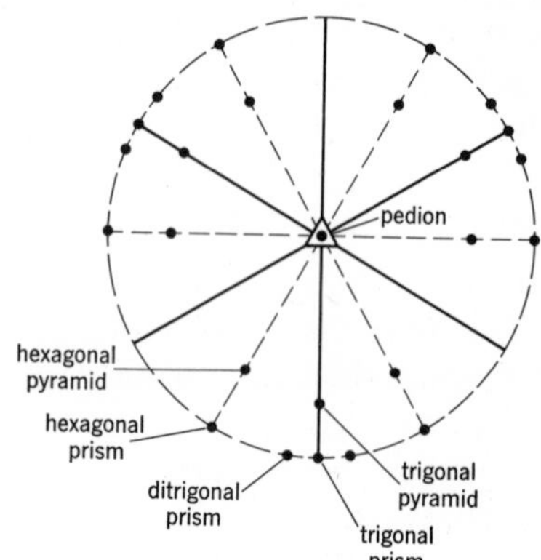

FIG. 110. Special positions of symmetry $3m$.

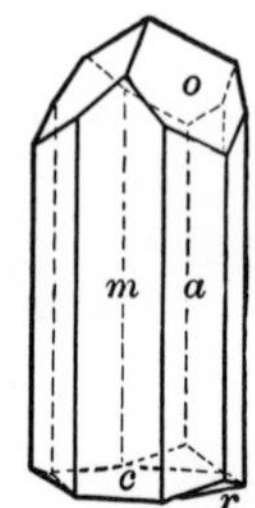

FIG. 111. Example of form development in class $3m$; tourmaline, $NaMg_3B_3Al_6Si_6O_{27}(OH)_4$.

Other inorganic representatives

$LiNaSO_4$
$KBrO_3$
$MgSO_3 \cdot 3H_2O$
$LiNa_3(SO_4)_2 \cdot 6H_2O$

Organic representatives

phenyl-*p*-tolyl ketone, $C_6H_5COC_6H_4CH_3$
hexamethyltetramine hydrobromide, $C_6H_{12}N_4 \cdot HBr$

Class $\bar{3}\frac{2}{m}$. The symmetry of this class and its repetition of a motif point are shown in Fig. 112. Special positions are shown in Fig. 113.

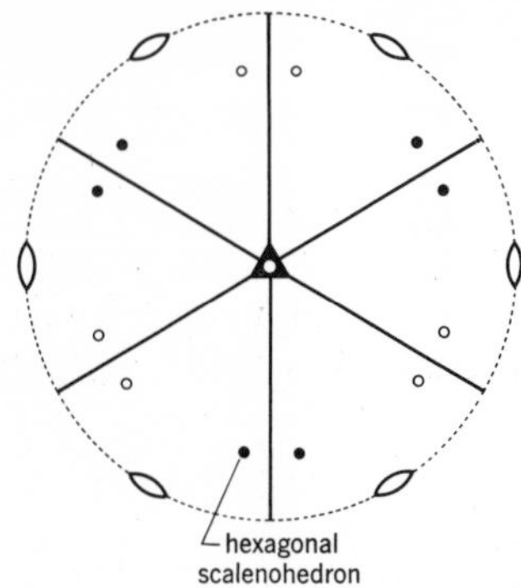

Fig. 112. Repetition of a point in the general position by symmetry $\bar{3}\,\frac{2}{m}$

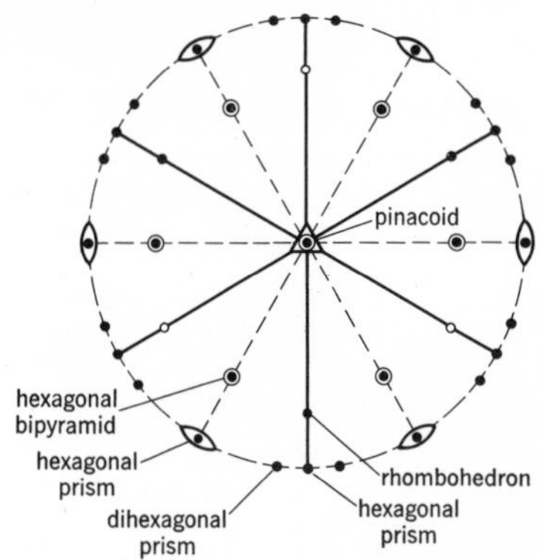

Fig. 113. Special positions of symmetry $\bar{3}\,\frac{2}{m}$.

Mineral representatives

corundum, Al_2O_3
hematite, Fe_2O_3, Fig. 114
calcite, $CaCO_3$ (and calcite group), Figs. 115, 116, and 117
brucite, $Mg(OH)_2$
whitlockite, $Ca_3(PO_4)_2$
aphthitalite, $(K,Na)_3Na(SO_4)_2$

Other inorganic representatives

As, Sb, Bi
$CdCl_2$
AsI_3
$CaCl_2 \cdot 6H_2O$
K_4CdCl_6
$NaNO_3$

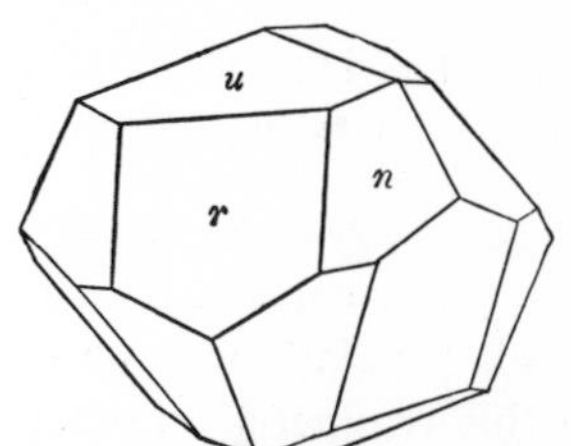

Fig. 114. Example of form development in class $\bar{3}\,\frac{2}{m}$: hematite, Fe_2O_3.

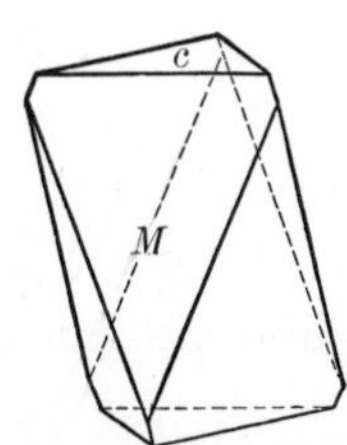

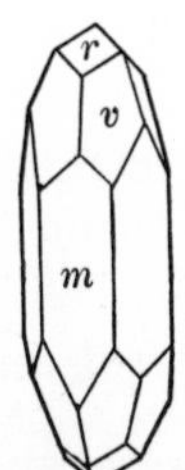

Fig. 115, Fig. 116, and Fig. 117. Examples of form development in class $\bar{3}\,\frac{2}{m}$: calcite, $CaCO_3$.

Organic representatives

tetraethylammonium bromide, $N(C_2H_5)_4Br$
tetraethylphosphonium iodide, $P(C_2H_5)I$
hexammine cobalt cyanide, $Co(CN)_6 \cdot Co(NH_3)_6$

Class 6. The symmetry of this class and its repetition of a motif point are shown in Fig. 118. Special positions are shown in Fig. 119. Since the symmetry contains no symmetry elements of the second sort, enantiomorphous crystals can occur in this class. Crystals showing form developments typical of this class have not been observed, but the following have been assigned to this symmetry on other evidence discussed in Chapter 11:

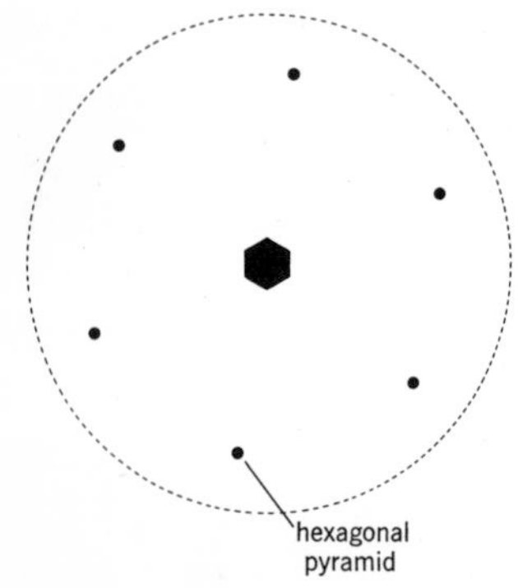

FIG. 118. Repetition of a point in the general position by symmetry 6.

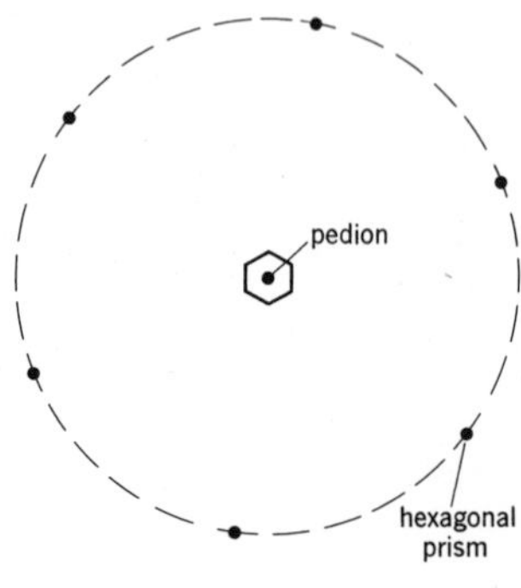

FIG. 119. Special positions of symmetry 6.

Mineral representatives

nepheline, $KNa_3Si_4Al_4O_{16}$

Other inorganic representatives

$LiKSO_4$

Organic representatives

iodoform, CHI_3
lead antimonyl tartrate, $Pb(SbO)_2(C_4H_4O_6)_2$
hydrocinchonine sulfate hendekahydrate, $(C_{19}H_{24}ON_2)_2 \cdot H_2SO_4 \cdot 11H_2O$

Class $\bar{6}$ $(= \frac{3}{m})$. The symmetry of this class and its repetition of a motif point are shown in Fig. 120. Special positions are shown in Fig. 121.

This is one of the two crystal classes without undoubted representatives. The other class is 432.

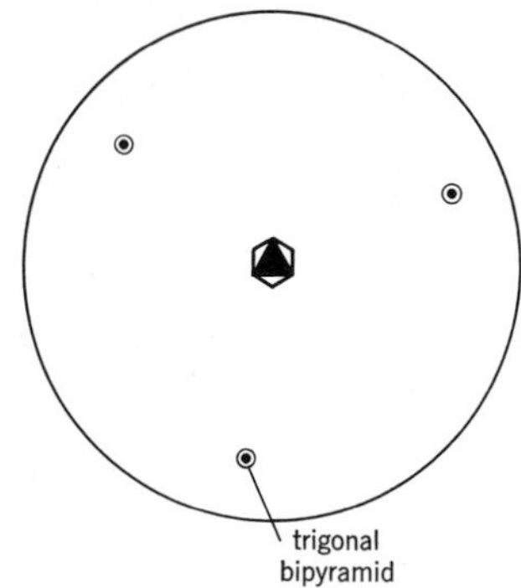

FIG. 120. Repetition of a point in the general position by symmetry $\bar{6}$.

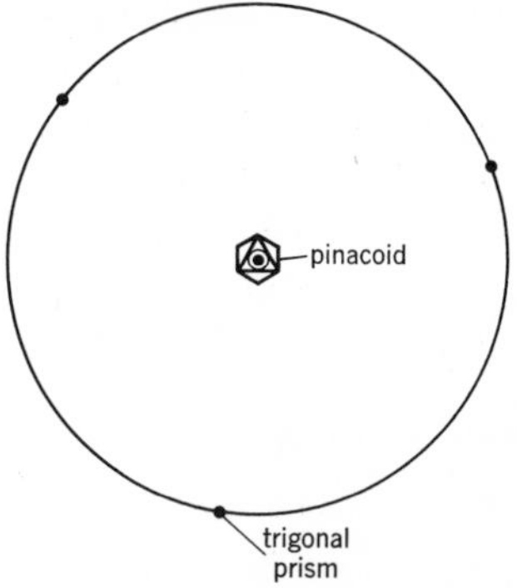

FIG. 121. Special positions of symmetry $\bar{6}$.

Class $\frac{6}{m}$. The symmetry of this class and its repetition of a motif point are shown in Fig. 122. Special positions are shown in Fig. 123.

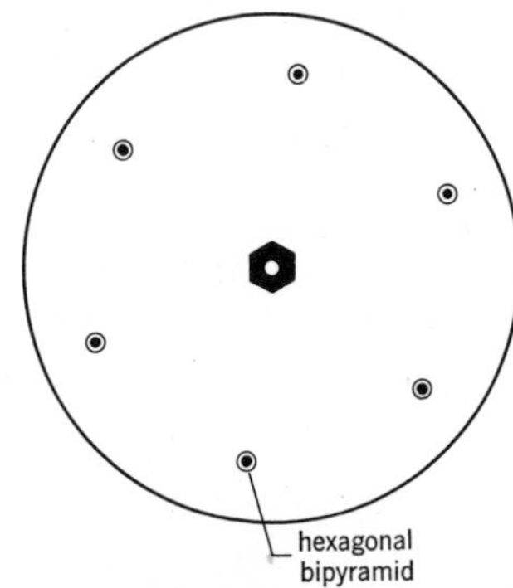

FIG. 122. Repetition of a point in the general position by symmetry $\frac{6}{m}$.

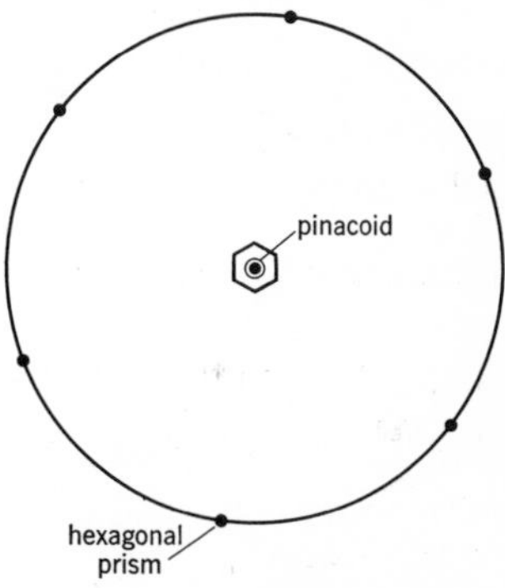

FIG. 123. Special positions of symmetry $\frac{6}{m}$.

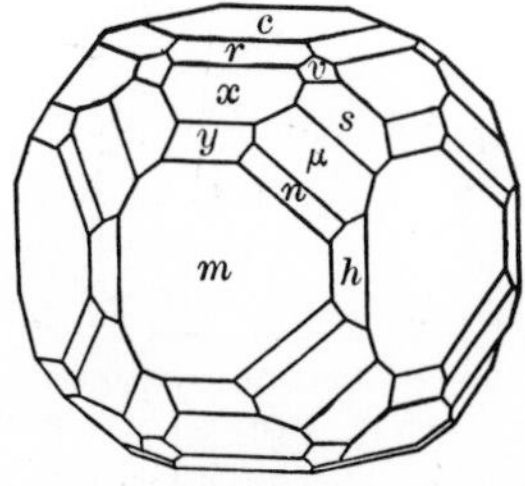

FIG. 124. Example of form development in class $\frac{6}{m}$: apatite, $Ca_5F(PO_4)_3$.

Mineral representatives

apatite, $Ca_5F(PO_4)_3$, Fig. 124, (and other members of the apatite group)
hanksite, $Na_{22}K(SO_4)_9(CO_3)_2Cl$

Other inorganic representatives

$La_2(SO_4)_3 \cdot 9H_2O$
$Ce_2(SO_4)_2 \cdot 9H_2O$

Organic representatives

(apparently none is known)

Class 622. The symmetry of this class and its repetition of a motif point are shown in Fig. 125. Special positions are shown in Fig. 126. Since the symmetry contains no symmetry elements of the second sort, enantiomorphous crystals can occur in this class. Crystals showing form developments typical of this class have not been observed, but the following have been assigned to this symmetry on other evidence discussed in Chapter 11:

Mineral representatives

high quartz, SiO_2
kalsilite, $KAlSiO_4$

Other inorganic representatives

$LiIO_3$
$LiAlSiO_4$
$BaAl_2O_4$

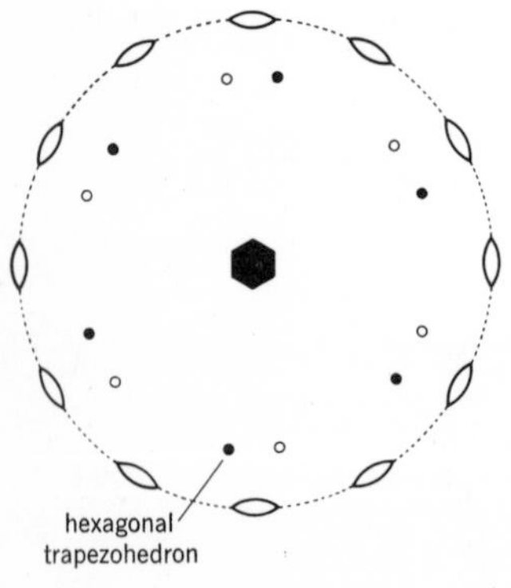

FIG. 125. Repetition of a point in the general position by symmetry 622.

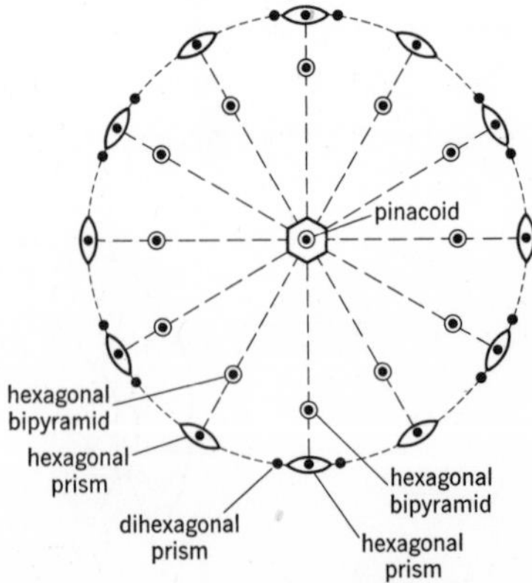

FIG. 126. Special positions of symmetry 622.

Organic representatives

dibenzalpentaerythritol, $C_{19}H_{20}O_4$
patchoulicamphor, $C_{15}H_{25}(OH)$
lead antimonyl tartrate-potassium nitrate, $Pb(SbO)_2(C_4H_4O_6)_2 \cdot KNO_3$

Class 6*mm*. The symmetry of this class and its repetition of a motif point are shown in Fig. 127. Special positions are shown in Fig. 128.

Mineral representatives

wurtzite, ZnS
greenockite, CdS
zincite, ZnO
bromellite, BeO, Fig. 129
iodyrite, AgI, Fig. 130
swedenborgite, $NaBe_4SbO_7$

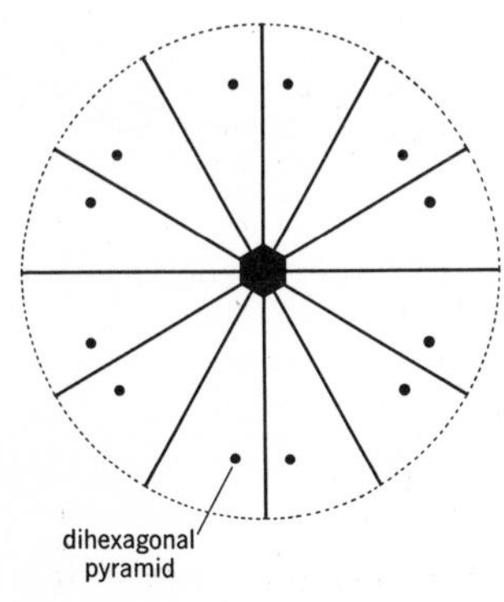

FIG. 127. Repetition of a point in the general position by symmetry 6*mm*.

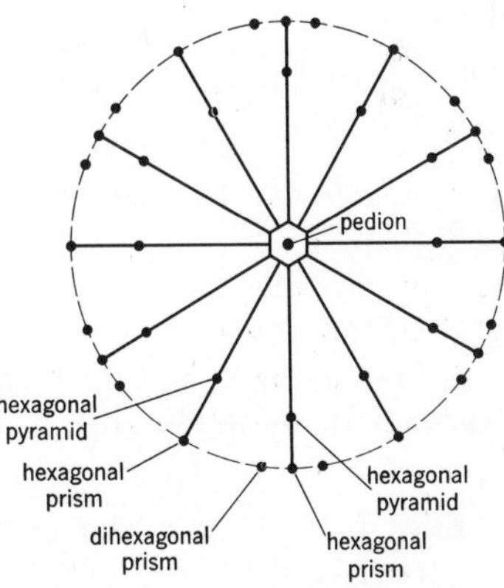

FIG. 128. Special positions of symmetry 6*mm*.

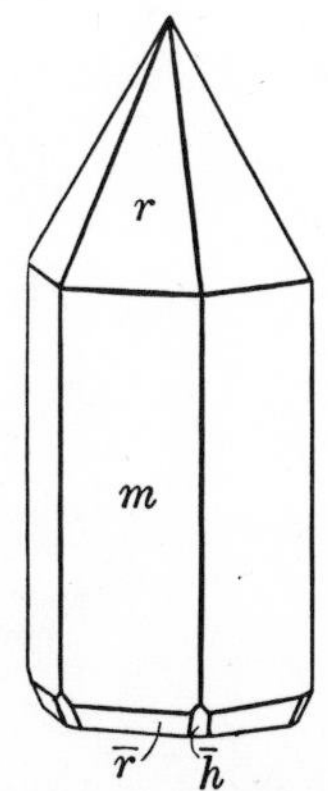

FIG. 129. Example of form development in class 6*mm*: bromellite, BeO.

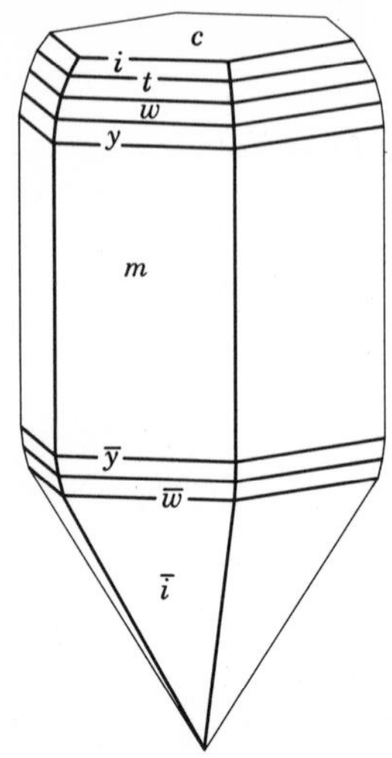

FIG. 130. Example of form development in class 6*mm*: iodyrite, AgI.

Other inorganic representatives

(apparently none not related to the wurtzite structure is known)

Organic representatives

triethylammonium chloride, $NH(C_2H_5)_3Cl$
piperidine thiocyano platinate, $Pt(CNS)_6(C_5H_{11}N)_2$

Class $\bar{6}m2$ $(= \frac{3}{m}\ m\ 2)$. The symmetry of this class and its repetition of a motif point are shown in Fig. 131. Special positions are shown in Fig. 132.

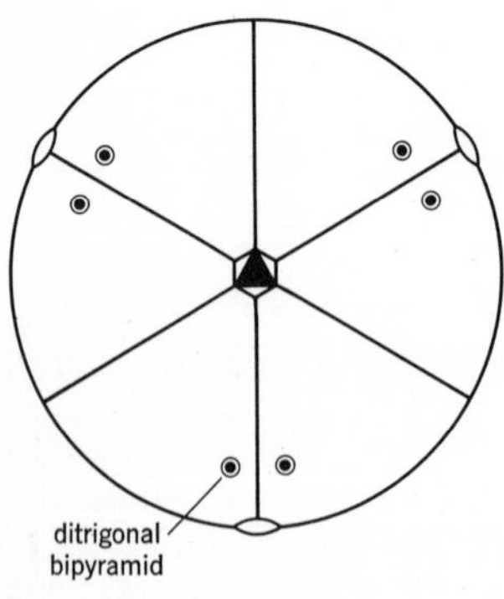

FIG. 131. Repetition of a point in the general position by symmetry $\bar{6}m2$.

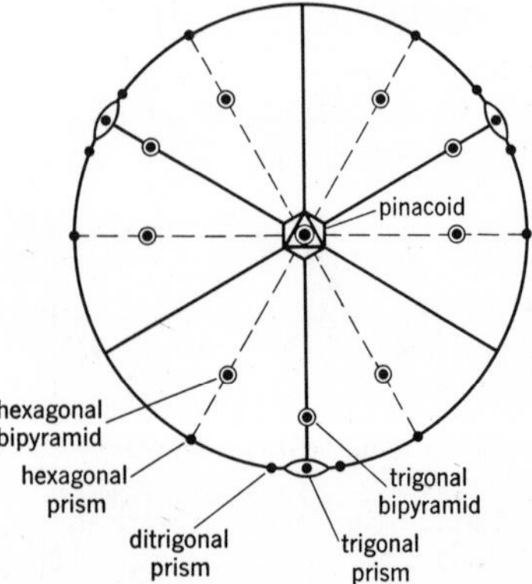

FIG. 132. Special positions of symmetry $\bar{6}m2$.

Mineral representatives

benitoite, $BaTiSi_3O_9$, Fig. 133
(possibly sychnasite, $(Ce,La)Ca(CO_3)_2F$)

Other inorganic representatives

none known

Organic representatives

none known

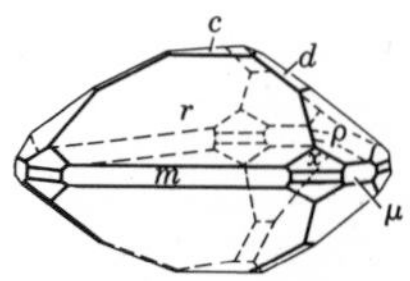

FIG. 133. Example of form development in class $\bar{6}m2$: benitoite, $BaTiSi_3O_9$.

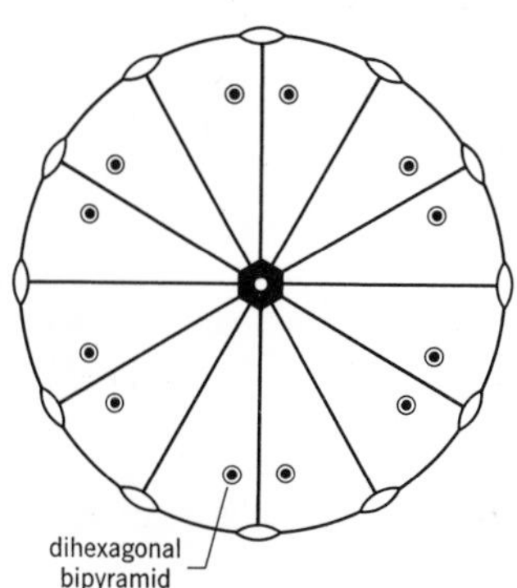

FIG. 134. Repetition of a point in the general position by symmetry $\frac{6}{m}\frac{2}{m}\frac{2}{m}$.

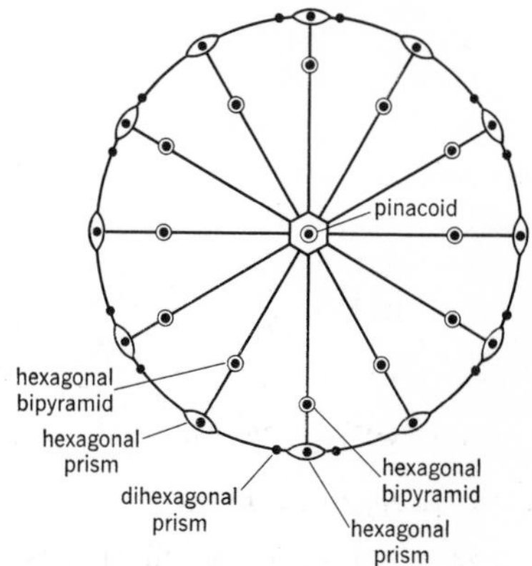

FIG. 135. Special positions of symmetry $\frac{6}{m}\frac{2}{m}\frac{2}{m}$.

Class $\frac{6}{m}\frac{2}{m}\frac{2}{m}$. The symmetry of this class and its repetition of a motif point are shown in Fig. 134. Special positions are shown in Fig. 135. Several of the common metals crystallize in this class.

Mineral representatives

covellite, CuS
beryl, $Be_3Al_2Si_6O_{18}$, Fig. 136

Other inorganic representatives

Be, Mg, Fig. 137, Zn, Cd, Hg
$(NH_4)_2SiF_6$
K_2SiF_6
$CeLaH(SO_4)_4$

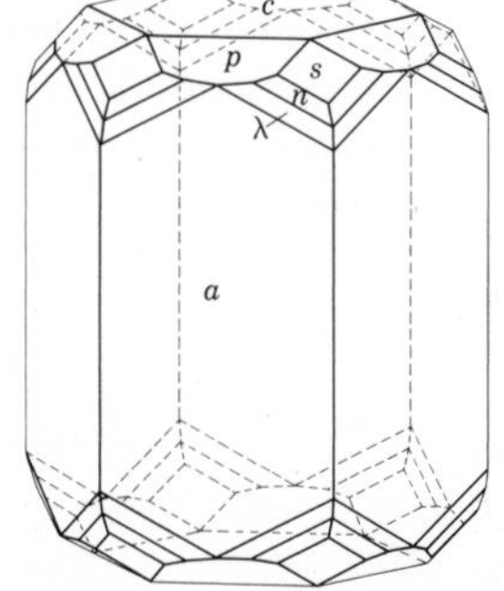

FIG. 136. Example of form development in class $\frac{6}{m}\frac{2}{m}\frac{2}{m}$: beryl, $Be_3Al_2Si_6O_{18}$.

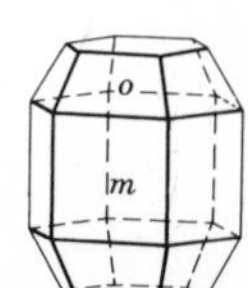

FIG. 137. Example of form development in class $\frac{6}{m}\frac{2}{m}\frac{2}{m}$: magnesium, Mg.

Organic representatives

styphnic acid, $C_6H(NO_2)_3(OH)_2$

trimethylethylammonium picrate, $(C_2H_5)(CH_3)_3NC_6H_2(NO_2)_3O$

The isometric system

The isometric system is unique in several respects: (*a*) It is the only system composed of classes containing more than one n-fold axis in which $n > 2$. (*b*) Each of its classes has four 3-fold axes. (*c*) Every form occurring in the system is a closed form and, therefore, can exist on a real crystal without the necessary occurrence of other forms. The reason for this is that four non-parallel planes are sufficient to enclose space, and the four 3-fold axes present in each point group of the system provide this as the minimum number of planes in any form. (*d*) The forms occurring in this system are unique to it; the pedion and pinacoid, which occur in all other systems, do not occur in the isometric system.

The forms of the isometric system are given in the following list. The numeral preceding the name of the form is the number of faces in the form.

4	*tetrahedron*	Fig. 138
6	*cube*	Fig. 139
8	*octahedron*	Fig. 140
12	*dodecahedron*	Fig. 141
12	*pyritohedron* (named from its common occurrence on crystals of the mineral pyrite)	Fig. 142
12	*tristetrahedron* (i.e., a polyhedron which can be derived by dividing each face of the tetrahedron into three faces)	Fig. 143
12	*deltohedron*	Fig. 144
12	*tetartoid*	Fig. 145
24	*tetrahexahedron* (i.e., a polyhedron which can be derived by dividing each face of the cube into four faces)	Fig. 146
24	*trapezohedron*	Fig. 147
24	*trisoctahedron* (i.e., a polyhedron which can be derived by dividing each face of the octahedron into three faces)	Fig. 148

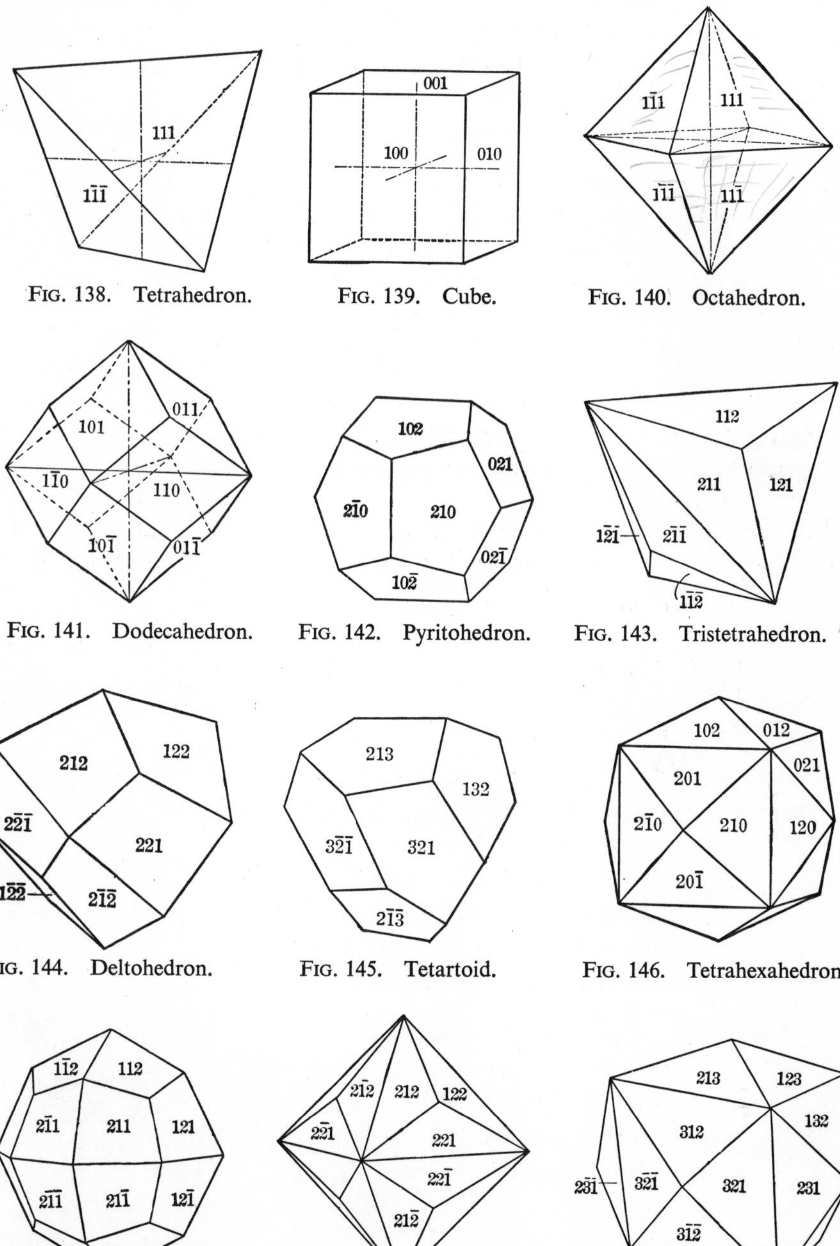

FIG. 138. Tetrahedron.

FIG. 139. Cube.

FIG. 140. Octahedron.

FIG. 141. Dodecahedron.

FIG. 142. Pyritohedron.

FIG. 143. Tristetrahedron.

FIG. 144. Deltohedron.

FIG. 145. Tetartoid.

FIG. 146. Tetrahexahedron.

FIG. 147. Trapezohedron.

FIG. 148. Trisoctahedron.

FIG. 149. Hextetrahedron.

24	*hextetrahedron* (i.e., a polyhedron which can be derived by dividing each face of the tetrahedron into six faces)	Fig. 149
24	*diploid* (i.e., a polyhedron composed of faces in pairs)	Fig. 150
24	*gyroid*	Fig. 151
48	*hexoctahedron* (i.e., a polyhedron which can be derived by dividing each face of the octahedron into six faces)	Fig. 152

The cube and octahedron occur in every class of the isometric system.

Class 23. The symmetry of this class and its repetition of a motif point are shown in Fig. 153. Special positions are shown in Fig. 154. Since the

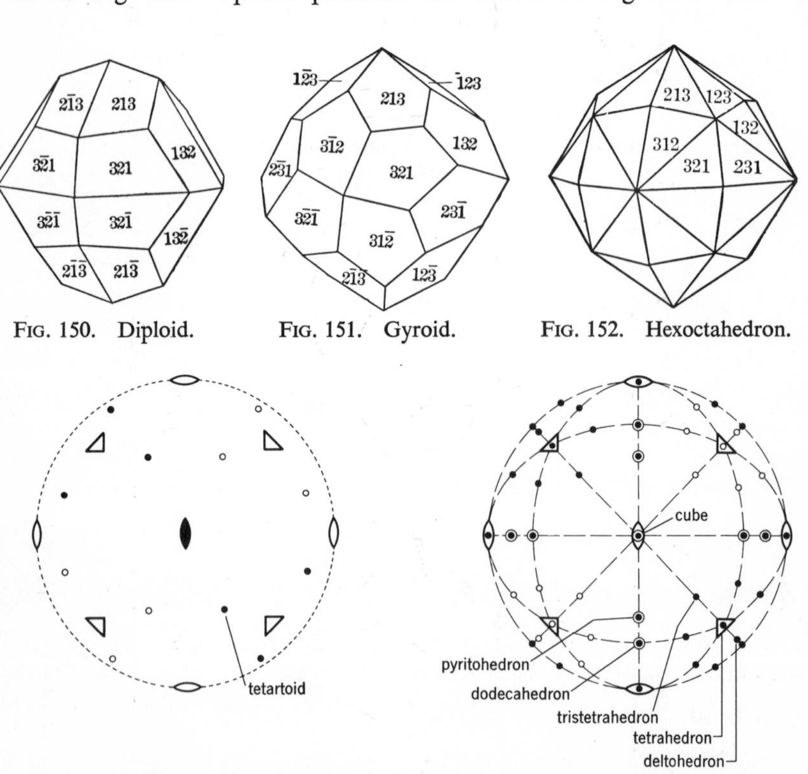

FIG. 150. Diploid.

FIG. 151. Gyroid.

FIG. 152. Hexoctahedron.

FIG. 153. Repetition of a point in the general position by symmetry 23.

FIG. 154. Special positions of symmetry 23.

Table 7. Forms occurring in the isometric system

Indices	Crystal classes				
	23	432	$\frac{2}{m}\bar{3}$	$\bar{4}3m$	$\frac{4}{m}\bar{3}\frac{2}{m}$
hkl	tetartoid	gyroid	diploid	hextetrahedron	hexoctahedron
hhl ($h > l$)	deltohedron	trisoctahedron	trisoctahedron	deltohedron	trisoctahedron
hhl ($l > h$)	tristetrahedron	trapezohedron	trapezohedron	tristetrahedron	trapezohedron
*hk*0	pyritohedron	tetrahexahedron	pyritohedron	tetrahexahedron	tetrahexahedron
111	tetrahedron	octahedron	octahedron	tetrahedron	octahedron
110	dodecahedron	dodecahedron	dodecahedron	dodecahedron	dodecahedron
100	cube	cube	cube	cube	cube

symmetry contains no symmetry elements of the second sort, enantiomorphous crystals can occur in this class.

Mineral representatives

ullmanite, NiSbS
cobaltite, CoAsS
langbeinite, $K_2Mg_2(SO_4)_3$

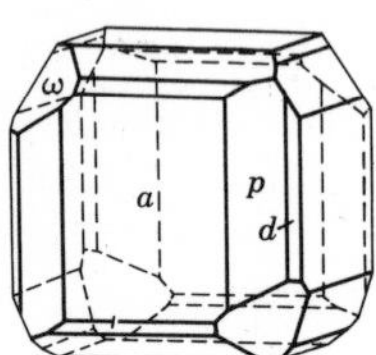

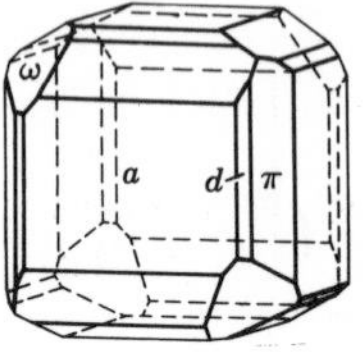

FIG. 155 and FIG. 156. Examples of enantiomorphous form development in class 23: left $NaClO_3$ (Fig. 155) and right $NaClO_3$ (Fig. 156).

Other inorganic representatives

$NaClO_3$, Figs. 155 and 156
$NaBrO_3$
$NaSrAsO_4 \cdot 9H_2O$
$Na_3SbS_4 \cdot 9H_2O$ (Schlippe's salt)
Na_2CaSiO_4

Organic representatives

sodium uranyl acetate, $Na(UO_2)\,(C_2H_3O_2)_3$
coniine alum, $(C_8H_{15}NH_3)Al(SO_4)_2 \cdot 12H_2O$
amylamine alum, $(C_5H_{11}NH_3)Al(SO_4)_2 \cdot 12H_2O$

Class 432. The symmetry of this class and its repetition of a motif point are shown in Fig. 157. Special positions are shown in Fig. 158. Since the symmetry contains no symmetry elements of the second sort, enantiomorphous crystals can occur in this class.

This is one of the two crystal classes without undoubted representatives. (The other class is $\bar{6}$.) Spurious form developments having the symmetry of this class have been found in Cu_2O (Fig. 159) and NH_4Cl (Fig. 160). The false symmetry is probably due to precipitation from a medium containing optically active matter, as suggested by a discussion in the next chapter.

Class $\frac{2}{m}\bar{3}$. The symmetry of this class and its repetition of a motif point are shown in Fig. 161. Special positions are shown in Fig. 162.

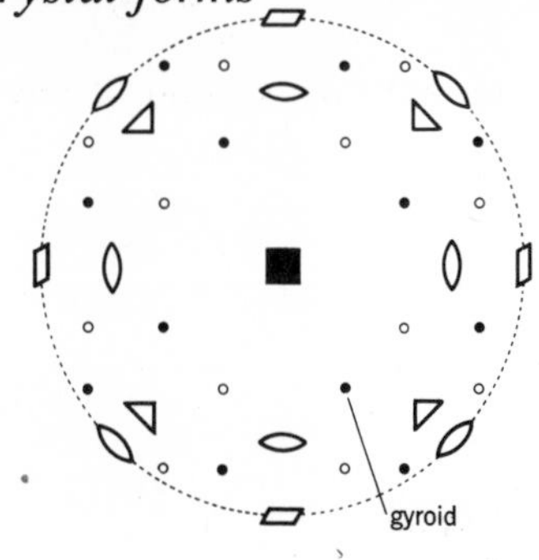

FIG. 157. Repetition of a point in the general position by symmetry 432.

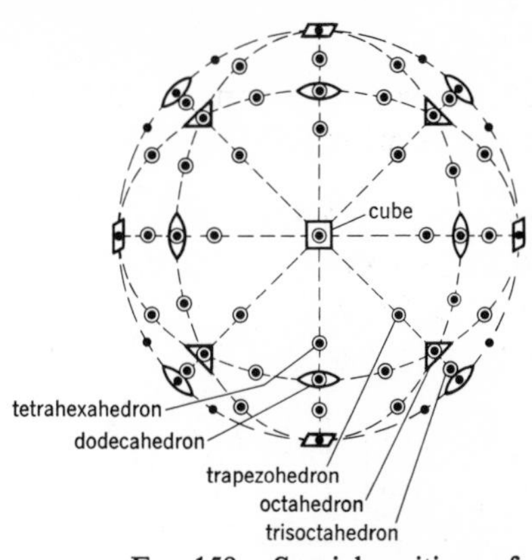

FIG. 158. Special positions of symmetry 432.

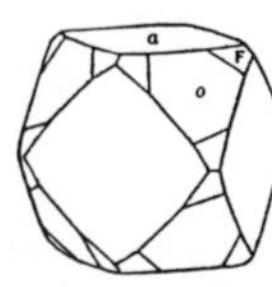

FIG. 159. Form development on Cu_2O having symmetry 432.

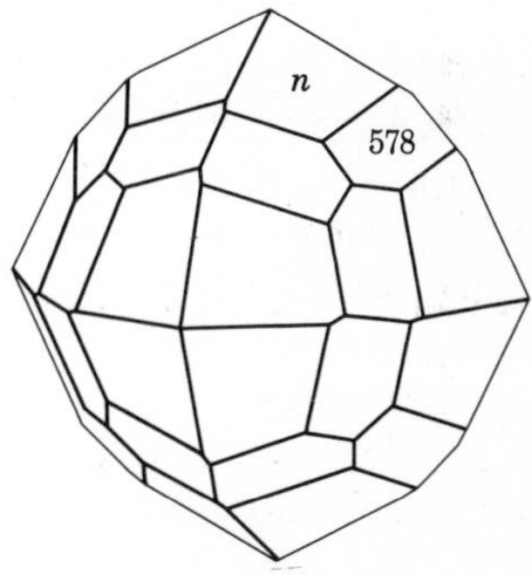

FIG. 160. Form development on NH_4Cl having symmetry 432.

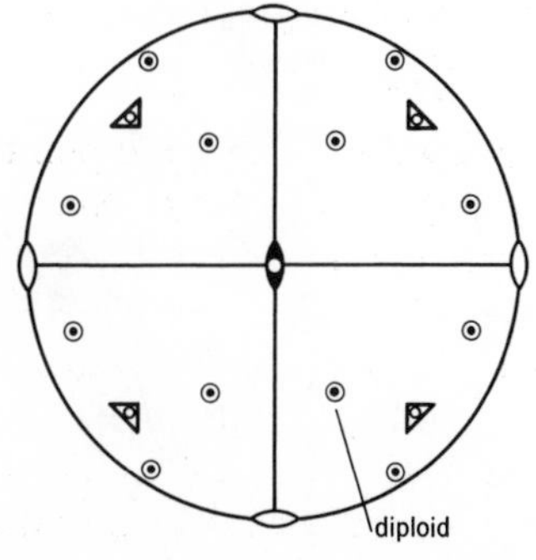

FIG. 161. Repetition of a point in the general position by symmetry $\frac{2}{m}\bar{3}$.

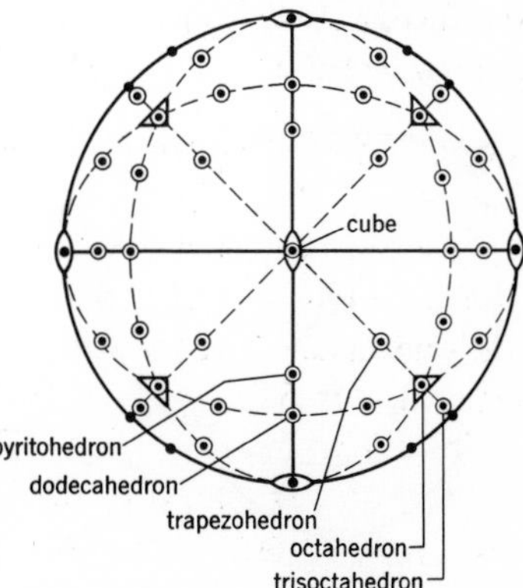

FIG. 162. Special positions of symmetry $\frac{2}{m}\bar{3}$.

Mineral representatives

pyrite, FeS_2, Figs. 163 and 164
sperrylite, $PtAs_2$
bixbyite, $(Fe, Mn)_2O_3$

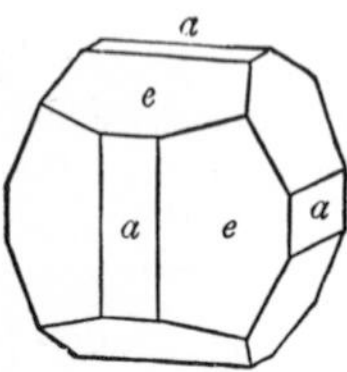

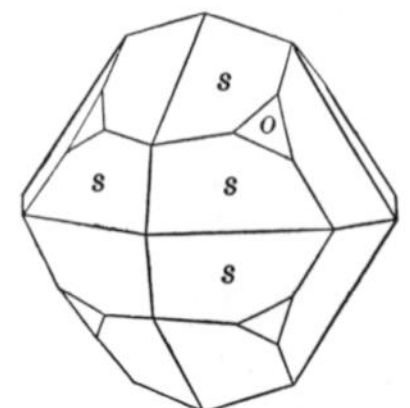

FIG. 163 and FIG. 164. Examples of form development in class $\frac{2}{m}\bar{3}$: pyrite, FeS_2.

Other inorganic representatives

alums, $KAl(SO_4)_2 \cdot 12H_2O$, etc.
$Ca(NO_3)_2$
$Sr(NO_3)_2$
$Ba(NO_3)_2$
$Pb(NO_3)_2$
$Zn(BrO_3)_2 \cdot 6H_2O$

Organic representatives

methylantiphenylhydroxamic acid, $C_6H_5C(OCH_3)NOH$

Class $\bar{4}3m$. The symmetry of this class and its repetition of a motif point are shown in Fig. 165. Special positions are shown in Fig. 166.

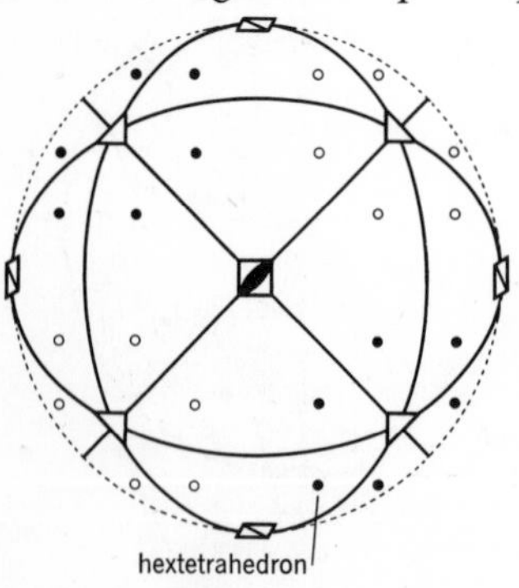
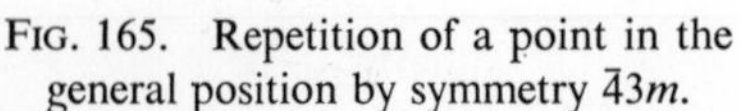

FIG. 165. Repetition of a point in the general position by symmetry $\bar{4}3m$.

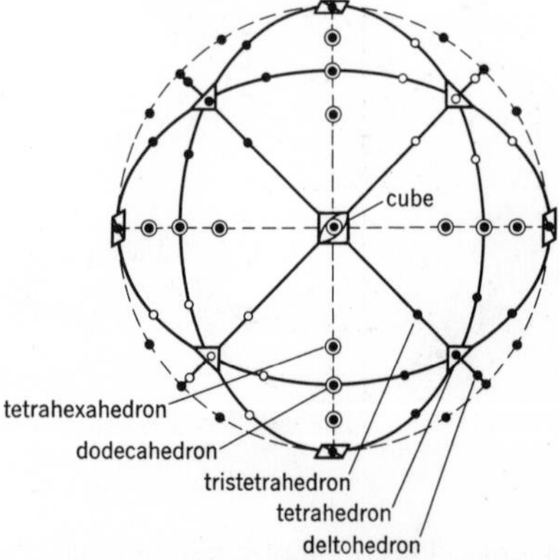

FIG. 166. Special positions of symmetry $\bar{4}3m$.

Mineral representatives

sphalerite, ZnS, Fig. 167
greenockite, ZnS
metacinnabarite, HgS
sulvanite, Cu_3VS_4
tetrahedrate, Cu_3SbS_3
tennantite, Cu_3AsS_3
eulytite, $Bi_4(SiO_4)_3$
marshite, CuI
rhodizite, $NaKLi_4Al_4Bo_3B_{10}O_{27}$
high boracite, $Mg_3B_7O_{13}Cl$, Fig. 168
pharmacosiderite, $Fe_3AsO_4(OH)_3 \cdot 5H_2O$
zunyite, $Al_{13}Si_5O_{20}(OH, F)_{18}Cl$

Other inorganic representatives

CuCl, CuBr, CuI
$Al(PO_3)_3$
Ag_3PO_4

Organic representatives

(apparently none is known)

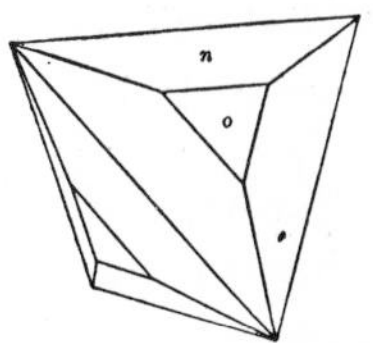

FIG. 167. Example of form development in class $\bar{4}3m$: sphalerite, ZnS.

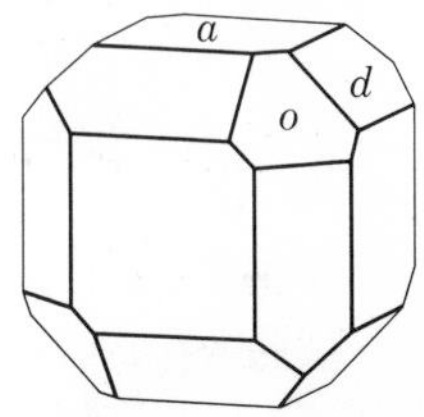

FIG. 168. Example of form development in class $\bar{4}3m$: high boracite, $Mg_3B_7O_{13}Cl$.

Class $\frac{4}{m}\bar{3}\frac{2}{m}$. The symmetry of this class and its repetition of a motif point are shown in Fig. 169. Special positions are shown in Fig. 170. Most of the ductile metals of commerce and many minerals belong to this class.

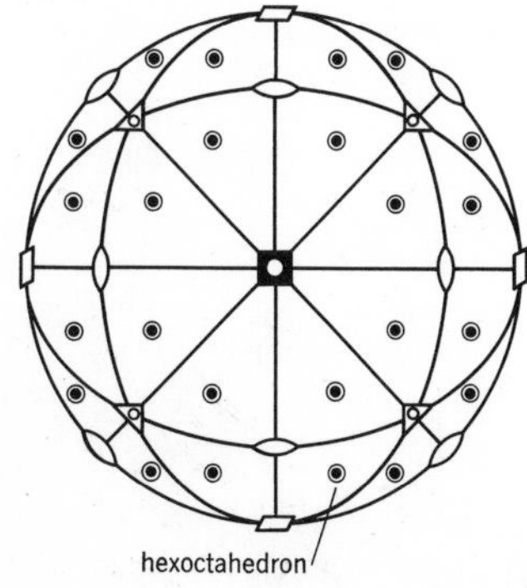

FIG. 169. Repetition of a point in the general position by symmetry $\frac{4}{m}\bar{3}\frac{2}{m}$.

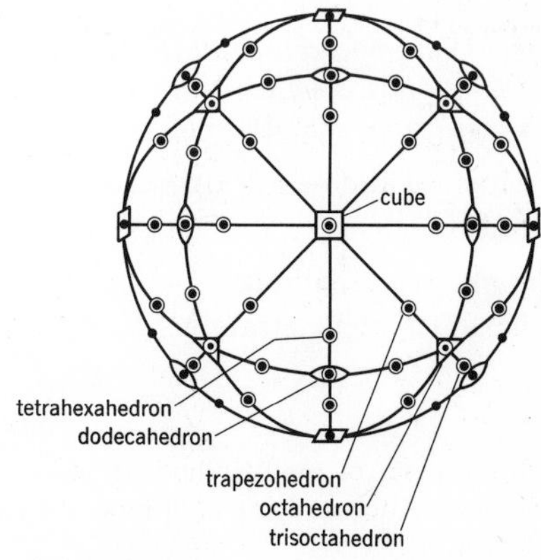

FIG. 170. Special positions of symmetry $\frac{4}{m}\bar{3}\frac{2}{m}$.

Mineral representatives

copper, Fig. 171
diamond
galena, PbS, Fig. 172
fluorite, CaF_2
eglestonite, Hg_4OCl_2, Fig. 173
cuprite, Cu_2O, Fig. 174
senarmontite, Sb_2O_3
arsenolite, As_2O_3
spinels, like $MgAl_2O_4$
garnets, like $Ca_3Al_2(SiO_4)_3$
sodalite, $Na_4Al_3(SiO_4)_3Cl$
lazurite, $Na_5Al_3(SiO_4)_3S$

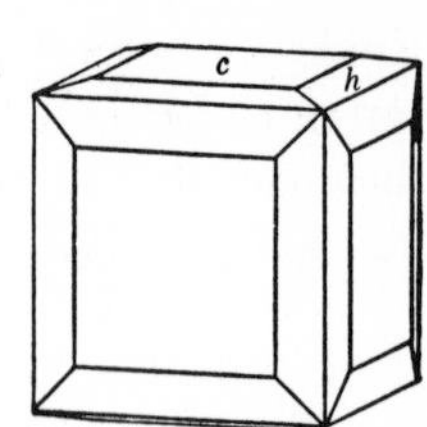

FIG. 171. Example of form development in class $\frac{4}{m}\bar{3}\frac{2}{m}$: copper.

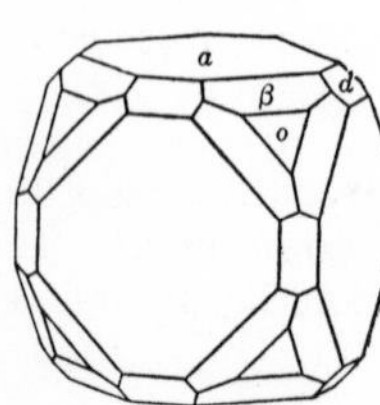

FIG. 172. Example of form development in class $\frac{4}{m}\bar{3}\frac{2}{m}$: galena, PbS.

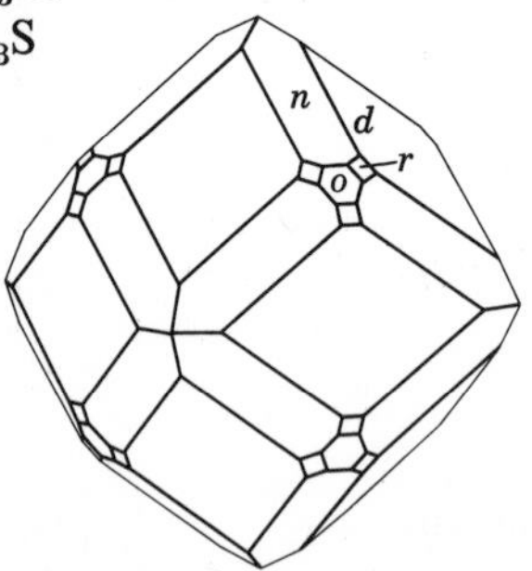

FIG. 173. Example of form development in class $\frac{4}{m}\bar{3}\frac{2}{m}$: eglestonite, Hg_4OCl_2.

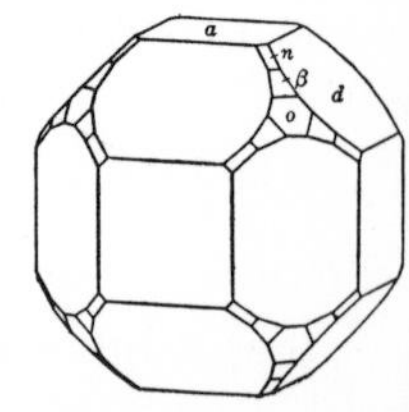

FIG. 174. Example of form development in class $\frac{4}{m}\bar{3}\frac{2}{m}$: cuprite, Cu_2O.

Other inorganic representatives

The metals Ag, Au, Fe, Pt, W, Si, Pb
Most alkali halides
Most alkaline-earth oxides, sulfides, and selenides
K_2PtCl_6

Organic representatives

hexamethylenetetramine, $(CH_2)_6N_4$

Exercises

1. Study a set of models showing idealized form development for crystals of various symmetries. After studying each model, record the following information you have found out about it:

crystal class
crystal system
name and indices of each form present

11 · Practical determination of point-group symmetry

Those who study crystals or their properties are frequently faced with the problem of determining the point-group symmetry of a particular species of crystal. It might be supposed that the morphological development of a crystal would constitute conclusive evidence of its symmetry, but there are pitfalls in using such evidence. The nature of the difficulties encountered in basing a symmetry determination on morphological development can be appreciated from the following examples.

Figure 1 shows a form development of the mineral quartz which reveals its true symmetry 32. The forms present are as follows:

hexagonal prism	m	$((10\bar{1}0))$
"positive" rhombohedron	r	$((10\bar{1}1))$
"negative" rhombohedron	z	$((01\bar{1}1))$
trigonal bipyramid	s	$((11\bar{2}1))$
trigonal trapezohedron	x	$((51\bar{6}1))$

This collection of forms is present on quartz crystals which have grown under favorable circumstances. When present, they plainly reveal the symmetry to be 32. Even if the general form, x, is absent, Fig. 2, the symmetry is still obviously 32. But, under other circumstances of growth, both the general form, x, and the form s may be missing, and the appearance of the crystal is that of Fig. 3. This collection of forms appears to have mirrors intersecting in the 3-fold axis, and the general symmetry of the collection of forms is $\bar{3}\frac{2}{m}$. Under other circumstances the "positive" and "negative" rhombohedron, r and z, may be developed to an equal extent, giving the crystal the appearance shown in Fig. 4. The symmetry of this form development appears to be $\frac{6}{m}\frac{2}{m}\frac{2}{m}$.

Another example of the difficulty of interpreting true symmetry from form development is afforded by the mineral nepheline. The true symmetry of this mineral is 6, yet its form development is usually $\frac{6}{m}\frac{2}{m}\frac{2}{m}$, Fig. 5, with no morphological hint of lower symmetry.

The nature of these difficulties and some methods of overcoming them are briefly discussed in this chapter.

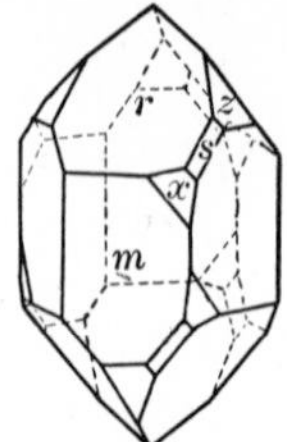

FIG. 1. Quartz, showing a general form development.

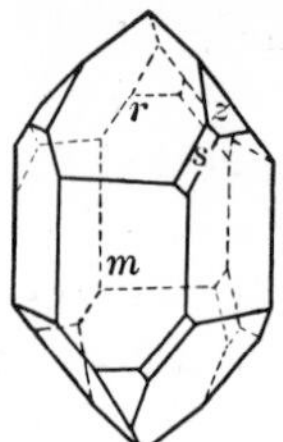

FIG. 2. Quartz, without general form *x*.

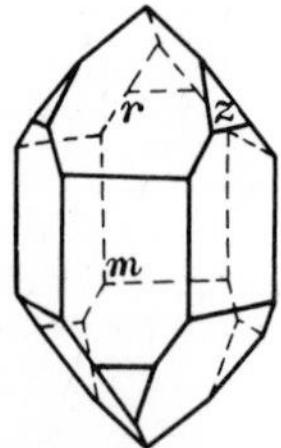

FIG. 3. Quartz, without forms *x* or *s*, but with unequal development of rhombohedrons *r* and *z*; apparent symmetry $\bar{3}\,\frac{2}{m}$.

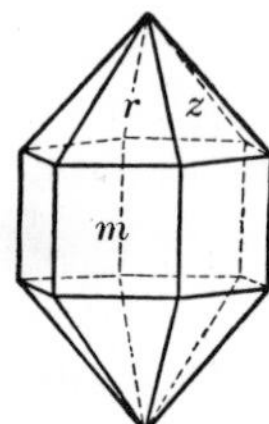

FIG. 4. Quartz, without forms *x* or *s*, and with equal development of rhombohedrons *r* and *z*; apparent symmetry $\frac{6}{m}\frac{2}{m}\frac{2}{m}$.

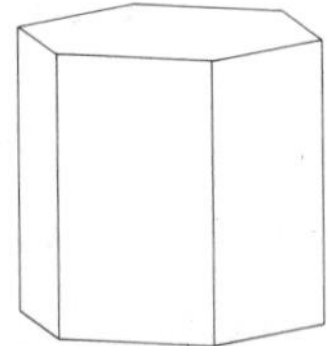

FIG. 5. Nepheline, $KNa_3Al_4Si_4O_{16}$, with form development suggesting incorrect symmetry $\frac{6}{m}\frac{2}{m}\frac{2}{m}$.

Theory of symmetry determination from morphology

Some of the difficulties of symmetry determination by using form development can be appreciated by reference to an empirical rule of form development first noticed by Bravais, and known as *Bravais' rule.* According to this rule the relative importance of several forms (that is, their relative area and frequency of occurrence) for a particular crystal species tends to be in the same order as their interplanar spacings. The interplanar spacings are concerned with lattice geometry alone. For a given unit cell and lattice type, the interplanar spacings are the same for all crystal classes of the system. The importance of form development in a crystal system, therefore, tends to follow the holosymmetric symmetry of the system. Only under favorable circumstances do crystals of the merosymmetric classes develop forms which degrade this holosymmetric appearance to reveal the true symmetry.

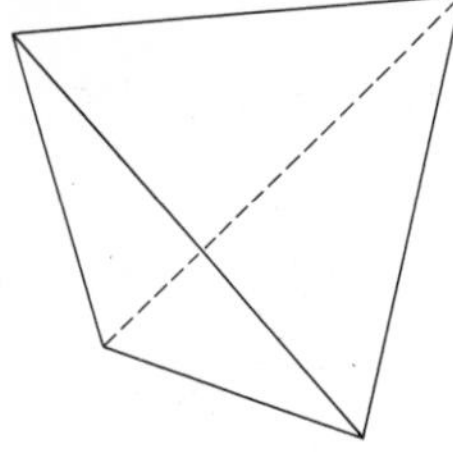

FIG. 6. "Positive" tetrahedron ((111)), symmetry $\bar{4}3m$.

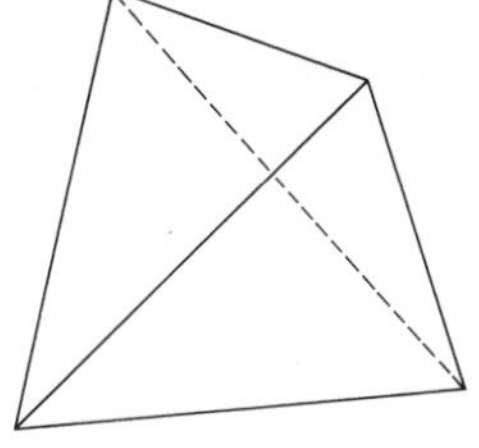

FIG. 7. "Negative" tetrahedron ((1$\bar{1}$1)), symmetry $\bar{4}3m$.

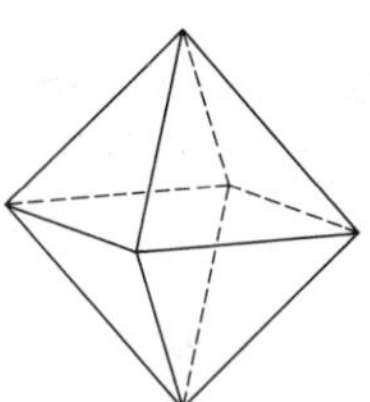

FIG. 8. Equal development of ((111)) and ((1$\bar{1}$1)), suggesting false symmetry $\frac{4}{m}\bar{3}\frac{2}{m}$.

There are two general ways in which this holosymmetric symmetry tends to appear. One way is the approximately equal development of *complementary* forms in the merosymmetric classes. For example, in the class $\bar{4}3m$, a very common form is the tetrahedron ((111)). This can take the form of a "positive" tetrahedron ((111)), Fig. 6, or a "negative" tetrahedron ((1$\bar{1}$1)), Fig. 7. Both can be present on the same crystal. If they are equally developed, the combination has the appearance of a single form, the octahedron, Fig. 8. This form development suggests the higher symmetry of the holosymmetric class $\frac{4}{m}\bar{3}\frac{2}{m}$. It was this equal development of the "positive" and "negative" rhombohedra which gave the quartz crystal of Fig. 4 the appearance of holosymmetric hexagonal symmetry.

A second way in which holosymmetry tends to appear is through the development of a special form of high symmetry. A good example of this is found in the isometric system. The cube, ((100)), and dodecahedron, ((110)), occur as special forms in each of the five classes of the system. Consequently any crystal that displays a form development consisting of only the cube or dodecahedron, or a combination of these having any ratio of areas whatever, gives no information as to its symmetry other than that it belongs to the isometric system.

In a similar way, certain other forms occur in more than one symmetry. The distribution of forms in the various point groups is shown in Tables 1, 2, 3, and 4. These tabulations are designed to aid in the determination of symmetry from morphological development. In the final columns of these tables are listed the symmetries which are characterized by a single general form alone. There are 19 symmetries so listed. This means that in 19 specific symmetries the finding of a crystal showing the general form alone determines the symmetry. In the 12 remaining symmetries the general form of these classes occurs as a special form in one or more other classes and hence cannot, by itself, serve to

Table 1. Distribution of forms in the triclinic, monoclinic, and orthorhombic systems

No. of faces	Name of form	Class								Unique form for
		1	$\bar{1}$	2	m	$\frac{2}{m}$	222	$2mm$	$\frac{2}{m}\frac{2}{m}\frac{2}{m}$	
1	pedion	+		+	+			+		
2	pinacoid		+	+	+	+	+	+	+	
2 2	dome sphenoid			+	+			+		
4	prism					+	+	+	+	
4	bisphenoid						+			222
4	pyramid							+		$2mm$
8	bipyramid								+	$\frac{2}{m}\frac{2}{m}\frac{2}{m}$

determine the symmetry of a crystal in its class. The tabulations also bring out the fact that sometimes the appearance of two special forms is sufficient to determine the class. Referring to Fig. 2 and the discussion in the first part of this chapter, the presence of the general form of class 32, namely the trigonal trapezohedron x, was not necessary to fix the symmetry. Table 3 shows that the simultaneous presence of two special forms, namely the rhombohedron, r, and the trigonal bipyramid, s, can occur only in class 32. Their presence in a combination therefore determines the class of a crystal on which they occur. These tables can be used in similar problems of symmetry determination from form development.

Note on twinning. A precaution should be noted here. It is possible for two or more individual crystals of low symmetry to intergrow in such a way as to

Table 2. Distribution of forms in the tetragonal system

No. of faces	Name of form	Class							Unique form for
		4	$\bar{4}$	$\frac{4}{m}$	422	$4mm$	$\bar{4}2m$	$\frac{4}{m}\frac{2}{m}\frac{2}{m}$	
1	pedion	+				+			
2	pinacoid		+	+	+		+	+	
4	tetragonal prism	+	+	+	+	+	+	+	
4	tetragonal pyramid	+				+			
4	tetragonal bisphenoid		+				+		
8	ditetragonal prism				+	+	+	+	
8	tetragonal bipyramid			+	+		+	+	
8	tetragonal trapezohedron				+				422
8	tetragonal scalenohedron						+		$\bar{4}2m$
8	ditetragonal pyramid					+			$4mm$
16	ditetragonal bipyramid							+	$\frac{4}{m}\frac{2}{m}\frac{2}{m}$

Table 3. Distribution of forms in the hexagonal system

No. of faces	Name of form	Class												Unique form for
		3	$\bar{3}$	32	$3m$	$\bar{3}\frac{2}{m}$	6	$\bar{6} = \frac{3}{m}$	$\frac{6}{m}$	622	$6mm$	$\bar{6}m2 = \frac{3}{m}m2$	$\frac{6}{m}\frac{2}{m}\frac{2}{m}$	
1	pedion	+			+		+				+			
2	pinacoid		+	+		+		+	+	+		+	+	
3	trigonal prism	+		+	+			+				+		
3	trigonal pyramid	+			+									
6	ditrigonal prism			+	+							+		
6	hexagonal prism		+	+	+	+	+		+	+	+	+	+	
6	trigonal bipyramid			+				+				+		
6	rhombohedron		+	+		+								
6	trigonal trapezohedron			+										32
6	ditrigonal pyramid				+									$3m$
6	hexagonal pyramid				+		+				+			
12	hexagonal bipyramid					+			+	+		+	+	
12	hexagonal scalenohedron					+								$\bar{3}\frac{2}{m}$
12	dihexagonal prism					+				+	+		+	
12	ditrigonal bipyramid											+		$\bar{6}m2$
12	hexagonal trapezohedron									+				$\bar{6}22$
12	dihexagonal pyramid										+			$6mm$
24	dihexagonal bipyramid												+	$\frac{6}{m}\frac{2}{m}\frac{2}{m}$

Table 4. Distribution of forms in the isometric system

No. of faces	Name of form	Class: 23	432	$\frac{2}{m}\bar{3}$	$\bar{4}3m$	$\frac{4}{m}\bar{3}\frac{2}{m}$	Unique form for
4	tetrahedron	+			+		
6	cube	+	+	+	+	+	
8	octahedron		+	+		+	
12	dodecahedron	+	+	+	+	+	
	pyritohedron	+		+			
	tristetrahedron	+			+		
	deltohedron	+			+		
	tetartoid	+					23
24	tetrahexahedron		+		+	+	
	trapezohedron		+	+		+	
	trisoctahedron		+	+		+	
	hextetrahedron				+		$\bar{4}3m$
	diploid			+			$\frac{2}{m}\bar{3}$
	gyroid		+				432
48	hexoctahedron					+	$\frac{4}{m}\bar{3}\frac{2}{m}$

mimic higher symmetry. In particular it is possible for such *twinned* intergrowths of merosymmetric crystals to mimic a single holosymmetric individual. This is one aspect of *twinning*, a topic not specifically discussed in this volume since its explanation lies not in geometry but in the physics of crystal growth.

Determination of symmetry by dissolution methods

The theory of symmetry determination from morphology is based on the notion that the growth form of a crystal must conform to its symmetry. In a

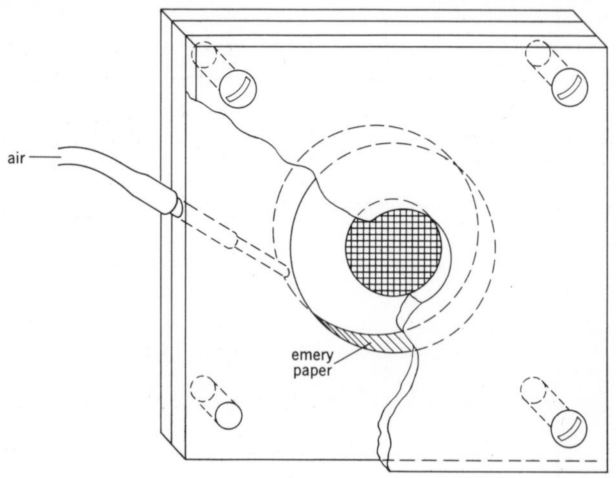

FIG. 9. Device for grinding spherical surfaces on crystals (modified after W. L. Bond).

similar manner the reverse growth, or solution of a crystal, must conform to its symmetry. There are two general ways in which dissolution of a crystal can be made to yield symmetry information: the study of dissolution forms and the study of etch figures. These correspond to megascopic and microscopic views of the dissolution process, respectively.

Dissolution forms. If a sphere ground from a single crystal is dissolved, the rates of solution in symmetrically equivalent directions should be the same, while the rates of solution in nonequivalent directions should not, in general, be the same. It is a comparatively easy matter to grind crystals into spheres and to perform such experiments. Figure 9 shows a simple apparatus used for grinding crystals to spheres. This consists essentially of a flat cylindrical chamber lined with fine emery paper. The crystal is placed in this chamber and blown about its periphery by a tangentially directed blast of air. When this device is used the surface of the crystal can usually be ground into a sphere in a matter of minutes or less.

Figure 10 shows spheres of crystals of the metal germanium after dissolution experiments with inorganic acids. It will be observed that, although the different concentrations of solvent result in different specific shapes, all have the

FIG. 10. Dissolution forms of spheres ground from germanium crystals. Both forms show symmetry $\frac{4}{m}\bar{3}\frac{2}{m}$.

symmetry $\frac{4}{m}\bar{3}\frac{2}{m}$, which is the correct symmetry of germanium. The end forms appear to be rounded polyhedral shapes approximating the crystal forms ((100)) and ((110)).

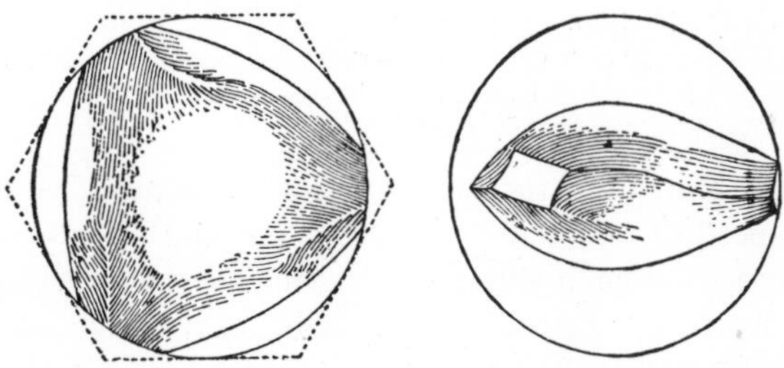

FIG. 11. Dissolution form resulting from etching a quartz sphere with hydrofluoric acid. The dissolution form shows symmetry 32 (from Dana's *Textbook of Mineralogy*).

Figure 11 shows the result of etching a quartz sphere with hydrofluoric acid. The symmetry of the final dissolution body is obviously 32, which is the correct symmetry of quartz.

Etch figures. An alternative dissolution experiment consists in applying the solvent to the natural crystal faces for only a short time. This experiment displays the nature of the beginning of the solution attack on the crystal structure from different directions. Instead of applying the solvent to the crystal for an extended time, it is usually applied to a crystal plane with a damp cloth or brush, and usually is not permitted to act more than a short time.

The solution action starts sporadically at various points on the crystal faces. The action appears to be initiated at imperfections in the crystal structure. The solvent eats back into the structure in various directions with velocities controlled by the speed of interaction of the solvent and structure in these directions. After a short time, a small *etch pit* or *etch figure* is developed at each point of solvent attack. Etch pits are usually shallow depressions bounded by approximately plane faces of high indices. The symmetry of each etch figure appearing in a crystal face should conform to the symmetry elements of the point group normal to that crystal face. The symmetry of the etch figure should therefore be that of one of the 10 plane point groups of Fig. 1, Chapter 7. Furthermore, the relation between the shapes and placement of etch figures on the various faces of a crystal should conform to the symmetry relations of these faces. The general shapes of the etch figures for the various symmetries, and their relations to one another, are shown in Figs. 12, 13, 14, and 15. In these figures the crystal shape is that expected for a holosymmetric morphological

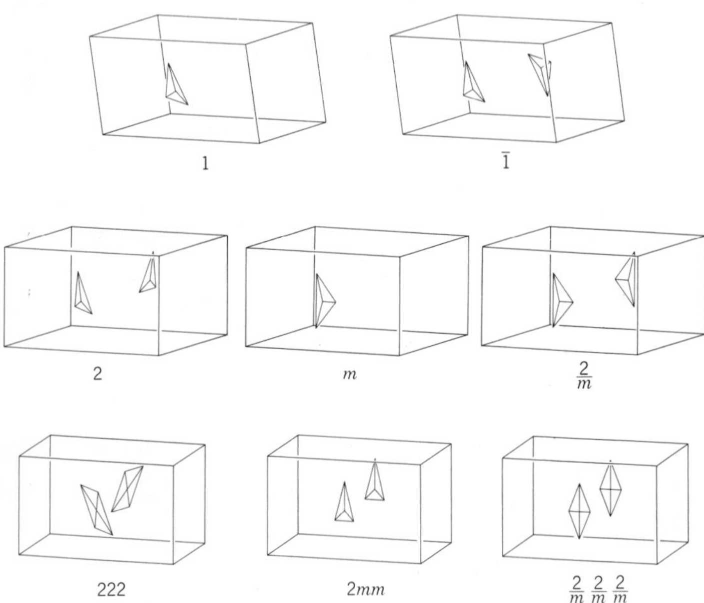

FIG. 12. Typical etch-figure appearances on triclinic, monoclinic, and orthorhombic crystals.

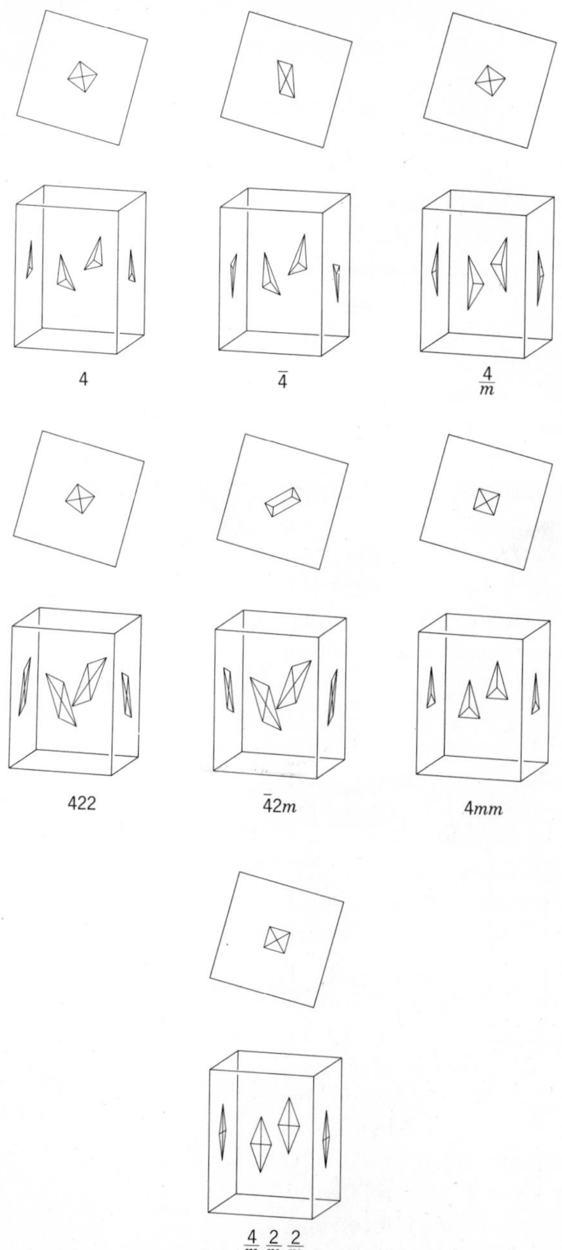

FIG. 13. Typical etch-figure appearances on tetragonal crystals.

development. The shape and distribution of the etch figures reveal the degradation of this holosymmetric symmetry wherever the true symmetry of the class requires it.

An actual photograph of etch figures on a prism face of apatite is shown in Fig. 16. The face in this illustration corresponds to the prism face in symmetry $6/m$ of Fig. 14, and the etch figures have the symmetry of the figures shown there. Figure 17 shows the etch figure produced on the basal plane. This also corresponds to symmetry $6/m$ of Fig. 14.

Etch-figure information as obtained from one solvent and concentration should not necessarily be regarded as conclusive. It is desirable that several different types of etch be tested in order to be sure that the specialized reaction of a particular solvent is not being observed.

It is essential to observe an important precaution when performing etch figure experiments: Solvents containing substances of left- or right-handed symmetry should not be used. A pair of scalenohedron faces of calcite etched by the action of a symmetrical solvent is shown in Fig. 18*a*. The action of left- and right-handed gluconodeltalactone on the same faces is shown in Figs. 18*b* and 18*c*. The left and right faces of the scalenohedron shown in the illustration are actually related by a mirror plane between them. Evidently a right-handed solvent acts differently on a left- and right-handed face, and so would fail to reveal the symmetry relation between them.

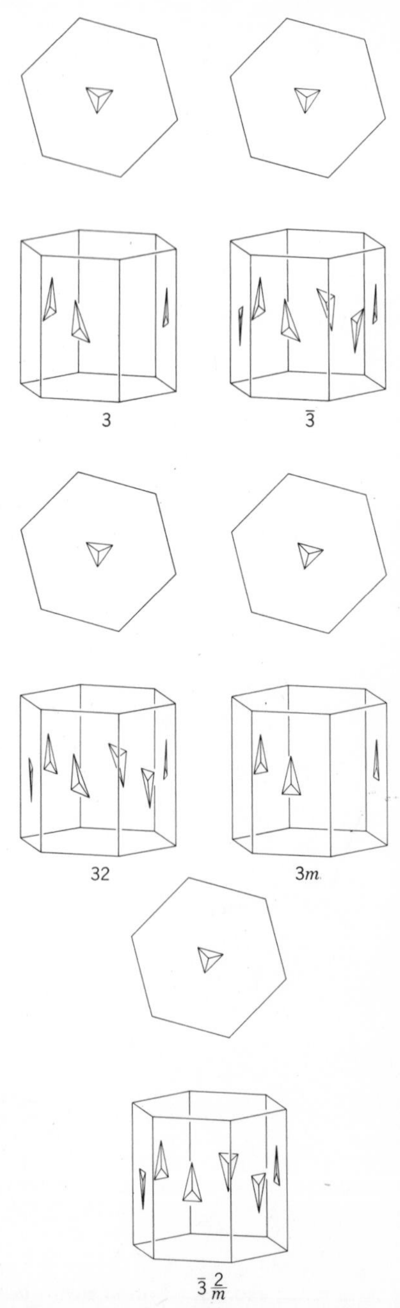

FIG. 14*a*. Typical etch-figure appearances on hexagonal crystals with 3 and $\bar{3}$ axes.

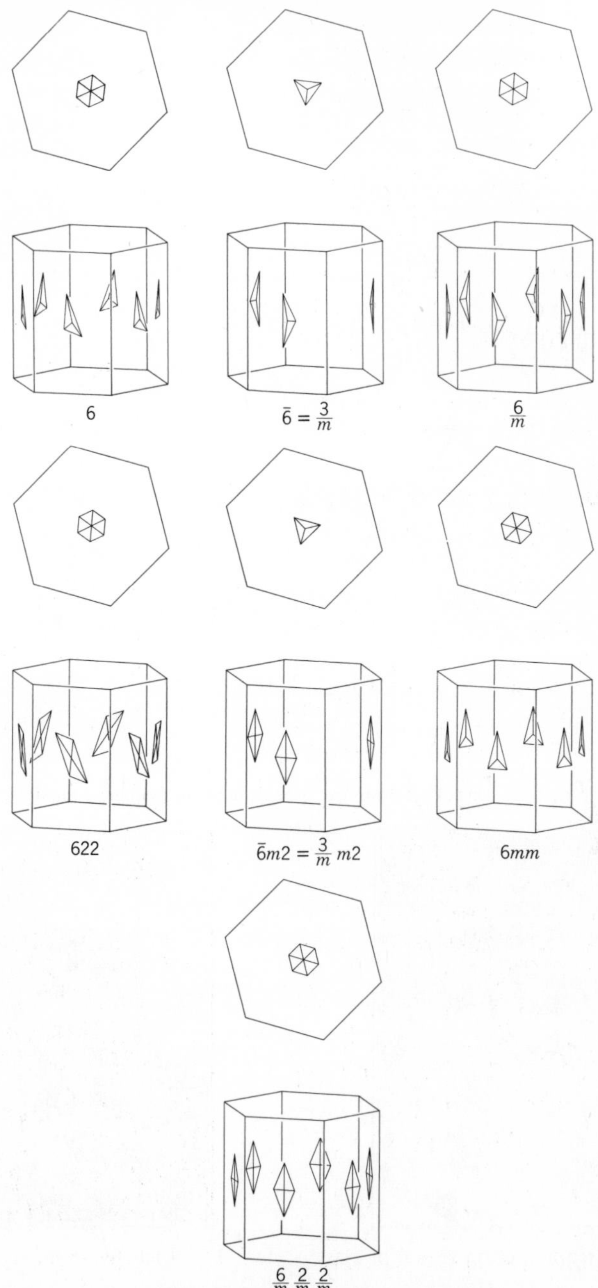

FIG. 14*b*. Typical etch-figure appearances on hexagonal crystals with 6 and $\bar{6}$ axes.

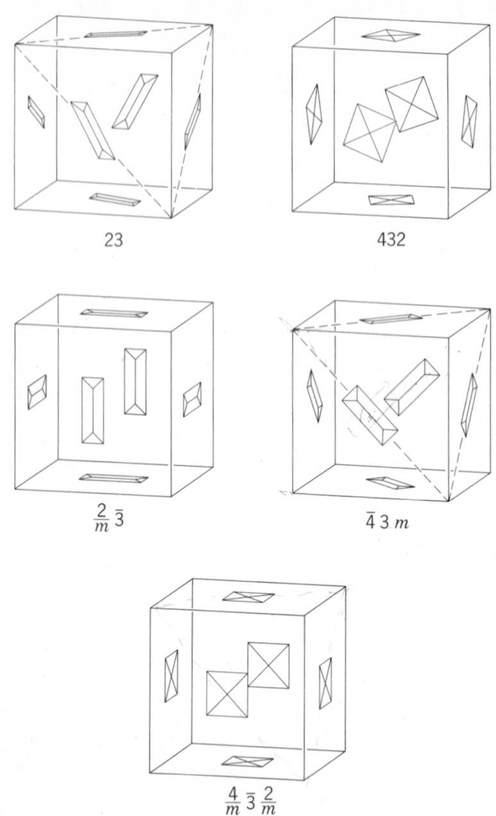

FIG. 15. Typical etch-figure appearances on isometric crystals.

FIG. 16. Etch figures on crystal of class $\frac{6}{m}$: etching produced by concentrated tartaric acid on $(10\bar{1}0)$ face of apatite, $Ca_5F(PO_4)_3$ (after Honess).

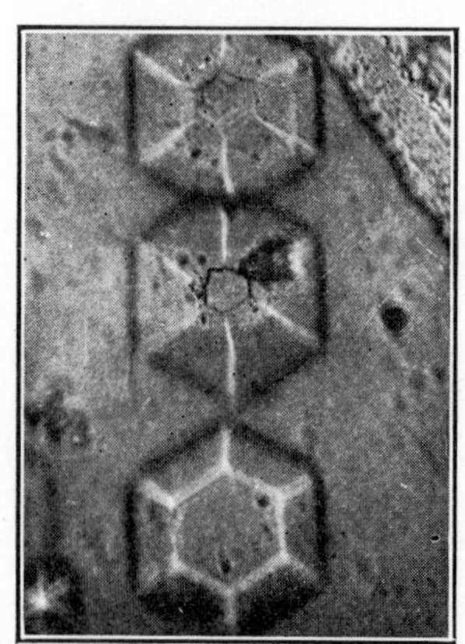

FIG. 17. Etch figure on crystal of class $\frac{6}{m}$: etching produced by hot concentrated tartaric acid on (0001) face of apatite, $Ca_5F(PO_4)_3$ (after Honess).

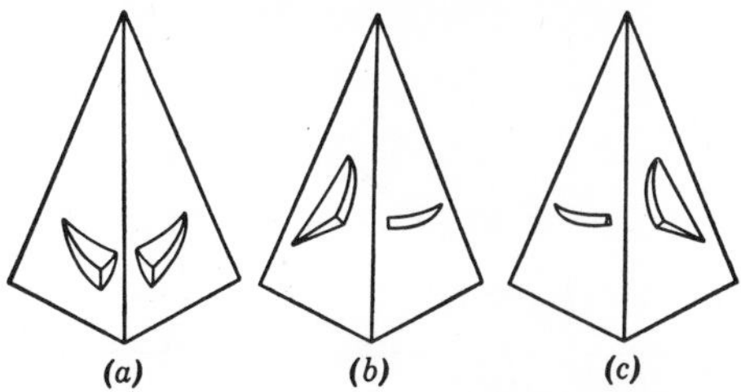

FIG. 18. Etch figures produced on a pair of neighboring scalenohedron faces of calcite with (*a*) citric acid, (*b*) left-gluconodeltalactone, (*c*) right-gluconodeltalactone (after Honess).

Symmetry and optical properties

Refractive indices and symmetry. The optical properties of crystals yield a certain amount of symmetry information. Since some of these properties of nonopaque crystals are very easily investigated with the aid of the polarizing petrographic microscope, an optical examination is usually made at once whenever it appears capable of aiding in assigning a crystal to the proper symmetry. In this section a brief outline is given of crystal optics as related to crystal symmetry. The information is summarized in Table 5.

The refractive indices of a crystal can be referred to an ellipsoid called the *indicatrix* which is regarded as having a fixed orientation with respect to the structure of the crystal. To find the refractive indices for light traveling in a particular direction, one passes a plane through the ellipsoid normal to this direction. This plane cuts the ellipsoid in a section which, in general, is an ellipse. The major and minor axes of this ellipse are proportional to the two refractive indices displayed by the crystal for light traveling in the given wave-normal direction.

The indicatrix must conform with the symmetry of the crystal. Since any section of an ellipsoid normal to a given symmetry axis is an ellipse, the ellipse must conform to the symmetry of that axis. If $n > 2$, the ellipse must have a 3-fold or greater symmetry, and the only way this can occur is that the ellipse must degenerate into a circle. Therefore tetragonal and hexagonal (including trigonal) crystals have indicatrices which are ellipsoids of rotation. Light traveling along the one special axis normal to this circular section has refractive indices proportional to the major and minor axes of a circle; such a wave, therefore, has only one refractive index and hence does not exhibit double refractions. Because of this unique axis, crystals having such an indicatrix are called *uniaxial*. These crystals have two refractive indices, ω and ε, corresponding to the equatorial and polar diameters of the ellipsoid.

Table 5. Optical properties of the crystal classes

	Optically anisotropic					Optically isotropic
	Biaxial 3 refractive indices, α, β, γ			Uniaxial 2 refractive indices, ω, ε		1 refractive index, n
	Inclined extinction	Inclined and parallel extinction	Parallel or symmetrical extinction			
	Triclinic dispersion of the optic axes	Monoclinic dispersion of the optic axes	Orthorhombic dispersion of the optic axes	No dispersion of the optic axis		
	Triclinic	Monoclinic	Orthorhombic	Tetragonal	Hexagonal	Isometric
Active; Enantiomorphous; Acentric	1	2	222	4 422	3 6 32 622	23 432
Active; Nonenantiomorphous; Acentric		m	$mm2$	$\bar{4}$ $\bar{4}2m$		
Inactive; Nonenantiomorphous; Acentric				$4mm$	$\bar{6}$ $\bar{6}m2$ $3m$ $6mm$	$\bar{4}3m$
Inactive; Nonenantiomorphous; Centric	$\bar{1}$	$\frac{2}{m}$	$\frac{2}{m}\frac{2}{m}\frac{2}{m}$	$\frac{4}{m}$ $\frac{4}{m}\frac{2}{m}\frac{2}{m}$	$\bar{3}$ $\frac{6}{m}$ $\bar{3}\frac{2}{m}$ $\frac{6}{m}\frac{2}{m}\frac{2}{m}$	$\frac{2}{m}\bar{3}$ $\frac{4}{m}\bar{3}\frac{2}{m}$

In crystals whose symmetries contain more than one axis for which $n > 2$, namely all isometric crystals, all sections of the indicatrix are circular and all refractive indices are the same. Such crystals are called optically *isotropic*.

Conversely, any crystals for which $n \lesseqgtr 2$ has an entirely general ellipsoid as an indicatrix. The symmetry of a general ellipsoid is $\frac{2}{m}\frac{2}{m}\frac{2}{m}$, and so it has three orthogonal elliptical sections whose intersections are of three different lengths. These three principal lengths represent three principal refractive indices, α (least), β (intermediate), and γ (greatest), of the crystal. For this reason the ellipsoid is called *triaxial*. There are two circular sections in a triaxial ellipsoid. Waves traveling normal to either of these circular sections have only one refractive index, β. Because of these two unique directions, a crystal having such an indicatrix is said to be optically *biaxial* (even though the indicatrix is a triaxial ellipsoid); i.e., it has two axes along which light may travel and display only one refractive index and therefore display no double refraction. The determination of isotropic, uniaxial, or biaxial character of a crystal is conveniently carried out with the aid of a petrographic polarizing microscope.

It is easy to subdivide biaxial crystals further. The basis for this is that the triaxial ellipsoid must have an orientation with respect to the crystal consistent with the symmetry of the crystal. This orientation can be readily determined by observing in what positions the crystal appears dark between crossed nicols. These positions are those of the major and minor diameters of the elliptical section which is normal to the direction of viewing the crystal. Such microscopic examination, then, usually permits placing a nonopaque crystal in the correct crystal system, except that tetragonal and hexagonal crystals cannot be separately distinguished.

Optical activity. Optical activity or optical rotatory power is another optical property useful in providing symmetry information. All crystals which belong to the classes lacking an operation of the second sort can occur in right- and left-handed forms. Crystals of these classes may also display optical activity; that is, when plane polarized light is transmitted through them, they may cause a right- or left-handed rotation of the plane of polarized light. This property is also theoretically possible in the nonenantiomorphous classes m, $mm2$, $\bar{4}$, and $\bar{4}2m$, although it has never been reliably observed in crystals having these symmetries. If experiment shows that a crystal is optically active, therefore, it must be assigned a nonholosymmetric crystal class in accordance with Table 5. The table shows, however, that, except for triclinic crystals, a 2-fold or 4-fold ambiguity still exists in the assignment of a crystal to the correct symmetry.

It should be emphasized that, although the symmetry of a crystal may permit it to display optical activity, the activity may be too small to be observed.

Only when optical activity is actually observed may a symmetry listed in the first section of Table 5 be inferred with certainty.

Piezoelectricity effect

Certain crystals have the property of becoming charged at opposite ends when subjected to compression (or tension), or, conversely, of expanding or contracting when placed in an electric field. This phenomenon is known as *piezoelectricity*, and crystals displaying it are said to be *piezoelectric*. When opposite ends of a crystal are equivalent by symmetry, they cannot behave differently when a crystal is compressed. This property is therefore excluded if the crystal has a center of symmetry since a centric character requires the opposite ends in any direction to be the same. The property is therefore prohibited to crystals belonging to the 11 centric classes and permitted only to crystals belonging to the 21 acentric classes. Furthermore, the high symmetry of class 432 causes its piezoelectric moduli to be zero. Therefore the effect cannot occur in 12 classes and may occur in only 20 of the 21 acentric classes. This distribution is shown in Table 6. This does not imply that crystals

Table 6. Piezoelectric properties of the crystal classes

Triclinic	Monoclinic	Orthorhombic	Tetragonal	Hexagonal		Isometric	Piezoelectric moduli
1	2 m	$2mm$	4 $4mm$	3 $3m$	6 $6mm$		hydrostatic, compression and torsion
				32	$\bar{6}$ $\bar{6}m2$		compression and torsion
		222	$\bar{4}$ 422 $\bar{4}2m$		622	23 $\bar{4}3m$	torsion
						432	nonpiezoelectric
1	$\frac{2}{m}$		$\frac{4}{m}$	$\bar{3}$	$\frac{6}{m}$	$\frac{2}{m}\bar{3}$	
		$\frac{2}{m}\frac{2}{m}\frac{2}{m}$	$\frac{4}{m}\frac{2}{m}\frac{2}{m}$	$\bar{3}\frac{2}{m}$	$\frac{6}{m}\frac{2}{m}\frac{2}{m}$	$\frac{4}{m}\bar{3}\frac{2}{m}$	

belonging to the 20 permitted acentric classes necessarily are noticeably piezoelectric, for the effect may be too small to detect.

Piezoelectricity has an important application in the control of oscillation frequency in electric circuits. An alternating field applied to a plate cut from a piezoelectric crystal causes it to expand and contract. If the period of alternation of the field is tuned to the natural frequency of mechanical vibration of the crystal, the crystal and circuit react with one another in a resonance phenomenon.

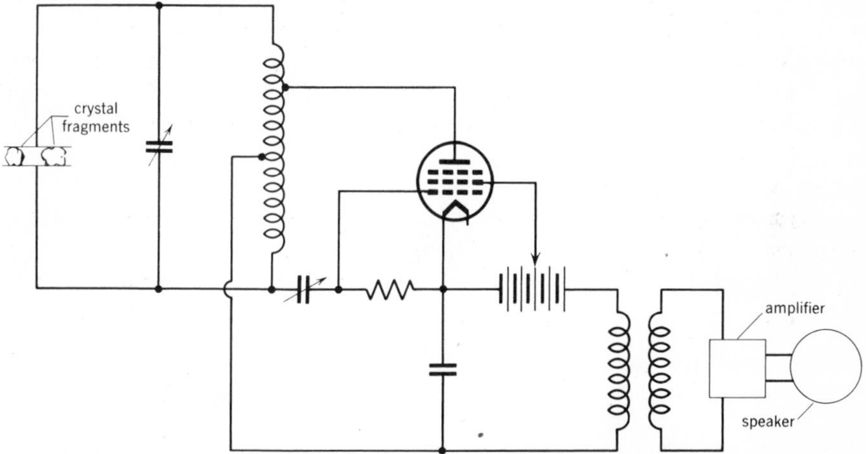

FIG. 19. Simple Giebe-Scheibe circuit for testing crystals for piezoelectric response.

This interaction is the basis of a common method of testing crystals for piezoelectricity. In the so-called Giebe-Scheibe method, the crystal fragments are placed between a pair of plates, Fig. 19, which form a part of an oscillating circuit which can be tuned by means of a condenser. When the condenser passes the position that brings the oscillation frequency of the circuit into resonance with the oscillation of a crystal fragment, a noise is produced in a loud speaker. If the test gives a positive result, one of the piezoelectric crystal classes of Table 6 is indicated. No certain symmetry conclusions can be drawn from a negative result.

Pyroelectric effect

Certain crystals have the property of becoming charged at opposite ends when their temperature is changed. This phenomenon is known as *pyroelectricity*, and the crystals displaying it are said to be *pyroelectric*. This different electrical behavior cannot occur at opposite ends of a crystal if they are symmetrically equivalent. Since a centric character causes the opposite ends in any direction to be the same, it is therefore prohibited to crystals belonging to the 11 centric classes and permitted to crystals belonging to the 21 acentric classes. Furthermore, crystals of those classes that can display pyroelectricity cannot do so along a *nonpolar direction*. For example, in symmetry 4, any direction normal to the 4-fold axis is transformed by the operation $A^2_{\pi/2}$ of the 4-fold axis into the opposite direction. Thus both the direction and its opposite are equivalent, so that the direction is nonpolar. On the other hand, any direction normal to the 3-fold axis in symmetry 3 is a

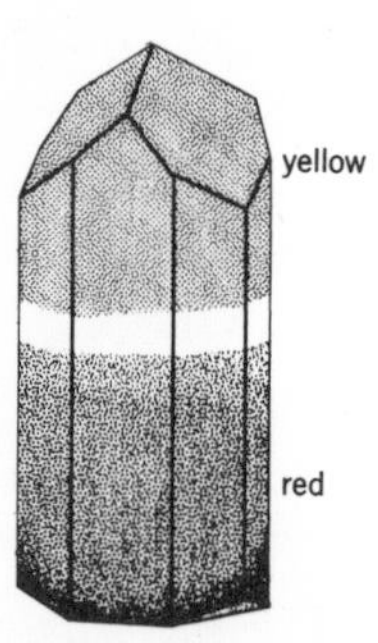

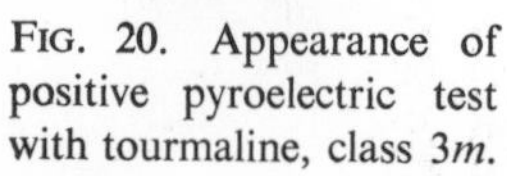

FIG. 20. Appearance of positive pyroelectric test with tourmaline, class $3m$.

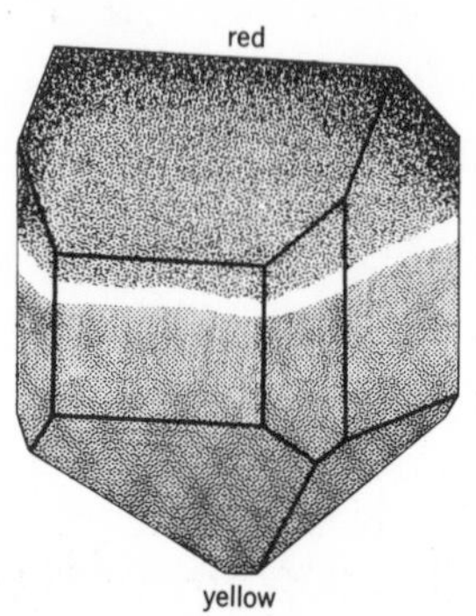

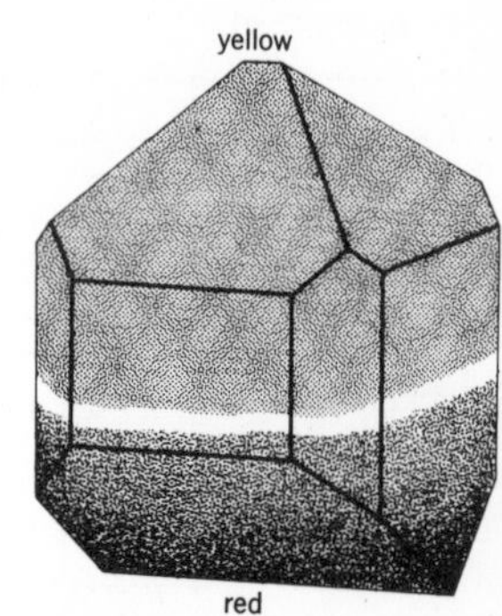

FIG. 21. Appearance of positive pyroelectric test with left tartaric acid (at left) and right tartaric acid (at right), class 2.

polar direction. Similarly, any direction making a general angle with the 4-fold axis mentioned above is a polar direction. A pyroelectric effect cannot occur at the ends of a nonpolar axis since symmetry requires them to behave the same.

There are a number of ways of making a test for pyroelectricity. A simple and spectacular test was devised by Kundt. Essentially this consists of blowing a dust of charged particles onto a crystal which has just been heated or cooled. The charged particles adhere to the parts of the crystal having the opposite charge. Both positively and negatively charged particles can be produced by starting with a dust composed of a mixture of red lead and sulfur. This mixture is placed in an aspirator bottle, and puffed out of a tube and through a muslin sieve at pleasure. The friction causes the sulfur to become negatively charged and the red lead to become positively charged. As the particles settle on the crystals, the sulfur adheres to the positively charged pole, coloring it yellow, and the red lead adheres to the negatively charged pole, coloring it red, Figs. 20 and 21. The pole that becomes *positive* on *heating* (or negative on cooling) is called the *analogous pole*; the pole that becomes *negative* on *heating* (or positive on cooling) is called the *antilogous pole*. A preferable way of changing temperature for a pyroelectric test is to heat the crystal, then remove its charge by touching it to metal, and permit it to cool. It can then be tested in the cooled state.

A variation of Kundt's method consists of burning magnesium ribbon under a bell jar. When the jar is filled with smoke it is placed over the crystal to be tested, which is resting on a glass plate. In response to the electrostatic field of a pyroelectric crystal the magnesia precipitates in filaments which outline the "lines of force" of the field.

Crystals tested for pyroelectricity frequently display a "false pyroelectric effect." This is really a piezoelectric effect induced by the strain caused by changing temperature. Fortunately the false effect and true effect occur for the same symmetries, so little ambiguity arises when a positive pyroelectric effect, of whatever cause, is observed.

Diffraction symmetry

Crystals can act as three-dimensional diffraction gratings for x-rays. The x-radiation diffracted by a crystal is customarily permitted to fall on a photographic film, where it leaves a record which (after development) is permanent and can be examined at leisure. Certain x-ray diffraction experiments on simple crystals give valuable symmetry information. Friedel was the first to point out that the intensities of x-ray "reflections" from the stacks of planes (hkl) and $(\overline{hkl})$ are the same, so that x-rays do not distinguish between a plane and its centrosymmetrically opposite plane, or between a direction and its opposite. On the other hand the intensity distribution of the x-ray diffraction experiment conforms to the other symmetry elements of the crystal. It is possible, therefore, to identify by x-ray diffraction experiments the point group of the crystal except that a symmetry center is added by the x-ray experiment whether present in the point group of the crystal or not. This means that 11 centric classes, column 2 of Table 1, Chapter 8, can be distinguished by x-ray experiments, but it is not known to which of the classes of the corresponding group of column 1 the crystal really belongs. Fortunately, experiments on optical activity, piezoelectricity, or pyroelectricity all tend to resolve this ambiguity and, therefore, to partly complement the x-ray diffraction experiments. This is brought out by Table 7.

The oldest diffraction method is the Laue method, which is performed by allowing general, unfiltered x-radiation to impinge upon a crystal and recording the diffracted radiation on a fixed flat film. It is now customary to study diffraction symmetry by using the precession or Weissenberg methods, which are used in the routine gathering of data for a crystal-structure analysis. These methods give the symmetry information in very elegant form. In addition to this purely pictorial test of symmetry there are both qualitative and quantitative tests for symmetry elements which serve to partly or completely determine the crystal symmetry by x-ray means.

Table 7. Crystal classes arranged according to certain distinguishing physical properties

System	Optical groups	X-ray groups (centric classes)	Included crystal classes	Piezo-electric classes	Optically active classes
Triclinic	Biaxial	$\bar{1}$	1 $\bar{1}$	1	1
Monoclinic		$\frac{2}{m}$	2 m $\frac{2}{m}$	2 m	2 m
Orthorhombic		$\frac{2}{m}\frac{2}{m}\frac{2}{m}$	222 $mm2$ $\frac{2}{m}\frac{2}{m}\frac{2}{m}$	222 $mm2$	222 $mm2$
Tetragonal	Uniaxial	$\frac{4}{m}$	4 $\bar{4}$ $\frac{4}{m}$	4 $\bar{4}$	4 $\bar{4}$
		$\frac{4}{m}\frac{2}{m}\frac{2}{m}$	422 $4mm$ $\bar{4}2m$ $\frac{4}{m}\frac{2}{m}\frac{2}{m}$	422 $4mm$ $\bar{4}2m$	422 $\bar{4}2m$

Table 7 (continued)

System	Optical groups	X-ray groups (centric classes)	Included crystal classes	Piezo-electric classes	Optically active classes
Hexagonal	Uniaxial	$\bar{3}$	3 $\bar{3}$	3	3
		$\bar{3}\frac{2}{m}$	32 $3m$ $\bar{3}\frac{2}{m}$	32 $3m$	32
		$\frac{6}{m}$	6 $\bar{6} = \frac{3}{m}$ $\frac{6}{m}$	6 $\bar{6}$	6
		$\frac{6}{m}\frac{2}{m}\frac{2}{m}$	622 $6mm$ $\bar{6}m2 = \frac{3}{m}m2$ $\frac{6}{m}\frac{2}{m}\frac{2}{m}$	622 $6mm$ $\bar{6}m2$	622
Isometric	Isotropic	$\frac{2}{m}\bar{3}$	23 $\frac{2}{m}\bar{3}$	23	23
		$\frac{4}{m}\bar{3}\frac{2}{m}$	432 $\bar{4}3m$ $\frac{4}{m}\bar{3}\frac{2}{m}$	$\bar{4}3m$	432

12 · The algebra of operations

Relations such as

$$A \cdot B = C \tag{1}$$

have been used in this book somewhat loosely up to this point. This kind of equation can often be employed as a compact expression of reasoning in some aspects of the discussion of space groups. It is therefore desirable to examine relations like (1) a little more closely before the study of space groups is initiated.

Representation of combinations by products

A sequence of operations can be represented by a sequence of symbols, such as $A, B, C, \cdots$. In earlier chapters it has been shown that a pair of operations may be equivalent to some other operation. Such a relation can obviously be expressed as an equation. This means that the operations can be manipulated symbolically by a kind of algebra.

It is possible to design an algebra so that an operation A, followed by an operation B, is represented by a sum $A + B$. It is also possible to represent it by a product, $A \cdot B$. This last convention is usually adopted for representing a combination of operations because it is also used in manipulating transformations of operations when expressed in matrix* form.

It will become apparent shortly that performing a pair of operations, A and B, in the order AB gives a result which is not, in general, the same as performing them in the reverse order BA. For this reason the terms of a product cannot, generally, be interchanged, or *permuted.* A peculiarity of the algebra of operations, therefore is that the symbols of a product are, in general, *nonpermutable* (or *noncommutative*). On the other hand, some particular pairs of operations can be shown to give the same result without regard to their order of performance. When this can be proved for a pair of operations, they are said to be *permutable*, or *commutative.* The condition for permutability is discussed in a subsequent section.

The addition of an operation to a sequence of operations, then, is represented by multiplication of terms representing the operations. But the order of

* See M. J. Buerger, *X-Ray Crystallography* (John Wiley & Sons, New York, 1942), Chapter 2.

multiplication is important, since terms in a sequence are not, in general, interchangeable. Adding a term, say Q, to a sequence AB, can be done in two ways, namely $Q \cdot AB$ and $AB \cdot Q$. In the first case, AB is said to be *premultiplied* by Q, and in the second AB is said to be *postmultiplied* by Q. The premultiplication $Q \cdot AB$ corresponds to *first* performing the operations Q, *then* performing the sequence of operations AB, whereas the postmultiplication corresponds to *first* performing the sequence of operations AB, *then* performing the new operation Q. In general these have different meanings.

Exponents

Since a repetition of the same operation is represented by $A \cdot A$, $A \cdot A \cdot A$, etc., it is a convention of this notation to represent $A \cdot A$ by A^2, $A \cdot A \cdot A$ by A^3, etc. In other words, the rules of exponents of ordinary algebra are adopted. A neat result of this is that

$$A \cdot A^{-1} = A^0, \tag{2}$$

also

$$A^{-1} \cdot A = A^0. \tag{3}$$

From the rule of exponents, A^0 must mean the operation A taken zero times, which is equivalent to no operation at all. In Chapter 2 it was noted that the operation meaning "no operation" is called the *identical operation.* Different authors represent this identical operation variously by the symbol 1, I, or E. Since the ordinary algebraic meaning of A^0 is 1, the symbol 1 is used in this book, so that (2) and (3) become

$$A \cdot A^{-1} = 1, \tag{4}$$

and

$$A^{-1} \cdot A = 1. \tag{5}$$

Equation (4) reads that an operation A, followed by an operation A^{-1}, are together equivalent to identity, that is, to no operation. Therefore, the symbol A^{-1} is an operation which annuls the A. This requires A^{-1} to be the reverse of A. (A^{-1} is usually called the *inverse* of A.) For example, if A_α is a rotation through angle α about axis A, then A_α^{-1} is the reverse rotation through angle α about A. In this example, then,

$$A_\alpha^{-1} = A_{-\alpha}. \tag{6}$$

Relations (4) and (5) provide the device for canceling a term or transferring an operation to the other side of an equation, which are the basic manipulations of this algebra. Suppose that one wishes to cancel the B on the left side of (1). This can be done by making use of a relation like (4) for operation B. Specifically, the operation B^{-1} is added at the right of the operations on both sides of equation (1), giving

$$A \cdot B \cdot B^{-1} = C \cdot B^{-1}. \tag{7}$$

But since, according to (4), the combination

$$B \cdot B^{-1} = 1, \tag{8}$$

equation (7) reduces to

$$A = C \cdot B^{-1}. \tag{9}$$

In the same way the operation A can be removed from the left side of (1) by using relation (5). Specifically, the operation A^{-1} is added at the left of the operations on both sides of (1), giving

$$A^{-1} \cdot A \cdot B = A^{-1} \cdot C. \tag{10}$$

By virtue of (5), (10) reduces to

$$B = A^{-1} \cdot C. \tag{11}$$

These two manipulations show that a term can be transferred from the beginning or end of a sequence of operations to the corresponding position on the other side of the equation provided the sign of the exponent is changed on transfer. In general, a term in the middle of a sequence cannot be transferred to the other side of an equation.

The inverse of a product

The sequence of operations $C^{-1}B^{-1}A^{-1}$ has the property of annulling the sequence ABC. That this is true is evident by applying a relation like (5) to the middle pair of the product in each stage of the following reduction:

$$\begin{aligned}(C^{-1}B^{-1}A^{-1})(ABC) &= C^{-1}B^{-1}A^{-1}ABC \\ &= C^{-1}B^{-1}BC \\ &= C^{-1}C \\ &= 1. \end{aligned} \tag{12}$$

A generalization of this is obviously

Theorem 1. *The inverse of a product is the product of the inverses in inverse order.*

The transformation of one operation by another

In carrying on the discussions in the next two sections it will be convenient to understand the meaning of a sequence of symbols of the form $A^{-1}BA$. It will be shown now that these three symbols mean the operation B after being transformed by A.

The proof is illustrated in Fig. 1. Let A and B be taken as rotations about axes A and B. As in Chapter 4, the axes are taken to intersect at the center of a sphere, and the motions of points on the surface of the sphere, under the influence of rotations A and B, are studied. Let the symbols [1], [2], [B], etc., stand for the points, 1, 2, B, etc., and let the symbols [2]A mean "point 2 transformed by operation A."

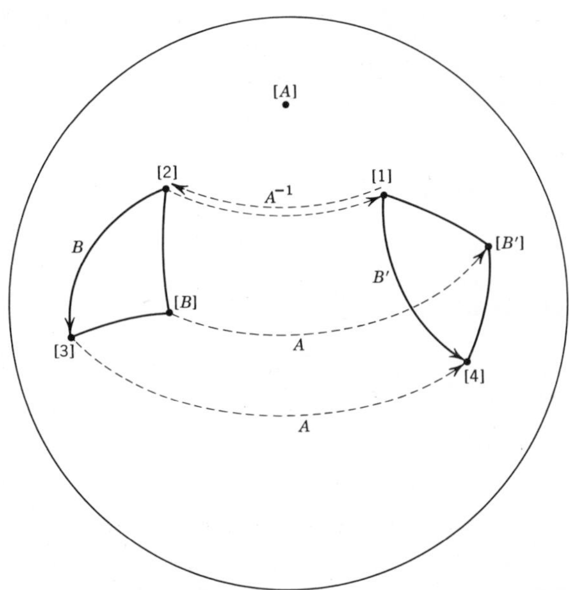

FIG. 1. Demonstration of the meaning of $A^{-1}BA$, where the A and B are rotational operations. The symbols in brackets are points; other symbols represent operations.

First choose any point [2]. Then, referring to Fig. 1,

$$[2]B \rightarrow [3] \tag{13}$$

Now, let the operation A act upon triangle [2B3]:

$$[2B3]A = [1B'4] \tag{14}$$

In other words, the operation of A transforms triangle [2B3] into triangle [1B'4]. The first triangle represents the action of operation B on any point [2]. The second triangle represents an operation exactly like B except that it takes place about a different point, [B'], a point to which A carries [B]. The operation B' at point [B'] is therefore said to be the operation B as transformed by A.

Next consider the relation between points [1] and [4]. The operation B' carries [1] into [4]:

$$[1]B' \rightarrow [4] \tag{15}$$

The points [1] and [4] are also related through the several operations which produce the sequence [1], [2], [3], [4]. In detail these operations are

$$[1]A^{-1} \rightarrow [2] \tag{16}$$

$$[2]B \rightarrow [3] \tag{17}$$

$$[3]A \rightarrow [4] \tag{18}$$

If these three operations are applied in sequence, the net result is

$$[1]A^{-1}BA \rightarrow [4] \tag{19}$$

Since (15) and (19) define the same transformation it follows that

$$A^{-1}BA = B'. \tag{20}$$

Theorem 2. *The sequence of operation $A^{-1}BA$ means the operation B as transformed by A.*

In this demonstration A and B were illustrated as operations of rotation. By making use of the same reasoning, other kinds of operations could be illustrated. The illustration as given can be adjusted so that A, or B, or both, are translations. For example, suppose A is to be regarded as a translation. To perform this conversion let the sphere expand to an indefinitely large size and let the rotation about [A] become indefinitely small. Then path [1] [2] becomes a straight line, and operation A becomes a translation. Since A is now a translation T, the specific form of (20) is

$$T^{-1}BT = B'. \tag{21}$$

This is an important relation which will be used in space-group derivation. It can be derived in a direct fashion by redrawing Fig. 1 so that [1] [2] is a straight line on a plane as in Fig. 2. Then the operation A becomes a translation of triangle [2B3] to [1B'4].

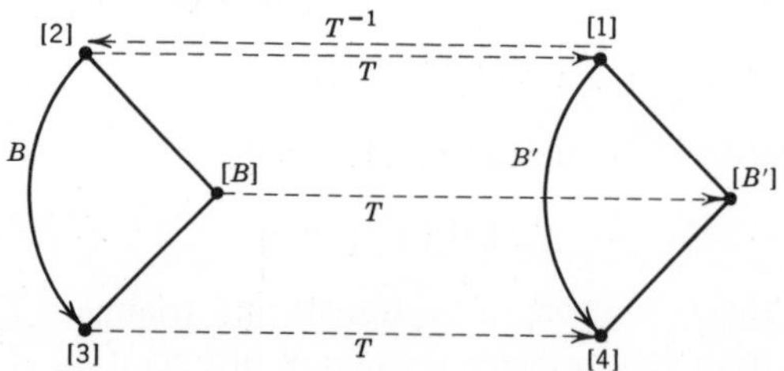

FIG. 2. Demonstration of the meaning of $T^{-1}BT$, where T is a translation and B is a rotation.

Condition for permutability

The two products AB and BA, composed of the same two terms in different orders, are called *conjugate products*. In general, $BA \neq AB$.

The discussion of the last section provides the key for judging when the terms of a product are permutable. When this is true, the conjugate products are equal:

$$BA = AB. \tag{22}$$

If both sides are premultiplied by A^{-1}, there results

$$A^{-1}BA = B. \tag{23}$$

This says that the operation A transforms operation B into itself. In other words, when (22) is true, operation A transforms B into itself. This relation is reciprocal, for if both sides of (22) are premultiplied by B^{-1}, the result is

$$A = B^{-1}AB. \tag{24}$$

This reveals that, when (22) is true, B transforms A into itself.

Theorem 3. *If operation A transforms B into itself, then operation B transforms A into itself, and the sequences of operations AB and BA are the same.*

Considered as vectors, any translation transforms any other translation into itself. Therefore products representing any pair of translations are permutable. Similarly any two rotations about the same axis can be represented by a product whose terms are permutable.

Meaning of the conjugate product

The meaning of the conjugate product can be readily ascertained with the help of the transformed operation $A^{-1}BA$. In a previous section this was shown, in general, to be the operation B as transformed by A. Let this transformed operation be designated B'. Then

$$A^{-1}BA = B'. \tag{25}$$

Let both sides be premultiplied by A, giving

$$BA = AB'. \tag{26}$$

Suppose, now, one has ascertained the meaning of AB, and one wishes to know the meaning of the permuted product BA. Relation (26) shows that the product BA is the same as its conjugate, but applied to the transformed operation B'.

Theorem 4. *If the meaning of AB is known, the meaning of BA is AB′, where B′ is the operation B as transformed by A.*

This relation has a converse. Either side of (26) may be regarded as the known form of the product, the meaning of the conjugate product being sought. In Theorem 4 the form AB is regarded as known and the meaning of BA is sought. Alternatively, the meaning of $B'A$ may be known and the meaning of

AB' is sought. Equation (25) shows that AB' is the same as $B'A$ but applied to operation B rather than B'. Since A transforms B to B', A^{-1} must transform B' to B. This provides a theorem somewhat similar to Theorem 4, namely,

Theorem 5. *If the meaning of* $B'A$ *is known, the meaning of* AB' *is* BA, *where* B *is the operation* B' *as transformed by* A^{-1}.

This theorem is useful in dealing with combinations of screw axes.

13 · Space groups isogonal with the monaxial point groups

In Chapter 2 it was shown that any repetition could be effected by a combination of a rotation, a reflection (or inversion), and a translation. In Chapter 4 it was shown that the first two of these could be neatly defined in terms of proper rotations and improper rotations, and all possible crystallographic combinations of these were found. But up to this point no systematic attempt has been made to combine these with translations. The results of combining translations with other operations are discussed in this and subsequent chapters. From a very general point of view it is evident that, since rotations, reflections, and translations are basic motions for repetition, rotation-translations (screws) and reflection-translations (glides) must exist as repetition operations. The existence of new symmetry elements corresponding to these operations will be established in more detail in this and later chapters.

Combinations of rotations and translations

Combination of a rotation and a perpendicular translation. In Chapter 7 the combination of a rotation and a perpendicular translation was derived as a preliminary to deriving the symmetrical space lattices. The result can be restated in the following theorem:

Theorem 1. *A rotation about an axis A through an angle α, followed by a translation, T, perpendicular to the axis, is equivalent to a rotation through the same angle α, in the same sense, but about an axis B located on the bisector of AA′ and at a distance $(T/2)$ cot $\alpha/2$ from AA′.*

This is briefly expressed by the equation

$$A_\alpha \cdot T_\perp = B_\alpha. \tag{1}$$

Since the rotation does not transform the translation into itself, the product $A_\alpha T_\perp$ is nonpermutable.

By premultiplying both sides of (1) by B^{-1}, it can be reset into another form:

$$B_\alpha^{-1} \cdot A_\alpha \cdot T_\perp = 1. \tag{2}$$

By postmultiplying both sides of (2) by T^{-1}, there results

$$B_\alpha^{-1} A_\alpha = T_\perp^{-1}. \tag{3}$$

Since $T_\perp^{-1}$ is simply another translation, $T'_\perp$, and since, according to (6) in Chapter 12, $B_\alpha^{-1} = B_{-\alpha}$, this can also be written

$$B_{-\alpha}A_\alpha = T'_\perp. \tag{4}$$

This predicts that the combination of two equal but opposite rotations about parallel axes is equivalent to a translation perpendicular to the axes.

Combination of a rotation and a parallel translation. Figure 1 illustrates the combination of a rotation through an angle α about an axis A with a translation $T_{\parallel}$ parallel with A. It is evident that the combination of motions PV and VQ produces a motion PQ, which can be described as a *screw motion.* Since the rotation transforms the translation into itself, Theorem 3 of Chapter 12 shows that the rotation and translation are permutable operations. This is also evident from Fig. 1, since paths PVQ and PUQ both give a net displacement of PQ.

Theorem 2. *A rotation about an axis, and a translation parallel to an axis, are permutable operations, and the combination is equivalent to a screw motion.*

This is briefly expressed as

$$A_\alpha \cdot T_{\parallel} = T_{\parallel} \cdot A_\alpha = A_{\alpha, T_{\parallel}}. \tag{5}$$

The symbol $A_{\alpha,\tau}$ is used to represent a screw motion about axis A. The rotation through angle α is called the *rotation component* of the screw, and the translation τ is called the *translation component* of the screw.

Combination of a rotation and a general translation. Any general translation can be resolved into its components perpendicular and parallel to a rotation axis. This would be expressed in vector notation as

$$\vec{T} = \vec{T}_\perp + \vec{T}_{\parallel}. \tag{6}$$

For the kind of operational algebra which was adopted in the last chapter, the combination of a motion followed by another motion is represented as a product, so that, in this notation, (6) would be expressed

$$T = T_\perp \cdot T_{\parallel}. \tag{7}$$

Now, combining a rotation with a general translation is the same as combining the rotation with either the right or left side of (7). The combination can be reduced as follows:

from (7): $A_\alpha \cdot T = A_\alpha \cdot T_\perp \cdot T_{\parallel}$

from (1): $= B_\alpha \cdot T_{\parallel}$

from (5): $= B_{\alpha, T_{\parallel}}$. (8)

This result is illustrated in Fig. 2, which is a generalization of part of Fig. 2 of Chapter 7. This means that, if the repetition scheme contains a rotation and a general translation the repetition scheme also contains a screw motion.

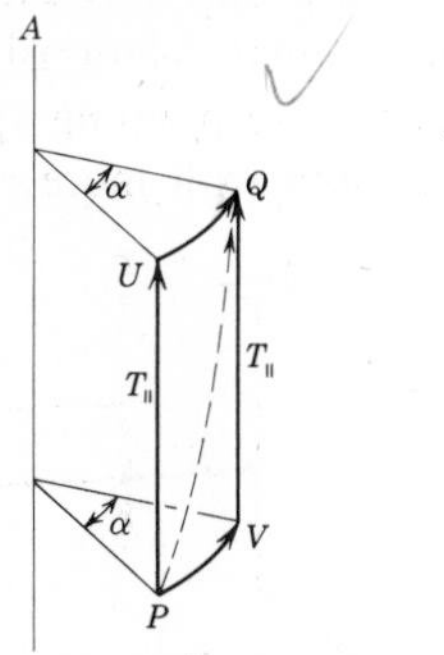

FIG. 1. Combination of a rotation, A_α, and a parallel translation, $T_{\parallel}$.

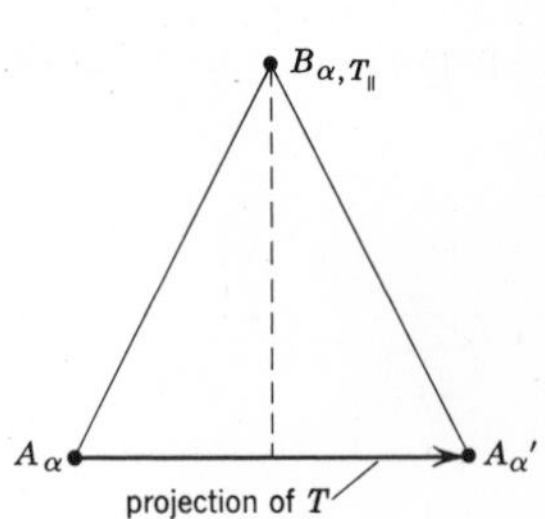

FIG. 2. Combination of a rotation, A_α and a general translation, T.

Importance of screw axes. The last section makes it obvious that repetition by screw motion must be accepted as a natural kind of repetition. To find all the space patterns, then, screw axes must be accepted as possible symmetry elements which can be combined with themselves and with other symmetry elements.

One immediately wonders how a screw axis would manifest itself in the appearance of a crystal as examined megascopically. This was illustrated in Figs. 1 and 2 of Chapter 10. The screw may be regarded as repeating an initial stack of planes to one or more new locations related by an angular period, α, and by a screw pitch τ. According to (8) this pitch is a translation which is of the order of magnitude of a cell edge. Obviously this translation interval cannot be detected by the naked eye, or even with a compound microscope, so that, whereas the angular relation of planes related by a screw axis is obvious, the translation is lost because of its comparatively negligible absolute magnitude. For this reason, if a 4-fold screw axis relates a sequence of faces of a crystal, as in Fig. 3, the crystal appears megascopically to have a 4-fold rotation axis. Conversely, if a crystal appears to have a 4-fold rotation axis, it cannot be ascertained from this whether the crystal pattern has a collection of translation-equivalent 4-fold pure rotation axes, or a collection of translation-equivalent 4-fold screw axes, nor can it be ascertained what the particular pitch of the screw axis is, if present.

This argument makes it plain that, to every point-group appearance of a crystal, in general there are several possible space patterns. These can be found by substituting appropriate sets of pure rotation axes or screw axes of various pitches, or both, successively for each pure rotation axis of the point group. This is the relation between point groups and space groups, and, in a rough way, it indicates how space groups can be derived by making use of the point groups already derived. In a preliminary way this also makes it apparent that the angular relations for each point-group axis carry over into the corresponding space groups, and that the angular relationships between different point-group axes are maintained in the corresponding space groups. Further aspects of this relationship will be discussed with more rigor shortly.

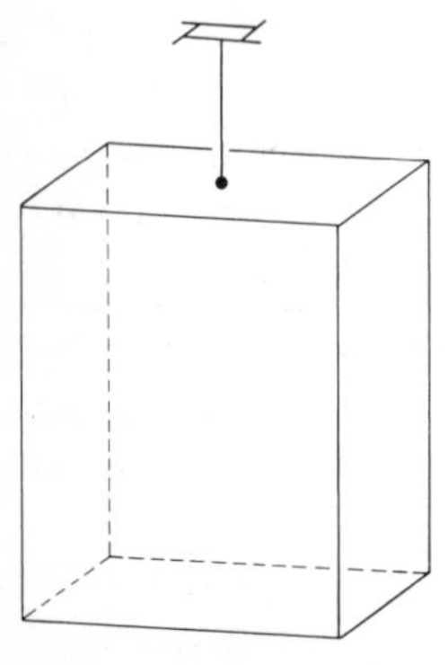

FIG. 3. Crystal surface related by a screw axis.

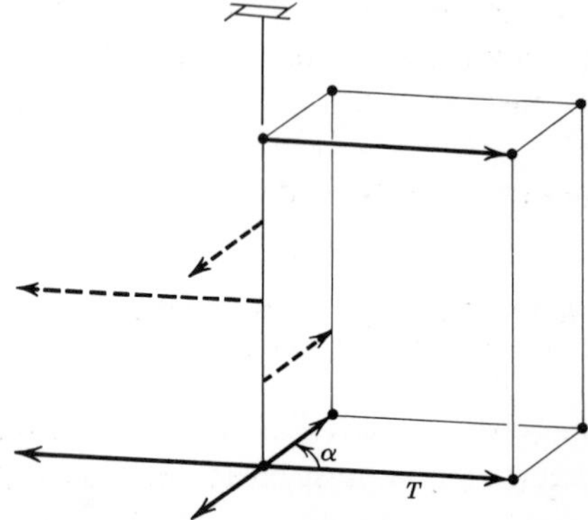

FIG. 4. Repetition of a translation, *T*, by a screw.

Possible values of the rotational component of screw operations. Since screw axes are important symmetry elements of space patterns, the question arises as to what values of the rotation angle α the screw operations can have. The screw motion might appear, at first sight, to repeat a perpendicular translation vector $\vec{T}$ like the directions of the treads of a spiral staircase, as shown in the broken lines of Fig. 4. But it must be remembered that vectors have merely magnitudes and directions, and not different origins. Therefore, although the rotational component of the screw repeats the vector T at an angle α from its original direction, the translation component of the screw does not affect it. This means that a screw axis and pure rotation axis of the same order, n, repeat a translation in the same way. The repetition of a translation was shown in Chapter 4 to limit n to 1, 2, 3, 4, and 6. It follows that the rotational components of screws can only be $2\pi/1$, $2\pi/2$, $2\pi/3$, $2\pi/4$, and $2\pi/6$.

This discussion makes it plain that both those pure rotation axes and screw axes which are crystallographically permissible are so located, with respect to translations, that they are symmetry elements of the translations of the lattice, that is, that their operations are capable of throwing the translations of the lattice into coincidence with themselves. An n-fold screw and n-fold pure rotation axis must have similar locations with respect to a particular set of translations to do this. This requires that the angles between screws, or screws and rotations, must be the same as those of the six permissible combinations of rotation axes derived in Chapter 4. This is further justification for using the word *isogonal* with respect to screws and rotation axes of the same n.

Possible values of the translational component of screw operations. It is evident that a pure rotation axis has the direction of a row of lattice points, and, from what was said in the last section, every screw has the direction of a row of lattice points too. The most general requirement on the translation, or *pitch*, component τ, of a screw must be as follows: After n screw operations have been concluded, the accumulation of rotations (each through angle α) has reached 2π, and the accumulated pitch intervals, namely $n\tau$, has attained some translation of the lattice in that direction, i.e., mt. In short,

$$n\tau = mt, \quad \text{where } n \text{ and } m \text{ are integers,} \tag{9}$$

so that the possible pitch values are

$$\tau = \frac{m}{n}\, t. \tag{10}$$

For example, the screws isogonal with a 6-fold rotation axis can have translation components of $\frac{m}{6}$ ths of a translation, t, specifically

$$\left.\begin{matrix} 0t, & \frac{1}{6}t, & \frac{2}{6}t, & \frac{3}{6}t, & \frac{4}{6}t, & \frac{5}{6}t, \\ \frac{6}{6}t, & \frac{7}{6}t, & \frac{8}{6}t, & \frac{9}{6}t, & \frac{10}{6}t, & \frac{11}{6}t, \\ \cdot & \cdot & \cdot & \cdot & \cdot & \cdot \end{matrix}\right\}. \tag{11}$$

But note that only the first row of this sequence is really distinct. The second row, for example, can be rewritten

$$0t + t,\ \tfrac{1}{6}t + t,\ \tfrac{2}{6}t + t,\ \tfrac{3}{6}t + t,\ \tfrac{4}{6}t + t,\ \tfrac{5}{6}t + t. \tag{12}$$

This is simply the first row of (11) plus a translation. Since every feature of the crystal is repeated by the translation of the lattice anyway, the first six values in (11) are repeated by the translation of the lattice, so that those of (12) follow from the first six in (11).

Note that the value $0t$ is included as a permissible translation component. This obviously corresponds to a pure rotation, so that pure rotation axes may be regarded as special cases of screws in which the translation component is zero.

The permissible screw axes and their designations. The last two sections discuss the permissible values of the rotation components and the translation components of permissible crystallographic screw operations. The results of these discussions for the five crystallographic values of n are listed in Table 1. The ways the several screw axes repeat a point are shown in Fig. 5.

Table 1. Permissible crystallographic screw axes

n		Permissible screws					
1	α	0					
	τ	0					
	Designation	1					
2	α	π	π				
	τ	0	$\frac{1}{2}t$				
	Designation	2	2_1				
3	α	$\frac{2\pi}{3}$	$\frac{2\pi}{3}$	$\frac{2\pi}{3}$			
	τ	0	$\frac{1}{3}t$	$\frac{2}{3}t$			
	Designation	3	3_1	3_2			
4	α	$\frac{\pi}{2}$	$\frac{\pi}{2}$	$\frac{\pi}{2}$	$\frac{\pi}{2}$		
	τ	0	$\frac{1}{4}t$	$\frac{2}{4}t$	$\frac{3}{4}t = -\frac{1}{4}t$		
	Designation	4	4_1	4_2	4_3		
6	α	$\frac{\pi}{3}$	$\frac{\pi}{3}$	$\frac{\pi}{3}$	$\frac{\pi}{3}$	$\frac{\pi}{3}$	$\frac{\pi}{3}$
	τ	0	$\frac{1}{6}t$	$\frac{2}{6}t$	$\frac{3}{6}t$	$\frac{4}{6}t = -\frac{2}{6}t$	$\frac{5}{6}t = -\frac{1}{6}t$
	Designation	6	6_1	6_2	6_3	6_4	6_5

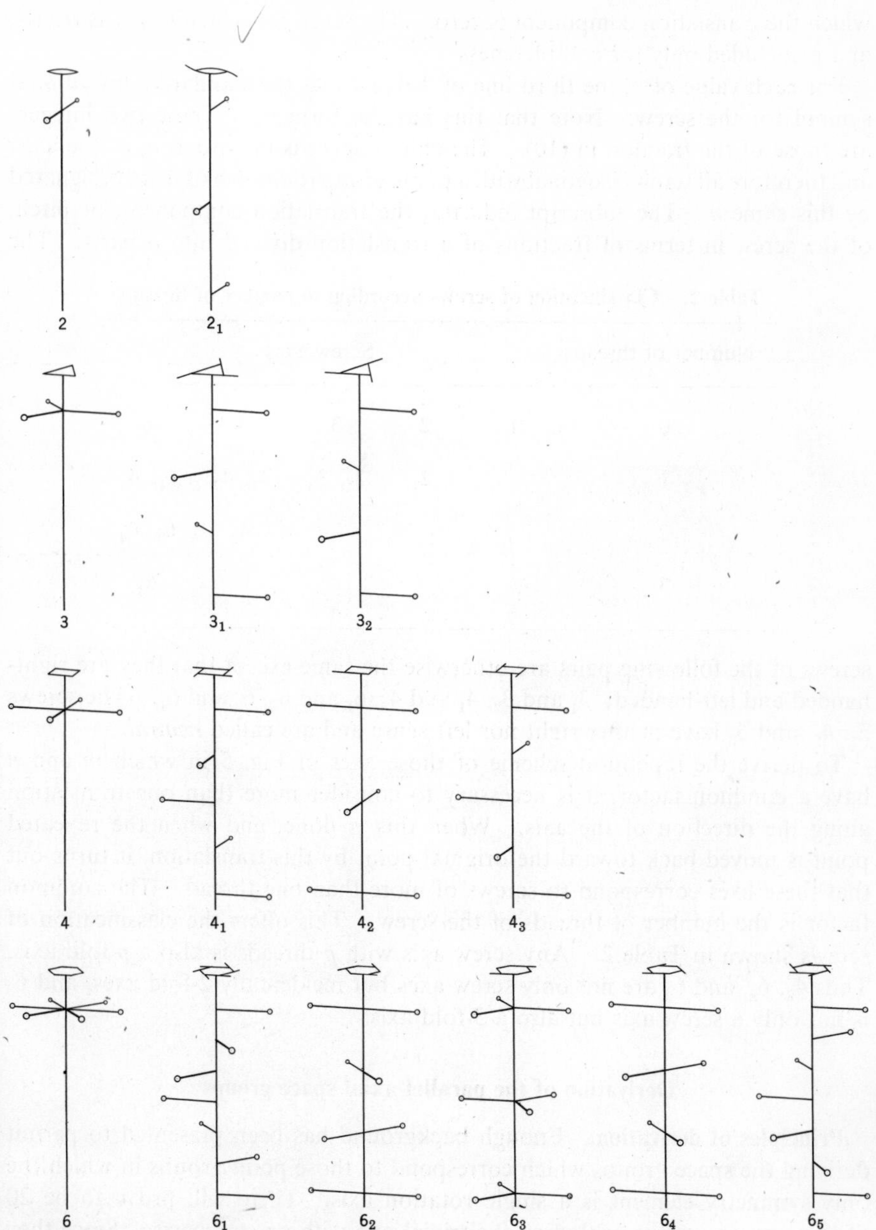

FIG. 5. The repetition of a point by the possible crystallographic screw axes.

In Table 1, the pure rotation axes are included as special cases of screws in which the translation component is zero. The screw for which $n = 1$ is trivial, and is included only for completeness.

For each value of n, the third line of Table 1 lists the standard conventional symbol for the screw. Note that this has the form n_m. These two integers are those of the fraction in (10). The chief integer is the order, n, of the axis, and therefore all screws isogonal with a point-group rotation axis n are designated by this same n. The subscript indicates the translation component, or pitch, of the screw in terms of fractions of a translation divided into n parts. The

Table 2. Classification of screws according to number of threads

Number of threads	Screw axes				
0	1	2	3	4	6
1		2_1	3_1, 3_2	4_1, 4_3	6_1, 6_5
2				4_2	6_2, 6_4
3					6_3

screws of the following pairs are otherwise the same except that they are right-handed and left-handed: 3_1 and 3_2, 4_1 and 4_3, 6_1 and 6_5, 6_2 and 6_4. The screws 2_1, 4_2, and 6_3 have neither right nor left sense and are called *neutral*.

To derive the repetition scheme of those axes of Fig. 5 in which m and n have a common factor, it is necessary to consider more than one translation along the direction of the axis. When this is done, and when the repeated point is moved back toward the original point by this translation, it turns out that these axes correspond to screws of more than one thread. The common factor is the number of threads of the screw. This offers the classification of screws shown in Table 2. Any screw axis with p threads is also a p-fold axis. Thus 4_2, 6_2, and 6_4 are not only screw axes but incidentally 2-fold axes, and 6_3 is not only a screw axis but also a 3-fold axis.

Derivation of the parallel-axial space groups

Principles of derivation. Enough background has been presented to permit deriving the space groups which correspond to those point groups in which the only symmetry element is a single rotation axis. There will prove to be 20 of these space groups, including the trivial one with no symmetry. Since they are characterized by sets of parallel axes, these can be called the parallel-axial space groups.

Table 3. Combinations of axes and lattices to be made in deriving the parallel-axial space groups

n	Isogonal screws	Lattices
1	1	P
2	2 2_1	P I
3	3 3_1 3_2	P R
4	4 4_1, 4_3 4_2	P I
6	6 6_1, 6_5 6_2, 6_4 6_3	P

The problem of deriving space groups is presented in its simplest form in deriving the space group corresponding to the point groups with a single rotation axis. The problem merely amounts to combining, in turn, each permissible screw having the same value of n with each of the several lattices consistent with that n. This gives several possible combinations for each point group. *The more complex space groups can be derived by following exactly the same procedure; the derivations are more difficult only because there are more elements to combine.* Fortunately, there are theoretical aids that help to simplify the derivation of the more complex space groups.

To derive the space groups corresponding with the point groups 1, 2, 3, 4, and 6, each of the isogonal screws for a specific value of n in Table 3 must be combined, in turn, with the translations of each of the lattices of Table 3 permitted to that value of n. The lattices are of two different varieties, primitive (P) and nonprimitive (I and R). The primitive lattices have primitive translations corresponding only to vectors between points at the cell vertices. The

Table 4. Nonequivalent translations of cells

Lattice	Nonequivalent translations			
2*P*	a	$a + b$	$a + b + c$	
	b	$a + c$		
	c	$b + c$		
2*I*	a	$a + b$	$a + b + c$	$\frac{1}{2}a + \frac{1}{2}b + \frac{1}{2}c$
	b	$a + c$		
	c	$b + c$		$\frac{1}{2}a + \frac{1}{2}b - \frac{1}{2}c$
3*P*	a_1	$a_1 + c$	$a_1 + a_2 + c$	
	c	$a_1 + a_2$		
3*R*	a_1	$a_1 + c$	$a_1 + a_2 + c$	$\frac{2}{3}a_1 + \frac{1}{3}a_2 + \frac{1}{3}c$
	c	$a_1 + a_2$		$\frac{1}{3}a_1 + \frac{2}{3}a_2 + \frac{2}{3}c$
4*P*	a_1	$a_1 + c$	$a_1 + a_2 + c$	
	c	$a_1 + a_2$		
4*I*	a_1	$a_1 + c$	$a_1 + a_2 + c$	$\frac{1}{2}a_1 + \frac{1}{2}a_2 + \frac{1}{2}c$
	c	$a_1 + a_2$		
6*P*	a_1	$a_1 + c$		
	c			

nonprimitive lattices have, in addition, translations corresponding to vectors from points at the cell vertices to one or more points within the cell. The translations of the *P*, *I*, and *R* cells are listed in Table 4. The components perpendicular and parallel to the axis of all translations of primitive cells are full cell edges only, whereas the components parallel to the axis of some translations of the nonprimitive cells are a half, or a third, of the edges of the cell.

To see how these translations combine with the general screw operation, a generalization of (8) can be used in which the pure rotation axis, A_α, of (8) is replaced by the more general screw $A_{\alpha,\tau}$:

$$A_{\alpha,\tau} \cdot T = B_{\alpha,\tau+T_\parallel}. \tag{13}$$

This can be interpreted for present purposes as follows: Whenever a screw operation (in which the pitch can be zero to include the case of a pure rotation) is combined with a translation of the cell, the new screw operation arising at location *B* (see Chapter 7) has a translation component (pitch) increased over that of the original screw at location *A* by an amount equal to the parallel component, $T_\parallel$, of the translation. For uniformity, let *a*, *b*, and *c* stand for the three translations corresponding to the edges of the unit cell, and let the axis *A* be taken parallel to the cell edge *c*. Then, whenever the screw $A_{\alpha,\tau}$ is combined with one of the translations listed for a cell in Table 4, the component of the translation along *c* is added to the screw operation at *B*. Whenever this component is $\vec{c}$, this does not affect the pitch of the screw, but when it is a fraction of $\vec{c}$ it does modify it. In primitive cells, no translations are fractions of a cell edge, and so the screw operations arise in their *B* positions from the *A* position without modification. When the cell is nonprimitive, however, the operations are modified.

The rotational components of the operations in the *B* positions were covered in detail in Chapter 7. To derive space groups, attention must be directed chiefly to the translation component in various *B* positions.

These principles are applied to the derivation of the space groups isogonal with point groups 1, 2, 3, 4, and 6 in the following sections.

Space groups isogonal with point group 1. According to Table 3 there is only one space group corresponding to point group 1, namely the one obtained by combining the translations of a primitive lattice with a 1-fold axis. The combination of *P* with 1 gives rise to the space group designated by the symbol *P*1. Since a 1-fold axis is trivial, this space group consists simply of the translations of a primitive lattice. This is indicated in Fig. 6 by the cell outline only.

Space groups isogonal with point group 2. The space groups based upon point group 2 are obtained by combining one of the axes 2 or 2_1 with the several nonequivalent translations of a cell of either a *P* or an *I* lattice. First consider combining either 2 or 2_1 with the translations of *P*. The projections of the translations of the cell are shown by arrows in Fig. 7. Consider the rotational components of the screws first. The rotations of a 2-fold axis at A, combined with the translations of the lattice, cause 2-fold rotations to arise at the three

FIG. 6. Space group $P1$.

new points, B, C, and D, shown in Fig. 7. The details of this combination were discussed in Chapter 7. Now consider the translation components of the screws. Every translation of the cell listed for $2P$ in Table 4 has a c component of either zero or unity. Therefore the $T_{\|}$ addition to the translation

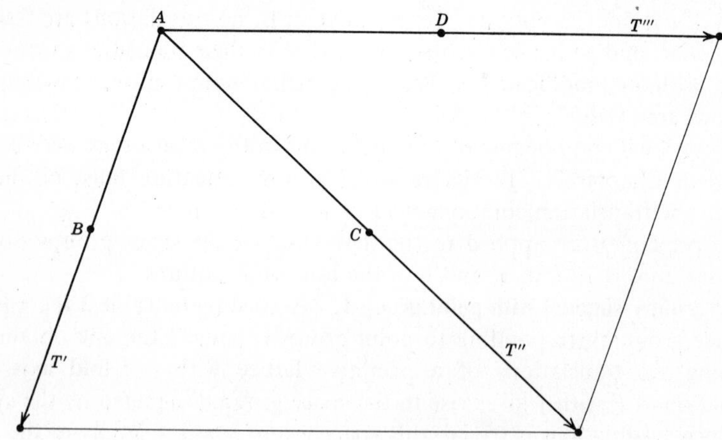

FIG. 7. The combination of a general 2-fold screw with the translations of P.

component on the right of (13) must be zero or unity. Thus all axes arising at the points B, C, and D in Fig. 7 have the same translation component as the axis placed at A. The two possible kinds of axis to place at A are 2 and 2_1.

The combinations of these axes with *P* therefore give rise to the space groups shown in Figs. 8 and 9, respectively. The combination of *P* with 2 is designated *P*2, and the combination of *P* with 2_1 is designated $P2_1$.

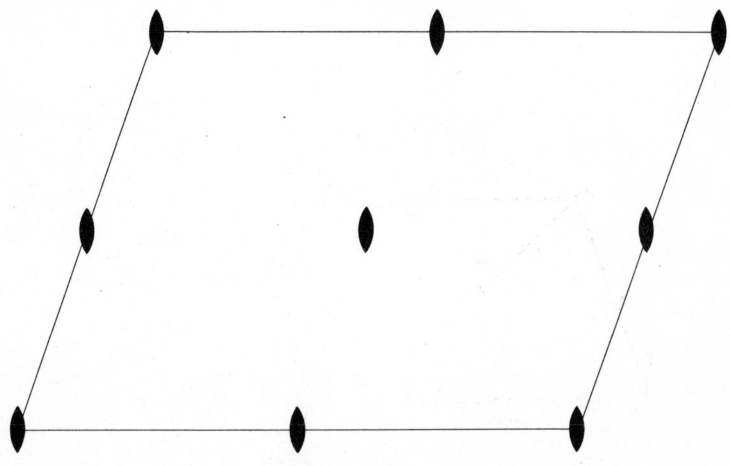

FIG. 8. *P*2.

Next consider the combination of *I* with 2, designated *I*2, and the combination of *I* with 2_1, designated $I2_1$. Table 4 shows that all the translations along the cell edges and face diagonals of *I* are the same as those of *P*. These translations give rise to the same screws at locations *B*, *C*, and *D* as did the translations of *P*. On the other hand the *I* lattice has cell translations along the cell diagonal with

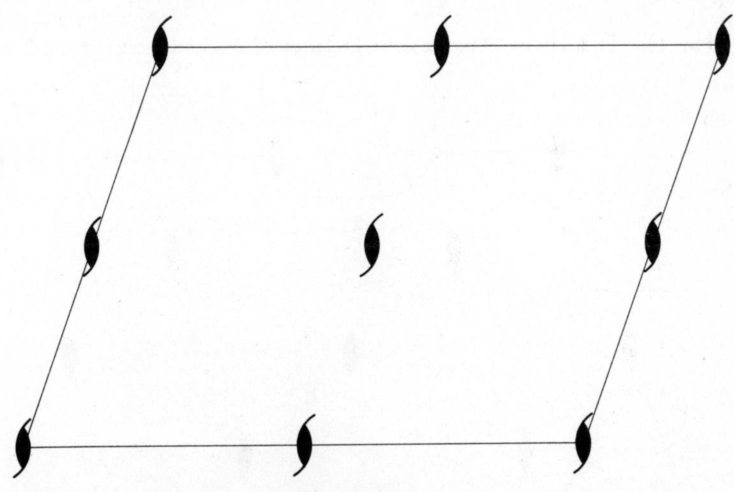

FIG. 9. $P2_1$.

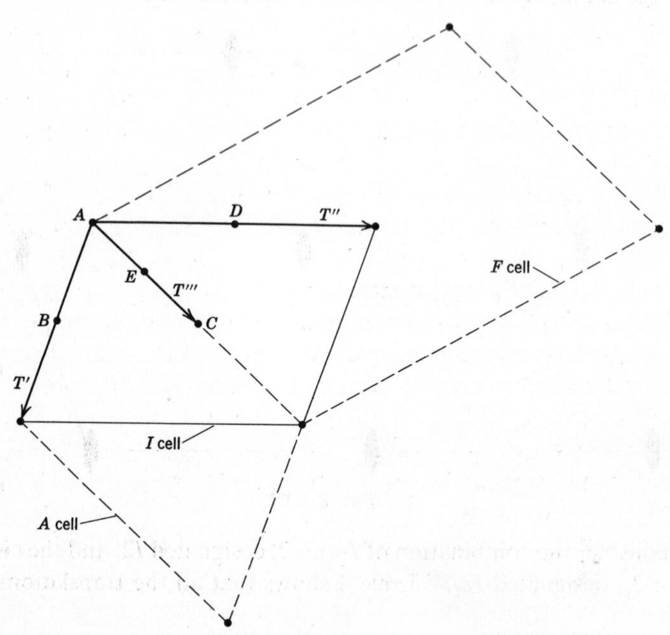

FIG. 10. Translations of the *I* cell, and relation of alternative cells, *A* and *F*, to *I*.

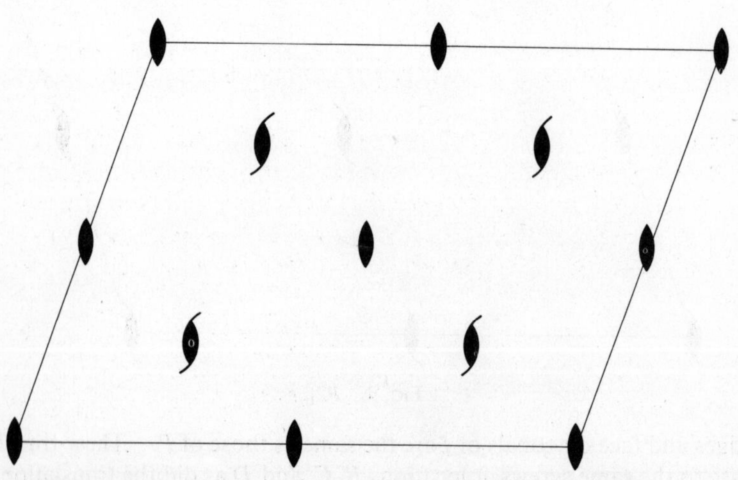

FIG. 11. *I*2.

components along c of $c/2$, Fig. 10. If this is inserted into (13) there results

$$A_{\alpha,\tau} \cdot T''' = E_{\alpha,\tau+c/2}. \tag{14}$$

This requires that, as a result of the diagonal translation, an operation appears halfway between the corners and center of the cell having a pitch increased by $c/2$ over that at the cell corner. Therefore, if the operation at the cell corner is a pure rotation, the operation at E is a screw with pitch $c/2$, and vice versa. Thus if a pure 2-fold rotation is placed at A, a 2_1 axis arises at E, and the result is as shown in Fig. 11, whereas if a 2_1 axis is placed at A, a pure 2-fold rotation axis arises at E. In both cases 2's are halfway between nearest 2_1's, and vice versa, so that the patterns of axes are the same. Thus $I2$ and $I2_1$ are the same space group; its conventional designation is $I2$.

(For later application it will sometimes be convenient to refer $I2$ to an end-centered lattice and sometimes to a face-centered lattice. This can be done by choosing different cells from the same set of axial symmetry elements. The relations among the I, A, and F lattices are shown by different cell outlines in Fig. 10. The space group "settings" or "orientations" called $I2$, $A2$, $B2$, and $F2$ in the first monoclinic setting become $I2$, $C2$, $A2$, and $F2$ in the second monoclinic setting.)

As a result of the above discussion it is evident that the only space groups isogonal with point group 2 are

$$P2,$$

$$P2_1,$$

$$\text{and } I2.$$

Since all 2-fold screws are neutral, these three space groups are neutral.

Space groups isogonal with point group 3. The space groups isogonal with point group 3 are obtained by combining one of the axes 3, 3_1, or 3_2 with the translations of lattice P or R. First consider combining the axes with P. If A is taken as a general 3-fold screw, its operations (omitting trivial operation 1) are $A_{2\pi/3,\tau}$, $A_{4\pi/3,2\tau}$. The projections of the nonequivalent translations of the cell of $3P$ are shown in Fig. 12. All the translations of P have components on c of zero or unity. The combinations of these translations with the screw operations are

$$\begin{aligned} A_{2\pi/3,\tau} \cdot T' &= B'_{2\pi/3,\tau}, \\ A_{4\pi/3,2\tau} \cdot T' &= B''_{4\pi/3,2\tau}, \\ A_{2\pi/3,\tau} \cdot T'' &= C'_{2\pi/3,\tau}, \\ A_{4\pi/3,2\tau} \cdot T'' &= C''_{4\pi/3,2\tau}. \end{aligned} \tag{15}$$

Since locations B' and C'' are identical, and B'' and C' are the equivalent, it is evident that the operations 1, $B_{2\pi/3,\tau}$, and $B_{4\pi/3,2\tau}$ exist at B' and C'. This

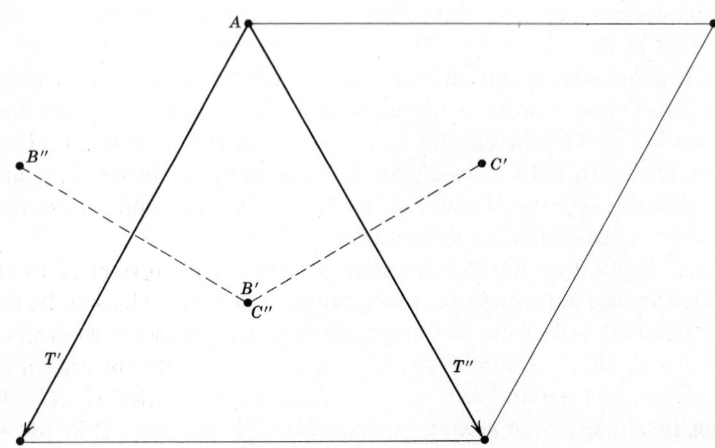

FIG. 12. The combination of a general 3-fold screw with the translations of *P*.

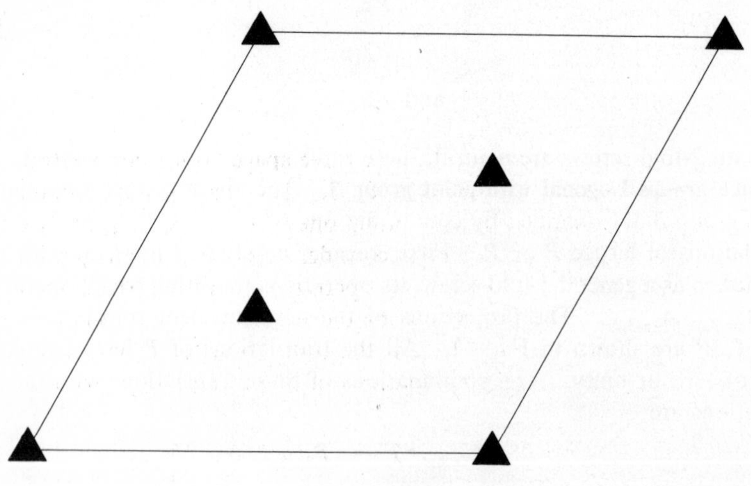

FIG. 13. *P*3.

means that, if a screw is placed at *A*, the translations of the lattice require identical screws at B' and C'. The three possible screws are 3, 3_1, and 3_2.

Consequently when combined with P they give $P3$ (Fig. 13), $P3_1$ (Fig. 14), and $P3_2$ (Fig. 15), respectively.

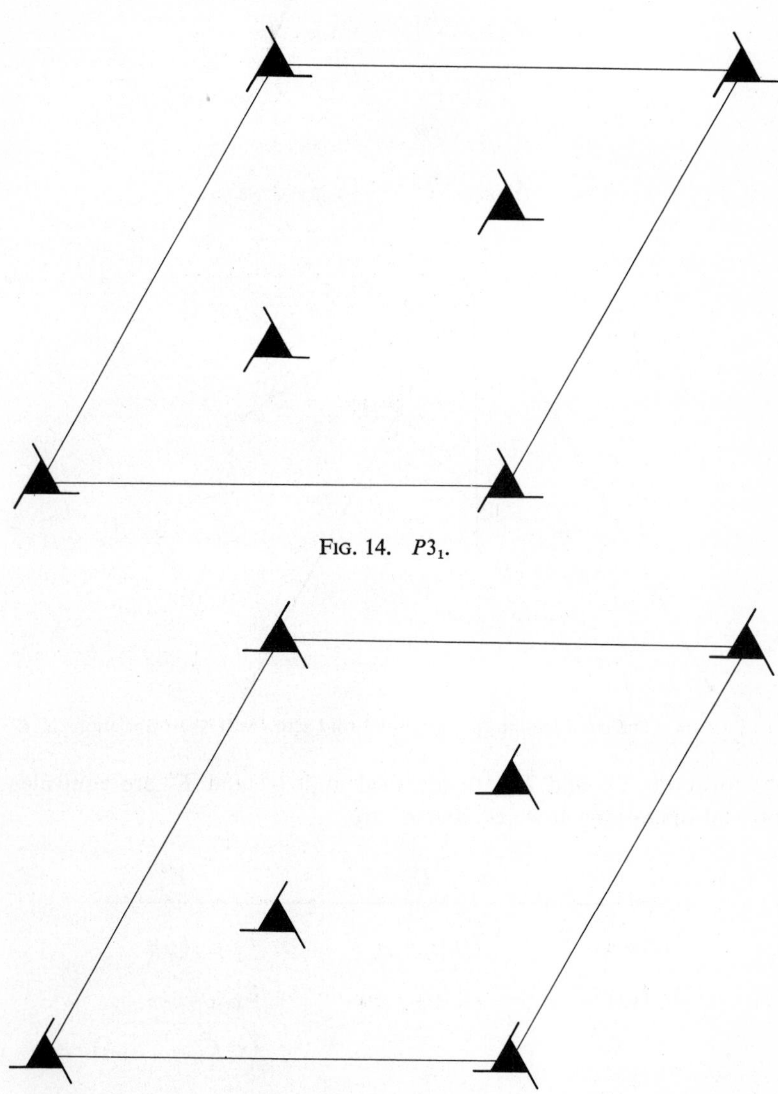

Fig. 14. $P3_1$.

Fig. 15. $P3_2$.

The translations of lattice R are the same as those of P with the addition of the two translations T''' and T'''' which terminate within the outline of the cell shown in Fig. 16. These have components on c of $\frac{1}{3}$ and $\frac{2}{3}$ respectively. The combination of these translations with the operations of a general 3-fold screw are

$$\begin{aligned}
A_{2\pi/3,\tau} \cdot T'''' &= D'_{2\pi/3,\tau+c/3},\\
A_{4\pi/3,2\tau} \cdot T'''' &= D''_{4\pi/3,2\tau+c/3},\\
A_{2\pi/3,\tau} \cdot T''''' &= E'_{2\pi/3,\tau+2c/3},\\
A_{4\pi/3,2\tau} \cdot T''''' &= E''_{4\pi/3,2\tau+2c/3}.
\end{aligned} \qquad (16)$$

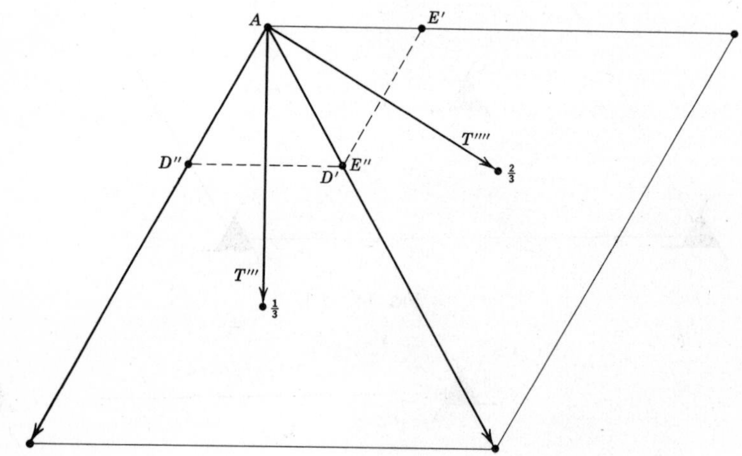

FIG. 16. The combination of a general 3-fold screw with the translations of *R*.

Since locations D' and E'' are identical and D'' and E' are equivalent, the nontrivial operations at A, D', and E' are

A	D'	E'
$A_{2\pi/3,\tau}$	$D'_{2\pi/3,\tau+c/3}$	$E'_{2\pi/3\ \tau+2c/3}$
$A_{4\pi/3,2\tau}$	$D'_{4\pi/3,2\tau+2c/3}$	$E'_{4\pi/3,2\tau+c/3}$
		$(\Leftrightarrow E'_{4\pi/3,2\tau+4c/3})$

It is evident that the operations of 3-fold screws exist at D' and E' and that the screws at the points of the triangle A, D', E' have pitch differences of $c/3$. If axes 3, 3_1, or 3_2 are placed at A, the axes at D' and E' are those shown in Table 5. All these patterns are the same, so that $R3$, $R3_1$, and $R3_2$ define the same space group, Fig. 17, which is customarily designated $R3$.

Table 5. Results of combining 3, 3_1, or 3_2 with R

Screw placed at A	τ for screw at A	Components of screws $D'_{2\pi/3,\ \tau+c/3}$	Components of screws $E'_{2\pi/3,\ \tau+2c/3}$	Screws at D'	Screws at D''	Designation of space group	
3	0	$2\pi/3,\ c/3$	$2\pi/3,\ 2c/3$	3_1	3_2	$R3$	Fig. 17
3_1	$c/3$	$2\pi/3,\ 2c/3$	$2\pi/3,\ c$	3_2	3	$R3_1 \Leftrightarrow R3$	Fig. 17
3_2	$2c/3$	$2\pi/3,\ c$	$2\pi/3,\ 4c/3$	3	3_1	$R3_2 \Leftrightarrow R3$	Fig. 17

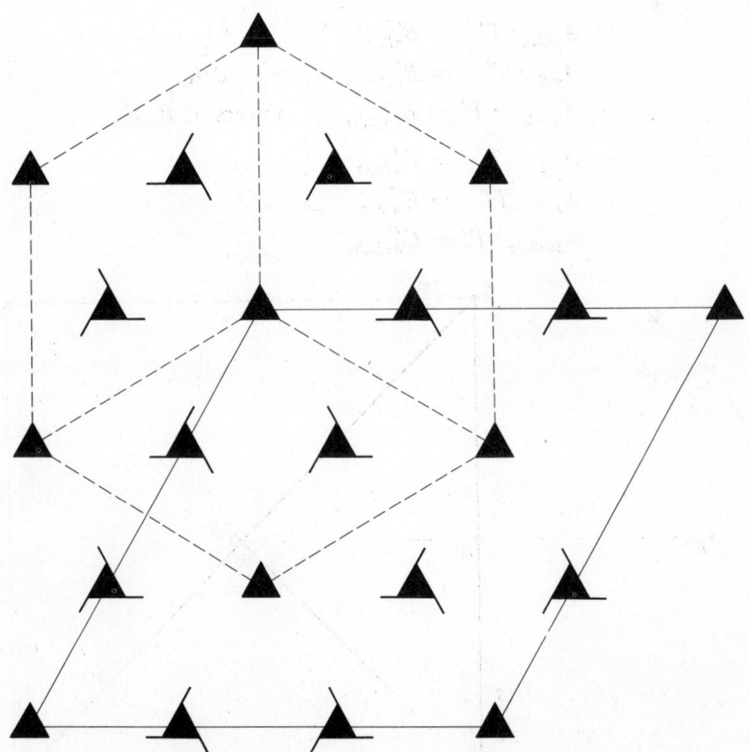

FIG. 17. $R3$. The full cell outlines a hexagonal cell; broken lines outline a rhombohedral cell.

As a result of this discussion it is evident that the space groups isogonal with point group 3 are

$$\begin{array}{ll} P3 & R3 \\ \begin{cases} P3_1 \\ P3_2 \end{cases} & \end{array}$$

The space groups related by braces are an enantiomorphous pair. Space groups $P3$ and $R3$ are *neutral*; i.e., they are composed of neutral screws, or else of neutral screws and equal numbers of screws of opposite sense.

Space groups isogonal with point group 4. The space groups isogonal with point group 4 are found by combining one of the axes 4, 4_1, 4_2, or 4_3, with the translations of lattice P or I. First consider combining the axes with P. If A is taken as a general 4-fold screw, its nontrivial operations are $A_{\pi/2,\tau}$, $A_{\pi,2\tau}$, and $A_{3\pi/2,3\tau}$. The projections of the nonequivalent translations of the cell of $4P$ are shown in Fig. 18. All the translations of P have components on c of zero or unity. The combinations of these translations with the screw operations are

$$\begin{aligned} A_{\pi/2,\tau}\cdot T' &= B'_{\pi/2,\tau}, \\ A_{\pi,2\tau}\cdot T' &= B''_{\pi,2\tau}, \qquad \longleftarrow B_{\pi,2\tau}, \\ A_{3\pi/2,3\tau}\cdot T' &= B'''_{3\pi/2,3\tau} \qquad \text{powers of } B_{\pi/2,\tau}, \end{aligned} \tag{17}$$

$$\begin{aligned} A_{\pi/2,\tau}\cdot T'' &= C'_{\pi/2,\tau}, \\ A_{\pi,2\tau}\cdot T'' &= C''_{\pi,2\tau}, \\ A_{3\pi/2,3\tau}\cdot T'' &= C'''_{3\pi/2,3\tau}. \end{aligned} \tag{18}$$

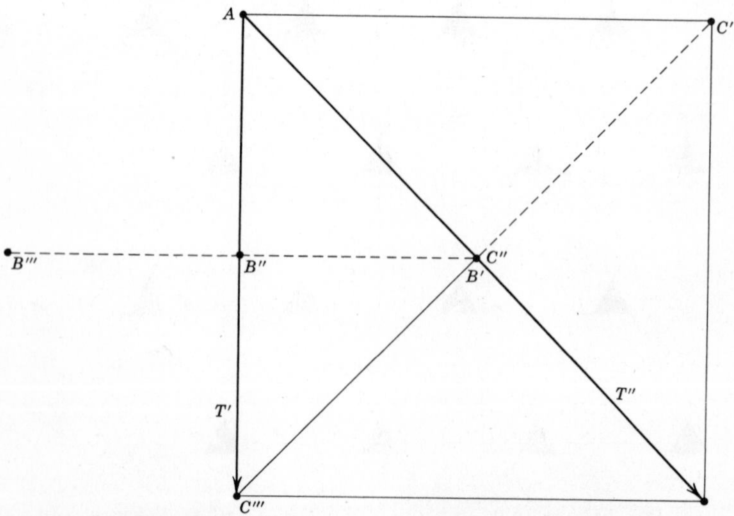

FIG. 18. The combination of a general 4-fold screw with the translations of P.

Table 6. Results of combining 4, 4_1, 4_2, or 4_3 with P

Screw placed at A	τ for screw at A	Components of screws		Screws at		Designation of space group	
		$B'_{\pi/2,\tau}$	$B''_{\pi,\tau}$	B'	C''		
4	0	$\pi/2,\ 0$	$\pi,\ 0$	4	2	$P4$	Fig. 19
4_1	$c/4$	$\pi/2,\ c/4$	$\pi,\ c/2$	4_1	2_1	$P4_1$	Fig. 20
4_2	$c/2$	$\pi/2,\ c/2$	$\pi,\ c$	4_2	2	$P4_2$	Fig. 22
4_3	$3c/4$	$\pi/2,\ 3c/4$	$\pi,\ 3c/2$	4_3	2_1	$P4_3$	Fig. 21

Locations B', C'', and B''' are equivalent or identical. At these points there appear the powers of the operations of the screw $B_{\pi/2,\tau}$. At point B'' there appear the operations of the screw $B_{\pi,2\tau}$. (The other points listed, namely C' and C''', are already equivalent to A and already contain the operations not assigned to other locations.) If axes 4, 4_1, 4_2, and 4_3 are placed successively at A, the results shown in Table 6 are obtained.

Next consider the combinations of 4-fold screws with the nonequivalent translations of lattice $4I$. The projections of three translations are shown in Fig. 23. The translations projecting as T' are the same as in the case of P, so that, in combination with the powers of operation of a screw at A, the operations on the right of (17) arise. In this case, however, the axis at B' is a simple translation-equivalent of the one at A. It is necessary to derive the further operations at D', D'', and D''' due to T''' whose component on c is $c/2$. These are

$$\begin{aligned} A_{\pi/2,\tau} \cdot T''' &= D'_{\pi/2,\tau+c/2}, \\ A_{\pi,2\tau} \cdot T''' &= D''_{\pi,2\tau+c/2}, \\ A_{3\pi/2,3\tau} \cdot T''' &= D'''_{3\pi/2,3\tau+c/2}. \end{aligned} \tag{19}$$

Note that the following locations are equivalent or identical: $D' \Leftrightarrow D''' \equiv B''$ of (17). Therefore there occur at the several locations of Fig. 23 the following operations:

A	B'' $(D' \Leftrightarrow D''' \equiv B'')$	D''
$A_{\pi/2,\tau}$	$D'_{\pi/2,\tau+c/2}$	$D''_{\pi,2\tau+c/2}$
$A_{\pi,2\tau}$	(17): $B''_{\pi,2\tau+2c/2}$	
$A_{2\pi,3\tau}$	$D'''_{3\pi/2,3\tau+3c/2}$	

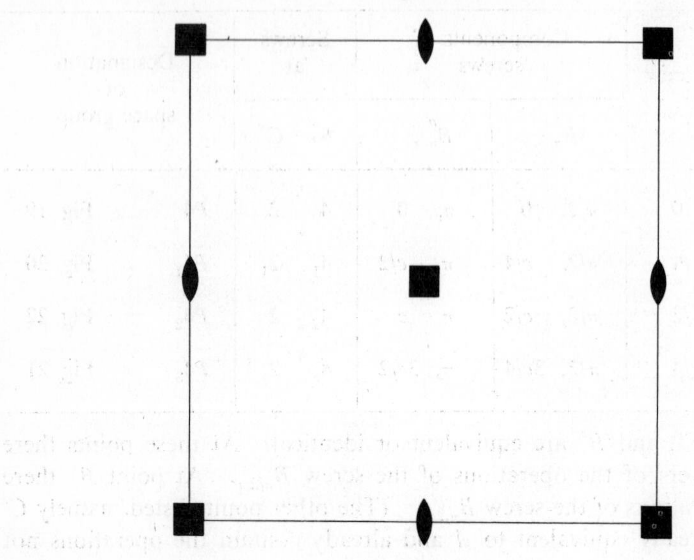

FIG. 19. *P*4.

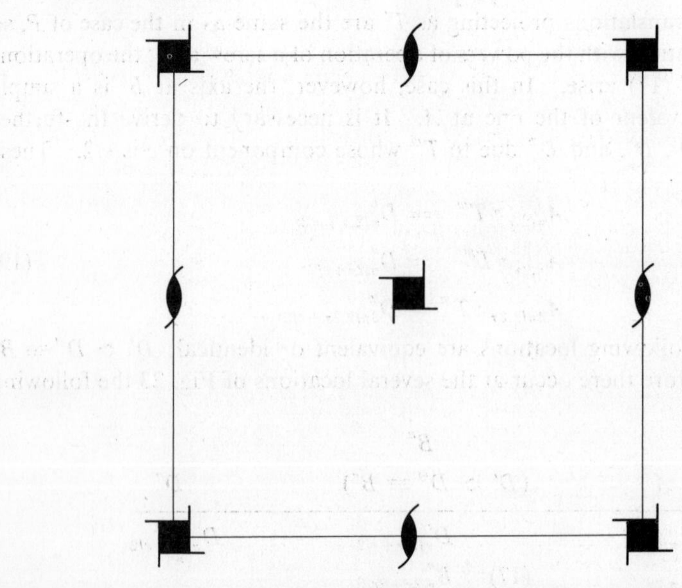

FIG. 20. $P4_1$.

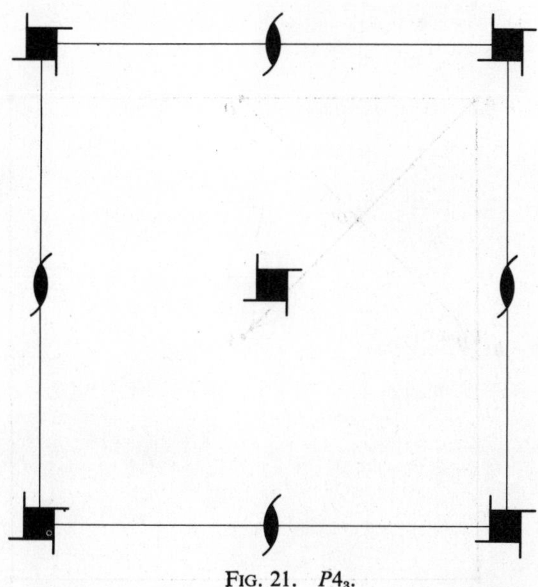

FIG. 21. $P4_3$.

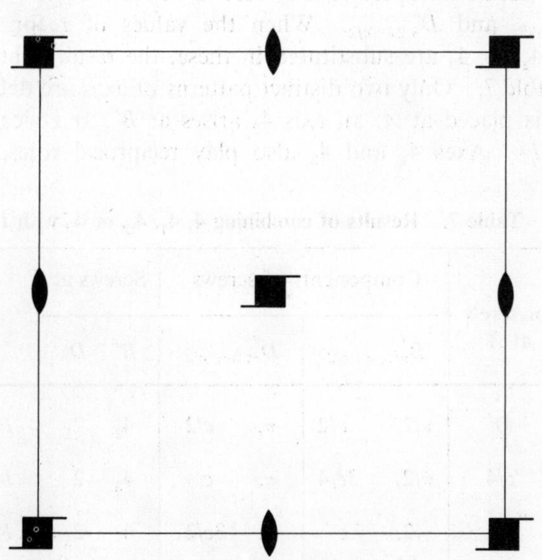

FIG. 22. $P4_2$.

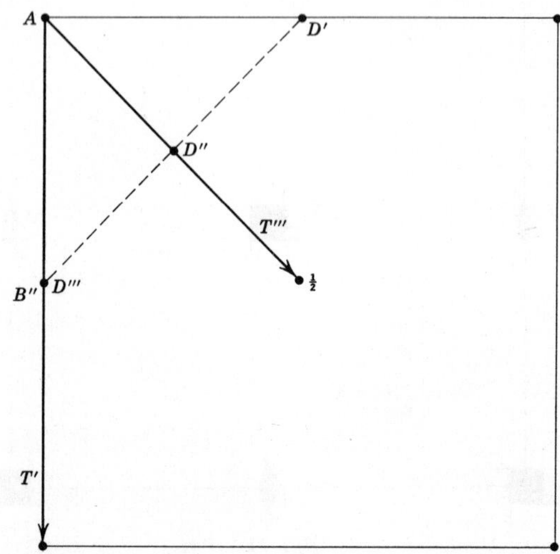

FIG. 23. The combination of a general 4-fold screw with the translations of *I*.

These are the nontrivial operations of screws whose first power operations are $A_{\pi/2,\tau}$, $B''_{\pi/2,\tau+c/2}$, and $D''_{\pi,2\tau+c/2}$. When the values of τ for the permissible screws 4, 4_1, 4_2, or 4_3 are substituted in these, the results obtained are those outlined in Table 7. Only two distinct patterns of axes are defined in Table 7. When axis 4 is placed at A, an axis 4_2 arises at B'', and vice versa, defining space group $I4$. Axes 4_1 and 4_3 also play reciprocal roles, defining space group $I4_1$.

Table 7. Results of combining 4, 4_1, 4_2, or 4_3 with *I*

Screw placed at A	τ for screw at A	Components of screws				Screws at		Designation of space group	
		$B''_{\pi/2,\,\tau+c/2}$		$D''_{\pi,\,2\tau+c/2}$		B''	D''		
4	0	$\pi/2$,	$c/2$	π,	$c/2$	4_2	2_1	$I4$	Fig. 24
4_1	$c/4$	$\pi/2$,	$3c/4$	π,	c	4_3	2	$I4_1$	Fig. 25
4_2	$c/2$	$\pi/2$,	c	π,	$3c/2$	4	2_1	$I4_2 \Leftrightarrow I4$	
4_3	$3c/4$	$\pi/2$,	$5c/4$	π,	$2c$	4_1	2	$I4_3 \Leftrightarrow I4_1$	

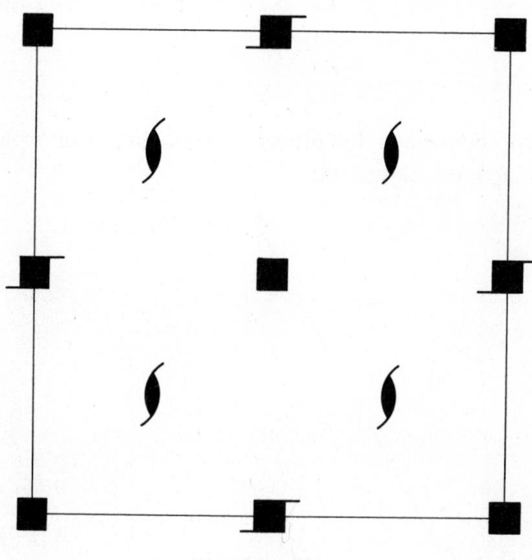

Fig. 24. *I*4.

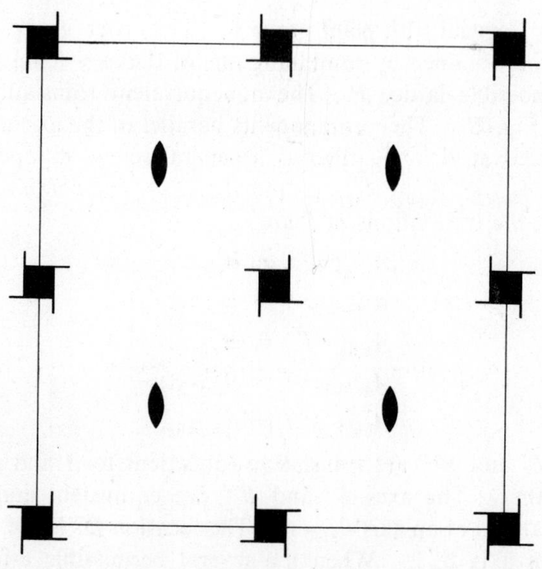

Fig. 25. $I4_1$.

The space groups corresponding to point group 4 are consequently

$$\begin{array}{ll} P4 & I4 \\ \left\{\begin{array}{l} P4_1 \\ P4_3 \end{array}\right. & I4_1 \\ P4_2 & \end{array}$$

The space groups connected by braces are an enantiomorphous pair. The other four space groups are neutral.

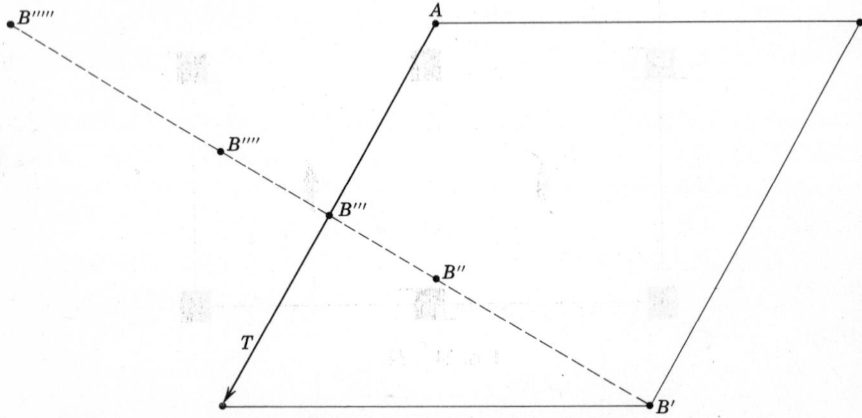

FIG. 26. The combination of a general 6-fold screw with the translations of *P*.

Space groups isogonal with point group 6. The space groups isogonal with point group 6 are obtained by combining one of the axes 6, 6_1, 6_2, 6_3, 6_4, or 6_5 with the one possible lattice *P*. The nonequivalent translations in the cell project as *T* in Fig. 26. Their components parallel to the axis at *A* are zero or unity. If the axis at *A* is regarded as a general screw, its operations can be listed as $A_{\pi/3,\tau}$, $A_{2\pi/3,2\tau}$, $A_{\pi,3\tau}$, $A_{4\pi/3,4\tau}$, and $A_{5\pi/3,5\tau}$. The combinations of these operations with the translations of *P* are

$$\begin{aligned} A_{\pi/3,\tau}\cdot T &= B'_{\pi/3,\tau}, \\ A_{2\pi/3,2\tau}\cdot T &= B''_{2\pi/3,2\tau}, \\ A_{\pi,3\tau}\cdot T &= B'''_{\pi,3\tau}, \\ A_{4\pi/3,4\tau}\cdot T &= B''''_{4\pi/3,4\tau}, \\ A_{5\pi/3,5\tau}\cdot T &= B'''''_{5\pi/3,5\tau}. \end{aligned} \tag{20}$$

The locations B' and B''''' are translation-equivalent to *A* and so need not be considered further. The axes B'' and B'''' are equivalent and comprise the nontrivial operations of an axis $B''_{2\pi/3,2\tau}$. The location B''' is the only nontrivial operation of an axis $B'''_{\pi,3\tau}$. When the several permissible 6-fold screws are placed at *A*, the new screws arising are those listed in Table 8.

Table 8. Results of combining 6, 6_1, 6_2, 6_3, 6_4, or 6_5 with *P*

Screw placed at *A*	τ for screw at *A*	Components of screws		Screws at		Designation of space group	
		$B''_{2\pi/3,\,2\tau}$	$B'''_{\pi,\,3\tau}$	B''	B'''		
6	0	$2\pi/3$, 0	π, 0	3	2	$P6$	Fig. 27
6_1	$c/6$	$2\pi/3$, $c/3$	π, $c/2$	3_1	2_1	$P6_1$	Fig. 28
6_2	$c/3$	$2\pi/3$, $2c/3$	π, c	3_2	2	$P6_2$	Fig. 30
6_3	$c/2$	$2\pi/3$, c	π, $3c/2$	3	2_1	$P6_3$	Fig. 32
6_4	$2c/3$	$2\pi/3$, $4c/3$	π, $2c$	3_1	2	$P6_4$	Fig. 31
6_5	$5c/6$	$2\pi/3$, $5c/3$	π, $5c/2$	3_2	2_1	$P6_5$	Fig. 29

This discussion shows that the space groups isogonal with point group 6 are the six space groups

$$\begin{array}{l} P6 \\ \left\{\begin{array}{l} P6_1 \\ P6_5 \end{array}\right. \\ \left\{\begin{array}{l} P6_2 \\ P6_4 \end{array}\right. \\ P6_3 \end{array}$$

The space groups related by braces are enantiomorphous pairs. The other two are neutral.

Résumé of the space groups isogonal with the monaxial point groups. As a result of the discussion of this chapter, all the space groups which are isogonal with the point groups having a single proper rotation axis have been derived. There are 20 such space groups, as follows:

$$\begin{array}{ccccc} P1 & P2 & P3 & P4 & P6 \\ & P2_1 & \left\{\begin{array}{l} P3_1 \\ P3_2 \end{array}\right. & \left\{\begin{array}{l} P4_1 \\ P4_3 \end{array}\right. & \left\{\begin{array}{l} P6_1 \\ P6_5 \end{array}\right. \\ & I2 & R3 & P4_2 & \left\{\begin{array}{l} P6_2 \\ P6_4 \end{array}\right. \\ & & & I4 & P6_3 \\ & & & I4_1 & \\ \hline 1 \;+ & 3 \;+ & 4 \;+ & 6 \;+ & 6 = 20 \end{array}$$

The space groups connected by braces are enantiomorphous pairs. The rest are neutral.

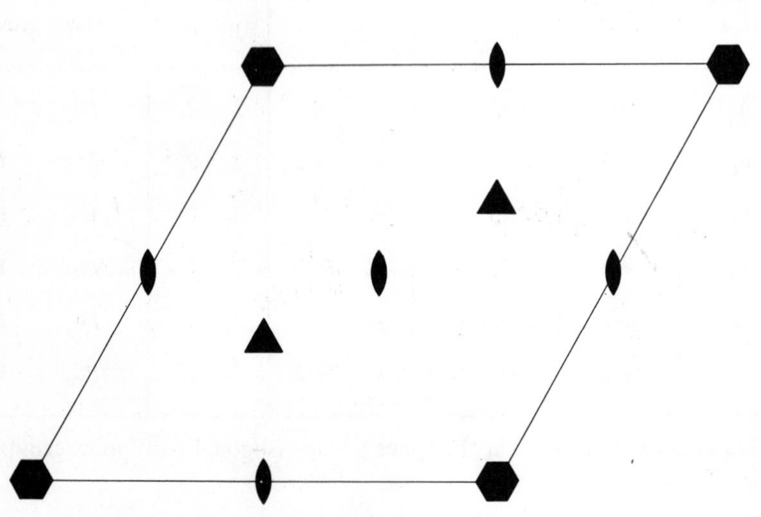

FIG. 27. $P6$.

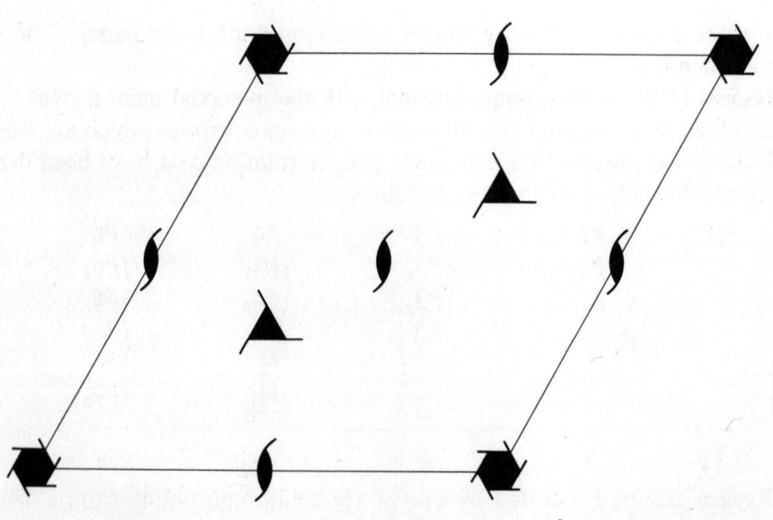

FIG. 28. $P6_1$.

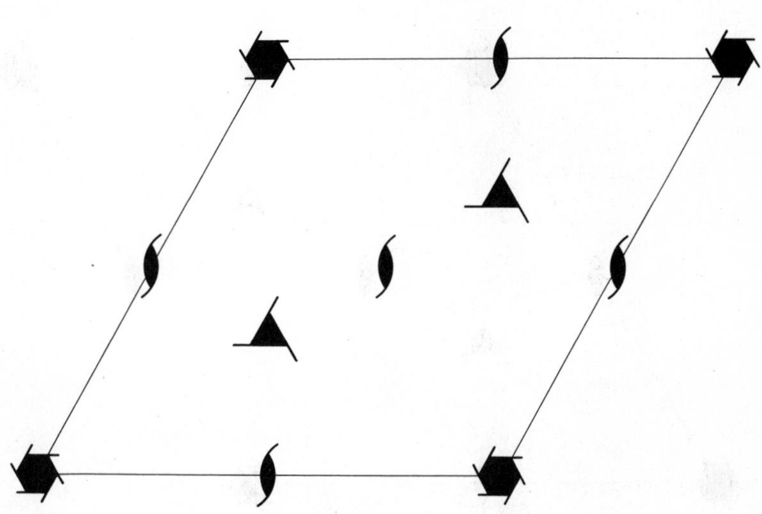

Fig. 29. $P6_5$.

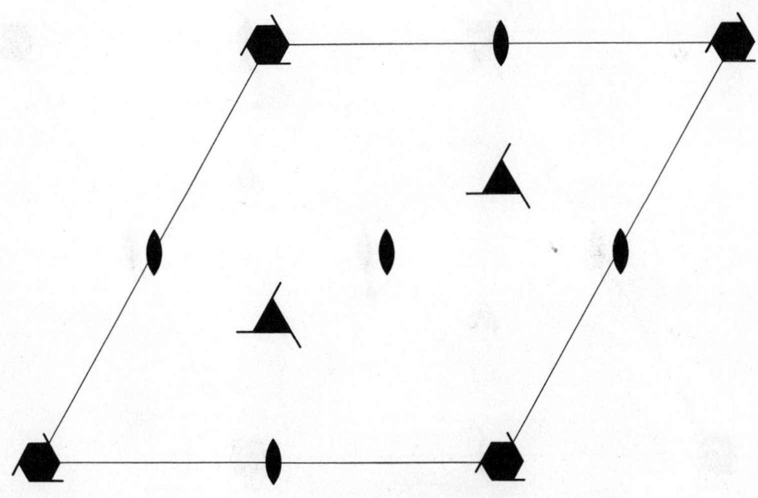

Fig. 30. $P6_2$.

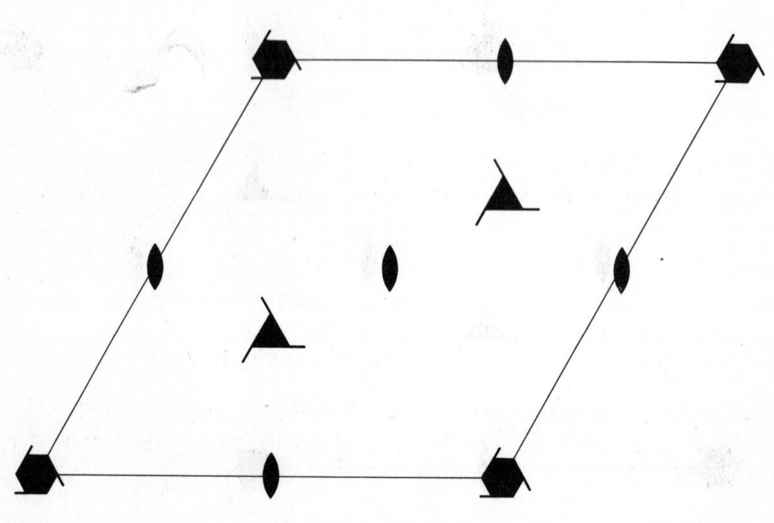

FIG. 31. $P6_4$.

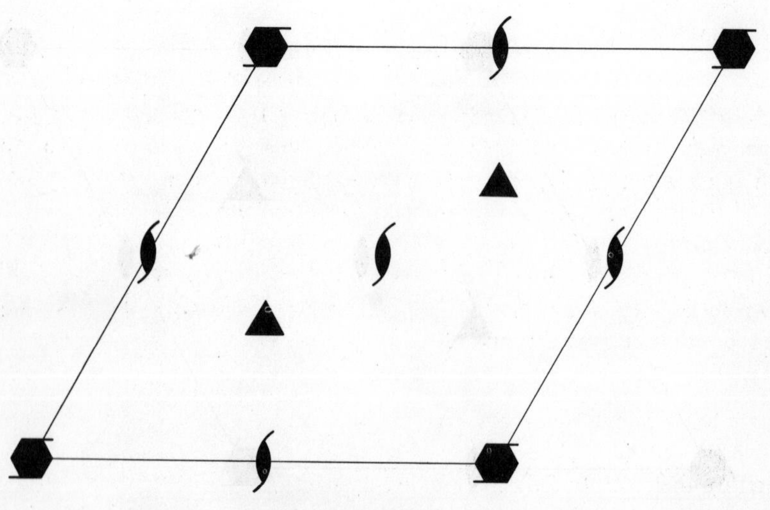

FIG. 32. $P6_3$.

14 · The dihedral space groups

In Chapter 13 all the space groups involving sets of parallel axes were systematically derived. In order to derive space groups concerned with axes which are not parallel it is first necessary to develop some theorems which permit forming combinations of rotations about axes which do not, in general, intersect.

Combinations involving non-parallel rotations

Combination of operations of two intersecting screws. In Chapter 4 it was shown that the combination of two rotations, A_α and B_β is the same as a third rotation, C'_γ, Fig. 1. This is written

$$A_\alpha \cdot B_\beta = C'_\gamma. \tag{1}$$

A very simple relation exists between α, β, and γ of (1) for the important special cases of the dihedral axial groups. In these cases $\alpha = \beta = \pi$. Solution of relation (17) of Chapter 4 shows that when U and V of that chapter (where $U = \alpha/2$, $V = \beta/2$, and $W = \gamma/2$) are $\pi/2$, then $w = W = \gamma/2 = \mu$. Relation (1) thus reduces to

$$A_\pi \cdot B_\pi = C'_{2\mu} \tag{2}$$

for the special case of the dihedral groups defined by 2-fold axes A and B. This simply means that, if two 2-fold rotations about axes A and B, which intersect at an angle μ, are combined, the result is a rotation of 2μ about a perpendicular axis C'. This case is of special importance in the derivation of the space groups of this chapter.

Now consider the more general combination of two screws A_{α,t_1} and B_{β,t_2} shown in Fig. 1. According to (5) of Chapter 13, these can be decomposed into the individual operations

$$A_{\alpha,t_1} = t_1 \cdot A_\alpha \tag{3}$$

and

$$B_{\beta,t_2} = B_\beta \cdot t_2. \tag{4}$$

Therefore their combination can be written

$$A_{\alpha,t_1} \cdot B_{\beta,t_2} = t_1 \cdot A_\alpha \cdot B_\beta \cdot t_2. \tag{5}$$

Relation (1) shows that the middle pair of terms is equal to C'_γ, so that (5) becomes

$$A_{\alpha,t_1} \cdot B_{\beta,t_2} = t_1 \cdot C'_\gamma \cdot t_2. \tag{6}$$

To interpret the terms on the right of (5), Theorem 5 of Chapter 12 can be applied. To show its specific application to this case, however, the relation

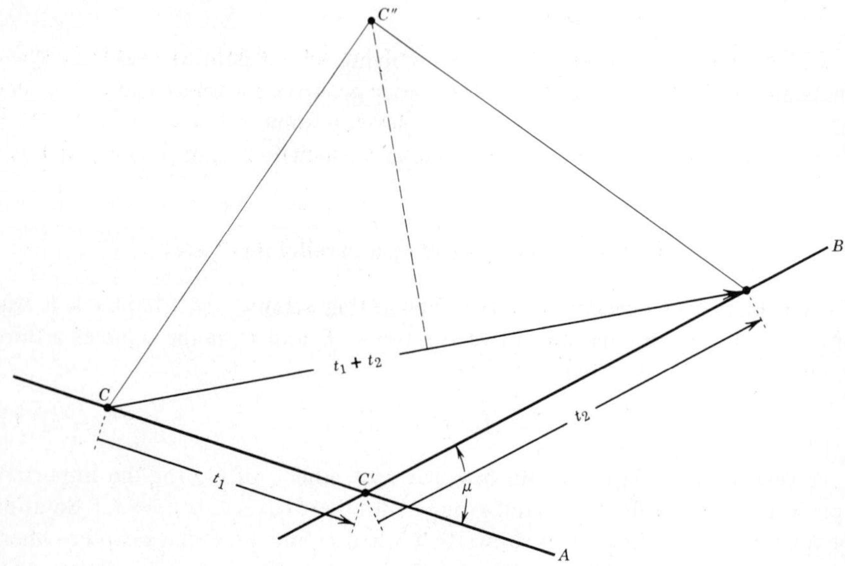

FIG. 1. Combination of two screws A_{α,t_1} and B_{β,t_2} intersecting at angle μ.

will be rederived using t_1 for A of the theorem. Consider the way the translation t_1 transforms a rotation of γ about C of Fig. 1. This can be symbolized as

$$t^{-1}C_\gamma t = C'_\gamma. \tag{7}$$

That is, a rotation through γ at C is transformed by the translation to a rotation through γ at C'. Now premultiply both sides of (7) by t, giving

$$tt^{-1}C_\gamma t = tC'_\gamma$$

or

$$C_\gamma t = tC'_\gamma. \tag{8}$$

This implies that, if the product on the right of (8) is permuted, it is equivalent to its conjugate but applied to an axis removed by t^{-1}.

The value of $t \cdot C'_\gamma$ given by (8) can now be substituted into (6), giving

$$A_{\alpha,t_1} \cdot B_{\beta,t_2} = C_\gamma \cdot t_1 \cdot t_2. \tag{9}$$

The terms on the right of (9) are now in the standard form of a rotation, C_γ, followed by a translation, $\vec{t_1} + \vec{t_2}$. The result of this combination is supplied by Theorem 1 of Chapter 13 if $\vec{t_1} + \vec{t_2}$ has no component parallel to C, or by Theorems 1 and 2 of Chapter 13, together, if $\vec{t_1} + \vec{t_2}$ has a component parallel to C_γ. In the event that α and β of (14) are both π, then axis C is perpendicular to the plane of A and B, so that $\vec{t_1} + \vec{t_2}$ has no component parallel to C. In this case the right of (9) is quite simple (Fig. 1):

$$A_{\pi,t_1} \cdot B_{\pi,t_2} = C''_{2\mu}. \tag{10}$$

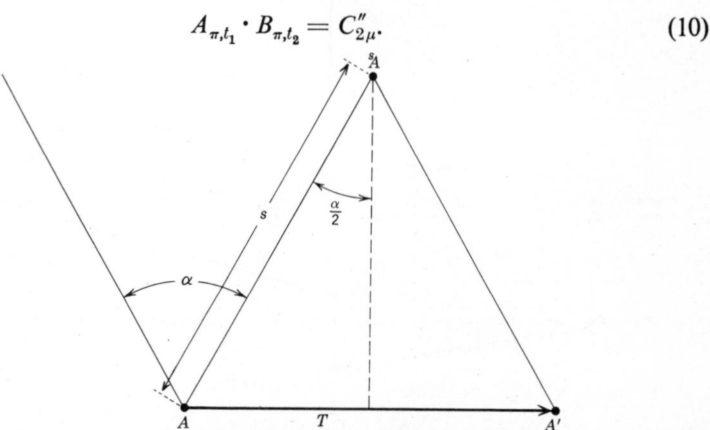

FIG. 2. The effect of displacing a rotation axis A_α by s.

That is, the result of combining two 2-fold screws whose axes A and B intersect at an angle μ is a rotation of 2μ about an axis C'' normal to the plane of A and B. The location of C'' with respect to C is found according to Theorem 1 of Chapter 13.

Effect of displacing an axis. In order to generalize the result of the last section to screws which do not intersect, it is necessary to know how the result of a rotation of α about an axis A compares with the result of a rotation of the same amount about a parallel axis ^sA, where ^sA stands for a "separated" axis. The comparison can be made by manipulating (1) of Chapter 13. The geometry is shown in Fig. 2, which is similar to Fig. 2 of Chapter 7. To bring out the relation between A_α and B_α, let the designation $^sA_\alpha$ be used instead of B_α. Then (1) of Chapter 13 is written

$$A_\alpha \cdot T_\perp = {}^sA_\alpha. \tag{11}$$

This supplies the required information in general form, namely that a rotation of α about a displaced axis is the same as the rotation about an undisplaced axis, followed by a perpendicular translation. It does not supply the relation between the translation T and the separation s. This can be readily found from Fig. 2. The relation is

$$\sin\frac{\alpha}{2} = \frac{T/2}{s} \tag{12}$$

so that

$$T_{\perp} = 2s\sin\frac{\alpha}{2}. \tag{13}$$

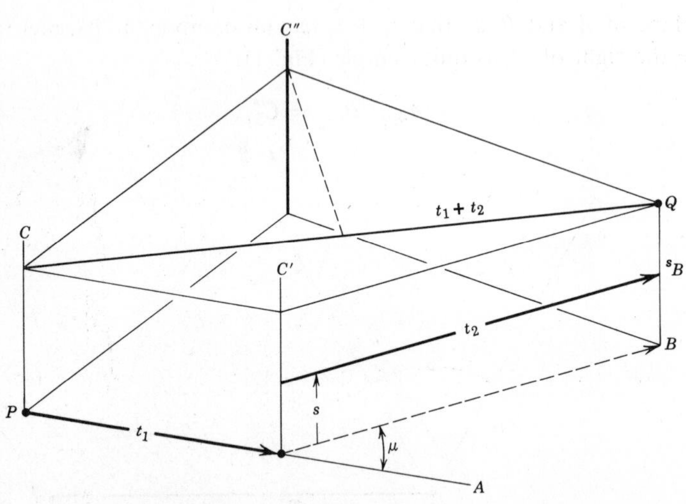

FIG. 3. Combination of two nonintersecting 2-fold screws A_{π,t_1} and $^sB_{\pi,t_2}$.

Combination of operations of two nonintersecting 2-fold screws. If one makes use of the results of the last two sections, it is a simple matter to find the result of combining two screw motions about axes which do not intersect, and which make an angle μ with one another.

First consider the special, but very important, case where the rotation components of both screws are π. This is illustrated in Fig. 3. The problem is to combine A_{π,t_1} with $^sB_{\pi,t_2}$. The operation $^sB_{\pi,t_2}$ can be formulated in terms of B_{π,t_2} by using relation (11):

$$^sB_{\pi,t_2} = B_{\pi,t_2} \cdot T_{\perp}. \tag{14}$$

The magnitude of the translation is given by (13):

$$\begin{aligned} T_{\perp} &= 2s\sin\frac{\alpha}{2} \\ &= 2s\sin\frac{\pi}{2} \\ &= 2s. \end{aligned} \tag{15}$$

Furthermore, reference to Fig. 2 shows that when $\alpha = \pi$ the directions of $T_\perp$ and s are the same. Therefore the specific values in (14) are

$$^{s}B_{\pi,t_2} = B_{\pi,t_2} \cdot 2s. \tag{16}$$

With this result, the combination of A_{π,t_1} with $^{s}B_{\pi,t_2}$ can be solved using the method involved in (6) to (10). The sequence of reduction is as follows:

$$A_{\pi,t_1} \cdot {}^{s}B_{\pi,t_2} = t_1 \cdot A_\pi \cdot {}^{s}B_\pi \cdot t_2. \tag{17}$$

Substituting from (16) this becomes

$$A_{\pi,t_1} \cdot {}^{s}B_{\pi,t_2} = t_1 \cdot A_\pi \cdot B_\pi \cdot 2s_\perp \cdot t_2. \tag{18}$$

In the last section it was pointed out that, when two 2-fold axes intersect at an angle μ, the result is a rotation through angle 2μ about an axis C' at right angles to both A and B. Therefore part of the right of (18) can be reduced as follows:

$$A_{\pi,t_1} \cdot {}^{s}B_{\pi,t_2} = t_1 \cdot C'_{2\mu} \cdot 2s_\perp \cdot t_2. \tag{19}$$

The first two terms on the right of (19) can be manipulated according to (8), giving

$$A_{\pi,t_1} \cdot {}^{s}B_{\pi,t_2} = C_{2\mu} \cdot (t_1 \cdot t_2) \cdot 2s_\perp \tag{20}$$

$$= C''_{2\mu,2s} \,. \tag{21}$$

This gives the same result as (10) except that the rotation about C'' is now a screw whose pitch is twice the separation, s, between axes A and B. This is a general form for combining 2-fold screws, and (10) is included as a special case in which $s = 0$.

Combination of operations for any two nonintersecting screws. The result of the last section can be generalized to include nonintersecting screws of any rotations α and β. The generalization arises partly from the fact that (13) cannot be reduced to merely a component perpendicular to the axis C'_γ as in (15), and partly from the fact that the value of γ is not simply 2μ, but rather one of the values given in Table 7 of Chapter 4. In spite of these complications, however, the combination of A_{α,t_1} with B_{β,t_2} still has the form like (20), specifically,

$$A_{\alpha,t_1} \cdot {}^{s}B_{\beta,t_2} = C'_\gamma \cdot (t_1 \cdot t_2) \cdot T. \tag{22}$$

But in this more general case both $\vec{t_1} + \vec{t_2}$ and $\vec{T}$ have parallel and perpendicular components on C_γ. As a consequence, a screw arises at C'' whose location is controlled by the value of γ and by the vector sum of the perpendicular components of t_1, t_2, and T, and whose pitch is the algebraic sum of the parallel components of t_1, t_2, and T.

A relation between space groups and point groups becomes obvious from the discussion of this and the preceding sections. The angular relation between axes in a point group are controlled by the Euler-type relation (1). To a particular set of values of α, β, and γ, there correspond, in general, several space groups whose angular relations are controlled by exactly the same Euler-type relation. These space groups are said to be *isogonal* with the point group. It is now quite clear that no space groups can exist whose angular relations are different from those of any point group. It follows that all axial space groups can be derived by combining the rotational operations of point groups with the translations of the permissible lattice types for these rotations.

Derivation of the space groups with nonparallel axes

General principle. The space groups with parallel axes were derived in the last chapter. In this chapter some of the more complex axial space groups are derived. The procedure to be adopted is to derive in this chapter the space groups isogonal with the dihedral classes 222, 32, 422, and 622. The derivation of the space groups isogonal with the isometric axial classes 23 and 432 follows a somewhat different procedure and is reserved for the next chapter.

In deriving the dihedral space groups, one merely adjusts Fig. 3 to the proper value of μ for the angle between neighboring nonequivalent axes in the particular dihedral group, and combines these with the nonequivalent translations of the cell. To derive all the space groups isogonal with a particular point group, t_1 and t_2 are allowed to take a general value or zero, and s is allowed to have a value consistent with the translation component $2s$ of the screw at C''. It should be observed that the only set of axes that can arise parallel to C must be one of the parallel-axial space groups derived in the last chapter. An easy method to follow, therefore, is to start with these space groups and fit s to the screw requirements of the principal axis with the aid of (21). The only variation, then, is determined by permitting the values of t_1 and t_2 to be zero or not zero.

Conventions in representing space groups. It is customary to orient the axis C, as used in equations in the preceding parts of this chapter, parallel to the crystallographic axis c. Space groups are usually shown in diagrams as seen looking along the c axis. In the space group isogonal with the dihedral point groups 222, 32, 422, and 622 the axis of greatest n is therefore c. In diagrams of these space groups, the axis C is seen end-on. The 2-fold axes A and B are perpendicular to C and therefore are seen with their translation components projected in correct scale on (001). If one were to look parallel to A (or B), this 2-fold axis, combined with the translations of the cell, would necessarily appear as one of the three groups $P2$, $P2_1$, or $I2$, Figs. 8–11 of Chapter 13, except that the cells are orthogonal and that the vertical direction is the coordinate axis

Z. It will be observed, in the illustrations just cited, that, when there is a particular kind of axis at level z, the same kind of axis occurs at $z + \frac{1}{2}$. Therefore, when looking *along* *Z*, i.e., down axis *C*, whatever axis *A* (or *B*) occurs at level $z + \frac{1}{2}$ is exactly superposed on a similar axis at level z. It is a convention to illustrate only one of these, and to indicate its z coordinate only if it differs from zero. The z coordinate is given as a fraction of the length of the c axis. Thus an axis, next to which is written the fraction $\frac{1}{4}$, means that this axis lies at a level $c/4$ above the level taken as zero. It also *implies* that a similar axis lies at level $c/4 + c/2 = 3c/4$. It is a further convention to represent a 2-fold screw parallel to the plane of the paper by an arrow with one barb, and a 2-fold pure rotation axis by an arrow with two barbs.

Space-group symbols. In the last chapter, as each space group was derived it was represented by a composite symbol consisting of a list of symbols representing the operations which were combined. For example, the combination of the operations of a primitive lattice with the operations of a 2-fold screw was represented by the symbol for the primitive lattice followed by the symbol for the screw axis, namely $P2_1$. The same general rule is followed for all space groups. In more complicated groups, however, it is vital to distinguish directions. For example, in combining the operations of the three axes 2, 2, and 2_1 with the translations of a lattice *C*, it is important to know whether the 2_1 axis is perpendicular to, or parallel with, the centered face. This requires the adoption of some conventions regarding the order in which the symbols for axes are written. The conventional sequence is as follows:

A space-group symbol consists of a sequence of four symbols. The first is a letter designating the lattice. Then comes a series of three symbols which show what symmetry elements are combined with the lattice translation to produce the space group. If the space group contains operations of the second sort these three symbols have the form of fractions in which the operations of the first sort are the numerators and the operations of the second sort are the denominators. In this chapter, no space groups with operations of the second sort are involved, so this becomes a sequence of three numbers representing three rotations, each of which has a subscript indicating the pitch of the screw, except that if the pitch is zero the subscript is omitted.

The order adopted in the "international" symbols is not the same for all crystals. The order is *C*, *A*, *B* for isometric, tetragonal, and hexagonal crystals, but *A*, *B*, *C* for orthorhombic crystals. The axis *C* is uniformly the crystallographic axis c, corresponding to the *Z* axis of the coordinate systems.

B lies in a "diagonal" plane. Therefore *B* coincides with the b axis for orthorhombic crystals (and for monoclinic and triclinic crystals when three symbols are used), with [110] for tetragonal and trigonal crystals, with [21·0] for hexagonal crystals, and with [111] for isometric crystals. An exception must be made for the locations of *A* and *B* in trigonal crystals unless a *C*-centered hexagonal lattice is admitted. The nature of the exception will be evident when trigonal crystals are discussed.

Space groups isogonal with 222. The space groups isogonal with 222 require axis C'' of Fig. 3 and equation (21) to be 2-fold. Therefore (21) has the specific form

$$A_{\pi,t_1} \cdot {}^{s}B_{\pi,t_2} = C''_{\pi,2s}. \tag{23}$$

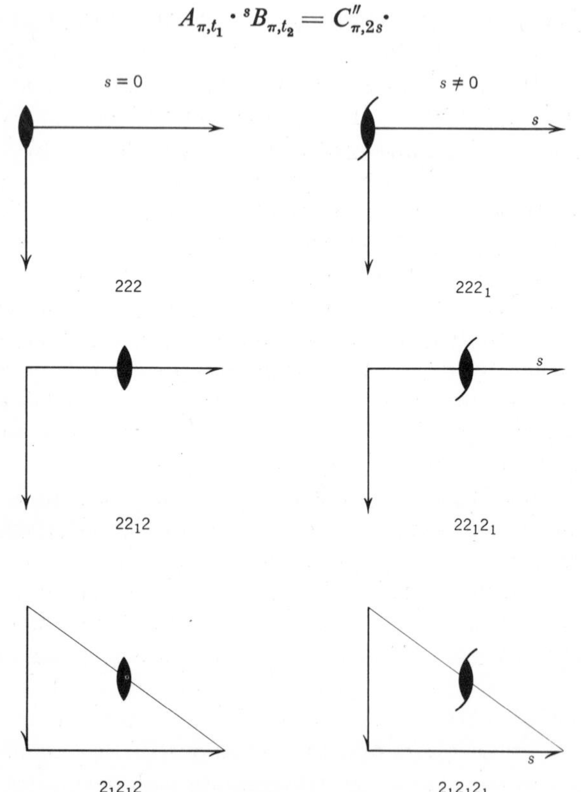

FIG. 4. The possible arrangements of three orthogonal 2-fold rotations or screws.

The axes A and B make an angle of $\pi/2$ with each other. If s in (23) is given a general value, and if t_1 and t_2 are allowed to assume values in turn such that both are zero, one is zero, neither is zero, the arrangements of axes shown in the right column of Fig. 4 result. If s is assigned the special value of zero, these degenerate to the arrangements shown in the left column. Each arrangement in Fig. 4 is assigned a symbol listing the characteristics of the axes in the order ABC''.

The space groups isogonal with 222 are derived by combining the axial sets of Fig. 4 with the translations of the orthorhombic lattices P, C, I, and F. These combinations need not be discussed in great detail since the combinations of each of the individual axes 2 and 2_1 with lattice translations have been discussed in detail in the last chapter.

For discussion purposes, let the general notation for the pitch of a screw be m, as in the last chapter. Then a 2-fold screw has the general form 2_m, where m is 1 for a true screw and zero for a pure rotation.

First consider the possible combination of $2_m2_m2_m$ with P. The only distinct combinations are such that all m's are zero, two m's are zero, one m is zero, or no m's are zero. Any other combinations are the same except for an interchange of A, B, and C'' axes, which amounts to a change in orientation or "setting" of the space group. Let the orientation be so chosen that, if the combination has one axis of one kind and two of another, the unique axis is C''. Then the only distinct combinations are represented by 222, 222_1, 2_12_12, and $2_12_12_1$. These are the combinations in the top and bottom rows of Fig. 4. (The middle row contains reorientations of 222_1 and 2_12_12.) These sets of axes are to be combined with the translations of a primitive lattice.

By making use of the arrangements of the three axes as shown in Fig. 4, and the way each of these combines with the translations of a primitive cell as shown in Figs. 8 and 9 of Chapter 13, the four space groups based upon a primitive lattice are determined at once. They are shown in Figs. 5-8 and are symbolized by $P222$, $P222_1$, $P2_12_12$, and $P2_12_12_1$.

Next, consider the possible combinations of $2_m2_m2_m$ with a lattice having one face centered. Let the centered face be C, and first observe how the axis A of Fig. 9 combines with the translations of the cell. If a screw A_{α,t_1} is placed at A, its translation equivalent occurs at A'' and a screw of $A_{\alpha,t_1+T_{\parallel}}$ arises at A'. From this it follows that, if A is a rotation, A' is a screw, and vice versa. This provides only one pattern, which is the same as Fig. 11, Chapter 13, but considered as cell outline A, Fig. 10, Chapter 13. Thus the A axes of Fig. 9 must be arranged in vertical sheets such that rotation axes and screw axes are alternately encountered from left to right. A similar discussion leads to a similar relation of B axes. Therefore the C-centered cell requires at the same time combinations $C222_m$, $C22_12_m$, $C2_122_m$, and $C2_12_12_m$. It remains only to permit m to assume the two permissible values of 0 and 1. The resulting space groups can be derived by using the designation 222_m, shown in the upper line of Fig. 4, and combining with the translations of C. The results are $C222$ and $C222_1$, shown in Figs. 10 and 11. Note that the conceivable space-group designations within each of the two following sets are the same space group:

$$C222 = C2_122 = C22_12 = C2_12_12.$$

$$C222_1 = C2_122_1 = C22_12_1 = C2_12_12_1.$$

The symbols in customary use are the simplest, which are the ones at the left of the above sequences.

Next consider the combinations of $2_m 2_m 2_m$ with the translation of lattice *I*. Figure 11 of Chapter 13 shows the combination of one of the 2_m's with *I*. Each

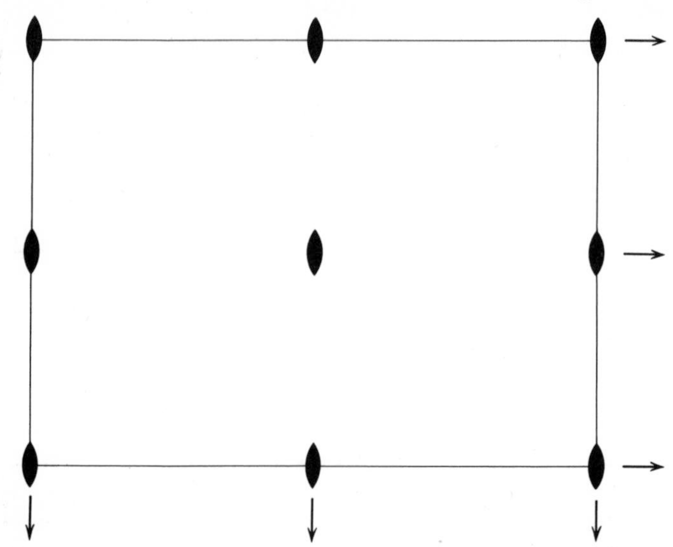

FIG. 5. Space group *P*222. The horizontal two-barbed arrows are horizontal 2-fold axes on level $z = 0$. Axes occurring at level z have translation mates at $z + \frac{1}{2}$.

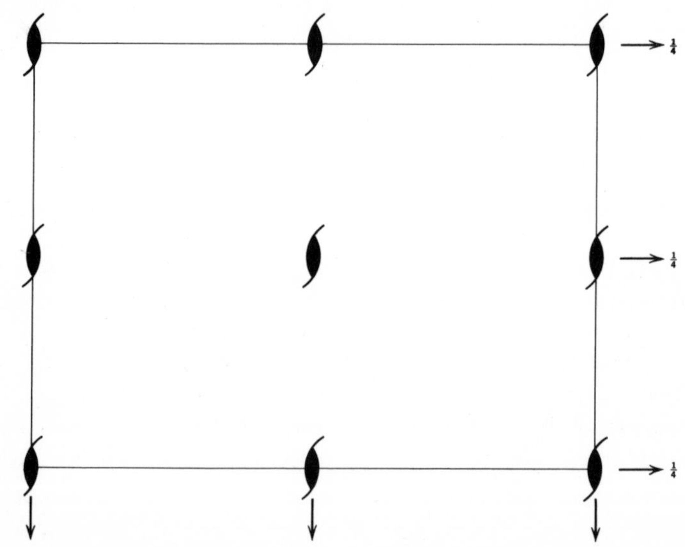

FIG. 6. Space group $P222_1$. Symbols with labels $\frac{1}{4}$ occur on a plane at level $z = \frac{1}{4}$. Axes occurring at level z have translation mates at $z + \frac{1}{2}$.

of the *A*, *B*, and *C*″ axes, combined with the translations of *I*, must give rise to such a pattern of axes, and it only remains to see how *A*, *B*, and *C*″ are related in space. As in the case of combination with lattice *P*, the possible combinations lie in the upper and lower rows of Fig. 4. The combination *I*222 is shown in

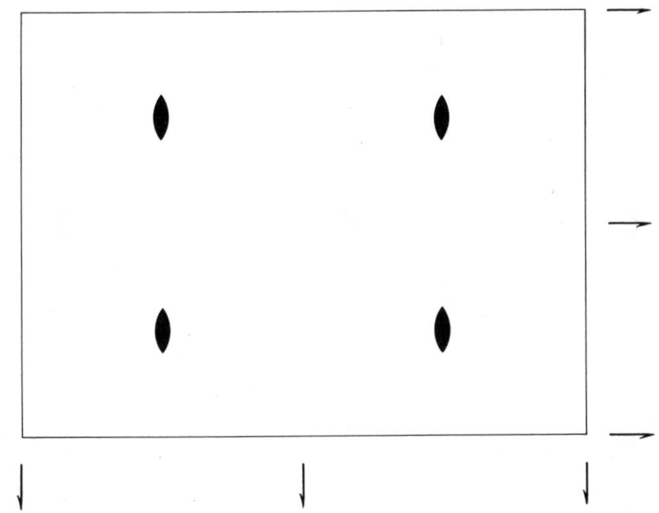

FIG. 7. Space group $P2_12_12$. The one-barbed arrows are horizontal 2-fold screw axes.

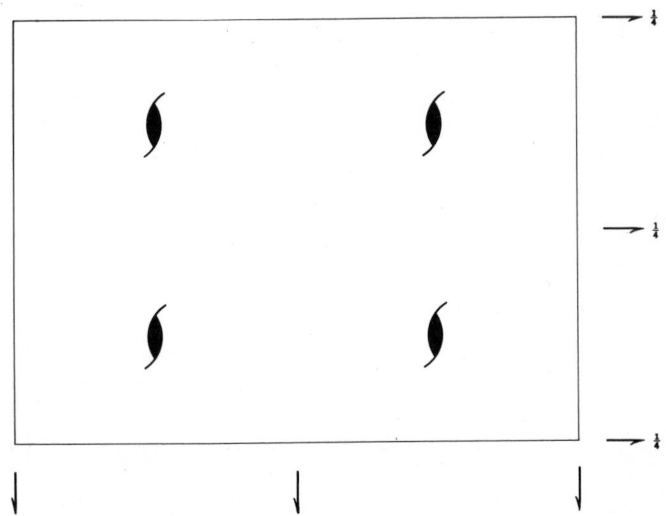

FIG. 8. $P2_12_12_1$.

Fig. 12, and the combination $I222_1$ is shown in Fig. 13. Observe that the combination *I*222 already contains $I2_12_12$, and that $I222_1$ already contains

$I2_12_12_1$. Therefore the conceivable space-group designations within each of the two following sets are the same space group:

$$I222 = I2_12_12.$$
$$I222_1 = I2_12_12_1.$$

The symmetrical designations $I222$ and $I2_12_12_1$ are customarily used.

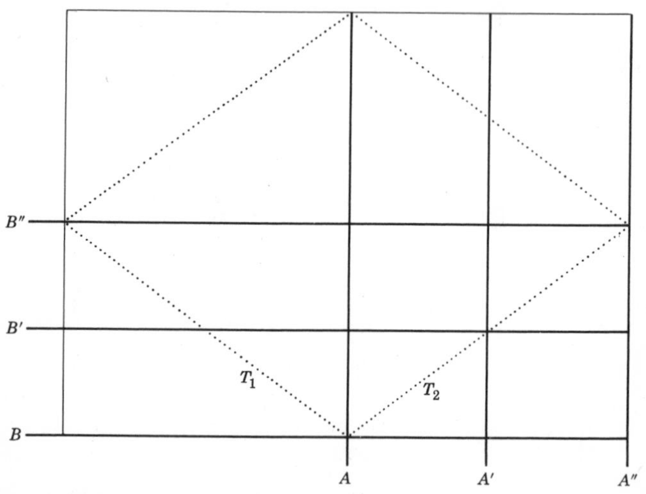

FIG. 9. Combinations of 2-fold screw axes A and B with translation T_2 of a C-centered lattice.

Finally, consider the combinations of $2_m2_m2_m$ with the translations of F. The patterns of axes of 2_m with F are shown in Fig. 11, Chapter 13, in which the F orientation of Fig. 10, Chapter 13, is used. Observe that each pattern contains both 2 and 2_1 axes. The combination $F222$ is shown in Fig. 14. Note that this contains all the combinations of the upper and lower rows of Fig. 4, so that the following combinations are the same space group:

$$F222 = F222_1 = F2_12_12 = F2_12_12_1.$$

The simplest designation $F222$ is given to this single possible F space group.

This discussion shows that there are 9 space groups isogonal with point group 222. These are

$P222$	$C222$	$I222$	$F222$
$P222_1$	$C222_1$	$I2_12_12_1$	
$P2_12_12$			
$P2_12_12_1$			

Since all 2-fold screws are neutral, all these space groups are neutral.

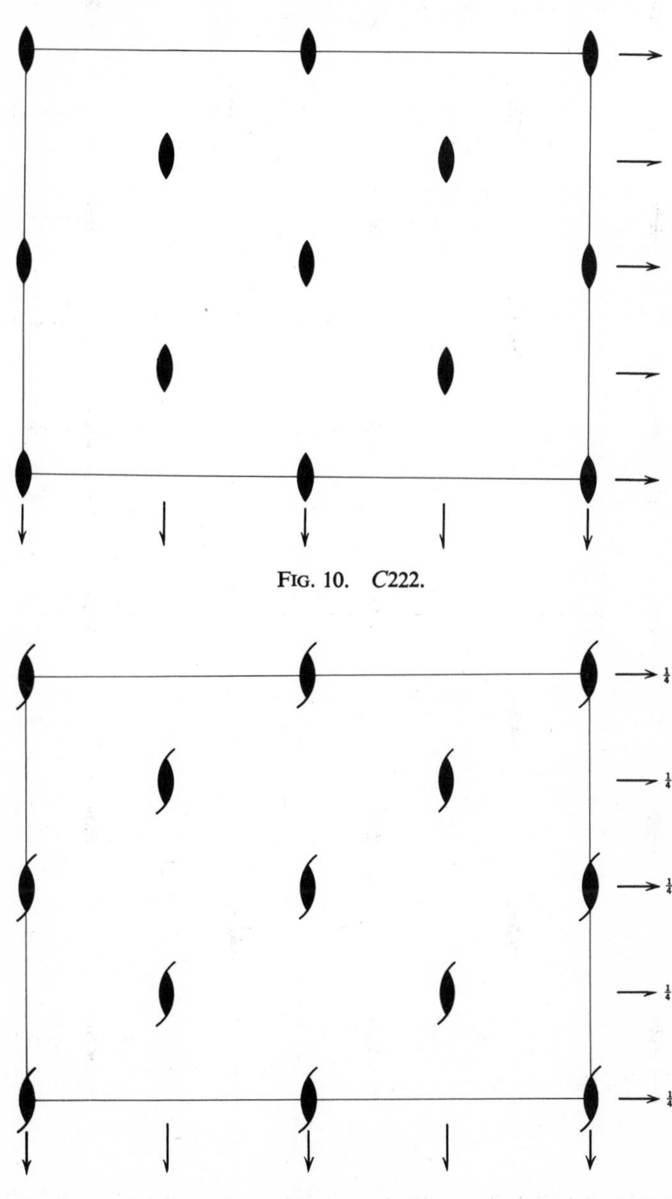

FIG. 10. *C*222.

FIG. 11. *C*222$_1$.

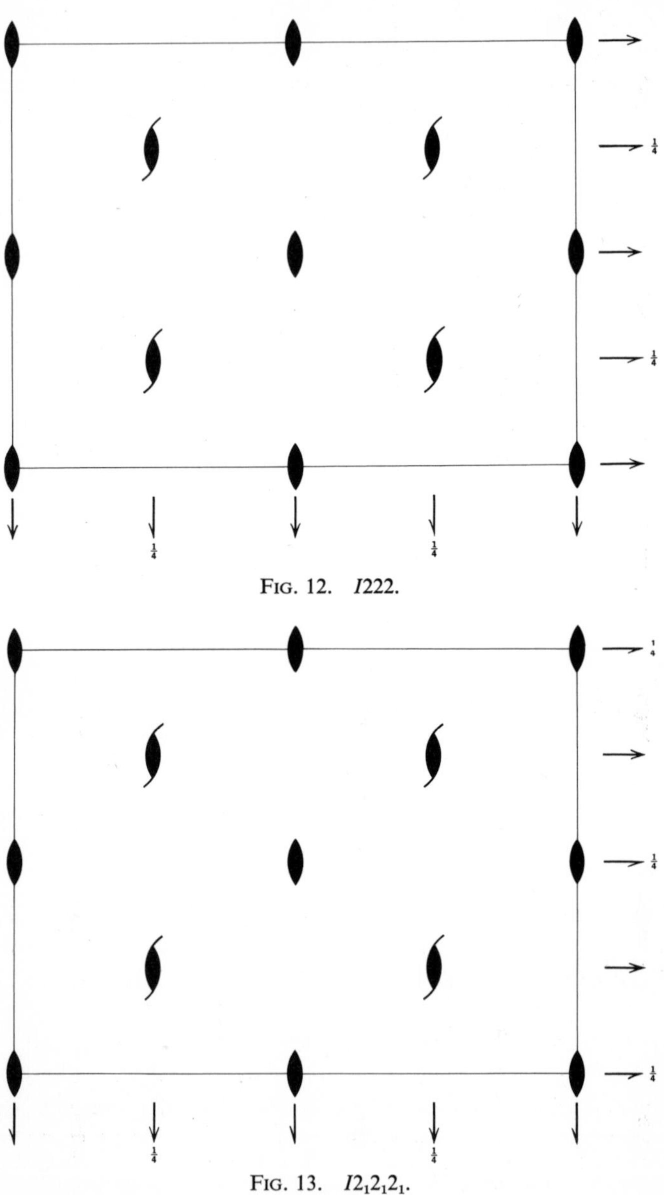

FIG. 12. $I222$.

FIG. 13. $I2_12_12_1$.

Space groups isogonal with point group 32. In symmetries in which one axis is 3 or greater, the order of listing the axes is $C''AB$. In trigonal symmetry the A and B axes are equivalent through the operation of axis C''. Therefore axis B is not specifically listed.

The trigonal space groups can be derived by combining $3_m 2_m 2_m$ with each of the two lattices *P* and *R*. Bearing in mind that the two 2-fold axes are equivalent, and therefore that both are 2's, or both are 2_1's, the only solutions of (21) and Fig. 3 are those shown in Fig. 15.

First consider the combinations of $3_m 2_m 2_m$ with lattice *P*. This lattice, when specialized sufficiently for a 3-fold axis, actually has hexagonal symmetry. Therefore, through each lattice point there is a set of three 2-fold axes along each *a* axis, shown as full lines in Fig. 16, and also three more 2-fold axes along the long diagonals of the diamond meshes. This means that, whereas the 3-fold axis of class 32 must be taken along the *c* axis, the 2-fold axes can be fitted either to the cell axes or to the long diagonals of the cells. Consequently there are two permissible orientations of 32 with respect to lattice *P*. By analogy with the tetragonal and hexagonal systems, the last position of the list of space-group symbols is accepted as the position of the axis along the cell diagonal. Therefore that permissible orientation in which there are 2-fold axes along the cell axes is written 321 (the 1 in this position indicating that there is no symmetry along the diagonal) while the other permissible orientation in which there are 2-fold axes along the cell diagonal is written 312 (the 1 in this position indicating that there is no symmetry along the cell axis). Therefore there are two categories of space groups having the primitive lattice, namely $P3_m 2_m 1$ and $P3_m 1 2_m$.

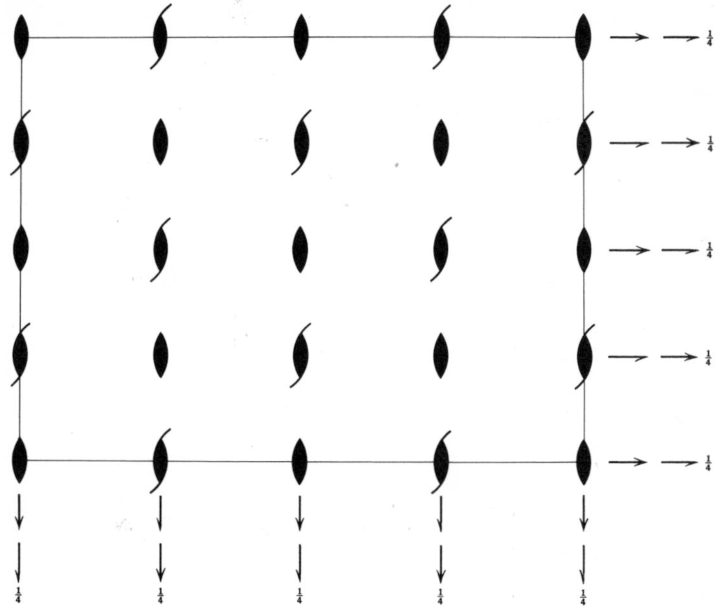

FIG. 14. *F*222.

First consider the combination $P3_m21$, i.e., the combination of the translations of the primitive lattice with the upper right of Fig. 15. Omit from preliminary consideration the axis ${}^sB$ at level s, Fig. 15. Then it is evident that the combination of the lattice translations and the 3_m produce a pattern of 3_m's like $P3_1$, Fig. 14 of Chapter 13. The 2-fold rotation axes intersect the 3_m

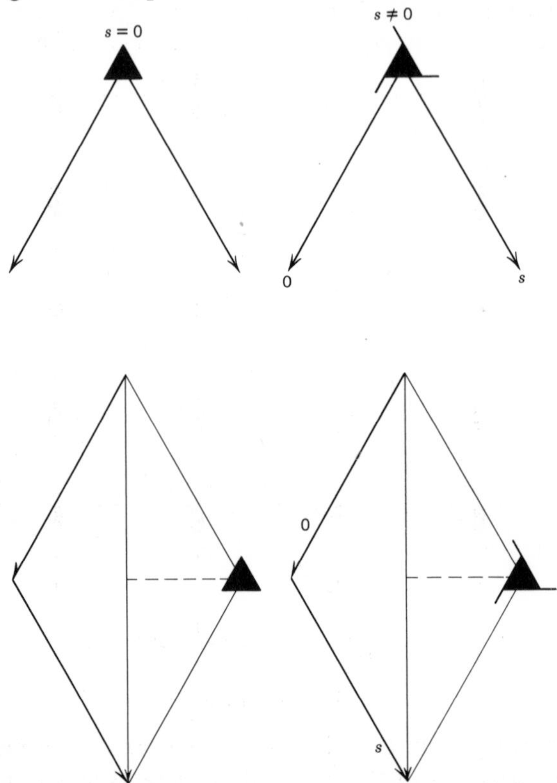

FIG. 15. The possible combinations of axes of the form $3_m2_m2_m$. In the combinations on the left side, the two horizontal screws are on the same level; on the right side they are at levels 0 and s respectively.

screws, according to the upper right of Fig. 15. Figure 17 illustrates the result of combining the operation $A_{\pi,}$ with a nonparallel axial translation: a screw $A_{\pi,a/2}$ occurs halfway along a translation. This requires that the pattern of 2-fold axes is the same as the patterns along the a axis of $C222$, Fig. 10; i.e., screws and pure rotation alternate.

Notice the relation of the 2-fold screw of Fig. 17 to the upper right 3-fold screw. These have the same relation as in the lower right of Fig. 15. This means that any combination $P3_m21$ contains $P3_m2_11$. Therefore all space groups with a primitive lattice and orientation 321 can be derived by using

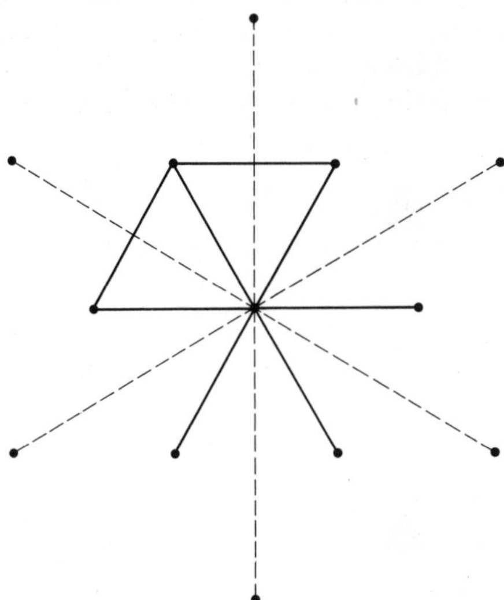

FIG. 16. Locations of two kinds of 2-fold axes in the primitive hexagonal lattice. The full lines are 2-fold axes parallel to cell edges while the broken lines are 2-fold axes parallel to the long diagonals of the hexagonal mesh.

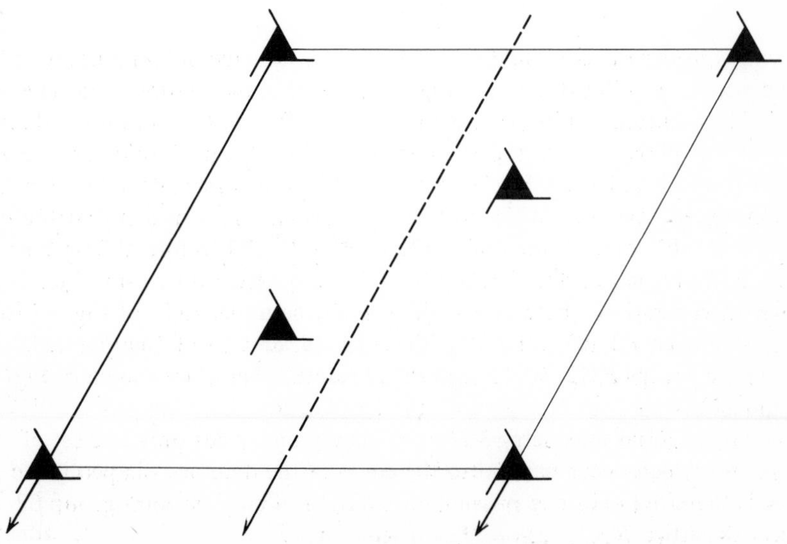

FIG. 17. Orientation 3_m21.

Fig. 17 and fitting the separation, *s*, between 2-fold axes of the upper right of Fig. 15, to the 3-fold screws of $P3$, $P3_1$, and $P3_2$ (Figs. 13, 14, and 15 of Chapter 13). The three space groups $P321$, $P3_121$, and $P3_221$ result. They are shown in Figs. 18, 19, and 20. (In the last two, the level designations differ from those shown in *International tables for x-ray crystallography* because of a 60° difference in orientation.)

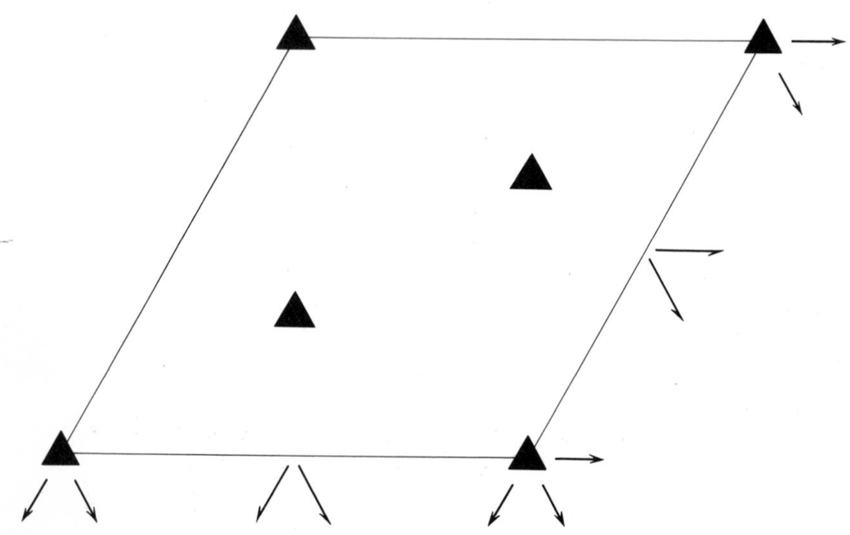

FIG. 18. *P*321.

Next, consider the combinations $P3_m12$. The scheme of combination of any 2-fold screw *A* is illustrated in Fig. 21. In this orientation, too, the non-parallel translations in (001) cause an alteration of parallel rotations and screws lying in this plane. Note the relation of the lower right 3-fold screw axis of Fig. 21 to the 2-fold screw just to its left. This is the same as the lower right of Fig. 15, except for a 30° difference in orientation. This means that the combination $P3_m12$ contains the combination $P3_m12_1$. Therefore all space groups with a primitive lattice and orientation 312 can be derived by using Fig. 21 and fitting the separation *s* between 2-fold axes of the upper right of Fig. 15 to the 3-fold screws of $P3$, $P3_1$, and $P3_2$ (Figs. 13, 14, and 15 of Chapter 13). The three space groups $P312$, $P3_112$, and $P3_312$ result. These are shown in Figs. 22, 23, and 24.

The lattice *R* has symmetry $\bar{3}\ 2/m$. This symmetry has only one set of three 2-fold axes which occur parallel to the edges of the diamond-shaped triple cell. There is therefore only one possible orientation of axes of point group 32 with respect to lattice *R*.

The possible space groups $R3_m2_m$ are obtained by combining the translations

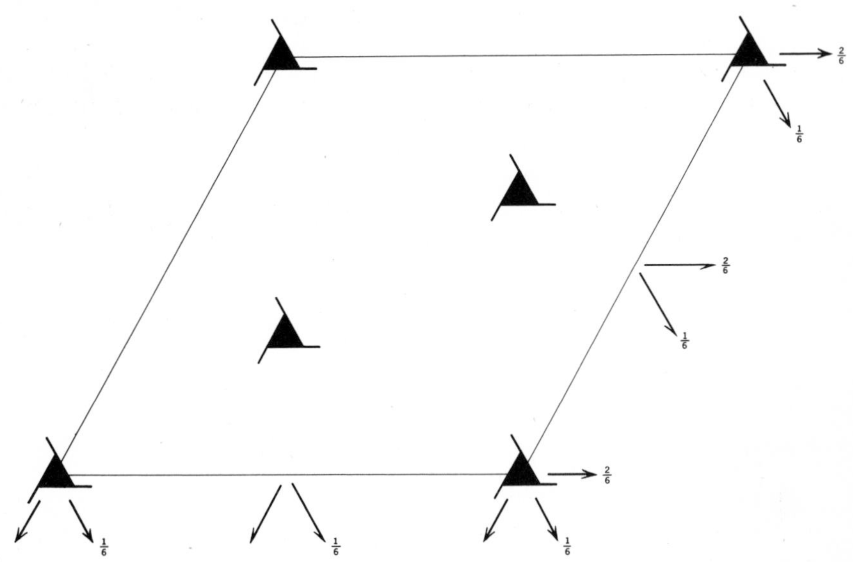

FIG. 19. $P3_121$. Horizontal axes at levels z, as shown, have translation mates at levels $z + \frac{1}{2}$.

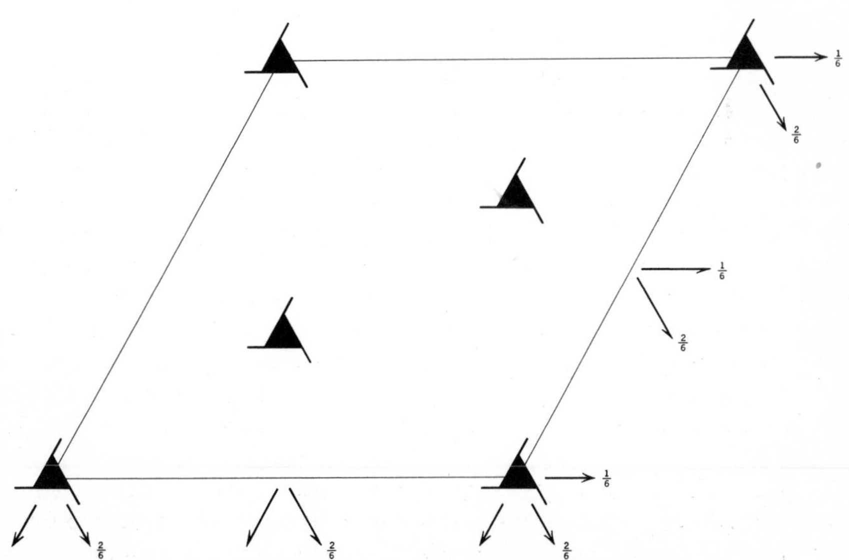

FIG. 20. $P3_221$. Horizontal axes at levels z, as shown, have translation mates at levels $z + \frac{1}{2}$.

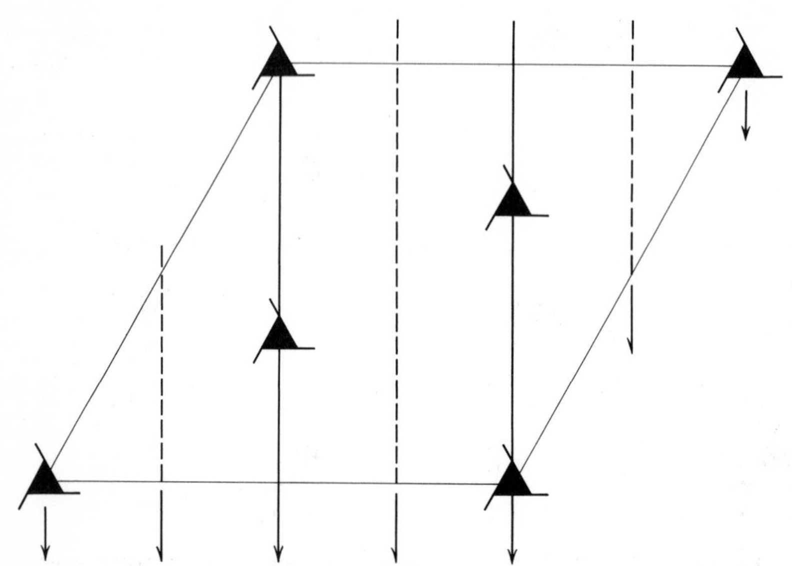

FIG. 21. Orientation 3_m12.

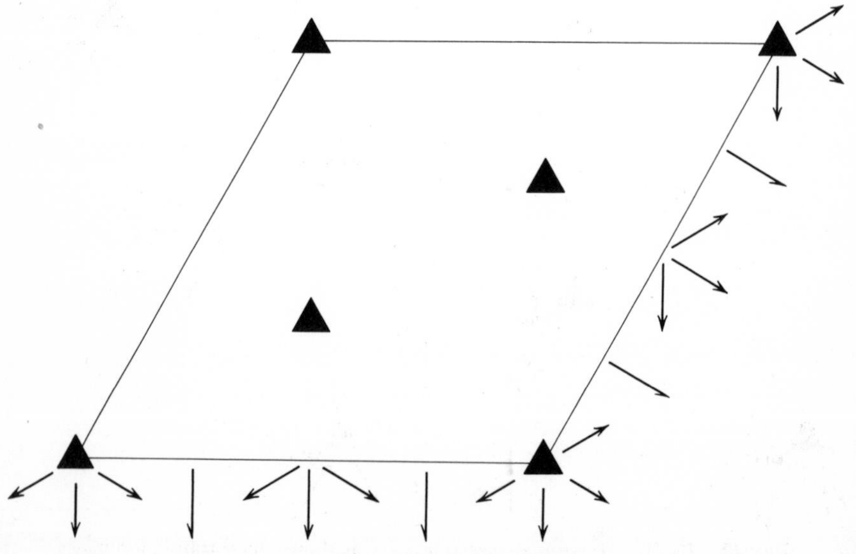

FIG. 22. *P*312.

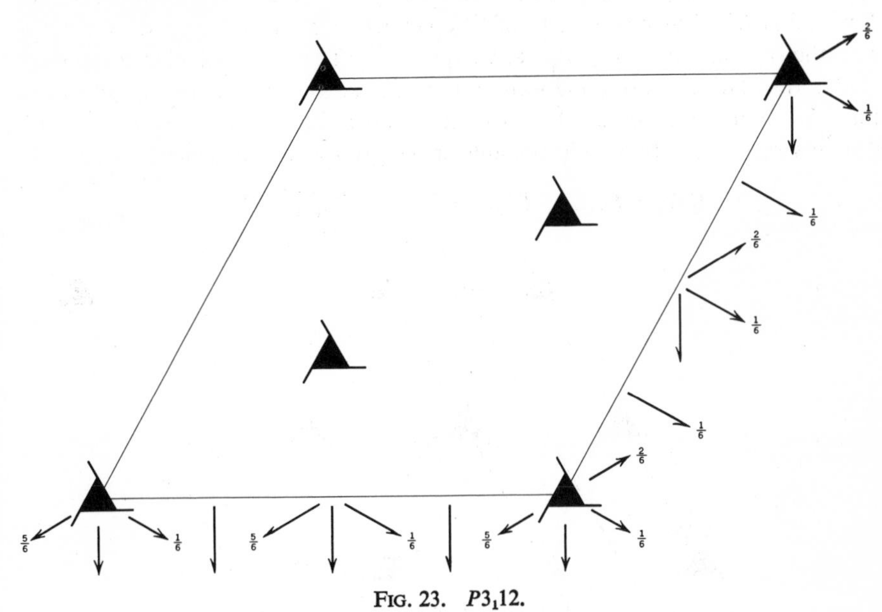

FIG. 23. $P3_112$.

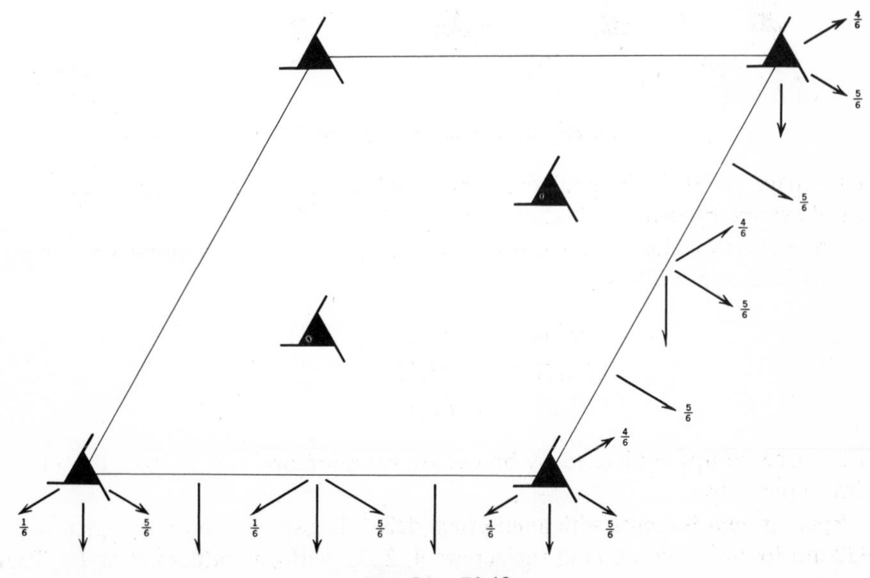

FIG. 24. $P3_212$.

of R with each of the possible axial combinations of Fig. 15. First consider the upper left axial set, which gives rise to space group $R32$. The combination of R with 3 is $R3$, shown in Fig. 17 of Chapter 13. The axis 2 must be combined with the translation T''' of Fig. 16, Chapter 13. The perpendicular component of this translation produces an alteration of rotations and screws as shown in Fig. 25. Note that Fig. 25 already contains all combinations shown in Fig. 15. For this reason the following possible space groups are the same:

$$R32 = R3_12 = R3_22 = R32_1 = R3_12_1 = R3_22_1.$$

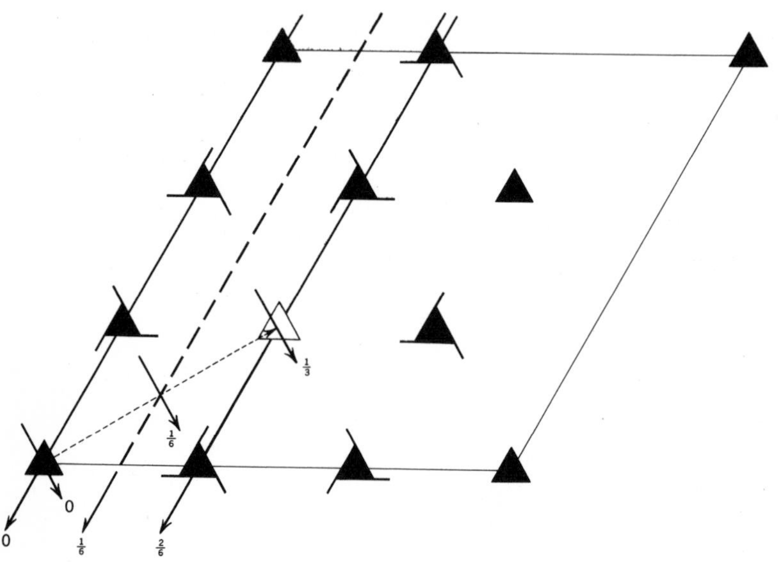

FIG. 25. Scheme of space groups $R3_m2_m$.

This space group is designated by the simplest symbol, $R32$. The completed set of symmetry elements is shown in Fig. 26.

The discussion just given shows that the space groups isogonal with point group 32 are the following:

$$\begin{array}{lll} P321 & P312 & R3 \\ \left\{\begin{array}{l} P3_121 \\ P3_221 \end{array}\right. & \left\{\begin{array}{l} P3_112 \\ P3_212 \end{array}\right. & \end{array}$$

The space groups connected by braces are enantiomorphous pairs. The other three are neutral.

Space groups isogonal with point group 422. The space groups isogonal with 422 are found by combining the screws $4_m2_m2_m$ with the lattices P or I. The combinations $4_m2_m2_m$ are shown in Fig. 27.

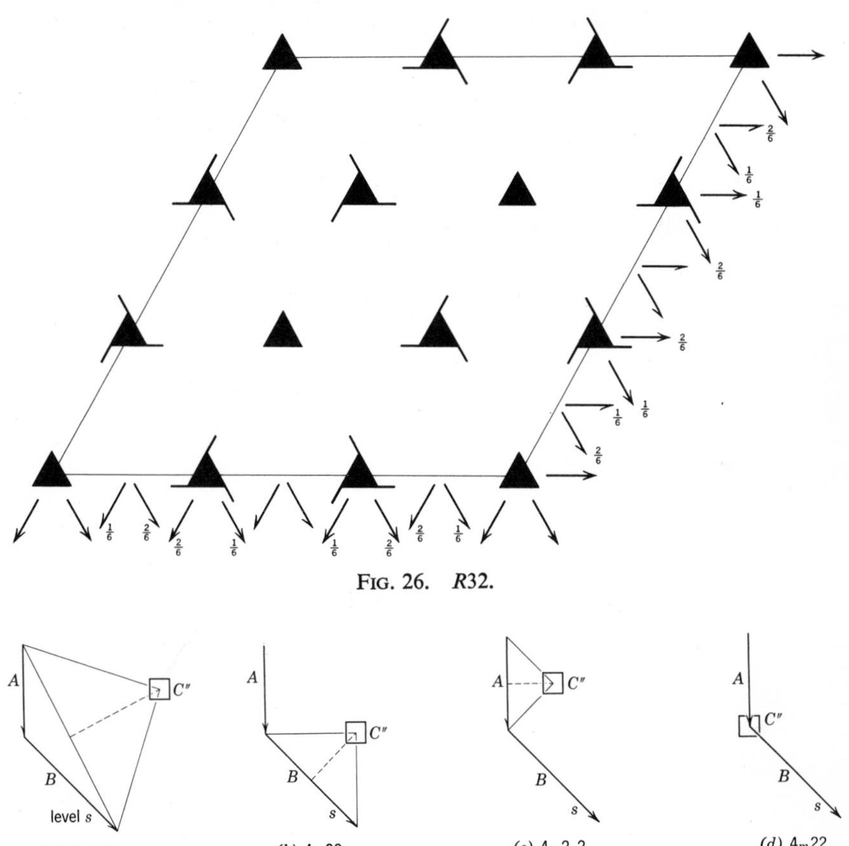

FIG. 26. *R*32.

FIG. 27. The possible combinations of axes of the form $4_m 2_m 2_m$.

Consider the general combinations $4_m 2_m 2_m$ with *P*. The translations of the primitive cell combine with the *A* rotations to yield space groups *P*2 or $P2_1$. The combination of the *B* rotations with *P* are illustrated in Fig. 28. If the screw at *B* is $B_{\pi,\tau}$ the nonparallel lattice translation $t_{[010]}$ combines with this to produce a screw at B' of characteristics $B'_{\pi,\tau+t/2}$. If *B* is a rotation, then B' is a screw, and vice versa. Thus all combinations $P4_m 2_m 2$ are automatically $P4_m 2_m 2_1$, so that it is only necessary to investigate space groups $P4_m 2_m 2$.

First consider the space groups of the form $P4_m 22$. From what has been said above, the general scheme of these space groups is as shown in Fig. 29. The value of *s* is fitted to the four possible screws 4, 4_1, 4_3, and 4_2 as shown in Figs. 30-33, yielding the four space groups *P*422, $P4_1 22$, $P4_3 22$, and $P4_2 22$.

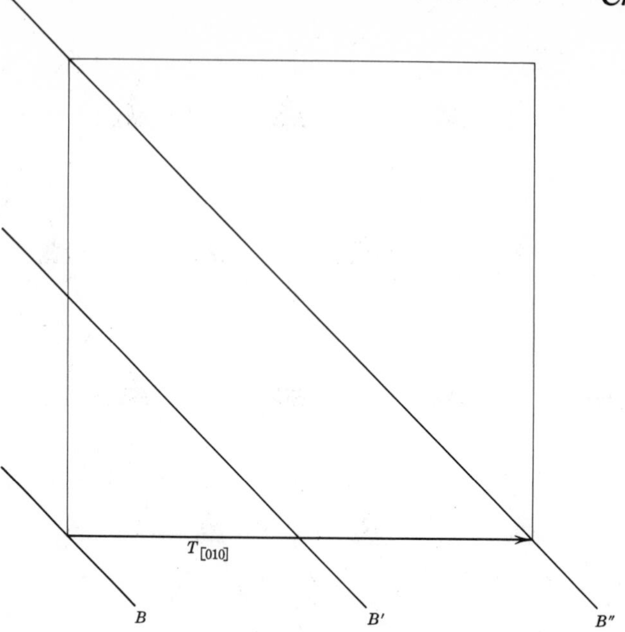

FIG. 28. Combination of the 2-fold screw axis *B* with the [010] translation of a tetragonal cell.

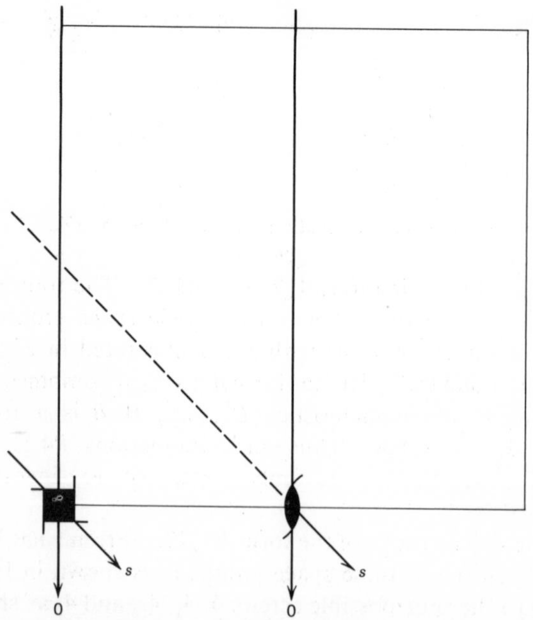

FIG. 29. Scheme of space groups $P4_m22$.

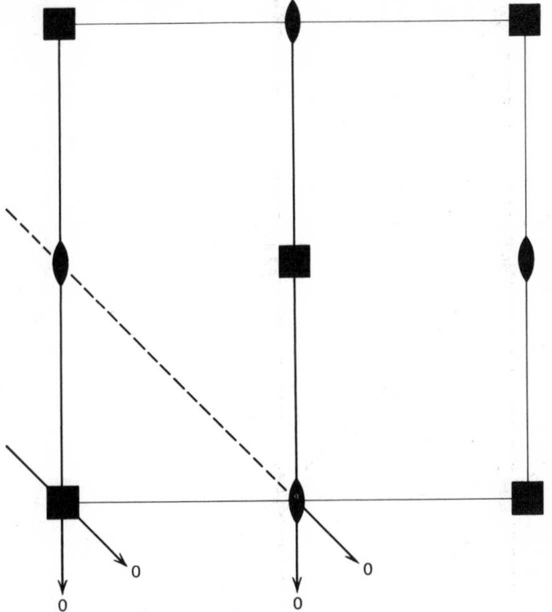

FIG. 30*a*. Scheme of *P*422.

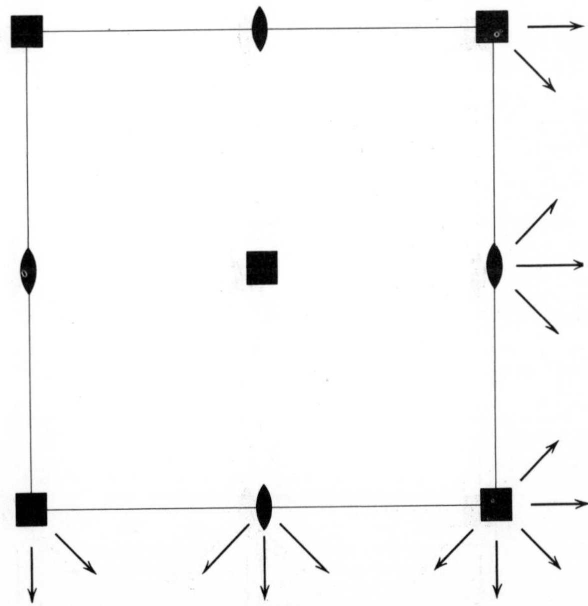

FIG. 30*b*. *P*422.

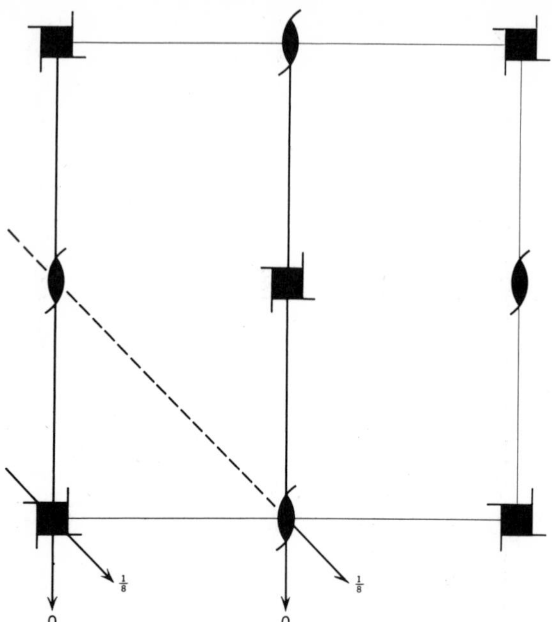

FIG. 31*a*. Scheme of $P4_122$.

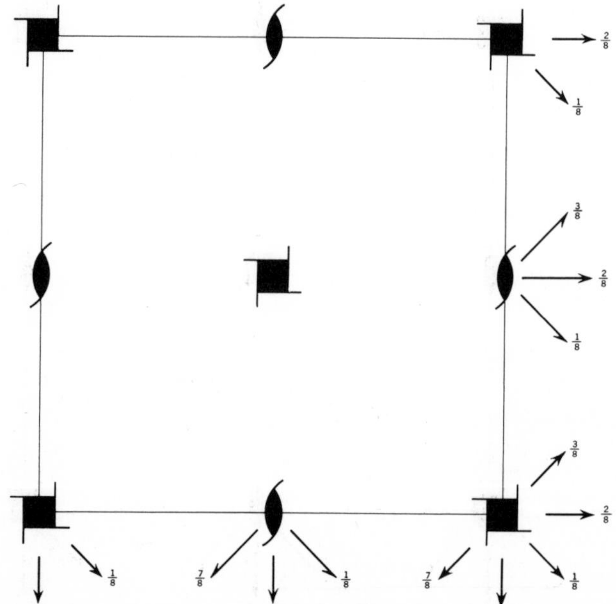

FIG. 31*b*. $P4_122$. Horizontal axes at levels z, as shown, have translation mates at levels $z + \frac{1}{2}$.

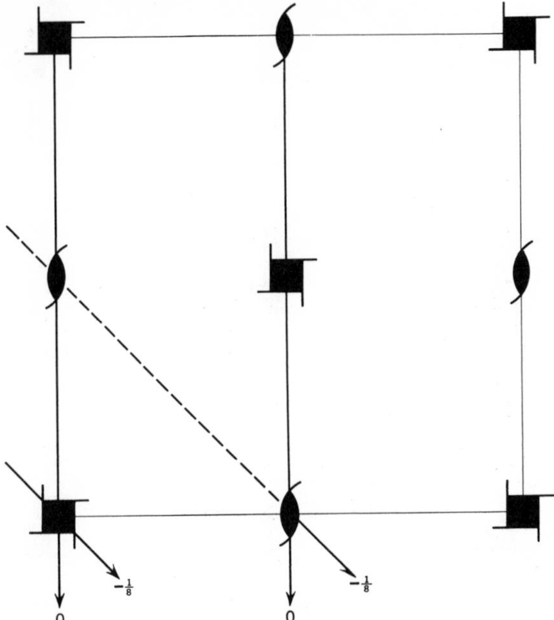

FIG. 32*a*. Scheme of $P4_322$.

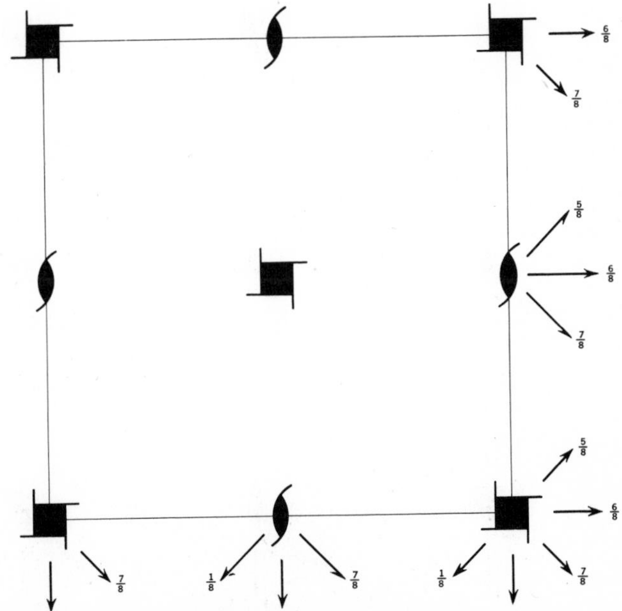

FIG. 32*b*. $P4_322$. Horizontal axes at levels z, as shown, have translation mates at levels $z + \frac{1}{2}$.

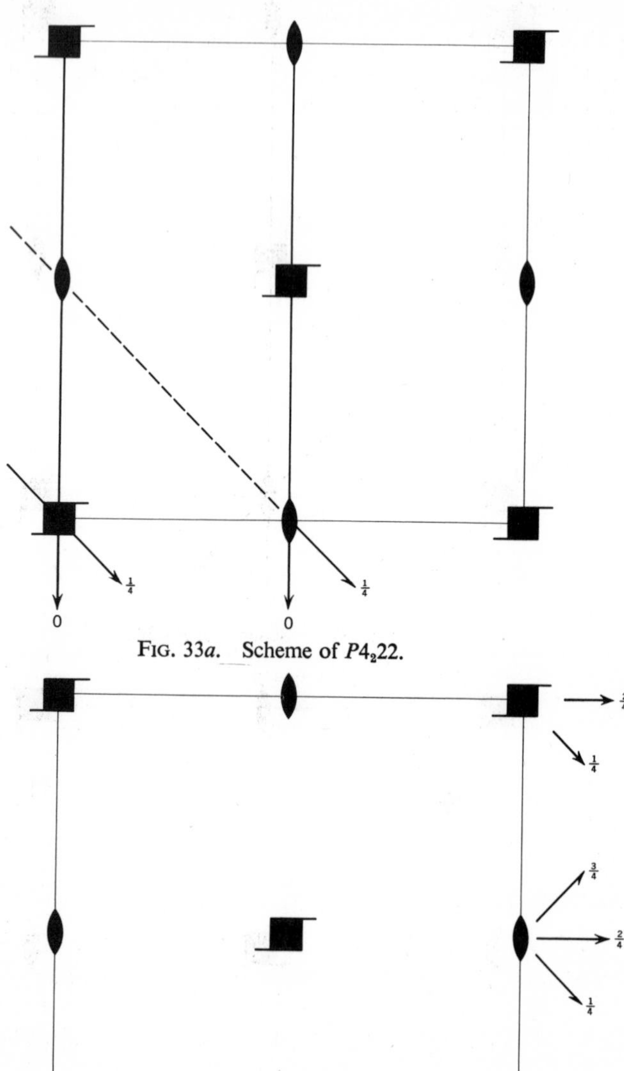

FIG. 33*a*. Scheme of $P4_222$.

FIG. 33*b*. $P4_222$. Horizontal axes at levels z, as shown, have translation mates at levels $z + \frac{1}{2}$.

Now consider the space groups of the form $P4_m 2_1 2$. If the center 4-fold screw of the cell is taken to correspond to Fig. 27(*c*) the general scheme of these space groups is as shown in Fig. 34. The value of *s* is fitted to the four possible screws as shown in Figs. 35–38, yielding the space groups $P42_12$, $P4_12_12$, $P4_32_12$, and $P4_22_12$.

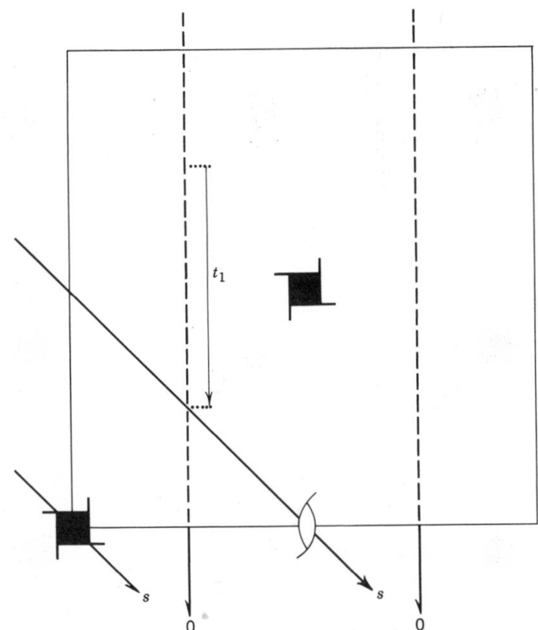

FIG. 34. Scheme of space groups $P4_m2_12$.

The space groups $I4_m2_m2_m$ contain the same operations of $P4_m2_m2_m$ plus additional operations due to the combinations of the body-diagonal translations of the cell with the rotations. The dotted translation in Fig. 39 repeats an *A* screw at level zero as an *A* screw at level $\frac{1}{4}$ with the added pitch of $a/2$. The translation repeats the *B* screw at level zero as a similar *B* screw at level $\frac{1}{4}$. If these additional operations are added to $P422$, space group $I422$, shown in Fig. 40, results. Since this contains all the situations shown in Fig. 27 for 4_0 and 4_2 axes, the following space groups are the same:

$$I422 = I42_12 = I4_222 = I4_22_12.$$

The simplest designation $I422$ is customarily used.

If the additional translations of *I* are added to $P4_122$, space group $I4_122$, shown in Fig. 41, results. Since this contains all the situations shown in Fig. 27 for 4_1 and 4_3 axes, the following space groups are the same

$$I4_122 = I4_12_12 = I4_322 = I4_32_12.$$

The designation $I4_122$ is customarily used.

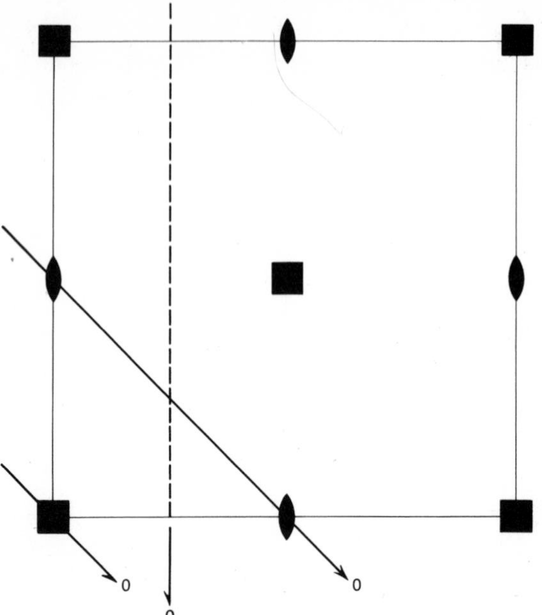

FIG. 35*a*. Scheme of $P42_12$.

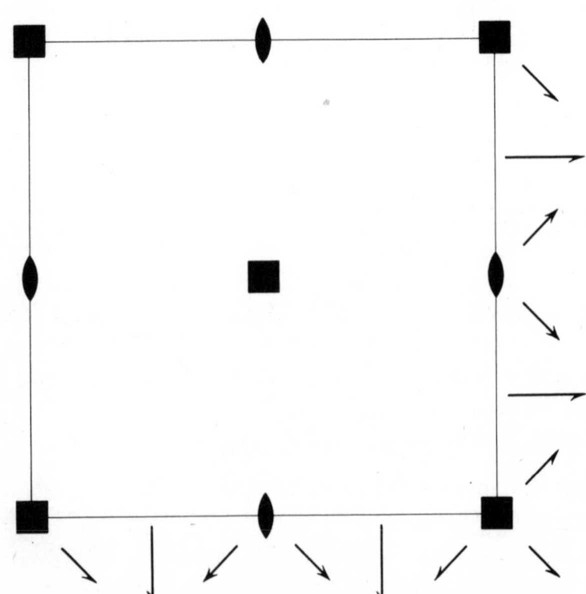

FIG. 35*b*. $P42_12$. Horizontal axes at levels z, as shown, have translation mates at levels $z + \frac{1}{2}$.

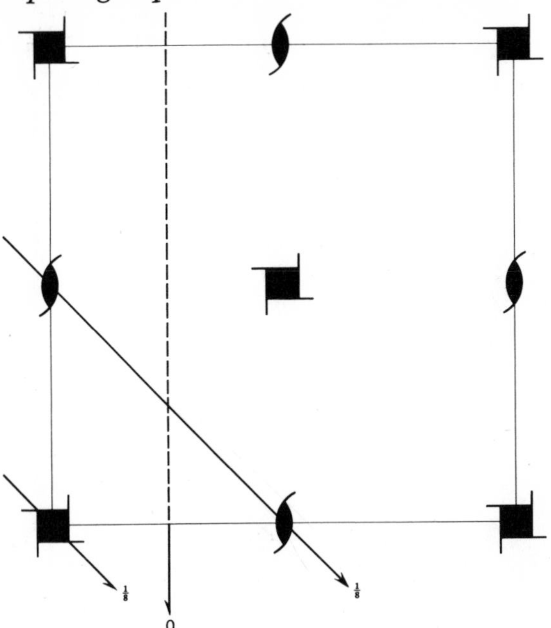

FIG. 36*a*. Scheme of $P4_12_12$.

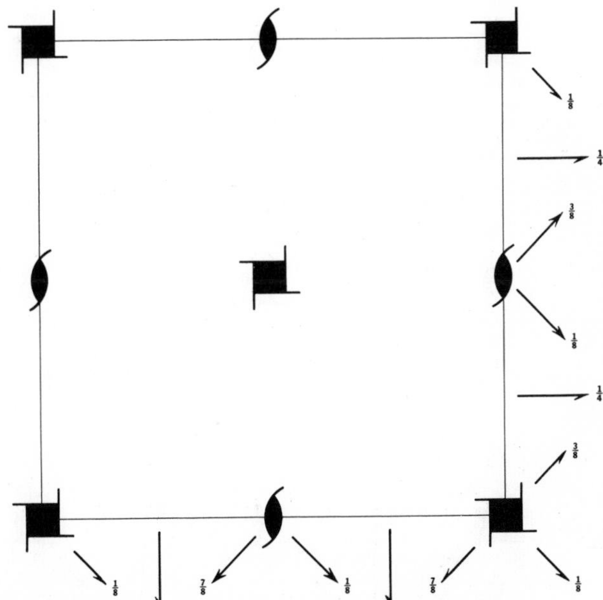

FIG. 36*b*. $P4_12_12$. Horizontal axes at levels z, as shown, have translation mates at levels $z + \frac{1}{2}$.

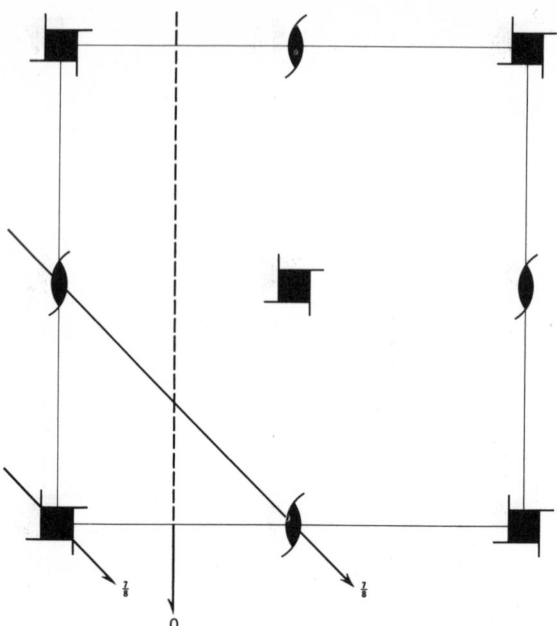

FIG. 37*a*. Scheme of $P4_32_12$.

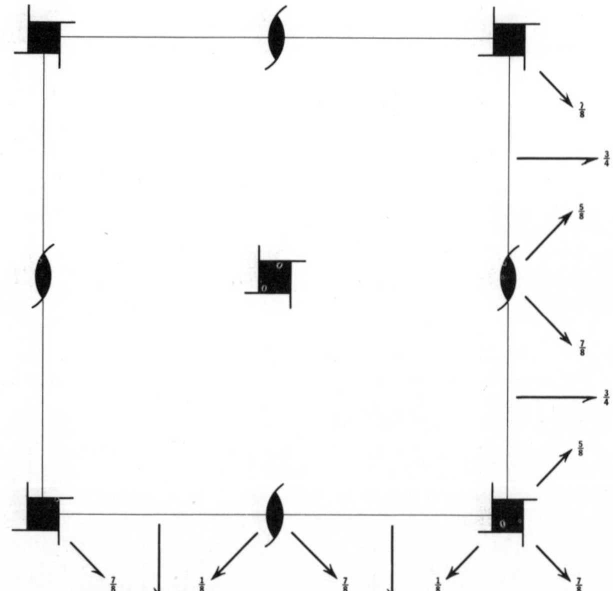

FIG. 37*b*. $P4_32_12$. Horizontal axes at levels z, as shown, have translation mates at levels $z + \frac{1}{2}$.

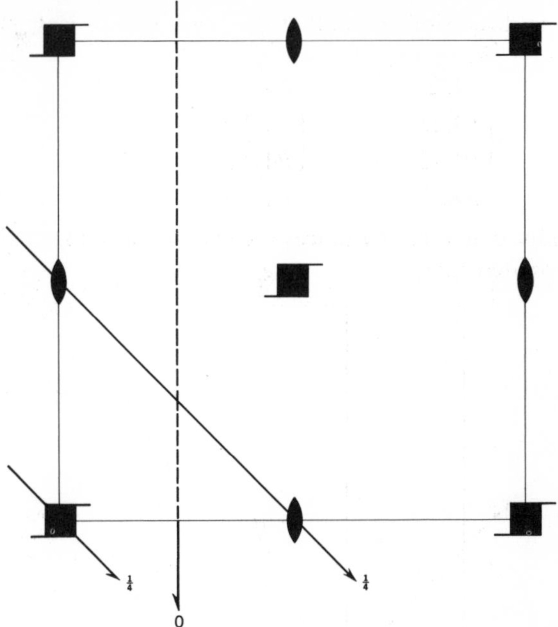

FIG. 38*a*. Scheme of $P4_22_12$.

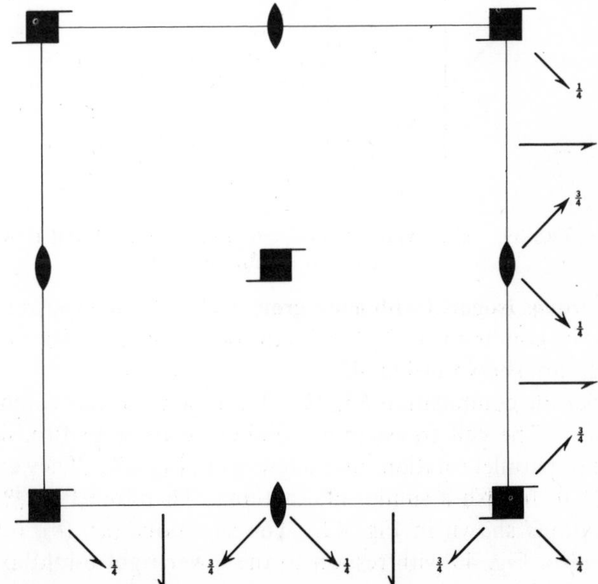

FIG. 38*b*. $P4_22_12$. Horizontal axes at levels z, as shown, have translation mates at levels $z+\frac{1}{2}$.

The foregoing discussion shows that the space groups isogonal with 422 are as follows:

$P422$	$P422$	$I422$
$\{P4_122$	$\{P4_12_12$	$I4_122$
$\{P4_322$	$\{P4_32_12$	
$P4_122$	$P4_22_12$	

The space groups connected by braces are enantiomorphous pairs. The other six space groups are neutral.

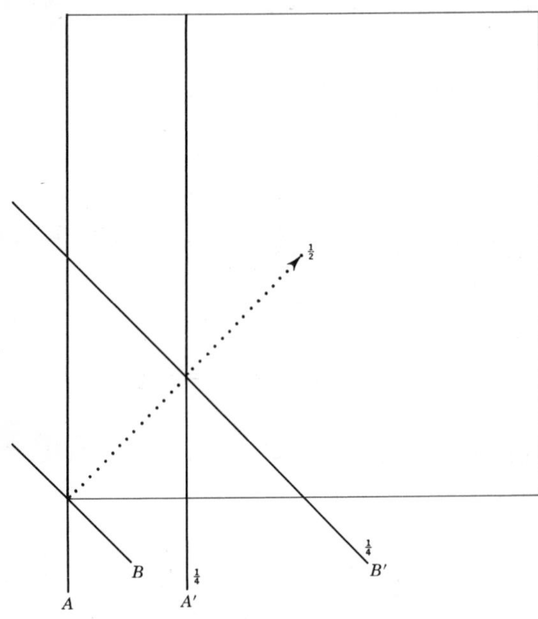

FIG. 39. The combination of 2-fold screw axes A and B with the centering translation of lattice I.

Space groups isogonal with point group 622. Space groups isogonal with 622 are found by combining $6_m2_m2_m$ with the one lattice P. The basic combinations of $6_m2_m2_m$ are shown in Fig. 42.

Consider the combination $P6_m22$. The scheme of this combination is shown in Fig. 43. The cell translations combine with A to furnish an alternating sequence of parallel rotations and screws as in Fig. 17. They combine with B as in Fig. 21 to furnish a similar alternation. Therefore Fig. 43 contains all the four situations shown in Fig. 42. The situations (*a*), (*b*), (*c*), (*d*) of Fig. 42 are labeled in Fig. 43 with respect to the lower right 6-fold axis. This means that the following space groups are the same:

$$6_m22 = 6_m2_12 = 6_m22_1 = 6_m2_12_1.$$

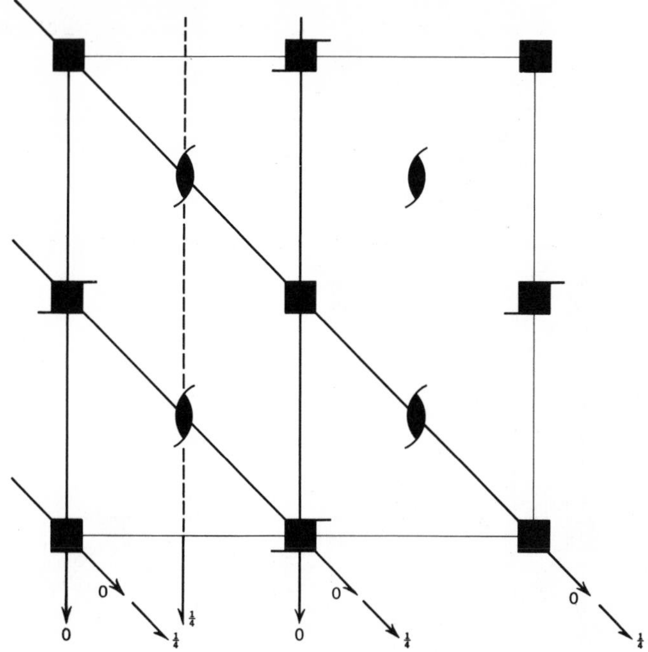

FIG. 40*a*. Scheme of *I*422.

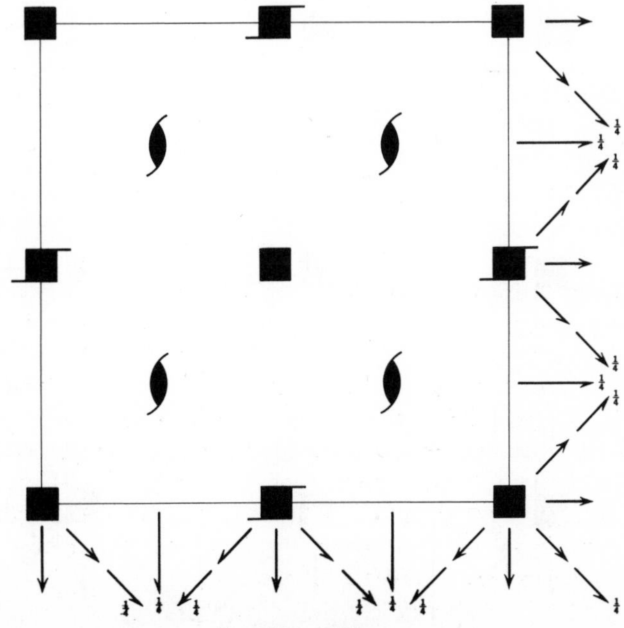

FIG. 40*b*. *I*422.

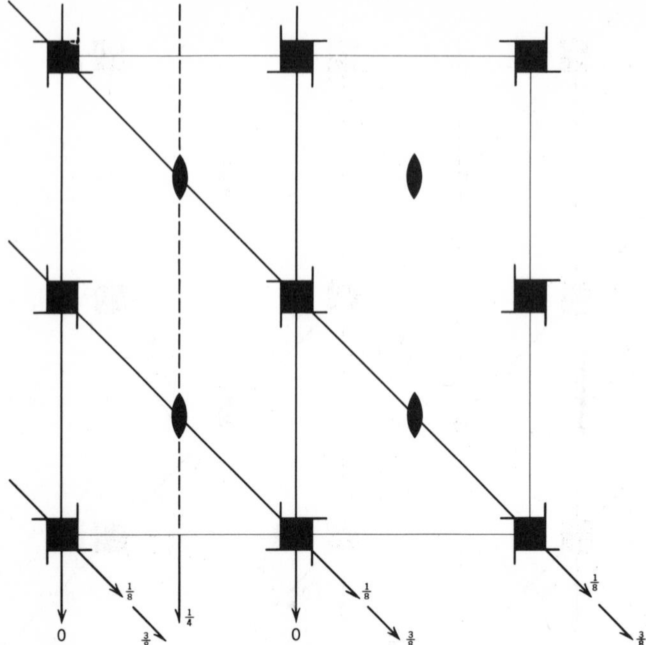

FIG. 41*a*. Scheme of $I4_122$.

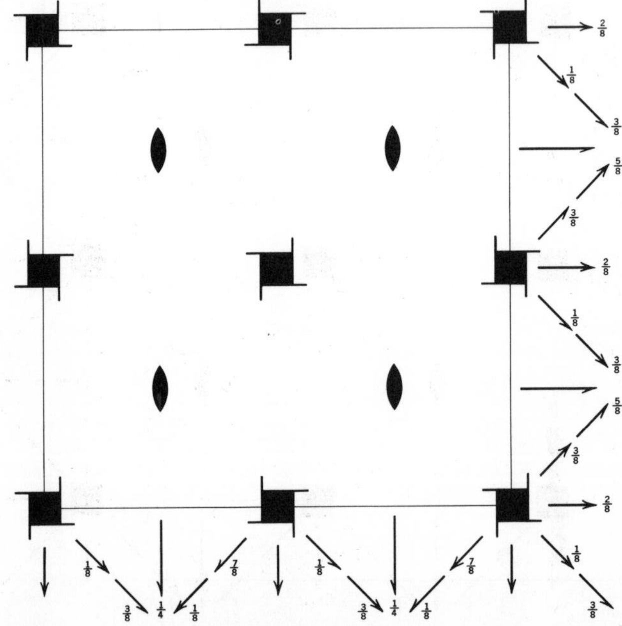

FIG. 41*b*. $I4_122$.

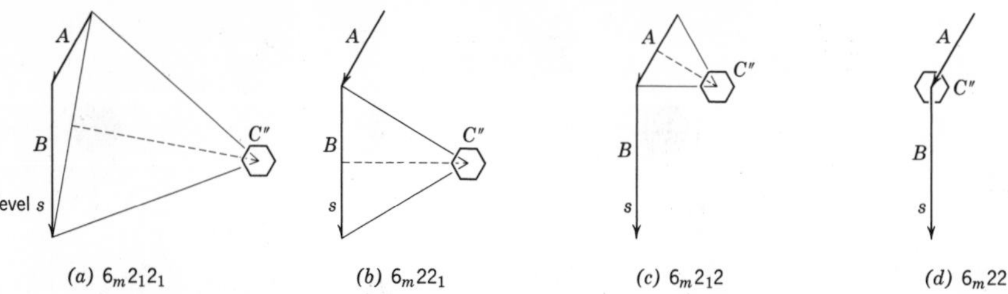

FIG. 42. The possible combinations of axes of the form $6_m 2_m 2_m$.

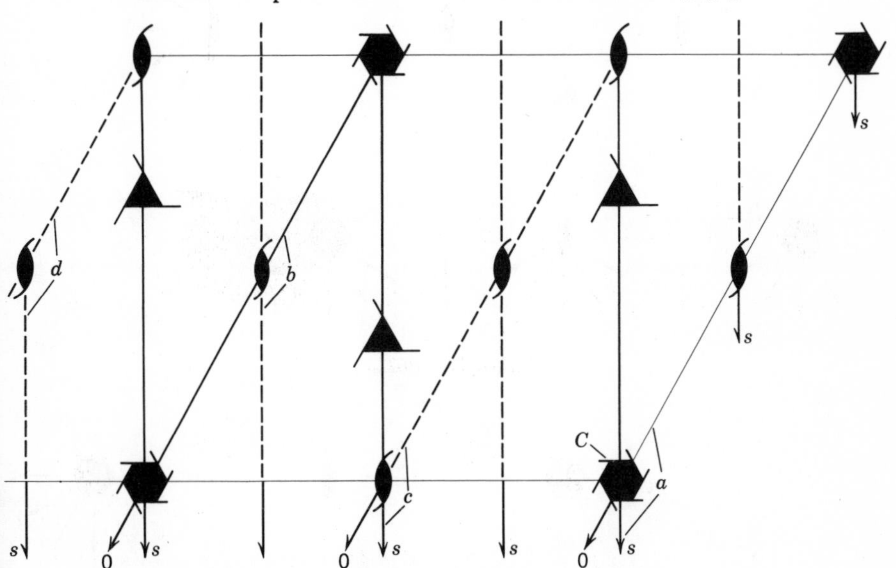

FIG. 43. Scheme of space groups $P6_m22$. The neighborhoods *a*, *b*, *c*, and *d* are the four situations of Fig. 42.

It remains only to adjust the value of *s* of Fig. 43 to the six possible screws 6, 6_1, 6_2, 6_3, 6_4, and 6_5. The resulting space groups (in a different order) are shown in Figs. 44–49.

This discussion shows that the following six space groups are isogonal with 622:

$$P622$$

$$\begin{cases} P6_122 \\ P6_522 \end{cases}$$

$$\begin{cases} P6_222 \\ P6_422 \end{cases}$$

$$P6_322$$

The space groups connected by braces are enantiomorphic pairs. The other two are neutral.

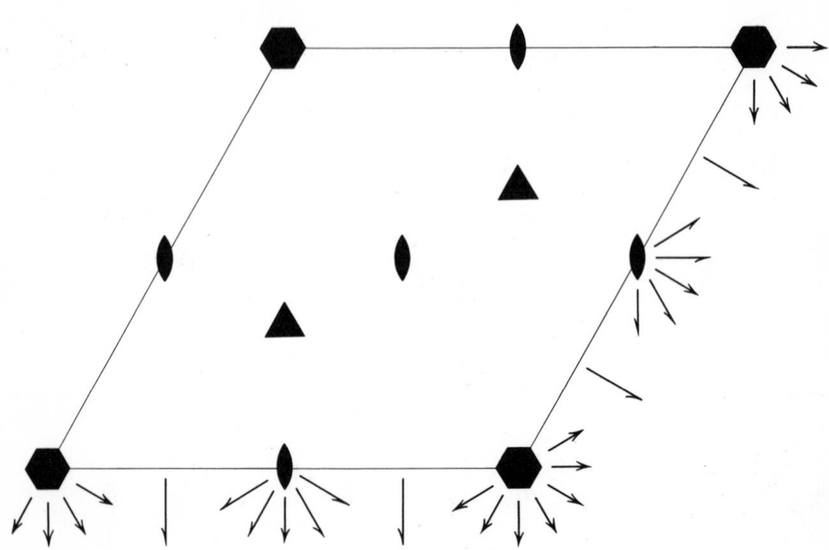

FIG. 44. *P*622.

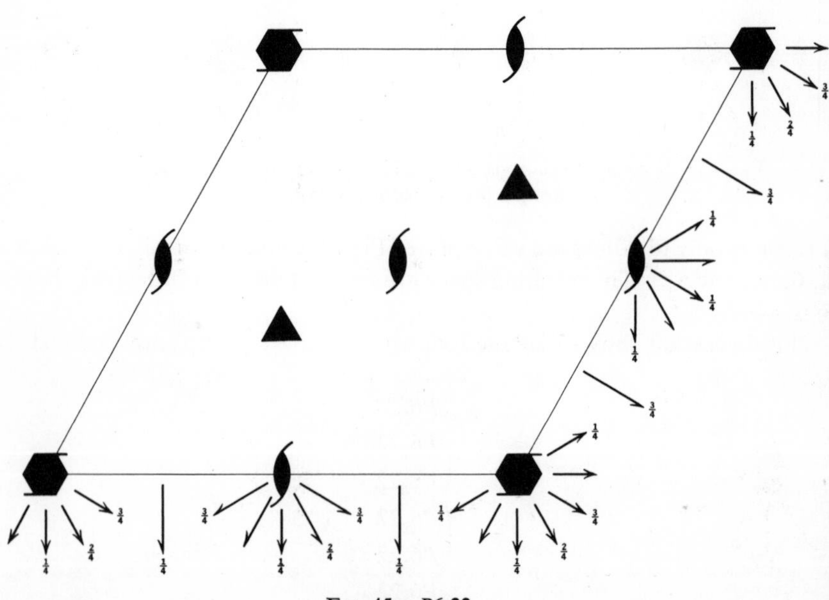

FIG. 45. $P6_322$.

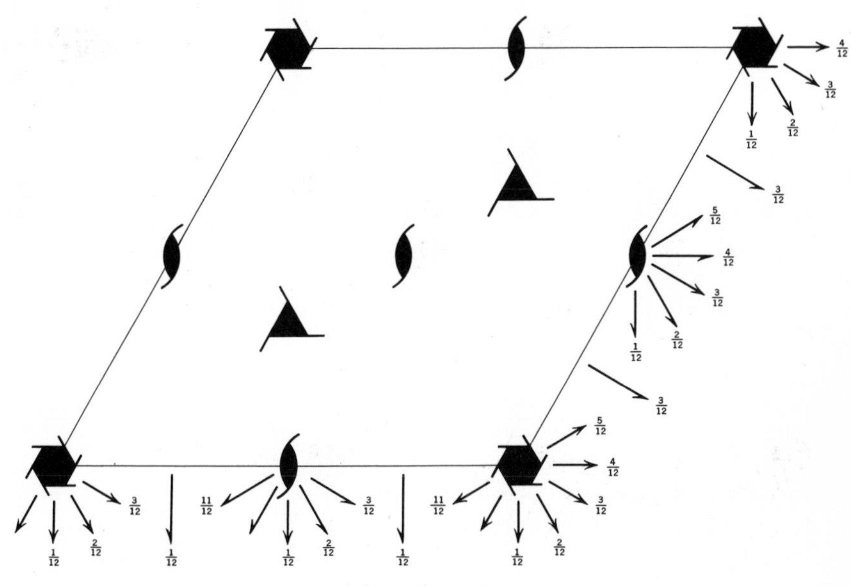

FIG. 46. $P6_122$.

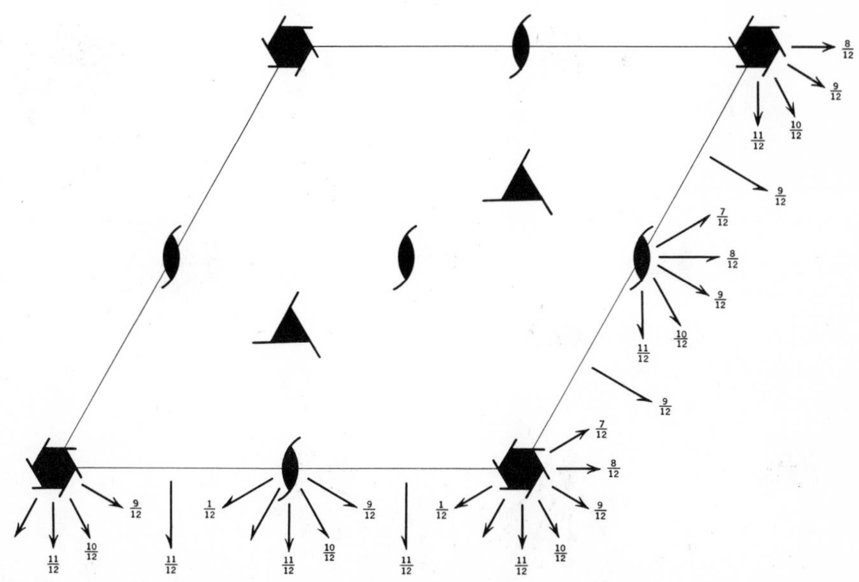

FIG. 47. $P6_522$.

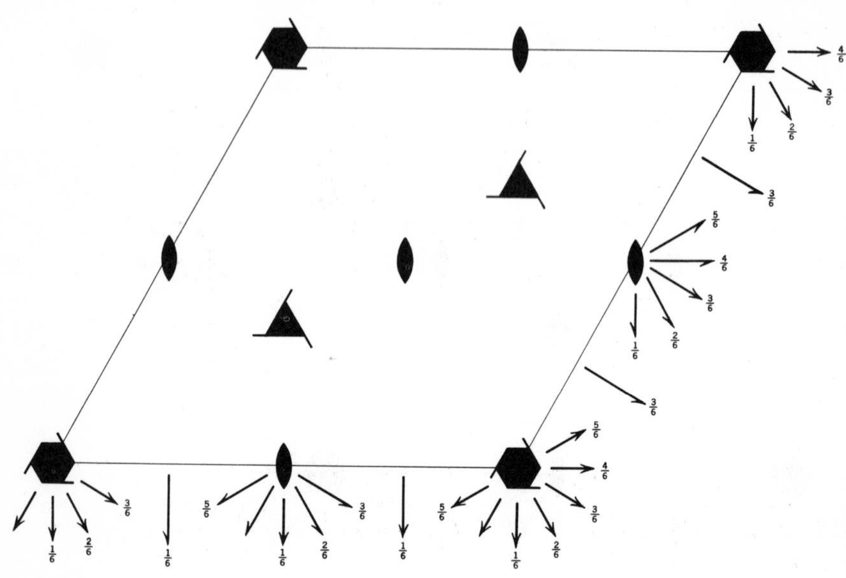

FIG. 48. $P6_222$.

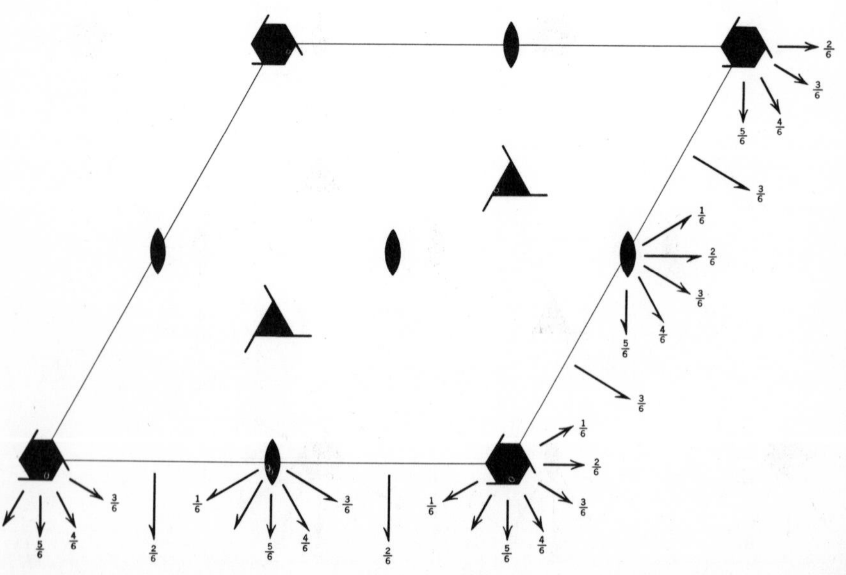

FIG. 49. $P6_422$.

Résumé of the dihedral space groups. As a result of the discussion of this chapter, all the space groups isogonal with the dihedral groups have been derived. There are 32 such groups, as follows:

$P222$	$P321$	$P422$	$P622$
$P222_1$	$P3_121$	$P4_122$	$P6_122$
$P2_12_12$	$P3_221$	$P4_322$	$P6_522$
$P2_12_12_1$	$P312$	$P4_222$	$P6_222$
$C222$	$P3_112$	$P42_12$	$P6_422$
$C222_1$	$P3_212$	$P4_12_12$	$P6_322$
$I222$	$R32$	$P4_32_12$	
$I2_12_12_1$		$P4_22_12$	
$F222$		$I422$	
		$I4_122$	

$$9 + 7 + 10 + 6 = 32$$

The space groups connected by braces are enantiomorphous pairs. The rest are neutral.

15 · The isometric axial space groups

The space groups of the isometric system can be derived by means of the same principles as used for deriving the dihedral space groups of the last chapter. This straightforward procedure is difficult only because it is difficult to visualize the combination of *any* two axes A and B of (22) of Chapter 14. A procedure that can be more readily visualized has been adopted in this book for the isometric system. It consists essentially of adding a new operation or symmetry element which transforms a previously derived space group into the new desired space group. In this way most of the details of groups already derived can be retained, and only a few new details need be sought.

Space groups isogonal with point group 23

Point group 23 was derived in Chapter 4 as a result of combining the three axes 233 by using Euler's relation. It can also be derived by adding the operations of a 3-fold axis to the operations of the orthorhombic point group 222, as suggested in Fig. 1. It follows that the 3-fold axis specializes each of the 2-fold axes by requiring them to be identical.

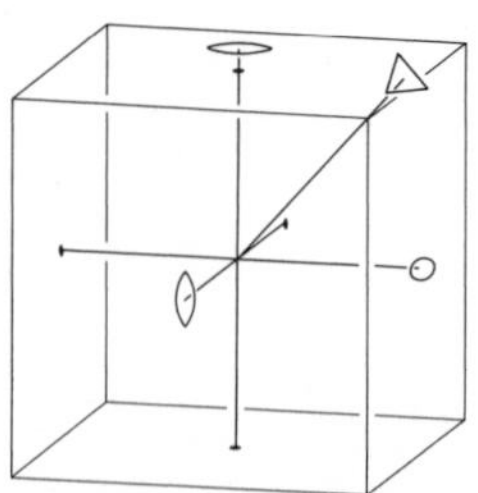

FIG. 1. Derivation of point group 23 from point group 222.

To find the space groups isogonal with 23, the operations of the various screws, isogonal with the several axes of point group 23, are combined with the translations of one of the permissible isometric lattices P, I, or F. First consider how the 3-fold screws and the lattices combine. Each of these isometric lattices is a specialization of a rhombohedral lattice, as shown in Figs. 2, 3, and 4. Therefore the combinations of any 3-fold screw with any isometric lattice

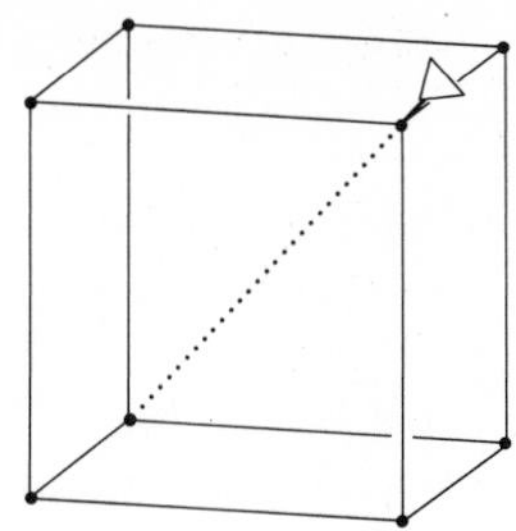

FIG. 2. Relation of isometric lattice *P* to rhombohedral lattice *R*.

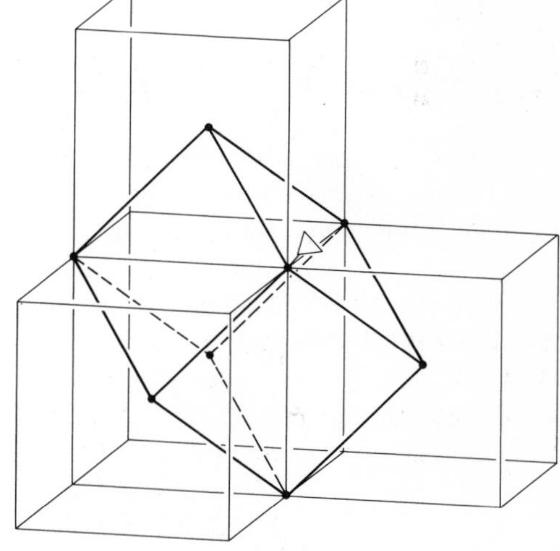

FIG. 3. Relation of isometric lattice *I* to rhombohedral lattice *R*.

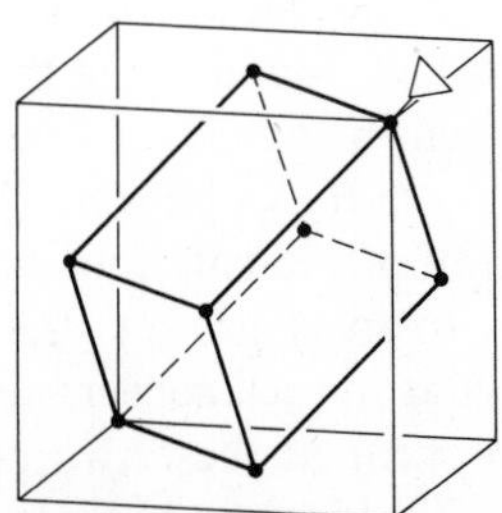

FIG. 4. Relation of isometric lattice *F* to rhombohedral lattice *R*.

produces an arrangement of symmetry axes the same as in space group *R*3 (Fig. 17, Chapter 13), parallel with each of the four 3-fold axes of point group 23. This set of axes contains 3, 3_1, and 3_2 axes.

Next consider the combination of three orthogonal 2-fold screws (which are isogonal with the 2-fold axes of Fig. 1) with the lattices *P*, *I*, and *F*. These are the space groups *P*222, $P222_1$, $P2_12_12$, $P2_12_12_1$, *C*222, $C222_1$, *I*222, $I2_12_12_1$, and *F*222 (Figs. 5–14, Chapter 14). The only ones of these that can become incorporated into isometric space groups are those whose three sets of axes can become equivalent by the axes of *R*3. In other words, just as the 3-fold axis of Fig. 1 requires the three 2-fold axes to be identical, so the space group *R*3 requires each of the three orthogonal sets of 2-fold axes of the isometric space groups to be identical. Of the nine axial orthorhombic space groups listed above, the only ones for which this is true are the following five symmetrical ones: *P*222, $P2_12_12_1$, *I*222, $I2_12_12_1$, and *F*222. In each of these space groups, the three sets of 2-fold axes necessarily become related by all the symmetry elements of each of the four *R*3 groups. If the relation of the 3-fold rotation to the above five groups can be found, the other axes of the *R*3 groups can be located. This can be readily found since a 3-fold rotation axis must transform the three sets of 2-fold axes into one another. The locations of the 3-fold axis which accomplish this are as shown in Figs. 5–9 for the five possible groups. These illustrations show only one octant of an isometric unit cell.

In this way the following new space groups are generated by adding a 3-fold axis to the five orthorhombic groups:

$$P222 \cdot 3 \rightarrow P23 \qquad \text{(Fig. 5, 10)},$$
$$P2_12_12_1 \cdot 3 \rightarrow P2_13 \qquad \text{(Fig. 6, 11)},$$
$$I222 \cdot 3 \rightarrow I23 \qquad \text{(Fig. 7, 12)},$$
$$I2_12_12_1 \cdot 3 \rightarrow I2_13 \qquad \text{(Fig. 8, 13)},$$
$$F222 \cdot 3 \rightarrow F23 \qquad \text{(Fig. 9, 14)}.$$

The new symmetry elements added to each of the groups on the left of the above list become groups *R*3 parallel to each 3-fold axis in point group 23. Starting with the locations of the 3-fold rotation axis given by Figs. 5–9, the locations of the 3_1 and 3_2 axes are found along the diagonal of the rhombohedra of Figs. 2, 3, and 4, as shown in Fig. 17 of Chapter 13. The complete distribution of symmetry elements are thus obtained. These are illustrated in Figs. 10–14.

The distribution of 3-fold rotation axes in the space groups isogonal with 23 are of two kinds. In space groups *P*23, *I*23, and *F*23 the 3-fold axis and three 2-fold axes intersect at the cell corners and also at the cell center. This requires point group 23 to occur at these two points, and consequently there intersect at these points four 3-fold axes and three 2-fold axes. The resulting distribution of pure 3-fold rotation axes for *P*23, *I*23, and *F*23 is shown in Fig. 15. On

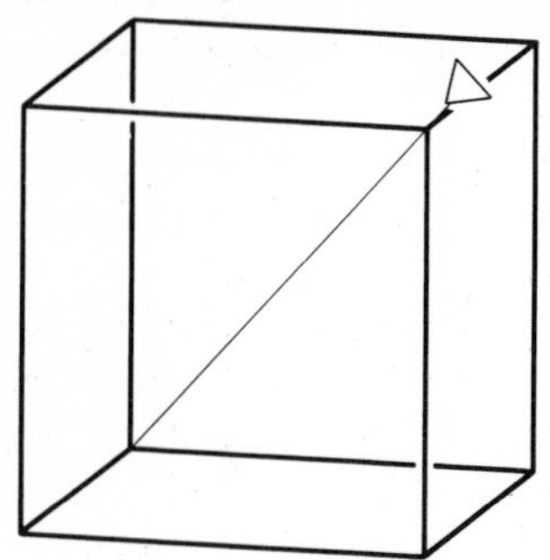

FIG. 5. $P222 \rightarrow P23$

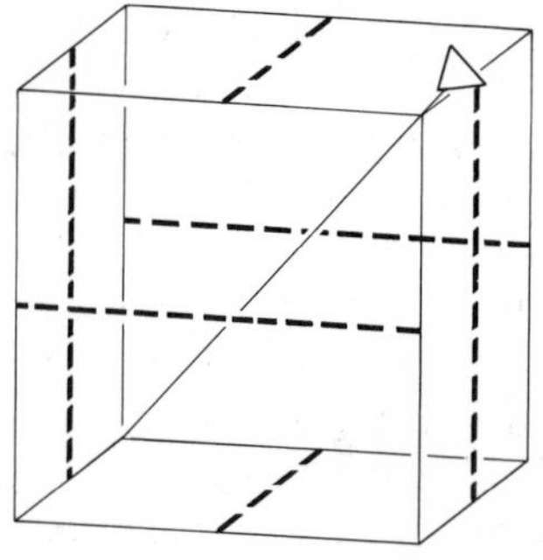

FIG. 6. $P2_12_12_1 \rightarrow P2_13$

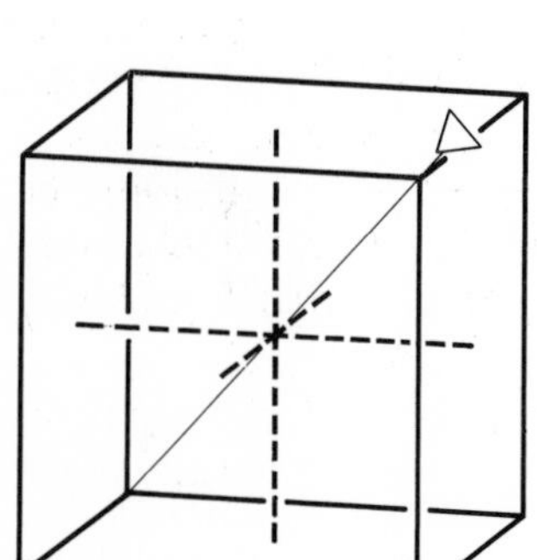

FIG. 7. $I222 \rightarrow I23$

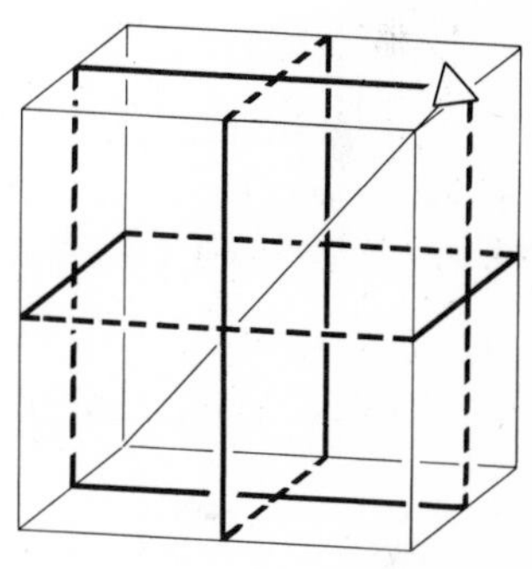

FIG. 8. $I2_12_12_1 \rightarrow I2_13$

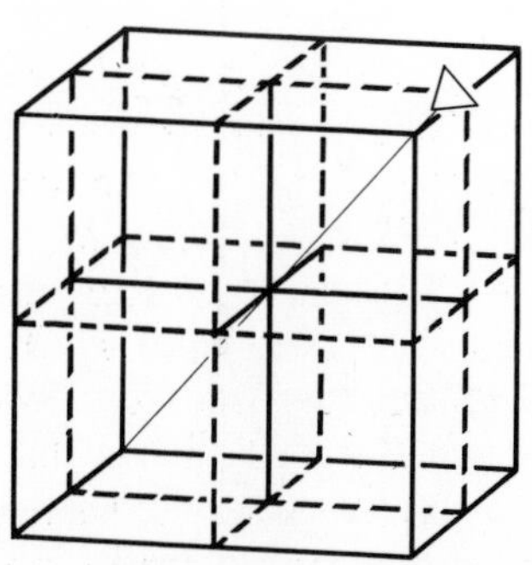

FIG. 9. $F222 \rightarrow F23$

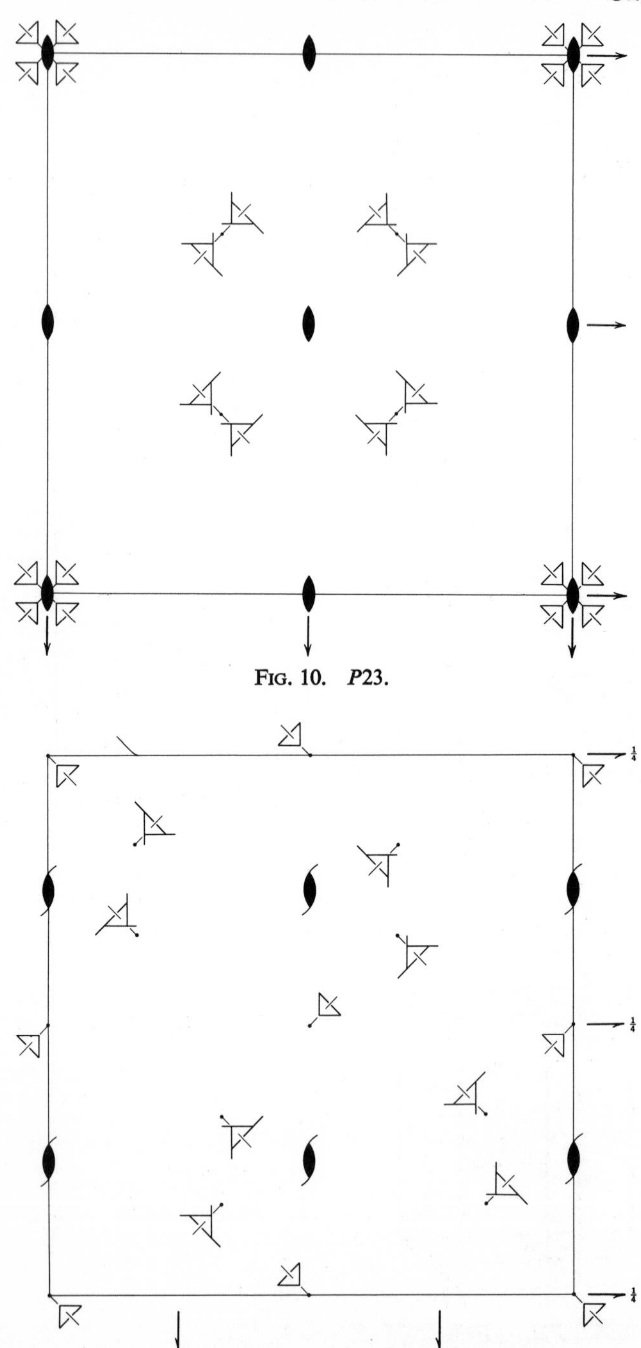

FIG. 10. *P*23.

FIG. 11. $P2_13$.

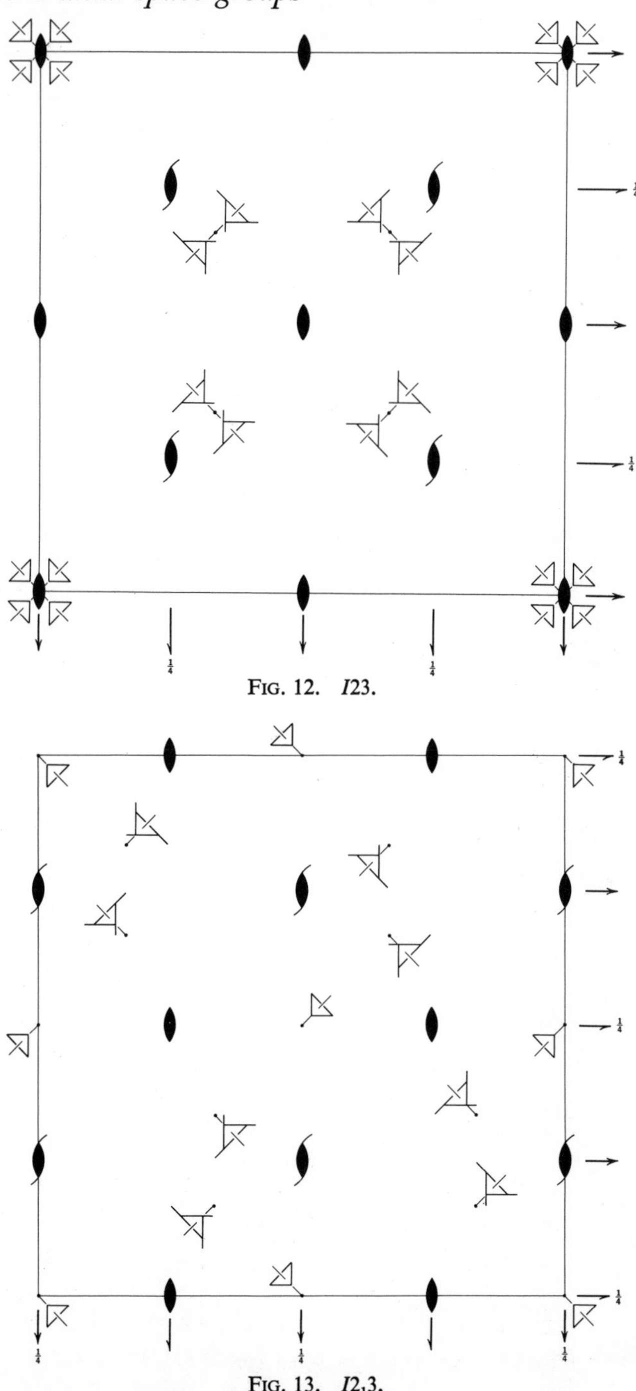

FIG. 12. *I*23.

FIG. 13. *I*$2_1$3.

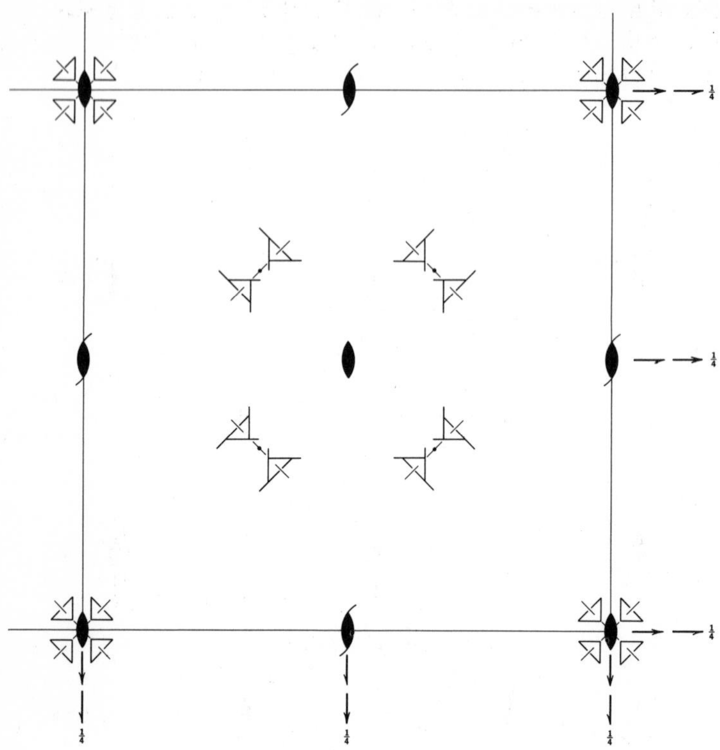

FIG. 14. *F*23. The diagram shows only one octant of the full cell.

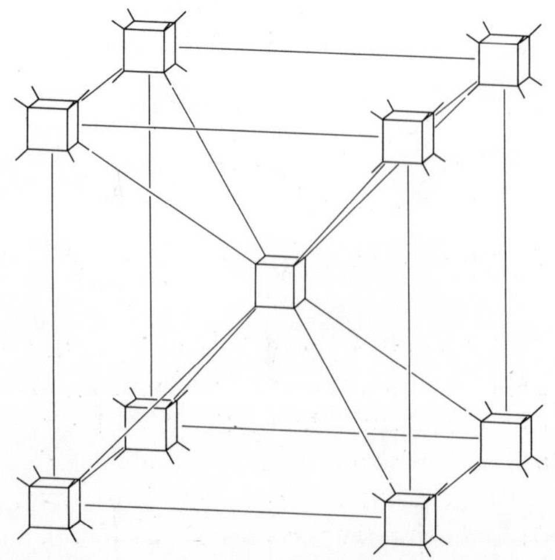

FIG. 15. Distribution of 3-fold axes in *P*23, *I*23, and *F*23.

the other hand, in space groups $P2_13$ and $I2_13$, the 3-fold axes intersect no other axes and so cannot form point group 23 at any point. In this case the 3-fold axes are distributed by the 2-fold screw axes as shown in Fig. 16.

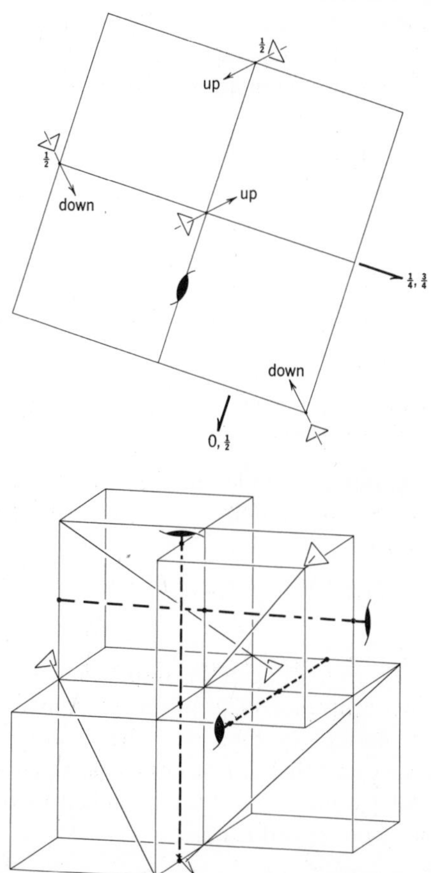

Fig. 16. Distribution of 3-fold axes in $P2_13$ and $I2_13$.

Space groups isogonal with point group 432

Theory of derivation. To find the space groups isogonal with 432, the operations of the various screws isogonal with the several axes of point group 432 are combined with the translations of one of the permissible isometric lattices *P*, *I*, or *F*. Figure 17 shows the arrangement of three axes of point group 432 whose operations are related. The relation is specifically

$$A_{2\pi/3} \cdot B_{\pi} = C_{-\pi/2}. \quad (1)$$

The migration of points under operations $A \cdot B$ is shown in the sequence $1 \rightarrow 2 \rightarrow 3$ in Fig. 18. This migration is clearly equivalent to $C_{-\pi/2}$.

The fact that the rotation about B is π makes it fairly easy to solve equation (22) of Chapter 14. If one looks down at the top of the cube in Fig. 17, the arrangement of axes is seen to be as in Fig. 19, except that A is actually above B, although shown somewhat separated in Fig. 19. Relation (1) holds for Fig. 19. Now consider the combination of A with a displaced B, specifically

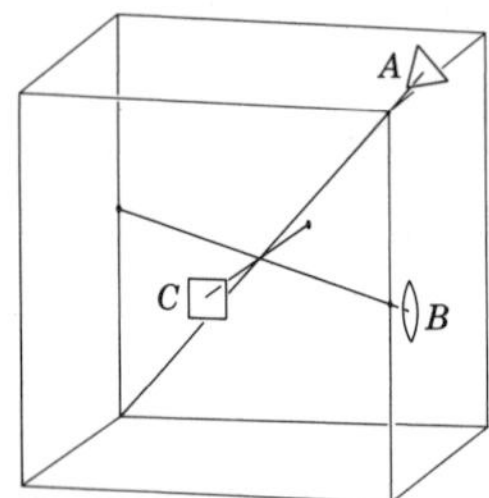

FIG. 17. Arrangement of related 3-fold, 2-fold, and 4-fold rotations in class 432.

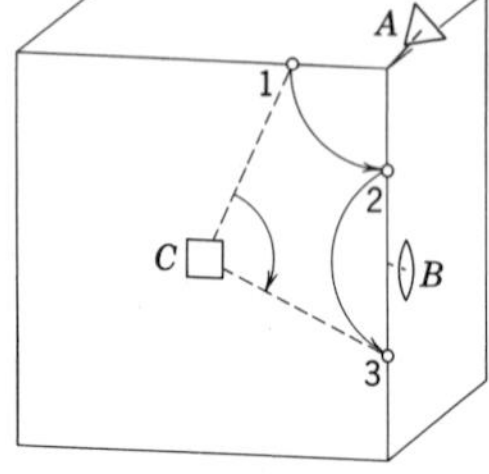

FIG. 18. Directions of related rotations in class 432.

${}^{s}B_{\pi}$, Fig. 20. The reasoning is similar to that leading to (21) of Chapter 14. The first step in analyzing the combination is to apply (16) of Chapter 14, but simplified so as to omit t_2:

$$A_{2\pi/3} \cdot {}^{s}B_{\pi} = A_{2\pi/3} \cdot B_{\pi} \cdot 2s \tag{2}$$

$$= C_{-\pi/2} \cdot 2s, \quad \text{from (1).} \tag{3}$$

The translation $T = 2s$, Fig. 21, can be resolved into $T_{\parallel}$ and $T_{\perp}$. The $T_{\perp}$ component causes the occurrence of a 4-fold screw at C'. This is illustrated by an end view of C and C' in Fig. 22. The $T_{\parallel}$ component adds itself to rotation $C_{-\pi/2}$. In the event that B is a nontrivial screw $B_{\pi,t}$, the components of t perpendicular and parallel to C must be added to the translation in (3). The more general forms of (2) and (3) are

$$A_{2\pi/3} \cdot {}^{s}B_{\pi,t} = A_{2\pi/3} \cdot B_{\pi} t \cdot 2s \tag{4}$$

$$= C_{-\pi/2} \cdot t,\ 2s$$

$$= C_{-\pi/2, t_{\parallel}+2s_{\parallel}} \cdot t_{\perp} \cdot 2s_{\perp}. \tag{5}$$

The arrangement of 3-fold axes in point group 432 is exactly the same as in point group 23. The point group 23 was derived in Chapter 4 as the combination 233. This implies that, whenever 3-fold axes are combined as in the isometric system, 2-fold axes arise as in point group 23. The only space groups isogonal with 23 are the five derived in the last section. These space groups consequently contain the only possible arrangements of 3-fold axes. Since 3-fold axes also occur in space groups isogonal with class 432, these same

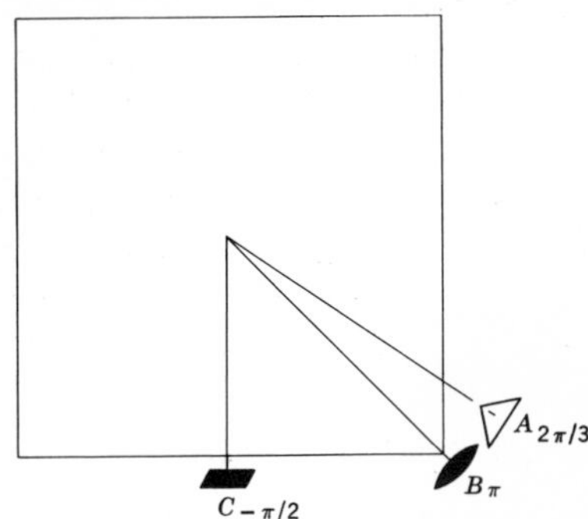

FIG. 19. Rotations of Fig. 17, seen looking approximately normal to upper face of cube.

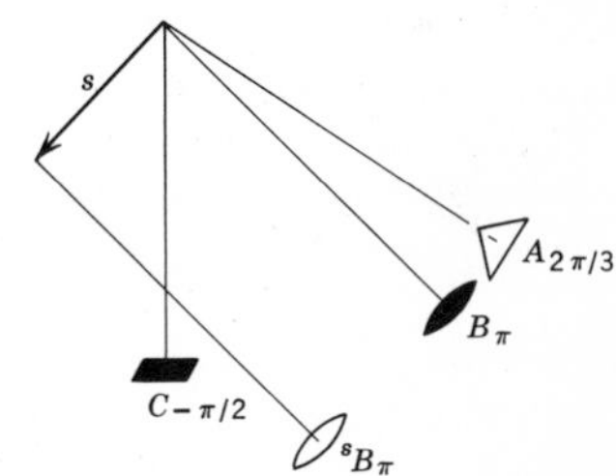

FIG. 20. Transformation of B_π in Fig. 19 to ${}^sB_\pi$.

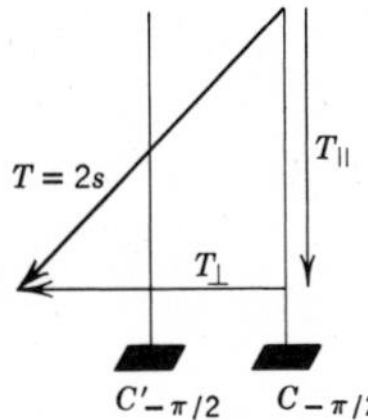

FIG. 21. Combination of $C_{-\pi/2}$ of Fig. 19 with T.

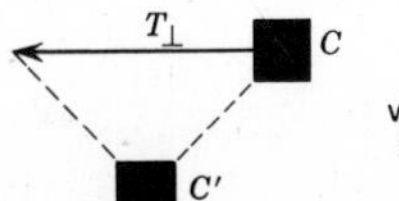

FIG. 22. View of Fig. 21 along axis C.

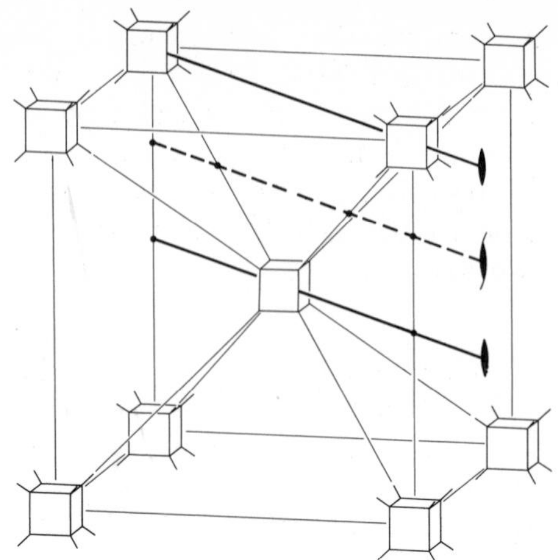

FIG. 23. Transformation of *P*23, *I*23, and *F*23 into themselves by means of 2 and 2_1 axes parallel to [110].

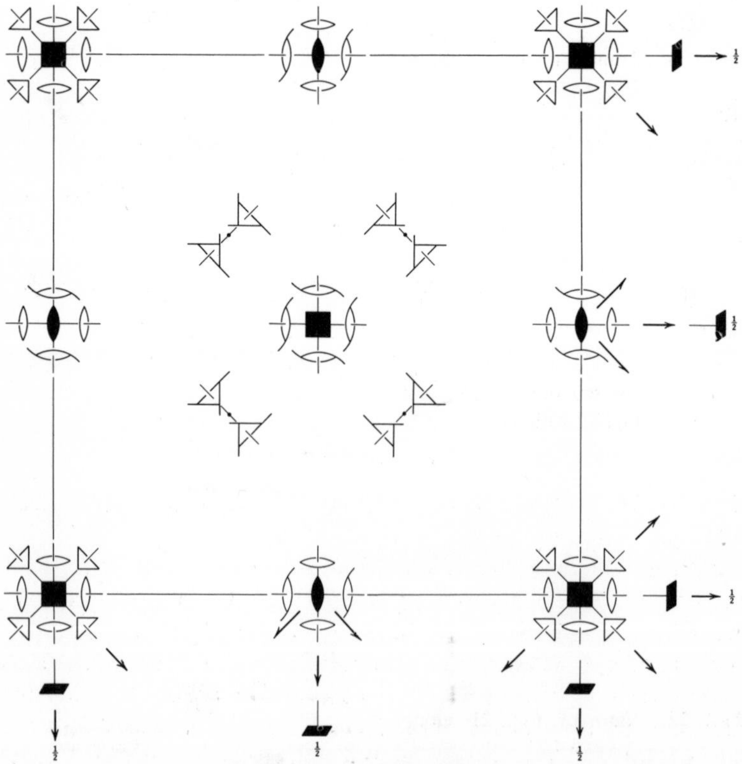

FIG. 24. *P*432.

arrangements of 3-fold axes must be contained in the space groups isogonal with 432. This is the same as saying that the space groups isogonal with 432 are based upon the five space groups of the preceding section, and that they can be found by adding appropriate operations to those five space groups.

The operation to be added is necessarily a 2-fold rotation or screw parallel to *B* of Fig. 17. This combines with the 3-fold axes to produce 4-fold axes

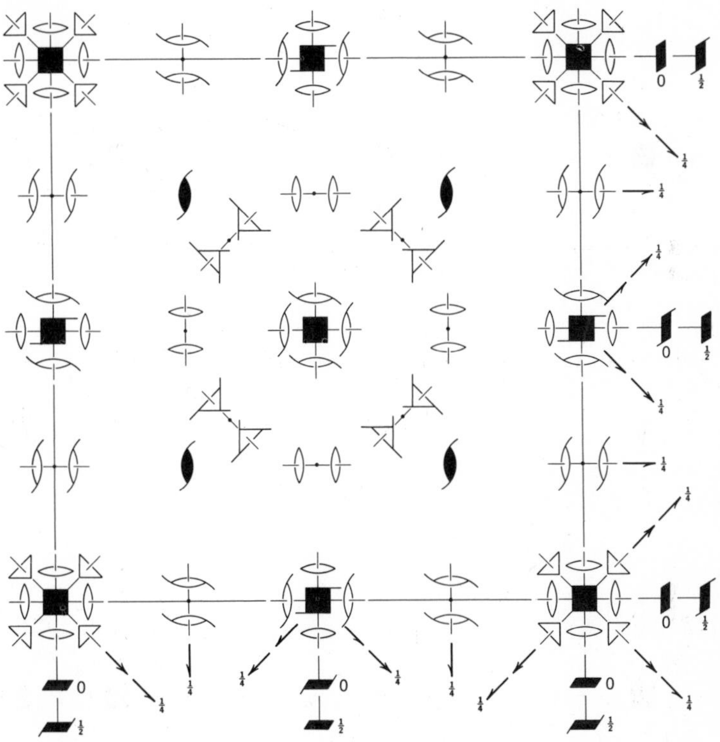

FIG. 25. *I*432.

according to (3) or (5). Whatever operation is added, it must transform the original space group into itself.

Space groups derivable from *P*23, *I*23, and *F*23. In space groups *P*23, *I*23, and *F*23 (Figs. 10, 12, and 14, respectively) the 3-fold axes intersect at cell corners and at the cell center, as shown in Fig. 15. As a consequence a collection of axes the same as in point group 23 occurs at these points. In *F*23 this group also occurs in the centers of octants, as shown in Fig. 9. The axes of the collection can be transformed into themselves by adding a 2-fold operation parallel to [110], either as a pure rotation through the symmetry locations 23, or as screws halfway between them as shown in Fig. 23.

First consider adding the pure 2-fold rotation through the locations where 3-fold axes intersect. This new operation transforms the intersection locations having symmetry 23 to symmetry 432. The original space groups then become new space groups as follows:

$P23 \cdot B_\pi \rightarrow P432$ (Fig. 24),
$I23 \cdot B_\pi \rightarrow I432$ (Fig. 25),
$F23 \cdot B_\pi \rightarrow F432$ (Fig. 26).

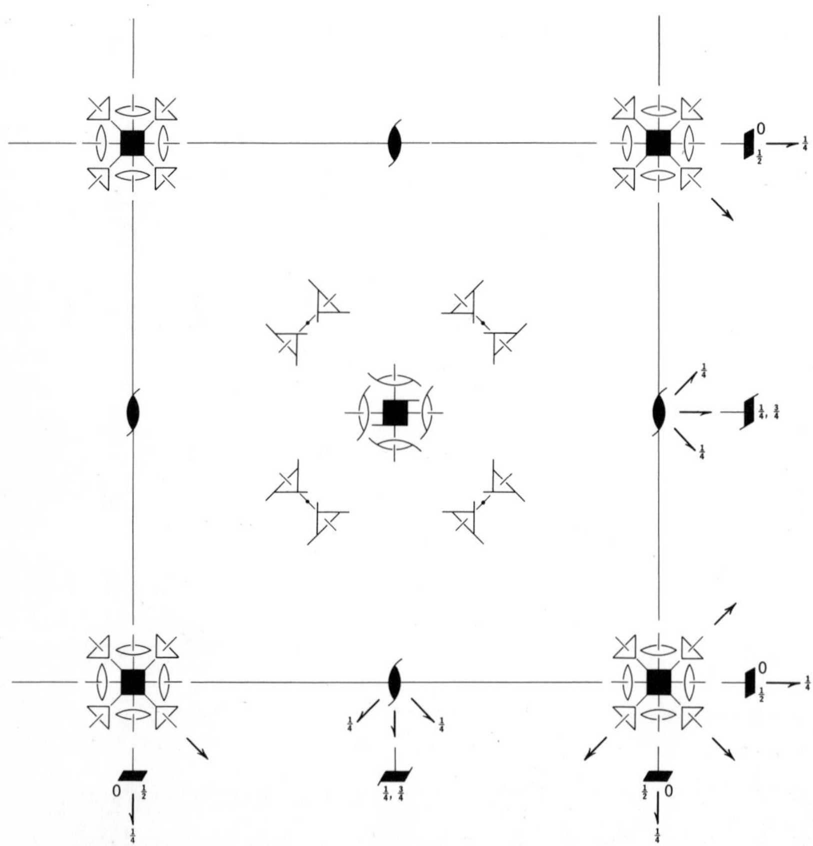

FIG. 26. *F*432. The diagram shows only one octant of the full cell.

The remaining symmetry elements of these space groups can be readily found because in the direction of each crystallographic axis there must occur one of the sets of axes isogonal with point group 422, as follows:

*P*432 contains 3 groups *P*422,
*I*432 ,, ,, ,, *I*422,
*F*432 ,, ,, ,, *I*422 in *F*422 orientation.

Next consider adding the 2-fold screw parallel to [110] but between intersections of 3-fold axes, as shown in Fig. 23. This operation already exists in *I*432, and so no new groups can be had by adding $B_{\pi,t}$ to *I*23. However, the operation does not exist in *P*432 or *F*432. Figure 5 shows that for *P*23 a diagonal screw halfway up the octant brings the crossings of 2-fold axes into

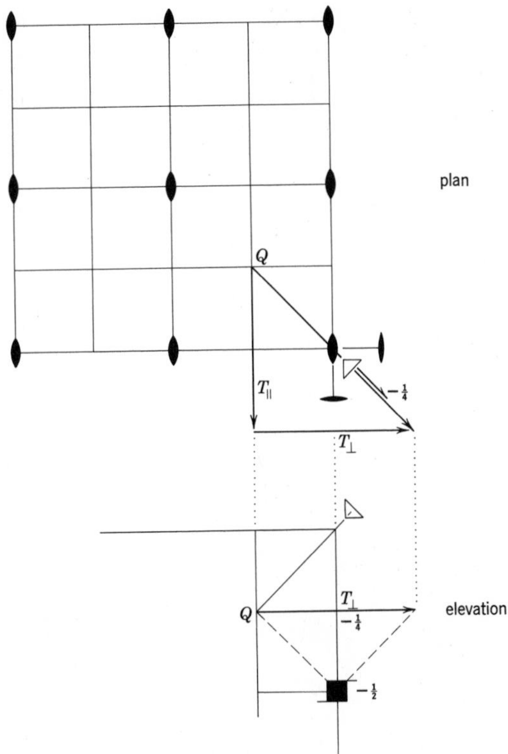

FIG. 27. Combination of *P*23 with 2_1 parallel to [110].

coincidence. The level of this screw is $-\frac{1}{4} = \frac{3}{4}$ (an equivalent screw arises at $+\frac{1}{4}$). Figure 9 shows that for *F*23 a diagonal screw at levels $-\frac{1}{8}$ or $-\frac{3}{8}$ from the top of the octant brings the crossing of 2-fold axes into coincidence.

The derivation of the characteristics of the new group is illustrated in Fig. 27. The operation $B_{\pi,T}$ is added at level $\frac{1}{4}$, or $\frac{3}{4} = -\frac{1}{4}$. The addition of $B_{\pi,T}$ at level $-\frac{1}{4}$ is specifically shown in Fig. 27. The screw and 3-fold rotation meet at point *Q*. Relation (5) can now be applied, with $s = 0$, since the axes intersect. The specific relation is

$$A_{2\pi/3} \cdot B_{\pi,t} = A_{2\pi/3} \cdot B_{\pi} \cdot t \tag{6}$$

$$= C_{-\pi/2} \cdot t \tag{7}$$

$$= C_{-\pi/2,t_{\|}} \cdot t_{\perp}. \tag{8}$$

The plan view in Fig. 27 shows the translation resolved into parallel and perpendicular components. The parallel component provides a screw pitch of $a/2$, where a is the cell edge. The screw is therefore 4_2. The perpendicular component locates the axis at a level $-\frac{1}{2}$ as shown in the elevation, Fig. 27. Therefore a new space group with a 4_2 axis is generated as follows:

$$P23 \cdot B_{\pi,t} \rightarrow P4_232 \qquad \text{(Fig. 28).}$$

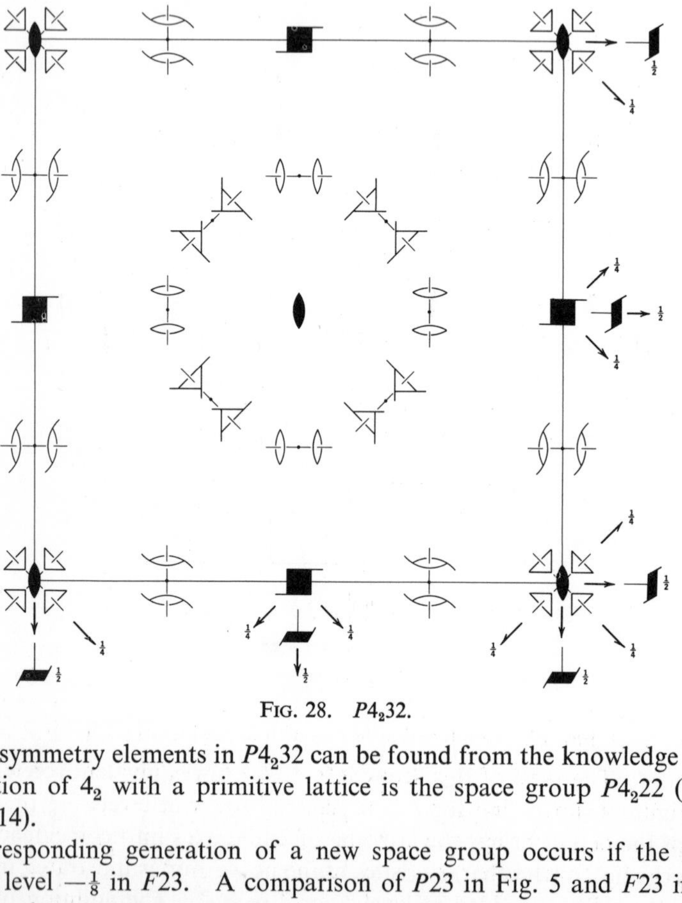

FIG. 28. $P4_232$.

The new symmetry elements in $P4_232$ can be found from the knowledge that the combination of 4_2 with a primitive lattice is the space group $P4_222$ (Fig. 33, Chapter 14).

A corresponding generation of a new space group occurs if the screw is added at level $-\frac{1}{8}$ in $F23$. A comparison of $P23$ in Fig. 5 and $F23$ in Fig. 9 shows that these arrangements of axes are the same except that the $F23$ arrangement is on half the scale of $P23$. The analysis given above, therefore, holds in $F23$ except that the scale is reduced by a factor of 2. As a result, whereas the 4-fold screw arising in $P23$ was 4_2, the half scale in $F23$ requires the pitch to be half value; accordingly the screw is 4_3. The new space group can be regarded as generated as follows:

$$F23 \cdot B_{\pi,t} \rightarrow F4_132 \qquad \text{(Fig. 29).}$$

Space groups derivable from $P2_13$ and $I2_13$. Space groups $P2_13$ (Fig. 6) and $I2_13$ (Fig. 8) both have a pattern of screw axes as shown in Fig. 30. These axes can be brought into coincidence with themselves by a diagonal 2-fold rotation at level $\frac{1}{8}$ or at level $\frac{3}{8}$. New groups isogonal with point group 432 can consequently be generated by adding diagonal rotations ${}^{s,\frac{1}{8}}B_\pi$ and ${}^{s,\frac{3}{8}}B_\pi$.

The combination of ${}^{s}B_\pi$ at a level $-\frac{1}{8}$ with the 3-fold axis is illustrated in Fig. 31. This makes specific use of (3). A 2-fold axis at the same level as ${}^{s}B$ would intersect the 3-fold axis at level $-\frac{1}{8}$. The combination $A_{2\pi/3}$ with B_π gives rise to $C_{-\pi/2}$ at level $-\frac{1}{8}$ as shown in the elevation. The displacement s causes a translation $T = 2s$ according to (15) of Chapter 14. The translation T can be broken down into $T_\perp$ and $T_\parallel$. The parallel component has a magnitude of $a/4$ and causes the rotation to become a screw $C_{-\pi/2,a/4}$. This is a left-hand screw 4_3. The perpendicular component causes a relocation of the axis (shown in the elevation) to level zero. Thus a set of axes $P4_3$ is generated parallel to a. The generation of this space group can be represented as

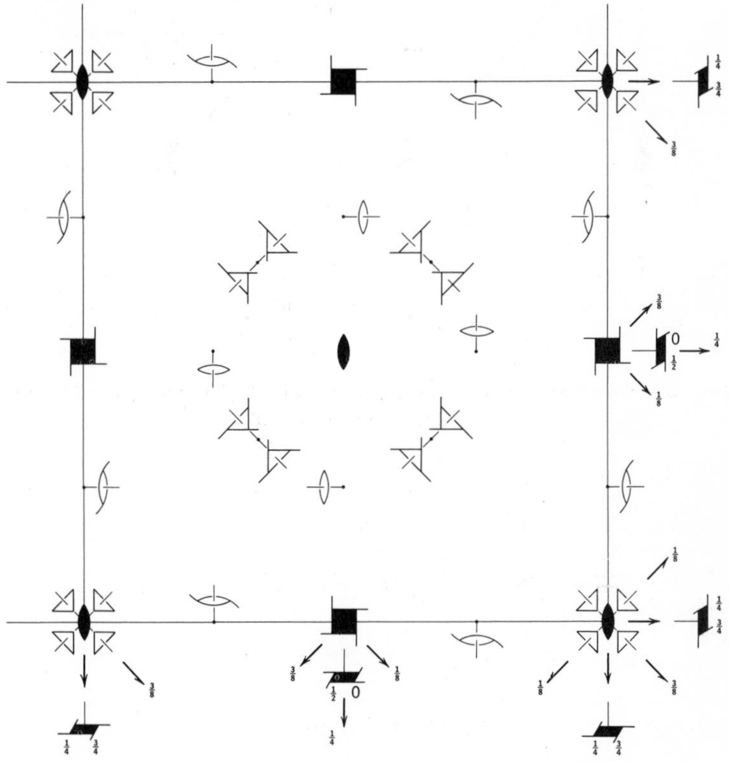

FIG. 29. $F4_132$. The diagram shows only one octant of the full cell.

$$P2_13 \cdot {}^{s,-\frac{1}{8}}B_\pi \rightarrow P4_332 \qquad \text{(Fig. 33).}$$

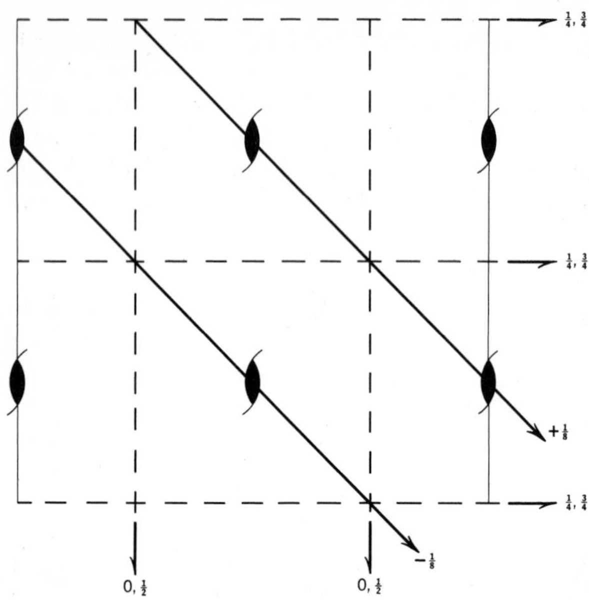

FIG. 30. Transformation of the 2-fold screws of $P2_13$ into themselves by 2-fold rotations parallel to [110].

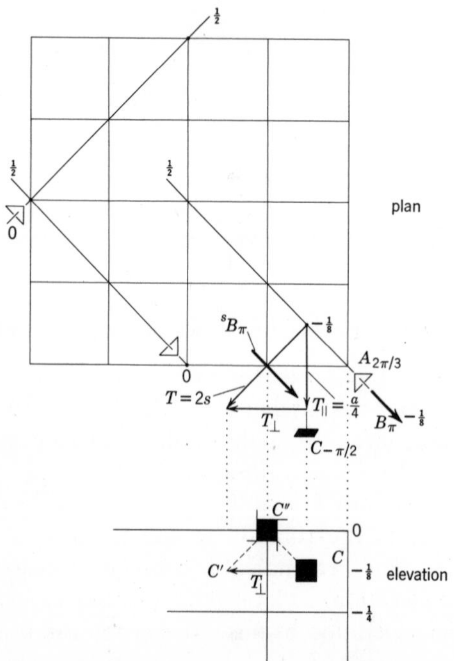

FIG. 31. Combination of ${}^sB_\pi$ with $A_{2\pi/3}$.

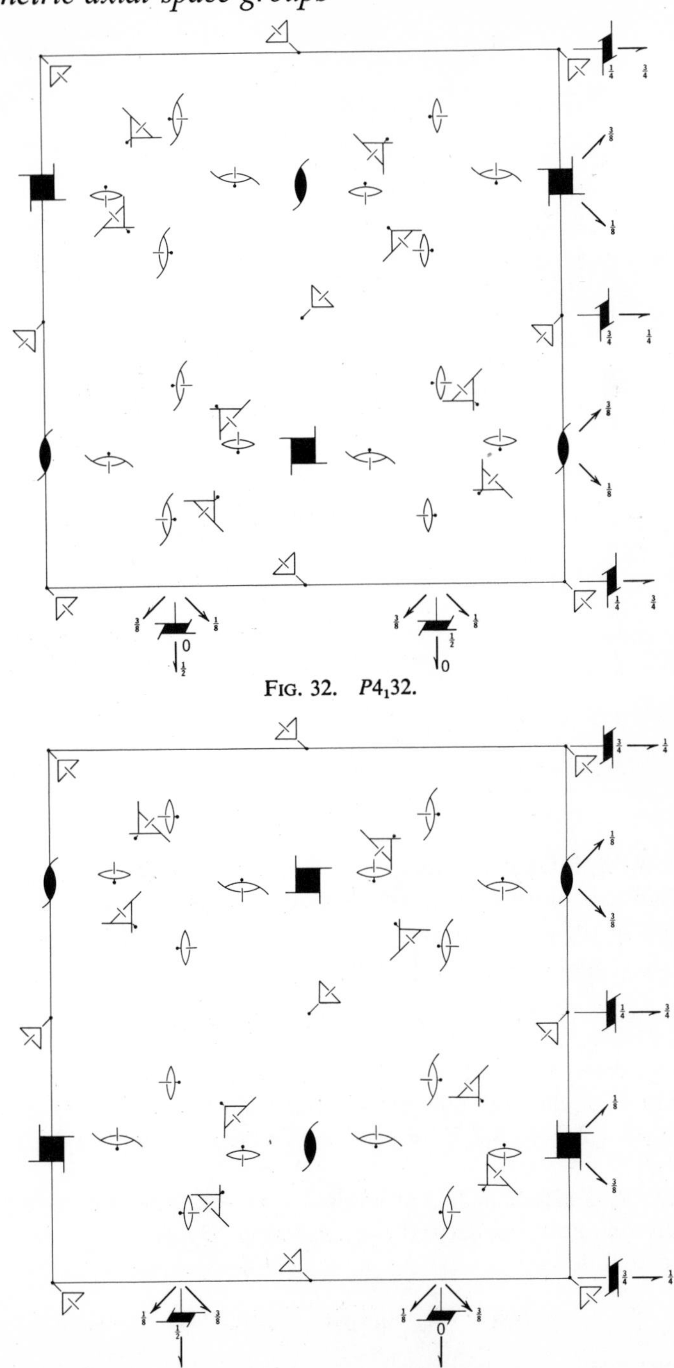

FIG. 32. $P4_132$.

FIG. 33. $P4_332$.

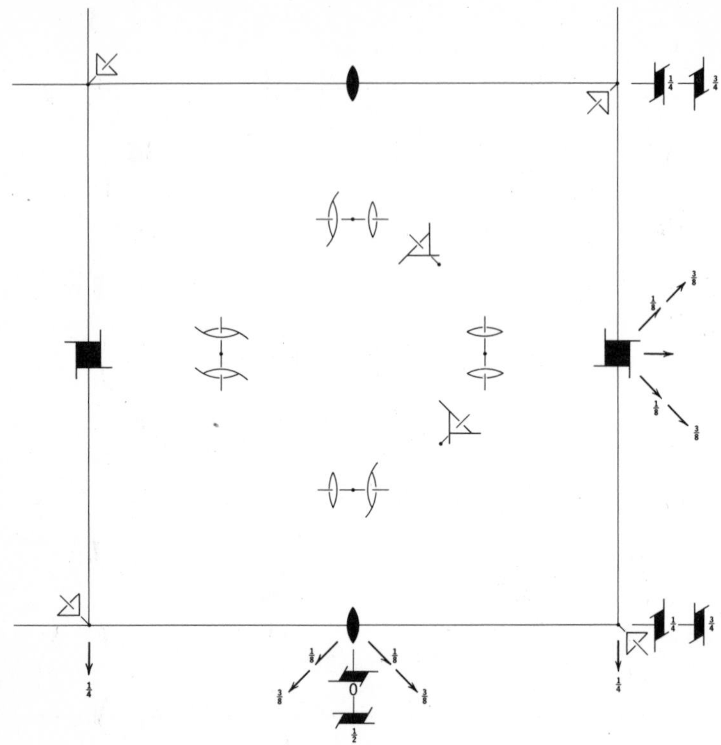

FIG. 34*a*. One octant of $I4_132$.

If the screw ${}^{s}B_{\pi}$ is taken at level $+\frac{1}{8}$, the intersection of B on a level $+\frac{1}{8}$ occurs with a 3-fold axis of another octant (Fig. 16) and in another direction. The combination of these two produces a right-handed screw 4_1. The generation of the resulting space group can be written

$$P2_13 \cdot {}^{s,+\frac{1}{8}}B_{\pi} \rightarrow P4_132 \qquad \text{(Fig. 32).}$$

The other symmetry elements of $P4_332$ and $P4_132$ can be derived by noting that, in the direction of each crystallographic axis a, there occurs a group obtained by combining 4_32_12 or 4_12_12, respectively, with P, giving $P4_32_12$ or $P4_12_12$, respectively.

If an axis ${}^{s}B_{\pi}$ is placed in $I2_13$ at levels $+\frac{1}{8}$ or $-\frac{1}{8}$, these become equivalent, so that only one group is derived by combining ${}^{s}B_{\pi}$ with $I2_13$. This can be represented as follows:

$$I2_13 \cdot {}^{s}B_{\pi} \rightarrow I4_132 \qquad \text{(Fig. 34).}$$

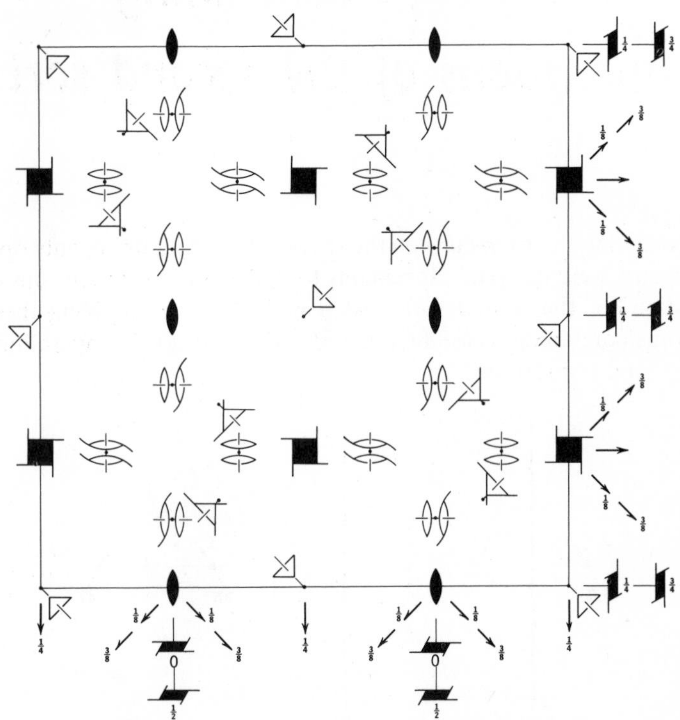

FIG. 34*b*. Full cell of $I4_132$ (drawn to half scale).

Résumé of isometric axial space groups. As a result of the discussion of this chapter, all the isometric axial space groups have been derived. There are 13 such groups, as follows:

$P23$	$P432$
$P2_13$	$\{P4_132$
$I23$	$\{P4_332$
$I2_13$	$P4_232$
$F23$	$I432$
	$I4_132$
	$F432$
	$F4_132$
5	+ 8 = 13

Only the two bracketed space groups are enantiomorphic pairs; the others are neutral.

16 · Space groups containing operations of the second sort

In the foregoing three chapters all the space groups containing only operations of the first sort were derived. It remains to derive those space groups containing operations of the second sort. As a preliminary to deriving these space groups, some combinations are first considered which involve operations of the second sort and translations.

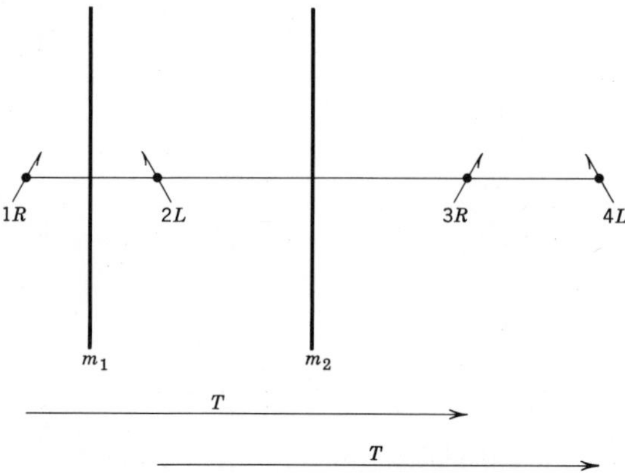

FIG. 1. Combination of a reflection and a translation perpendicular to the plane of the reflection.

Combinations of operations of the second sort with translations

Combination of a reflection and perpendicular translation. Equation (6) of Chapter 6 provides the relation

$$\underbrace{m_1 \cdot m_2}_{\mu} = A_{2\mu}. \tag{1}$$

This applies to two mirrors intersecting at an angle μ. If the point of intersection is allowed to approach infinity while the angle approaches zero, the left side of this relation approaches the limit of two parallel mirrors separated by an interval s, while the right side approaches a translation of magnitude $2s$. This limiting relation is so important that it is illustrated for strictly parallel planes in Fig. 1. This illustration shows that

$$(1R) \cdot m_1 \quad = (2L), \tag{2}$$

$$(2L) \cdot m_2 \quad = (3R), \tag{3}$$

$$\therefore \quad (1R) \cdot m_1 \cdot m_2 = (3R). \tag{4}$$

It is evident from Fig. 1 that this same displacement is produced by a translation T:

$$(1R) \cdot T = (3R). \tag{5}$$

Since the two displacements are the same, the transformations producing them are equal, so that

$$m_1 m_2 = T. \tag{6}$$

This can be easily manipulated to give

$$m_2 = m_1^{-1}\, T. \tag{7}$$

Now, just as A_π and A_π^{-1} $(=A_{-\pi})$ are the same, so the operations of a reflection and its inverse are the same, so that m can be used to replace m^{-1} in (3), giving

$$m_1 T = m_2. \tag{8}$$

This relation can be confirmed geometrically from Fig. 1.

Combination of an inversion and a translation. To combine an inversion with a translation it is convenient to use a relation established in Chapter 4, specifically that $\bar{1} = \tilde{2}$. This relation requires that an inversion is the same as a 2-fold rotation combined with a reflection, i.e.,

$$i_1 = A_\pi \cdot m_{1,\perp}. \tag{9}$$

Note that each operation on the right of (9) transforms the other into itself, so that they are permutable. The combination of an inversion and a translation can be formulated using (9), as follows:

$$i_1 \cdot T = A_\pi \cdot m_{1,\perp} \cdot T. \tag{10}$$

The result of the last two operations of (10) is known from (8). When this is substituted in (10) it can be written and reduced as follows:

$$\begin{aligned} i_1 \cdot T &= A_\pi \cdot m_{2,\perp} \\ &= i_2. \end{aligned} \tag{11}$$

This shows that an inversion, i_1, followed by a translation results in another inversion, i_2, at a distance of half a translation from the original inversion. The relation is graphically illustrated in Fig. 2.

Combination of a rotoreflection and a translation parallel to the axis. The deduction of the last section can be generalized by applying it to any rotoreflection. Let the rotoreflection be represented by A_{α,m_1}. The combination of this operation with a translation parallel to the axis of the rotation is as follows:

$$\begin{aligned} A_{\alpha,m_1} \cdot T &= A_\alpha \cdot m_1 \cdot T \\ &= A_\alpha \cdot m_2 \\ &= A_{\alpha,m_2}. \end{aligned} \tag{12}$$

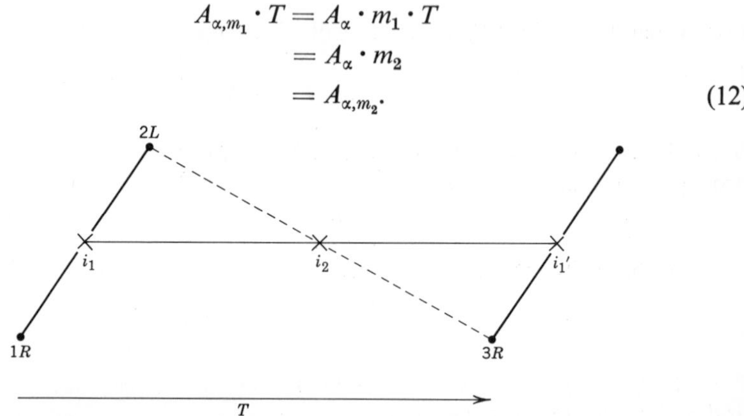

FIG. 2. Combination of an inversion and a translation.

The notation in (12) is the same as in (8). The meaning of (12) is that any rotoreflection, defined by rotation A_α and plane m_1, followed by a translation parallel to the axis, is equivalent to a similar rotoreflection halfway along the translation. The new rotoreflection is defined by the same rotation A_α, but combined with a plane m_2. This result is useful in deducing space groups isogonal with rotoreflection or rotoinversion axes.

Combination of a reflection and a parallel translation. If a reflection is combined with a translation parallel to the plane of reflection, the combination is called a *glide reflection*, or simply a *glide*. Each of these two operations transforms the other into itself, and so they are permutable.

The repetition of a point by repeated application of the operation of a glide reflection is illustrated in Fig. 3. The plane of the reflection is a symmetry element of the resulting pattern and is called a *glide plane*.

The operation of a glide reflection is said to have a *reflection component*, *m*, and a *translation component*, τ. The operation can be symbolized as m_τ. For the special case that $\tau = 0$, a glide reflection becomes a pure reflection, *m*. Figure 3 shows that two successive glide operations are equivalent to a lattice translation, *t*.

In diagrams showing symmetry elements, a pure reflection plane, seen edge-on, is represented by a solid line. A glide plane, seen edge-on, is represented by a line interrupted in various ways as illustrated in Fig. 4. If the view is along the translation component, the line is dotted; if the view is normal to the

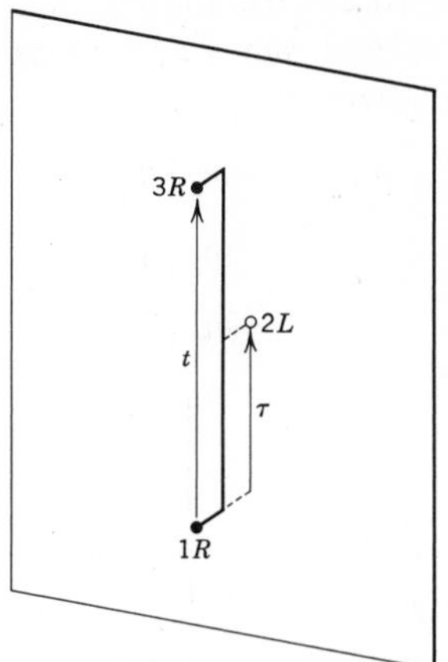

FIG. 3. Repetition of a point by a glide reflection.

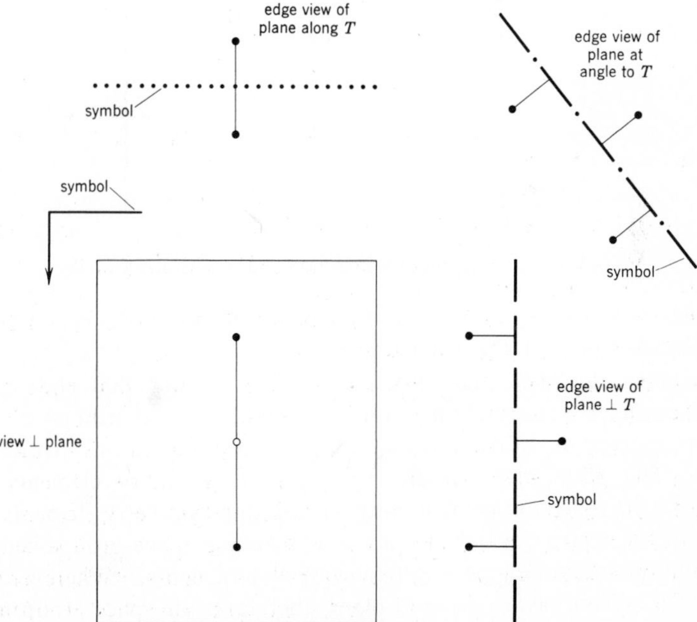

FIG. 4. The representations of a glide plane in different views.

translation, the line is dashed; if the view is somewhere between these, the line is dot-and-dashed.

Combination of a reflection and a general translation. The combination of a reflection and a general translation results in a glide. This is illustrated in Fig. 5 and can be readily demonstrated analytically. To do this the translation is resolved into components perpendicular and parallel with the glide plane. The deduction is then as follows:

$$\begin{aligned} m_1 \cdot T &= m_1 \cdot T_\perp \cdot T_\parallel \\ &= m_2 \cdot T_\parallel \\ &= m_{2,T_\parallel}. \end{aligned} \tag{13}$$

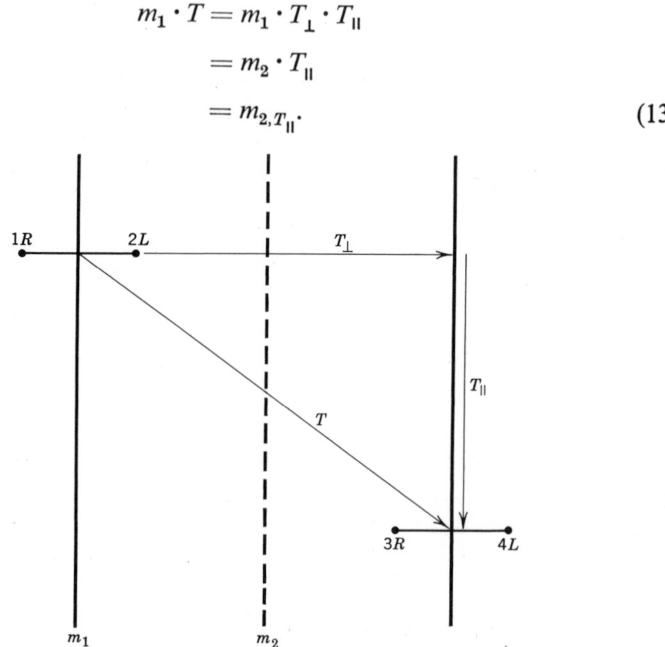

FIG. 5. Combination of a reflection and a general translation.

The location of m_2 follows (8), and so the new glide plane occurs at a distance of half a translation from the original plane.

Importance of glides. The last section demonstrated that glide reflections must be expected as normal operations of repetition. Accordingly glide planes must be accepted as ordinary symmetry elements in repetitions involving translations. The glide plane among space-group symmetry elements bears a relation to the reflection plane among point-group symmetry elements which is similar to the relation which the screw axis among space groups bears to the pure rotation axis among point-group symmetry elements. Wherever the point group of a crystal has a reflection plane, therefore, the space group may have sets of parallel reflection planes, glide planes, or both. Glide planes are thus isogonal with reflection planes.

It will often be convenient to speak of both pure reflection planes and glide planes as belonging to the general category of glide planes. From this point of view a reflection plane is a glide plane whose translation component is zero. This generalization is the same as was used when a pure rotation axis was regarded as a screw axis whose translation component was zero.

Symbols for reflection planes and glide planes. The presence of characteristic reflection planes or glide planes is indicated by an appropriate entry in the space-group symbol. Whereas the symbol for a rotation axis is a number,

Table 1. Symbols used for glide planes

Symbol	Significance of symbol	Translation component
a	axial glides	$\frac{a}{2}$
b		$\frac{b}{2}$
c		$\frac{c}{2}$
n	diagonal glide	$\frac{a}{2}+\frac{b}{2}$, $\frac{a}{2}+\frac{c}{2}$ or $\frac{b}{2}+\frac{c}{2}$
d	"diamond" glide	$\frac{a}{4}+\frac{b}{4}$, $\frac{a}{4}+\frac{c}{4}$ or $\frac{b}{4}+\frac{c}{4}$
m	"mirror"	zero

the symbol for a plane is a letter. A pure reflection plane is symbolized by m. Glide planes are symbolized by letters which denote the direction of the translation component of the glide in terms of fractions of the cell edges. The letters used for various glide planes and their significances are given in Table 1. The "diamond" glide, d, occurs where the glide is half a "centering" translation of the cell.

The particular letter reveals the direction of the glide; the orientation of the glide plane is revealed by its position in the space-group symbol. Each possible plane is perpendicular to a possible rotation axis. The symbol for a glide is therefore placed with the perpendicular axis. The axis symbol occupies the numerator of a "fraction," and the glide symbol occupies the denominator.

In abbreviated symbols, the symbols for some axes are omitted, in which event the fractional form is not used.

The combination of a glide and a general translation. The result of combining a glide with a general translation can be readily found. Let the component of the translation parallel to the glide plane be different from the translation component, τ, of the glide. Then the combination can be formed as follows:

$$\begin{aligned} m_{1,\tau} \cdot T &= m_1 \cdot \tau \cdot T_{\parallel} \cdot T_{\perp} \\ &= m_1 T_{\perp} \cdot \tau \cdot T_{\parallel} \\ &= m_2 \cdot \tau \cdot T_{\parallel} \\ &= m_{2,\tau+T_{\parallel}}. \end{aligned} \tag{14}$$

The result of the combination is accordingly a glide plane at a perpendicular distance of half a translation from the original glide plane, and having translation components $\vec{\tau} + \vec{T}_{\parallel}$.

Combination of a screw and a perpendicular glide. Because of the special importance of 2-fold screws in symmetry combinations, it will prove useful to know the result of combining a 2-fold screw axis and a perpendicular glide plane. This can be found as follows:

$$\begin{aligned} A_{\pi,t} \cdot m_{\tau} &= A_{\pi} \cdot t \cdot m \cdot \tau \\ &= A_{\pi} \cdot m \cdot t' \cdot \tau \\ &= i_1 \cdot t' \cdot \tau \\ &= i_1 t^{-1} \tau \\ &= i_2. \end{aligned} \tag{15}$$

Here t' is the translation t as transformed by m. The net result of this combination is an inversion i_2. The inversion center is removed from the intersection location i_1 by the translation $t^{-1}\tau$ as illustrated in Fig. 6. The reduction of this general case to the three special ones is illustrated in Figs. 7, 8, and 9.

Procedure in deriving complex space groups

In Chapter 7 a procedure was established for deriving complex symmetries from simple ones. Specifically, the eleven symmetries containing only rotations of the first sort were established by first principles; those containing also operations of the second sort were then derived by adding a permissible second-sort operation to each of the eleven axial symmetries.

The general theory of this procedure was as follows: All symmetries, even those containing operations of the second sort, necessarily contain operations of the first sort. That is, all symmetries contain rotation axes, including the trivial axis 1. Such axes can be combined in only eleven different ways. Therefore every symmetry contains one of these eleven sets of rotation axes as a base

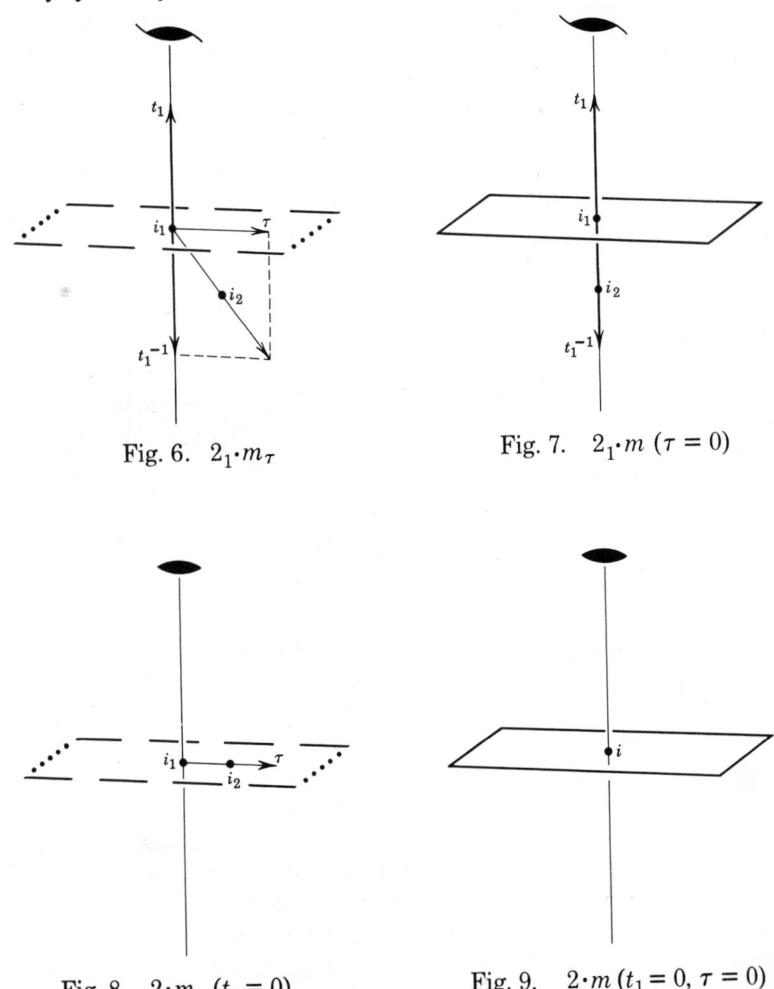

Fig. 6. $2_1 \cdot m_\tau$

Fig. 7. $2_1 \cdot m$ $(\tau = 0)$

Fig. 8. $2 \cdot m_\tau$ $(t_1 = 0)$

Fig. 9. $2 \cdot m$ $(t_1 = 0, \tau = 0)$

FIGS. 6–9. Combinations of various 2-fold screws and perpendicular glides, of the form $2_n \cdot m_\tau$.

or frame. Let such a set of axes be called an *axial frame*. Now, starting with one of the eleven symmetries, all the symmetries having this particular axial frame and also containing operations of the second sort can be found by adding symmetry operations of the second sort to this frame. When this has been systematically done, all symmetries based upon this axial frame have been found. In order that the axial frame should remain the same axial frame after the new operation is added, *it is essential that the new operation transform the axial frame into itself.* If this did not occur, the new axial frame would not be the same as the one used to start (if indeed it is even one of the eleven permissible combinations), and therefore the new symmetry would not be one based upon the frame selected.

This is a basic procedure for discovering complex sets of symmetry elements. Its use can be extended to finding the space groups containing operations of the second sort. Every such space group must have as an axial frame one of the axial space groups derived in the last three chapters. The more complex space groups based upon each axial frame can be found by adding permissible operations of the second sort to the particular axial frame. If the procedure is followed systematically so as to exhaust all possibilities, all remaining space groups will be encountered. There are limitations on the nature of the added operation:

1. The operation can be added only so that its orientation with respect to the axial frame is the same as that of the isogonal operation which is added to the isogonal axial frame to produce the isogonal point group.

2. The character of the operation must be such as to transform the axial frame into itself.

Except for the 4-fold rotoinversion, all operations of the second sort can be resolved into rotations and reflections, or rotations and inversions. Thus all point groups of the second sort, except $\bar{4}$, were derived from the eleven axial frames by systematically adding to them reflections and inversions. Correspondingly, all space groups except those isogonal with $\bar{4}$ can be derived from the space axial frame by adding operations isogonal with reflections and inversions, specifically glides having all permissible directions of translation components, and inversions.

Certain axial space groups cannot be transformed into themselves by an operation of the second sort. Any member of the enantiomorphic pairs of space groups is transformed by any operation of the second sort into its enantiomorph, not into itself. Such space groups cannot be axial frames. Only the 43 neutral space groups listed at the end of the last three chapters can be used as axial frames. It was for this reason that the "neutral" category was established. In the event that the neutral axial frame contains both left-handed and right-handed screws, the location of the operation of the second sort is considerably restricted.

Triclinic space groups

Point group $\bar{1}$. The only operation isogonal with an inversion is an inversion. The only space group isogonal with $\bar{1}$ is therefore obtained by combining an inversion with the only lattice permissible to class $\bar{1}$, namely P. The resulting space group is $P\bar{1}$. The properties of this space group are deduced by combining an inversion, i, with the translations of P. According to (11), each translation combines with the original inversion to produce a new inversion displaced from the original one by half a translation. Seven new centers (making eight in all) therefore arise as the result of the translations $\vec{a}$, $\vec{b}$, $\vec{c}$, $\vec{a}+\vec{b}$, $\vec{a}+\vec{c}$, $\vec{b}+\vec{c}$, $\vec{a}+\vec{b}+\vec{c}$. The space group is illustrated in Fig. 10.

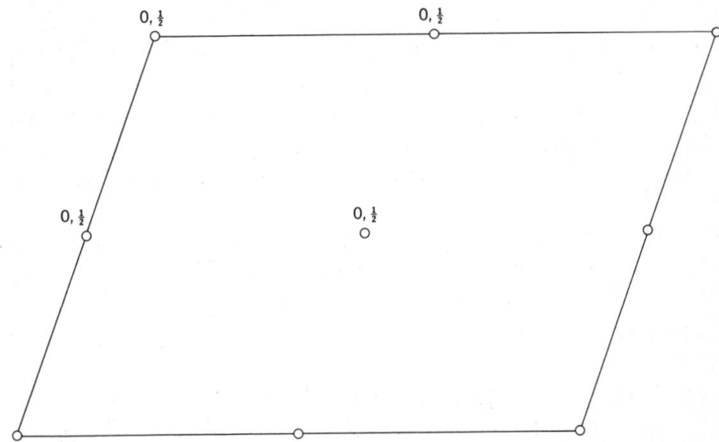

FIG. 10. Space group $P\bar{1}$. The open circles are inversion centers. They occur in a set at level $z = 0$. Translation mates also occur at level $z = \frac{1}{2}$, as indicated. In diagrams which follow, only centers on levels $z \neq 0$ are ordinarily labeled; translation mates at $z + \frac{1}{2}$ are ordinarily unlabeled.

Monoclinic space groups

Point group *m*. Class m contains only a reflection plane. The symmetry elements isogonal with this reflection plane are a reflection plane m and a glide plane m_τ. The space groups isogonal with m are therefore found by combining either of these with the permissible lattices for class m, namely P or I. (The lattice I can also be described as A or B by choosing an alternative cell.) In the following discussion the first monoclinic setting is adopted, that is, with the symmetry plane parallel to (001), but symbols are also given in parentheses for the second setting, in which the symmetry plane is parallel to (010).

When a mirror m is combined with translation $\vec{c}$ a new mirror m' arises at level $z = c/2$. When m is combined with any other translation, the component of the translation parallel to the plane is a full cell translation, and so the combination is a glide m_τ whose translation component is a full cell translation.

Such a glide is the same as a mirror, which is already present. The result of combining m with P is therefore space group Pm, shown in Fig. 11.

If a glide is combined with the translations of P, the translation component of the glide must be half of a cell translation parallel to the plane; i.e., it must be $\vec{a}/2$, $\vec{b}/2$, or $\vec{a}/2 + \vec{b}/2$. The resulting space groups are called Pa, Pb, and Pn (Pa, Pc, or Pn in the second orientation). All these have the same general

Table 2. Combination of possible glide planes with body-centering translation

Plane at level $z = 0$		Components of translation parallel to glide plane	Resulting plane at level $z = \frac{1}{4}$	
Designation	τ		τ	Designation
m	0	$\frac{a}{2} + \frac{b}{2}$	$\frac{a}{2} + \frac{b}{2}$	n
a	$\frac{a}{2}$	$\frac{a}{2} + \frac{b}{2}$	$a + \frac{b}{2} \Leftrightarrow \frac{b}{2}$	b
b	$\frac{2}{b}$	$\frac{a}{2} + \frac{b}{2}$	$\frac{a}{2} + b \Leftrightarrow \frac{a}{2}$	a
n	$\frac{a}{2} + \frac{b}{2}$	$\frac{a}{2} + \frac{b}{2}$	$a + b \Leftrightarrow 0$	m

symmetry characteristics, illustrated as Pb in Fig. 12. These are accordingly regarded as one space group. The different symbols Pa, Pb, and Pn serve to reveal the choice of cell edges with respect to the direction of the translation component of the glide.

Next consider combining m_τ with the translations of I. This lattice has the same translations as P, plus the additional translation $\vec{a}/2 + \vec{b}/2 + \vec{c}/2$. The space groups Im and Ib therefore also contain the symmetry elements of Pm and Pb and have, in addition, symmetry elements due to the combination of m_τ with $\vec{a}/2 + \vec{b}/2 + \vec{c}/2$. The $c/2$ component produces a glide at levels $c/4$ (and $3c/4$) whose translation components are provided by the combination

$$m_\tau T_{||} = m_{\tau+a/2+b2}. \qquad (16)$$

When τ is assigned its permissible values, the combinations resulting are those shown in Table 2. The resulting four space groups could be designated

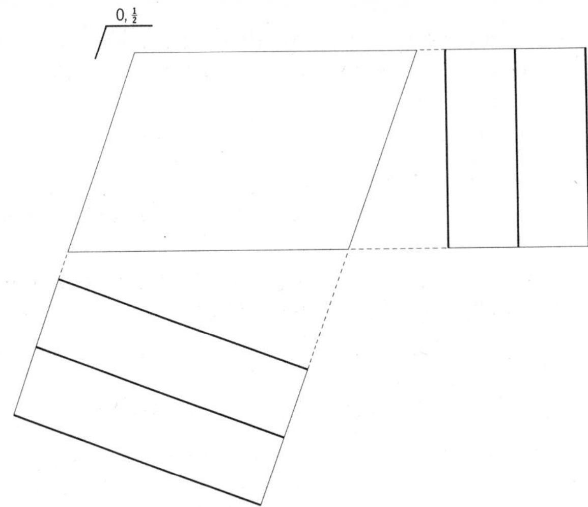

FIG. 11. Space group *Pm*. The three projections show the conventional representations of the mirrors looking along the three cell axes. The symbol to the upper left of the cell represents a mirror which is parallel to the plane of the paper at level $z = 0$. A parallel plane occurs at level $z = \frac{1}{2}$.

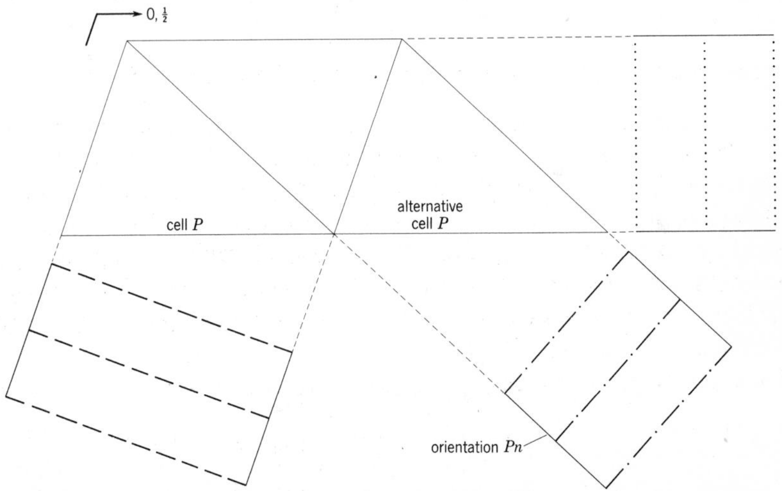

FIG. 12. Space group *Pb*. Three of the projections show the conventional representations of the glide planes when seen along the three cell axes. Orientation *Pn* shows the appearance of the same space group when the cell axes are chosen in such a way that one of the two cell axes parallel to the glide plane is not chosen parallel to the translation component of the glide plane. The symbol to the upper left of the cell represents a glide plane which is parallel to the plane of the paper at level $z = 0$. Another occurs at level $z = \frac{1}{2}$. The translation component is in the direction of the arrow, namely in the direction of the cell edge *b*.

In, *Ib*, *Ia*, and *Im*. But it will be observed that, except for an origin shift of $z = \frac{1}{4}$, the following pairs are identical:

$$Im = In \qquad (Im = In), \qquad \text{Fig. 13,}$$

$$Ia = Ib \qquad (Ia = Ic), \qquad \text{Fig. 14.}$$

Sometimes these space groups based upon *I* are referred to the less symmetrical cell *B* in order to permit using a reduced cell. These cells are outlined in Figs. 13 and 14. When this is done the glide directions change with respect to the cell axes, and the space-groups symbols become

$$Bm = Ba \qquad (Cm = Cc), \qquad \text{Fig. 13,}$$

$$Bb = Bn \qquad (Ca = Cn), \qquad \text{Fig. 14.}$$

The space groups isogonal with *m* are therefore the following four:

$$Pm \qquad (Pm)$$

$$Pa \Leftrightarrow Pb \Leftrightarrow Pn \qquad (Pa \Leftrightarrow Pc \Leftrightarrow Pn)$$

$$Im \Leftrightarrow Bm \qquad (Im \Leftrightarrow Cm)$$

$$Ia \Leftrightarrow Bb \qquad (Ia \Leftrightarrow Ca)$$

Point group $\frac{2}{m}$. Point group $2/m$ contains the three symmetry elements 2, *m*, and *i*. The space groups isogonal with this point group can therefore be found by combining the space groups isogonal with any two of the point groups 2, *m*, or $\bar{1}$. The combination adopted here is equivalent to combining the space groups isogonal with 2 and $\bar{1}$. The actual procedure is to start with each of the space groups isogonal with 2 as an axial frame and add the operation *i* in a location such that it transforms the frame into itself. This requires the inversion to be added on an axis (labeled i_1) or halfway between axes (labeled i_2). Six space groups result, as follows:

$$P2 \cdot i_1 = P2/m \qquad \text{Fig. 15}$$

$$P2 \cdot i_2 = P2/b \qquad \text{Fig. 16}$$

$$P2_1 \cdot i_1 = P2_1/m \qquad \text{Fig. 17}$$

$$P2_1 \cdot i_2 = P2_1/b \qquad \text{Fig. 18}$$

$$I2 \cdot i_1 = I2/m \qquad \text{Fig. 19}$$

$$I2 \cdot i_2 = I2/b \qquad \text{Fig. 20.}$$

The location and characteristics of the reflection planes resulting from these combinations are readily found with the aid of Figs. 6, 7, 8, and 9.

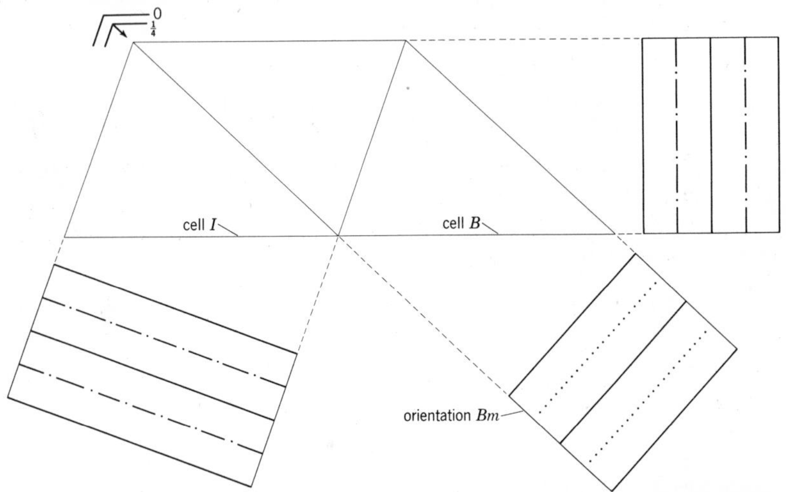

FIG. 13. Space group *Im*. If the *B*-centered cell is chosen, the space group is labeled *Bm*. The two symbols to the upper left of the cell indicate two kinds of reflection planes parallel to the plane of the paper. One is a mirror at level $z = 0$; the other is a glide plane at level $z = \frac{1}{4}$ with translation component parallel to the diagonal of cell *I*.

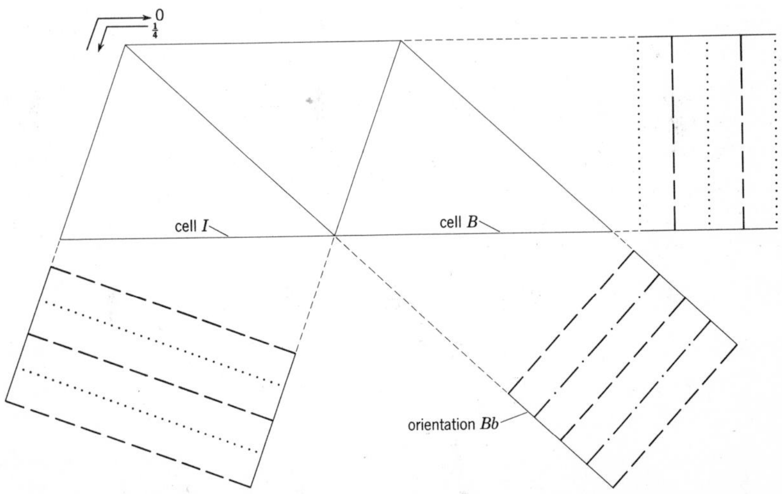

FIG. 14. Space group *Ia*. If the *B*-centered cell is chosen, the space group is labeled *Bb*. The two symbols to the upper left of the cell indicate two kinds of glide planes parallel to the plane of the paper. One is a glide plane at level $z = 0$ with translation component parallel to *b* of cell *I*; the other is a glide plane at level $z = \frac{1}{4}$ with translation component parallel to *a* of cell *I*.

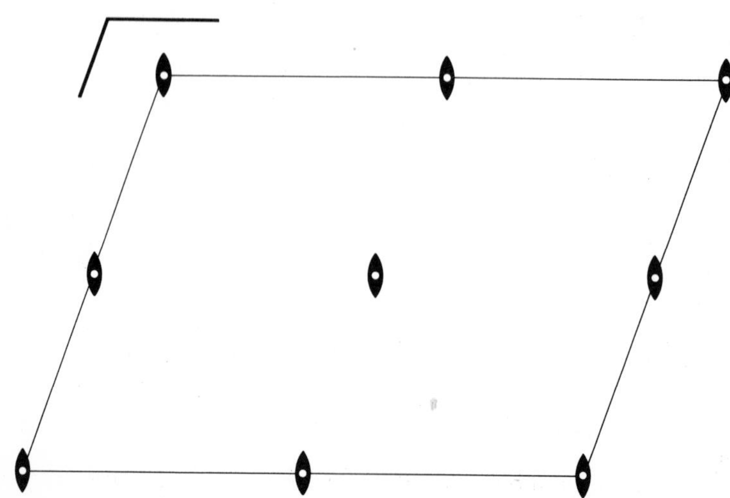

FIG. 15. $P\frac{2}{m}$. The symbol to the upper left of the cell represents a mirror which is parallel to the paper at level $z = 0$. Symmetry elements at level z have translation mates at level $z + \frac{1}{2}$.

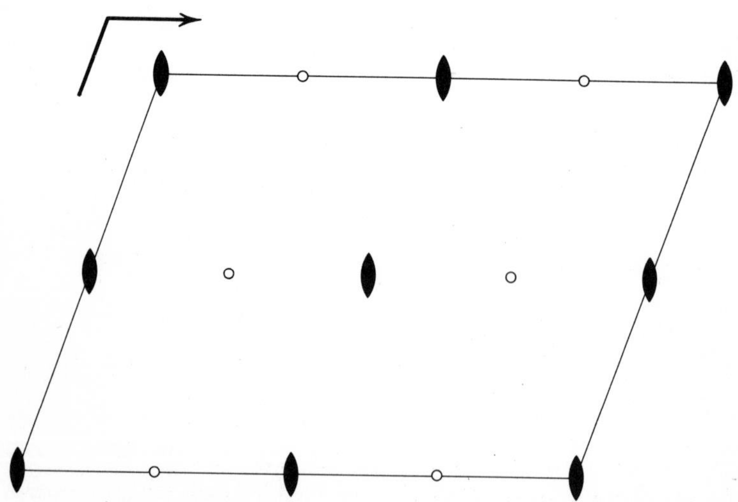

FIG. 16. $P\frac{2}{b}$. The symbol to the upper left of the cell represents a glide plane which is parallel to the paper at level $z = 0$. The translation component is in the direction of the arrow, namely in the direction of the cell edge b.

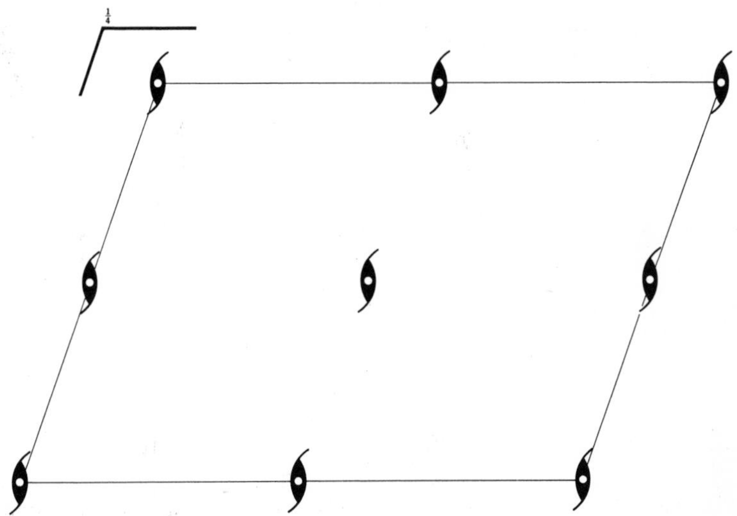

FIG. 17. $P\dfrac{2_1}{m}$. The symbol to the upper left of the cell is a reflection plane parallel to the plane of the paper at level $z = \frac{1}{4}$. The open circles are inversion centers at level $z = 0$.

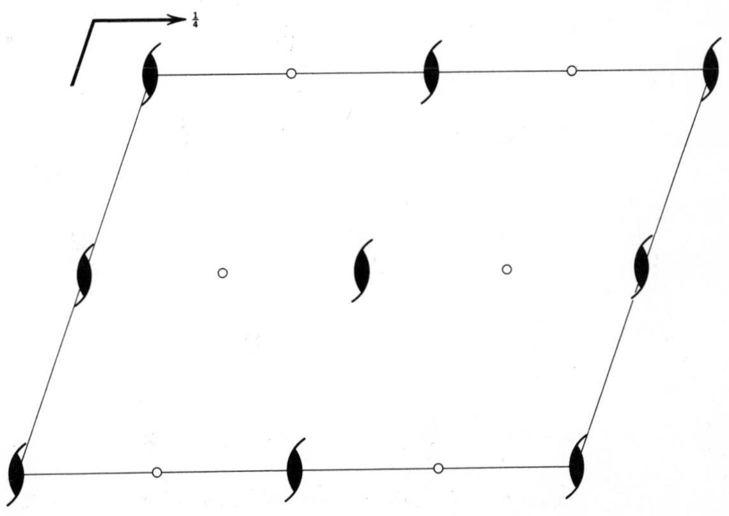

FIG. 18. $P\dfrac{2_1}{b}$.

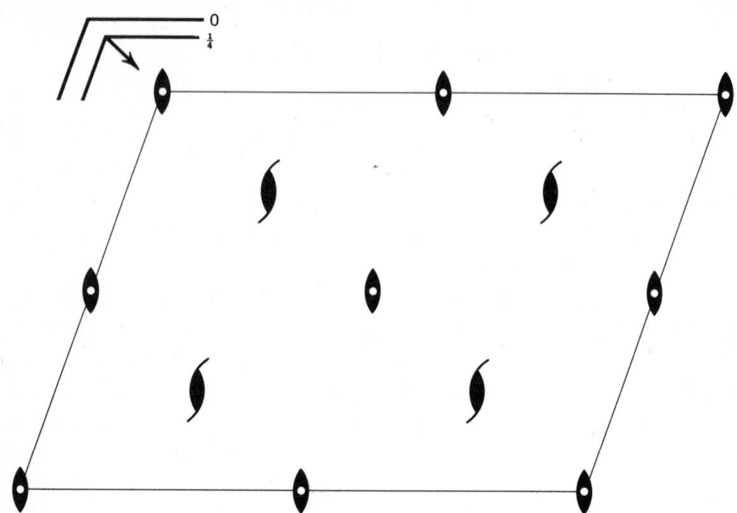

FIG. 19. $I\frac{2}{m}$. The two symbols to the upper left of the cell indicate two kinds of reflection planes parallel to the plane of the paper. One is a mirror at level $z = 0$; the other is a glide plane at level $z = \frac{1}{4}$ with translation component parallel to the cell diagonal.

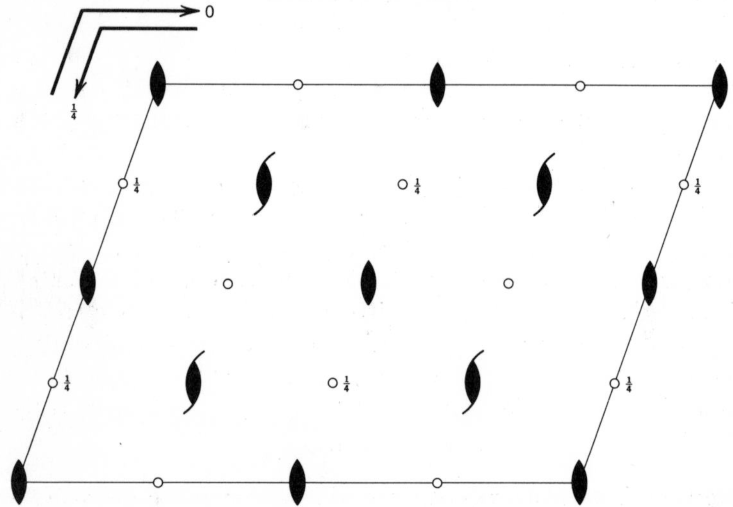

FIG. 20. $I\frac{2}{b}$. The two symbols to the upper left of the cell indicate two kinds of glide planes parallel to the plane of the paper. One is a glide plane at level $z = 0$ with translation component parallel to b; the other is a glide plane at level $z = \frac{1}{4}$ with translation component parallel to a.

Orthorhombic space groups

Point group *mm*2. The point group *mm*2 contains two orthogonal planes intersecting in a 2-fold axis. It can be derived by starting with axial frame 2 and adding a single reflection plane m_1. The combination produces the second orthogonal plane m_2. In a similar way the space groups isogonal with *mm*2 can be found by starting with the axial frames isogonal with 2 and adding an operation isogonal with m_1.

The axial frames isogonal with 2 are *P*2, $P2_1$, and *I*2. Since, however, orthorhombic crystals can be referred to lattices *P*, *I*, *C*, and *F*, provision must be made to start with these axial frames in all permissible forms. Specifically these are *P*2, $P2_1$, *I*2, *F*2, *C*2, and *A*2. The last two possibilities arise since the cell of *C*2 is centered on a face perpendicular to the 2-fold axis whereas the cells of either *A*2 and *B*2 are centered on a face parallel to the 2-fold axis. Both general possibilities are represented by *C*2 and *A*2.

To each of these six axial frames an operation isogonal with m_1 must be added. In general this is a glide plane with translation component zero, axial or diagonal. If m_1 is taken perpendicular to the *a* axis these translation components must be 0, $c/2$, $b/2$, or $b/2 + c/2$. The designations of the corresponding planes are *m*, *c*, *b*, and *n*. The orientations and translation characteristics of these planes are now fixed, but their locations with respect to a 2-fold screw are not. The location must be such as to transform the axial frame into itself. This requires the location of the plane to contain a row of axes, or to be halfway between a row of axes, i.e., at $x = 0$ or $x = \frac{1}{4}$. The second location is designated here by a superscript *s* preceding the symbol of the plane; i.e., if *m* is through $x = 0$, ${}^s m$ is through $x = \frac{1}{4}$.

The combinations of 2 and 2_1 with *m*, *c*, *b*, *n*, ${}^s m$, ${}^s c$, ${}^s b$, and ${}^s n$ are systematically outlined in Table 3. Each such combination results in a glide m_τ in the m_2 location perpendicular to m_1. These combinations are readily deduced with the aid of the algebra of operations. This is merely outlined in Table 1, but a typical combination will now be discussed in detail. Consider the combination 2_1 with ${}^s b$, which is the second last combination of Table 3. The plane of ${}^s b$ is displaced from a possible location *b* by a translation *s*. Let the operation of *b* be $m_{1,b/2}$, and let that of ${}^s b$ be ${}^s m_{1,b/2}$. Then, by virtue of (8)

$$m_{1,b/2}T = {}^{T/2}m_{1,b/2}. \tag{17}$$

Thus every displaced plane can be replaced by a similar plane through the axis, plus a translation. This translation is 2*s*, so that (17) is

$$m_{1,b/2} \cdot 2s = {}^s m_{1,b/2}. \tag{18}$$

This is the first combination carried out in Table 3. The actual value of *s* must be $a/4$ in order to transform two similar axes which are separated by $a/2$ into

Table 3. Combinations of 2-fold screws and parallel glides

Original combination		Equivalent combination resulting from moving plane to axis			Characteristics of resulting reflection				Combination designation
Designation	Separation s of plane and axis	Translation of screw	New translation, T, of (17)	Translation of plane	Σ translations	Separation of plane and axis	Translation of plane	Symbol	
$2\,m$	0	0	0	0	0	0	0	0	$mm2$
$2\,c$	0	0	0	$\frac{c}{2}$	$\frac{c}{2}$	0	$\frac{c}{2}$	c	$cc2$
$2\,b$	0	0	0	$\frac{b}{2}$	$\frac{b}{2}$	$\frac{b}{4}$	0	${}^{s}m$	$b\,{}^{s}m2$
$2\,n$	0	0	0	$\frac{b}{2}+\frac{c}{2}$	$\frac{b}{2}+\frac{c}{2}$	$\frac{b}{4}$	$\frac{c}{2}$	${}^{s}c$	$n\,{}^{s}c2$
$2\,{}^{s}m$	$\frac{a}{4}$	0	$\frac{a}{2}$	0	$\frac{a}{2}$	0	$\frac{a}{2}$	a	${}^{s}ma2$
$2\,{}^{s}c$	$\frac{a}{4}$	0	$\frac{a}{2}$	$\frac{c}{2}$	$\frac{a}{2}+\frac{c}{2}$	0	$\frac{a}{2}+\frac{c}{2}$	n	${}^{s}cn2$
$2\,{}^{s}b$	$\frac{a}{4}$	0	$\frac{a}{2}$	$\frac{b}{2}$	$\frac{a}{2}+\frac{b}{2}$	$\frac{b}{4}$	$\frac{a}{2}$	${}^{s}a$	${}^{s}b\,{}^{s}a2$
$2\,{}^{s}n$	$\frac{a}{4}$	0	$\frac{a}{2}$	$\frac{b}{2}+\frac{c}{2}$	$\frac{a}{2}+\frac{b}{2}+\frac{c}{2}$	$\frac{b}{4}$	$\frac{a}{2}+\frac{c}{2}$	${}^{s}n$	${}^{s}n\,{}^{s}n2$
$2_1\,m$	0	$\frac{c}{2}$	0	0	$\frac{c}{2}$	0	$\frac{c}{2}$	c	$mc2_1$
$2_1\,c$	0	$\frac{c}{2}$	0	$\frac{c}{2}$	0	0	0	m	$cm2_1$
$2_1\,b$	0	$\frac{2}{2}$	0	$\frac{b}{2}$	$\frac{b}{2}+\frac{c}{2}$	$\frac{b}{4}$	$\frac{c}{2}$	${}^{s}c$	$b\,{}^{s}c2_1$
$2_1\,n$	0	$\frac{c}{2}$	0	$\frac{b}{2}+\frac{c}{2}$	$\frac{b}{2}$	$\frac{b}{4}$	0	${}^{s}m$	$n\,{}^{s}m2_1$
$2_1\,{}^{s}m$	$\frac{a}{4}$	$\frac{c}{2}$	$\frac{a}{2}$	0	$\frac{a}{2}+\frac{c}{2}$	0	$\frac{a}{2}+\frac{c}{2}$	n	${}^{s}mn2_1$
$2_1\,{}^{s}c$	$\frac{a}{4}$	$\frac{c}{2}$	$\frac{a}{2}$	$\frac{c}{2}$	$\frac{a}{2}$	0	$\frac{a}{2}$	a	${}^{s}ca2_1$
$2_1\,{}^{s}b$	$\frac{a}{4}$	$\frac{c}{2}$	$\frac{a}{2}$	$\frac{b}{2}$	$\frac{a}{2}+\frac{b}{2}+\frac{c}{2}$	$\frac{b}{4}$	$\frac{a}{2}+\frac{c}{2}$	${}^{s}n$	${}^{s}b\,{}^{s}n2_1$
$2_1\,{}^{s}n$	$\frac{a}{4}$	$\frac{c}{2}$	$\frac{a}{2}$	$\frac{b}{2}+\frac{c}{2}$	$\frac{a}{2}+\frac{b}{2}$	$\frac{b}{4}$	$\frac{a}{2}$	${}^{s}a$	${}^{s}n\,{}^{s}a2_1$

each other. If this is substituted into the $2s$ of (18), and if the right and left sides are interchanged, it becomes

$$^{s}m_{1,b/2} = m_{1,b/2} \cdot a/2. \tag{19}$$

This transformation gives the second set of columns of Table 3 from the first set.

Next the 2-fold axis is combined with this glide and translation. For the combination $2_1\ {}^{s}b$ under discussion this calls for adding the operation $A_{\pi,c/2}$ to (19):

$$A_{\pi,c/2} \cdot {}^{s}m_{1,b/2} = A_{\pi,c/2} \cdot m_{1,b/2} \cdot a/2. \tag{20}$$

Since translations and parallel rotations are permutable, and since translations and parallel reflections are permutable, the right side of (20) can be rearranged to bring together A_π and m_1, as follows:

$$A_{\pi,c/2} \cdot {}^{s}m_{1,b/2} = A_\pi \cdot m_1 \cdot a/2 \cdot b/2 \cdot c/2. \tag{21}$$

The combination $A_\pi \cdot m_1$ is a perpendicular reflection m_2, according to (10) of Chapter 8. Therefore (21) becomes

$$A_{\pi,c/2} \cdot {}^{s}m_{1,b/2} = m_2 \cdot a/2 \cdot b/2 \cdot c/2. \tag{22}$$

Since m_1 was perpendicular to a, m_2 is perpendicular to b. Therefore the translations $a/2$ and $c/2$ are parallel translations whereas $b/2$ is a perpendicular translation. Now, the combination of a mirror and a perpendicular translation is

$$m_2 \cdot T_\perp = {}^{T/2}m_2. \tag{23}$$

Since $T_\perp$ is $b/2$, this is specifically

$$m_2 \cdot b/2 = {}^{b/4}m_2. \tag{24}$$

The parallel components of (22) become translation components of the glide plane. The net result is

$$A_{\pi,c/2} \cdot {}^{s}m_{1,b/2} = {}^{b/4}m_{2,a/2+c/2}. \tag{25}$$

The correct designation of this glide plane is ^{s}n. In a similar manner all other permissible combinations are reduced in Table 3.

Lattice P. While Table 3 primarily shows the results of combining various screws with various parallel glides, it can also be used to derive space groups based upon primitive lattices. The translations of the lattice combine with 2 or 2_1 to produce axial frames $P2$ or $P2_1$, and combine with each glide to produce a set of parallel glides, according to (14). The space groups which result would be those designated by prefixing the symbol P to the symbols shown in the last column of Table 3. These are listed in Table 4. Several of these become identical in pairs by a 90° rotation about the 2-fold axis. This is indicated by a notation such as *Pma*2 $\cong$ *Pbm*2. The equality sign $\cong$ signifies "equivalent by change of orientation." Table 4 shows that there are 10 space groups based upon *P* isogonal with *mm*2. These are illustrated in Figs. 21-30.

Lattice I. To derive space groups based upon other lattices than *P* it is necessary only to add the additional translations characteristic of the centered lattice to the space groups already derived. An equivalent procedure is to add to each of the space groups already derived the additional axes of the centered axial frame which the primitive axial frame lacks. This is perhaps the simplest visual procedure, and it is followed here.

Table 4. Space groups isogonal with *mm*2 based upon *P*

*Pmm*2,	Fig. 21	$Pmc2_1$,	Fig. 27
*Pcc*2,	Fig. 22	($Pcm2_1 \cong Pmc2_1$)	
*Pbm*2,	Fig. 23	$Pbc2_1$,	Fig. 28
*Pnc*2,	Fig. 24	$Pnm2_1$,	Fig. 29
(*Pma*2 $\cong$ *Pbm*2)		($Pmn2_1 \cong Pnm2_1$)	
(*Pcn*2 $\cong$ *Pnc*2)		($Pca2_1 \cong Pbc2_1$)	
*Pba*2,	Fig. 25	$Pbn2_1$,	Fig. 30
*Pnn*2,	Fig. 26	($Pna2_1 = Pbn2_1$)	

The axial frame *I*2 is shown in Fig. 11, Chapter 13. When specialized to the orthogonal axes of the orthorhombic system it is as shown in Fig. 31. This contains the same axes as *P*2 plus the addition of 2-fold screws in the center of each quarter cell. The space groups based upon *I* can therefore be found by adding the operation of one of these axes to the ten distinct space groups listed in Table 4. When added to *Pmm*2 (Fig. 21) the new screw operation combines with the two displaced mirrors to form the combinations $2_1\,{}^s m$. Table 3 shows this to be the same as *n*. The result is shown in Fig. 32. This new space group is called *Imm*2, but it actually contains four combinations of screws and glides, of which three are distinct, as follows:

$$Imm2 = Inn2$$
$$= Inm2_1 \ (\cong Imn2_1).$$

This means that three of the distinct combinations of Table 3 have been encountered in one space group.

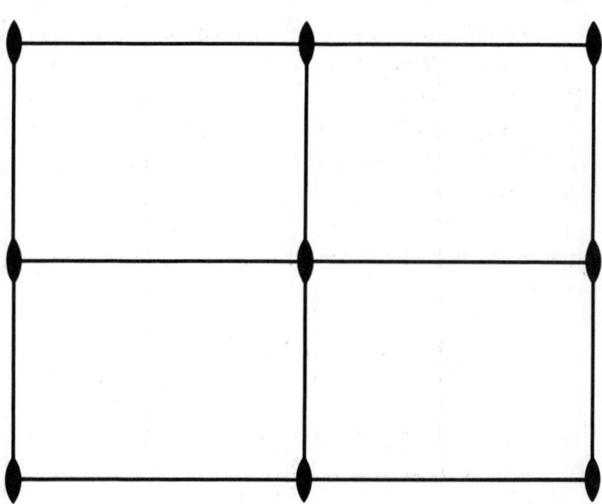

FIG. 21. *Pmm*2.

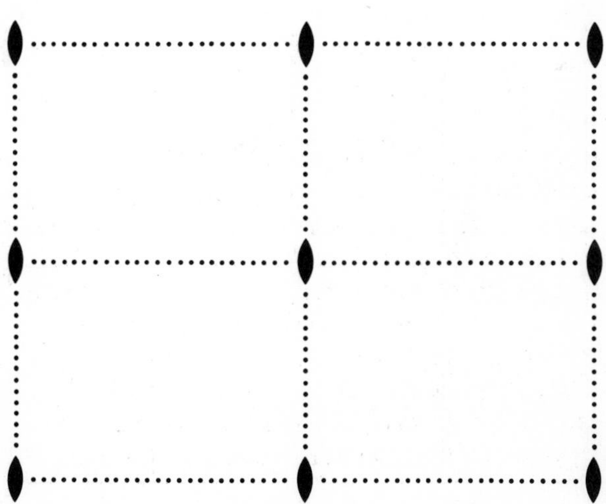

FIG. 22. *Pcc*2.

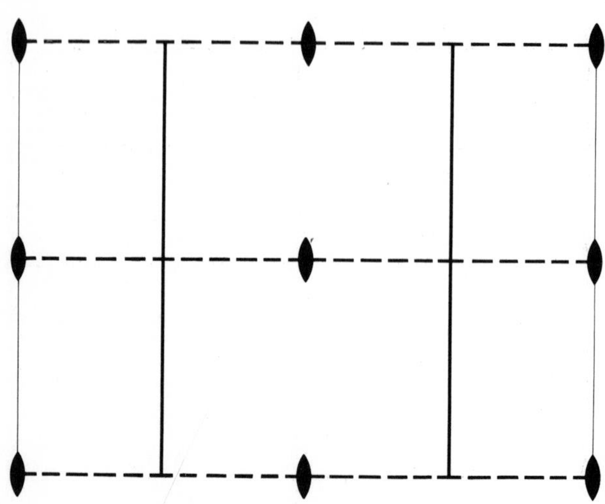

FIG. 23. *Pbm*2.

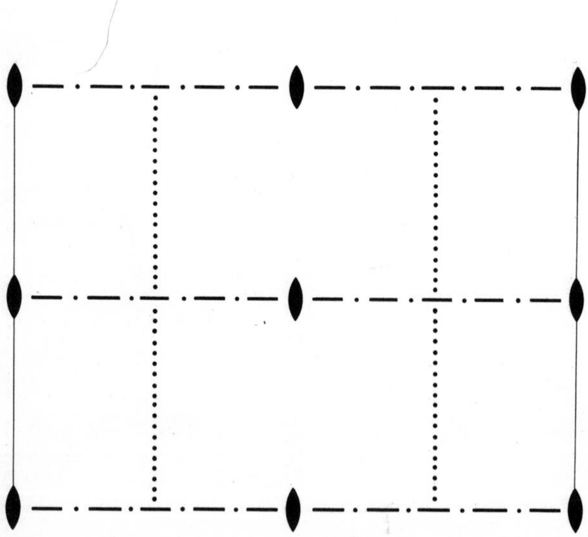

FIG. 24. *Pnc*2.

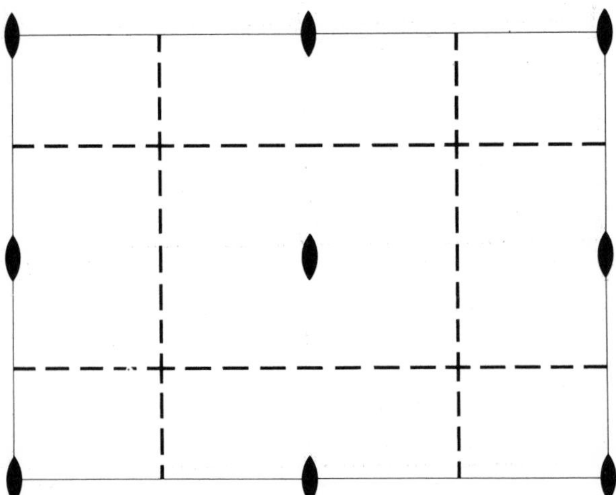

FIG. 25. *Pba*2.

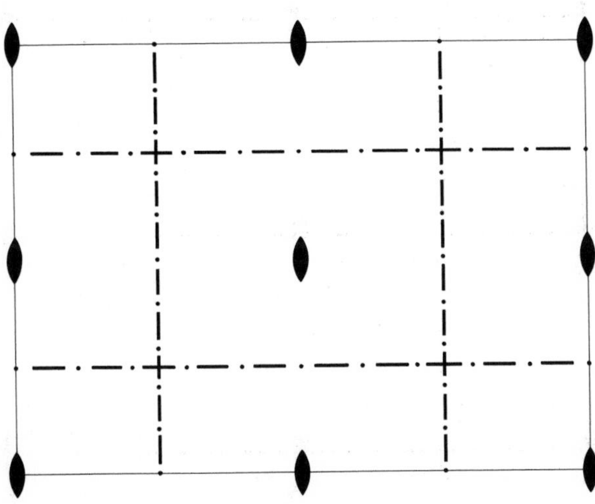

FIG. 26. *Pnn*2.

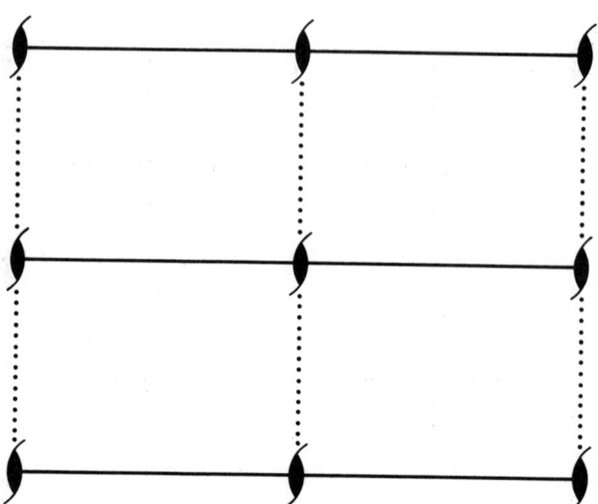

FIG. 27. $Pmc2_1$.

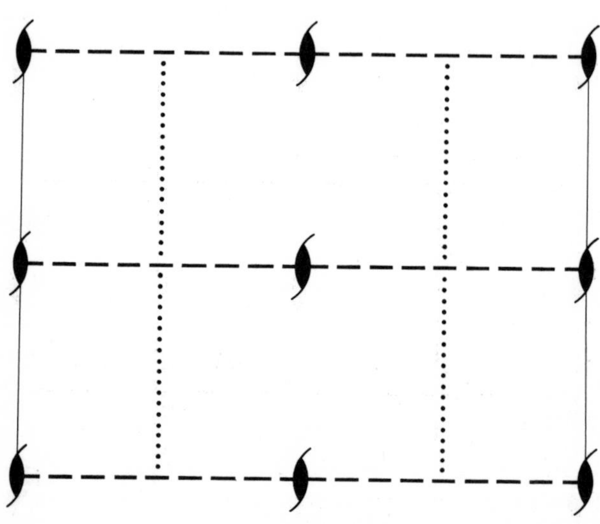

FIG. 28. $Pbc2_1$.

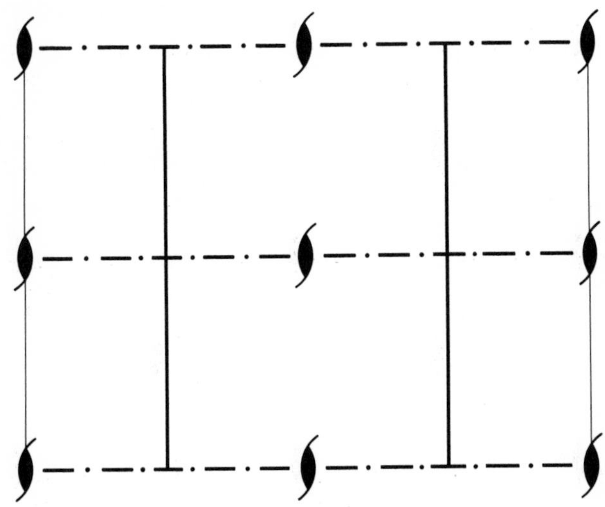

FIG. 29. $Pnm2_1$.

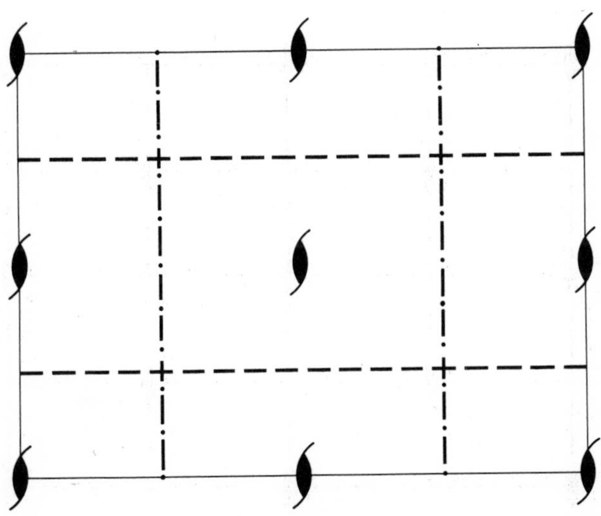

FIG. 30. $Pbn2_1$.

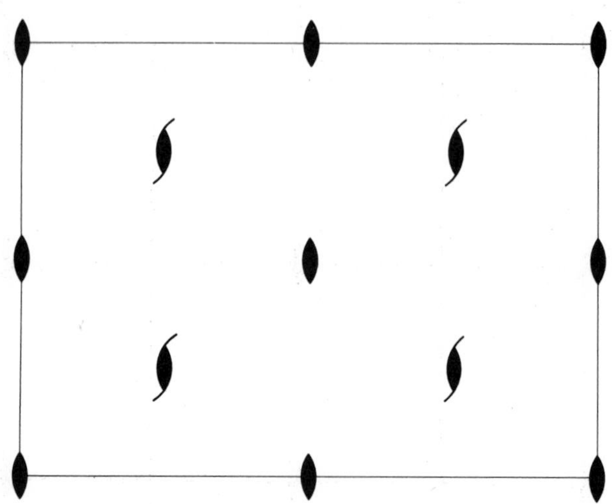

FIG. 31. *I*2. (Repeated from Chapter 13, Fig. 11, but referred to orthogonal axes.)

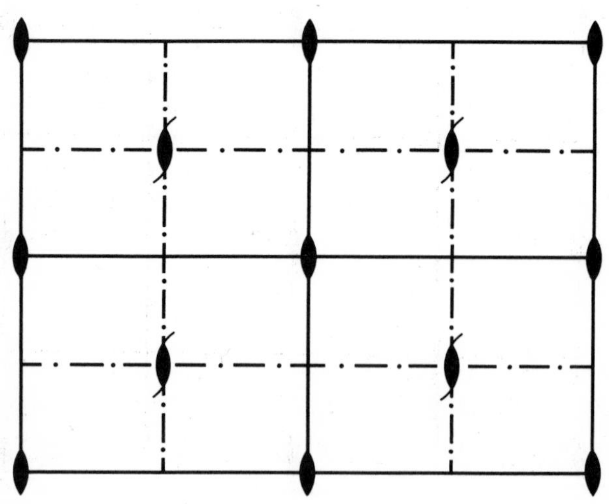

FIG. 32. *Imm*2.

When the additional operation of I is added to $Pcc2$ (Fig. 22), Table 3 shows that the result of combining 2_1 with ${}^s c$ is a. The new space group is shown in Fig. 33. It is customarily symbolized as $Iba2$, but it actually contains four combinations of screws and glides, of which three are distinct, as follows:

$$\begin{aligned} Iba2 &= Icc2 \\ &= Ibc2_1 \ (\cong Ica2_1). \end{aligned}$$

When the additional operation of I is added to $Pbm2$ (Fig. 23), the result is shown in Fig. 34. The two new combinations are $2_1\,{}^s b_1 = {}^s n_2$ and $2_1 m_2 = c_1$. The new space group is called $Ibm2$, but it actually contains four distinct combinations of screws and glides, as follows:

$$\begin{aligned} Ibm2 &= Icn2 \\ &= Ibn2_1 \\ &= Icm2_1. \end{aligned}$$

All the ten distinct combinations of Table 3 have now been encountered, so that all space groups based upon I have been derived.

Lattice C. In the axial frames $C2$ and $C2_1$ the distribution of axes is the same as in $P2$ and $P2_1$ respectively, but for orthorhombic symmetry an orthogonal cell is chosen so that the specific distributions of axes are as shown in Figs. 35 and 36 respectively. These have the same axes as $P2$ and $P2_1$ respectively, plus an additional similar axis in the center of each quadrant. The space groups based upon C can therefore be found by adding a 2-fold rotation operation to the six distinct upper combinations of Table 3, and by adding a 2-fold screw operation to the four distinct lower combinations of Table 3.

When a 2-fold rotation characteristic of $C2$ is added to $Pmm2$, two new combinations $2\,{}^s m = a$ appear, according to Table 3. The resulting space group is shown in Fig. 37. Although this is called $Cmm2$, it contains four combinations of Table 3, of which three are distinct, as follows:

$$\begin{aligned} Cmm2 &= Cba2 \\ &= Cma2 \ (\cong Cbm2). \end{aligned}$$

When a 2-fold rotation characteristic of $C2$ is added to $Pcc2$ two new combinations $2\,{}^s c = n$ appear. The resulting space group is shown in Fig. 38. Although this is designated $Ccc2$, it contains four combinations of Table 3, of which three are distinct, as follows:

$$\begin{aligned} Ccc2 &= Cnn2 \\ &= Cnc2 \ (\cong Ccn2). \end{aligned}$$

This exhausts all the distinct combinations of Table 3 with 2-fold rotation axes, and so exhausts the space groups based upon axial frame $C2$.

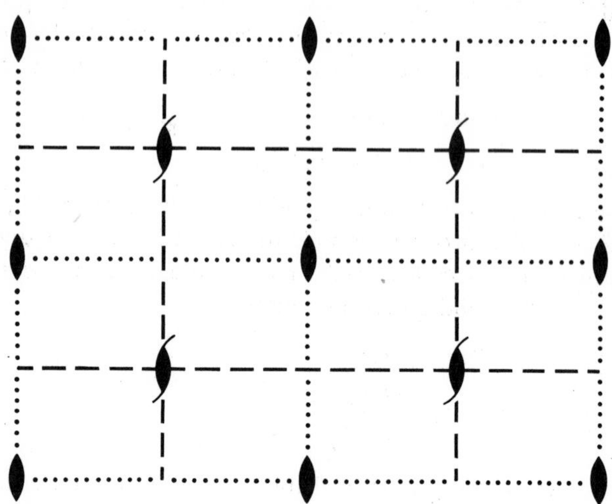

FIG. 33. *Iba*2.

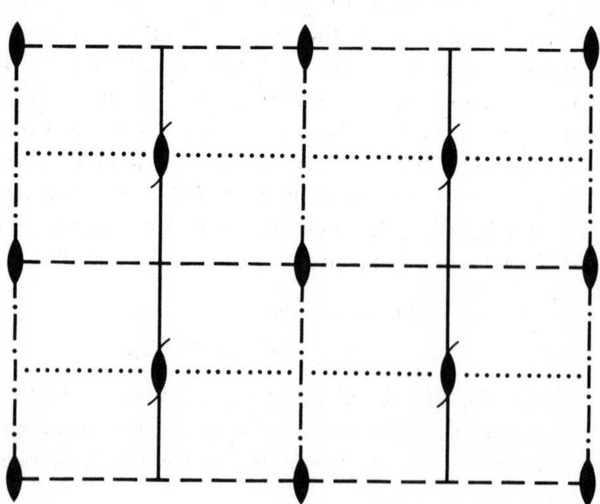

FIG. 34. *Ibm*2.

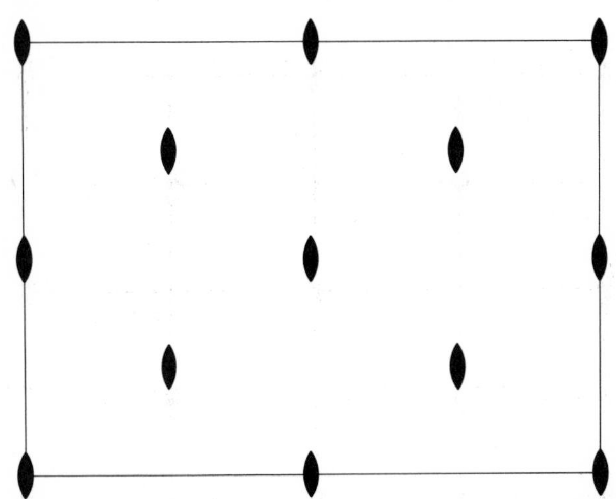

FIG. 35. *C*2. The distribution of symmetry elements is the same as in *P*2 (Chapter 13, Fig. 8), but the cell is chosen so that it is *C*-centered.

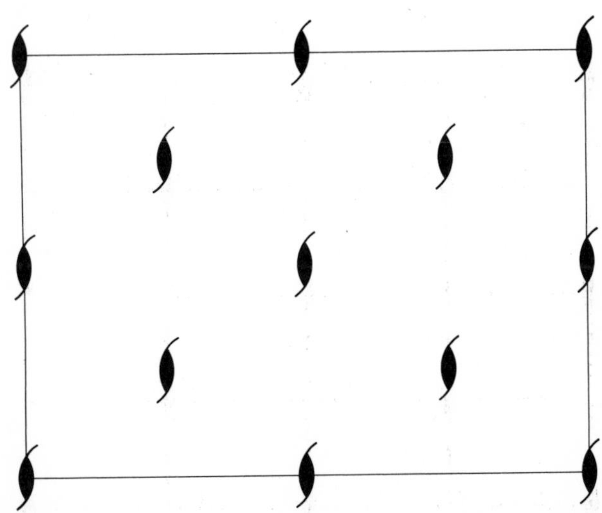

FIG. 36. $C2_1$. The distribution of symmetry elements is the same as in $P2_1$ (Chapter 13, Fig. 9), but the cell is chosen so that it is *C*-centered.

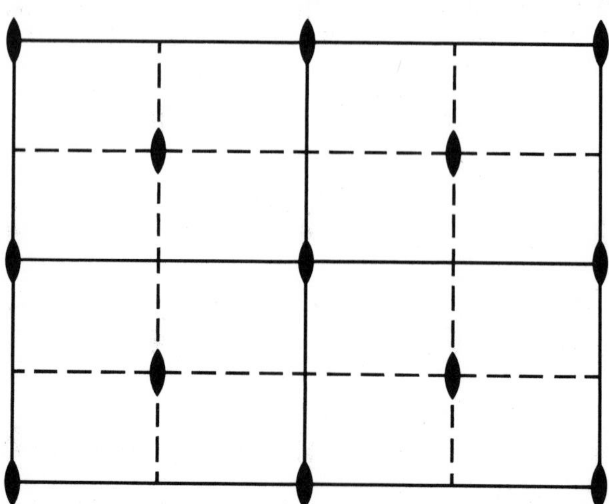

FIG. 37. *Cmm*2.

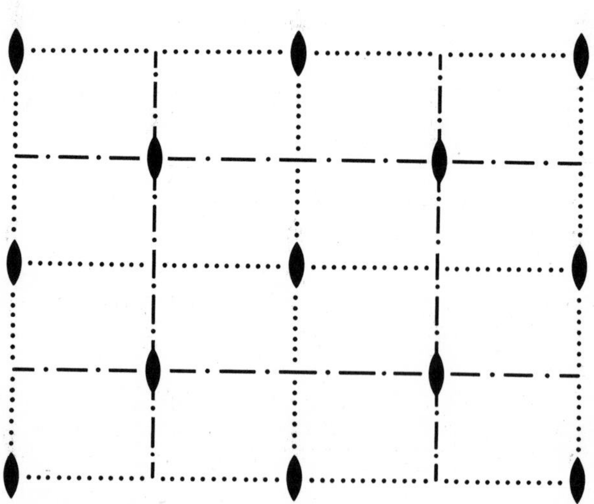

FIG. 38. *Ccc*2.

When a 2-fold screw characteristic of $C2_1$ is added to $Pmc2_1$, the combinations $2_1\,{}^sm_1 = n_2$ and $2_1\,{}^sc_2 = a_1$ arise. The resulting space group is shown in Fig. 39. Although this group is called $Cmc2_1$, it actually contains four distinct combinations, as follows:

$$\begin{aligned} Cmc2_1 &= Cbn2_1 \\ &= Cmn2_1 \\ &= Cbc2_1. \end{aligned}$$

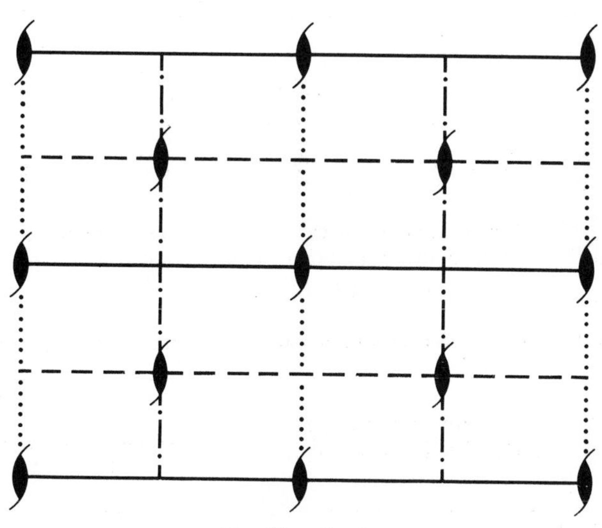

FIG. 39. $Cmc2_1$.

These are the only distinct combinations of the lower part of Table 3, and so exhaust the space groups based upon C.

Lattice A. The axial frame $A2$ in the orthorhombic system can be regarded as a specialization of the monoclinic $I2$ in such a way that an orthogonal cell centered on the A face results. The arrangement of axes in orthorhombic $A2$ is shown in Fig. 40.

Two new features occur in deriving space groups isogonal with $mm2$ and based upon the axial frame $A2$. In the first place, the centering on A and the lack of centering on B requires that the kinds of glide planes parallel to these planes are different. For a primitive lattice, combinations like $ma2$ and $bm2$ would be the same space group by interchange of axes. But the axes cannot be interchanged in an A-centered lattice, for in the first combination the mirror is parallel to the centered face, in the second it is parallel to an uncentered face. Another new feature is that the permissible glide planes parallel to the centered face are different from those previously considered. The lattice translations

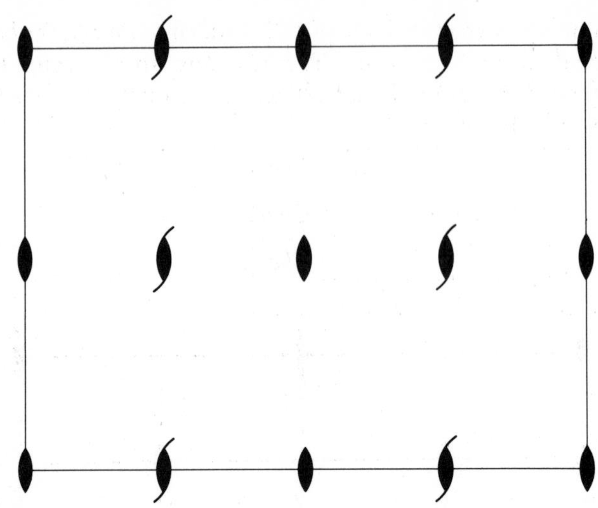

FIG. 40. *A*2. The distribution of symmetry elements is the same as in *I*2 (Chapter 13, Fig. 11), but the cell is chosen so that it is *A*-centered, as indicated in Chapter 13, Fig. 10.

Table 5. Combinations of 2-fold screws with parallel *d*-glides
(separation, $s = a/4$)

Original combination		Equivalent combination resulting from moving plane to axis			Characteristics of resulting reflection		
Designation	Separation s of plane and axis	Translation of screw	New translation, T, of (17)	Translation of plane	Σ translations	Separation of plane and axis	Translation of plane
$2d$	0	0	0	$\frac{b}{4}+\frac{c}{4}$	$\frac{b}{4}+\frac{c}{4}$	$\frac{b}{8}$	$\frac{c}{4}$
$2^s d$	$\frac{a}{4}$	0	$\frac{a}{2}$	$\frac{b}{4}+\frac{c}{4}$	$\frac{a}{2}+\frac{b}{4}+\frac{c}{4}$	$\frac{b}{8}$	$\frac{c}{4}$
$2_1 d$	0	$\frac{c}{2}$	0	$\frac{b}{4}+\frac{c}{4}$	$\frac{b}{4}+\frac{3c}{4}$	$\frac{b}{8}$	$\frac{3c}{4}$
$2_1^s d$	$\frac{a}{4}$	$\frac{c}{2}$	$\frac{a}{2}$	$\frac{b}{4}+\frac{c}{4}$	$\frac{a}{2}+\frac{b}{4}+\frac{3c}{4}$	$\frac{b}{8}$	$\frac{a}{2}+\frac{3c}{4}$

parallel to A are b, c, and $b/2 + c/2$. This permits glides with translation components of 0, $b/2$, $c/2$, and $b/4 + c/4$, whose designations are m, b, c, and d. There are some curious interrelations among these. Since $b/2 + c/2$ is a lattice translation, the glides $b/2$ and $c/2$ are together equivalent to a lattice translation. Therefore either one of these, followed by a lattice translation, equals the other. Therefore the glide b and c are the same. Furthermore, the glide n, which is possible in a primitive lattice, is equivalent to a mirror when parallel to A. This is because the translation component of n is $b/2 + c/2$; therefore a reflection followed by this translation is a reflection followed by a lattice translation, which is equivalent to a mirror. Finally, the glide d, whose translation component is $b/4 + c/4$, although permissible parallel to A, cannot be used because it results in glides with nonpermissible translation components parallel to (010). This is established in Table 5.

As a result of this discussion it is evident that the only permissible and distinct glide planes parallel to A are m ($= n$) and b ($= c$). These can be placed through an axis of Fig. 40, or halfway between similar axes, i.e., at $x = 0$ or $x = a/4$. To investigate the characteristics of the space groups it is only necessary to investigate the combination of these planes with the 2 and 2_1 axes with the aid of Table 3. The four combinations are as follows:

(1)
$$2 \cdot m_1 = m_2,$$
$$2_1 \cdot m_1 = c_2;$$
result: space group *Amm*2, Fig. 41.

(2)
$$2 \cdot b_1 = {}^s m_2,$$
$$2_1 \cdot b_1 = {}^s c_1;$$
result: space group *Abm*2, Fig. 42.

(3)
$$2 \cdot {}^s m_1 = a_2,$$
$$2_1 \cdot {}^s m_1 = n_2;$$
result: space group *Ama*2, Fig. 43.

(4)
$$2 \cdot {}^s b_1 = {}^s a_2,$$
$$2_1 \cdot {}^s b_1 = {}^s n_2;$$
result: space group *Aba*2, Fig. 44.

Lattice F. The axial frame $F2$ in the orthorhombic system can be regarded as a specialization of the monoclinic $I2$ in such a way that an orthogonal cell

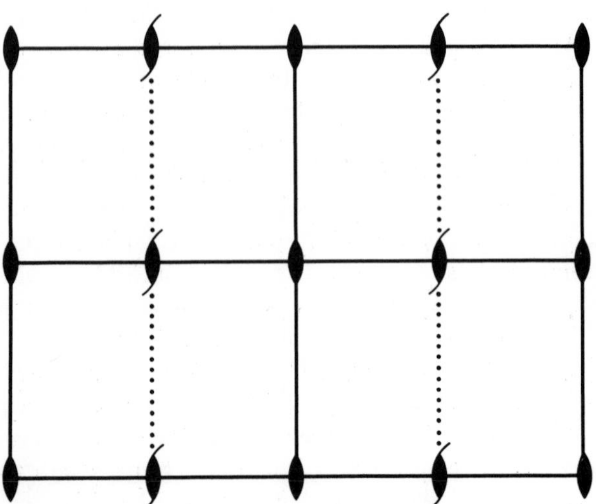

FIG. 41. *Amm*2.

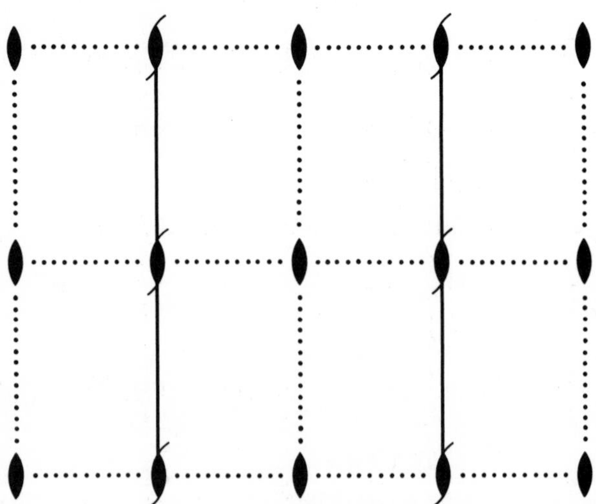

FIG. 42. *Abm*2. (Note that, in *A*-centered cells, *b* glides and *c* glides are the same.)

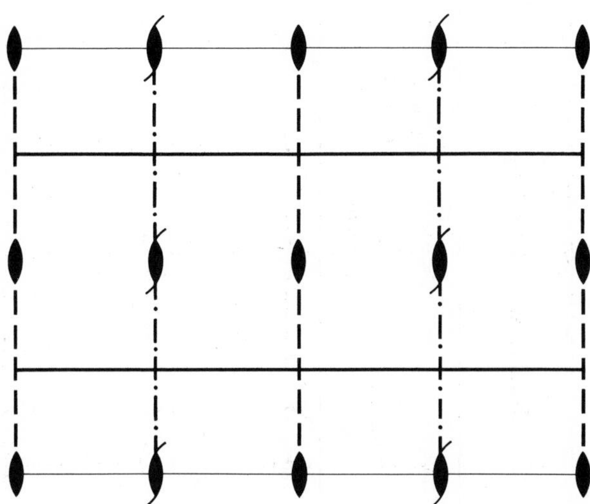

FIG. 43. *Ama*2.

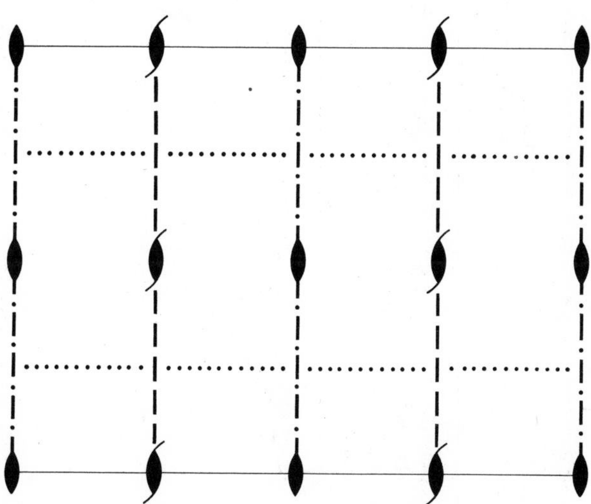

FIG. 44. *Aba*2. (Note that, in *A*-centered cells, *b* glides and *c* glides are the same.)

Table 6. Combinations of 2-fold screws with parallel *d*-glides (separation, $s = a/8$)

Original combination		Equivalent combination resulting from moving plane to axis			Characteristics of resulting reflection			
Desig-nation	Separa-tion s of plane and axis	Transla-tion of screw	New translation, T, of (17)	Transla-tion of plane	Σ translations	Separa-tion of plane and axis	Transla-tion of plane	Symbol
$2\,{}^{s}d^{+}$	$\frac{a}{8}$	0	$\frac{a}{4}$	$\frac{b}{4}+\frac{c}{4}$	$\frac{a}{4}+\frac{b}{4}+\frac{c}{4}$	$\frac{b}{8}$	$\frac{a}{4}+\frac{c}{4}$	${}^{s}d^{+}$
$2\,{}^{s}d^{-}$	$\frac{a}{8}$	0	$\frac{a}{4}$	$\frac{b}{4}-\frac{c}{4}$	$\frac{a}{4}+\frac{b}{4}-\frac{c}{4}$	$\frac{b}{8}$	$\frac{a}{4}-\frac{c}{4}$	${}^{s}d^{-}$
$2_1\,{}^{s}d^{+}$	$\frac{a}{8}$	$\frac{c}{2}$	$\frac{a}{4}$	$\frac{b}{4}+\frac{c}{4}$	$\frac{a}{4}+\frac{b}{4}-\frac{c}{4}$	$\frac{b}{8}$	$\frac{a}{4}-\frac{c}{4}$	${}^{s}d^{-}$
$2_1\,{}^{s}d^{-}$	$\frac{a}{8}$	$\frac{c}{2}$	$\frac{a}{4}$	$\frac{b}{4}-\frac{c}{4}$	$\frac{a}{4}+\frac{b}{4}+\frac{c}{4}$	$\frac{b}{8}$	$\frac{a}{4}+\frac{c}{4}$	${}^{s}d^{+}$

centered on all three planes A, B, and C results. The arrangement of axes in the orthorhombic $F2$ is shown in Fig. 45.

The translations of the F lattice parallel to the A face are b, c, and $b/2 + c/2$. The glides permissible to the lattices therefore would appear to have permissible translation components of 0, $b/2$, $c/2$, and $b/4 + c/4$. The only distinct permissible planes are therefore m, c, and d. Note that d can have components $b/4 + c/4$ (called d^+ in Table 5) or $b/4 - c/4$ (called d^- in Table 6). The d

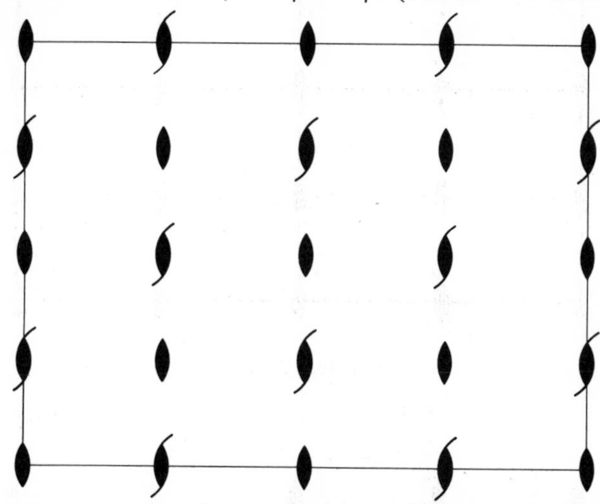

FIG. 45. $F2$. The distribution of symmetry elements is the same as in $I2$ (Chapter 13, Fig. 11), but the cell is chosen so that it is F-centered, as indicated in Chapter 13, Fig. 10.

glides can transform the axes of Fig. 45 into themselves when located at $x = a/8$, while the m reflection and c glide can transform the axes into themselves when located at $x = 0$.

The combination of $F2$ with m turns out to involve the combination of $F2$ with c, so that $Fmm2 = Fcc2$. Only two distinct space groups are therefore based upon $F2$, corresponding to combination with m and with ${}^{s}d$. The symmetry elements of these space groups can be readily found by combining the four axes in the neighborhood of the origin which are not translation equivalent, with plane m or d, as follows:

$$F2 \cdot m\text{: (Table 3),}$$

$$\left.\begin{aligned} {}^{00}2 \cdot m_1 &= m_2, \\ {}^{\frac{1}{4}\frac{1}{4}}2\ {}^{s}m_1 &= a_2 \Leftrightarrow c_2, \\ {}^{0\frac{1}{4}}2_1 m_1 &= c_2, \\ {}^{\frac{1}{4}0}2_1\ {}^{s}m_1 &= n_2 \Leftrightarrow m_2. \end{aligned}\right\} \begin{matrix}\text{Space group } Fmm2, \\ \text{Fig. 46.}\end{matrix}$$

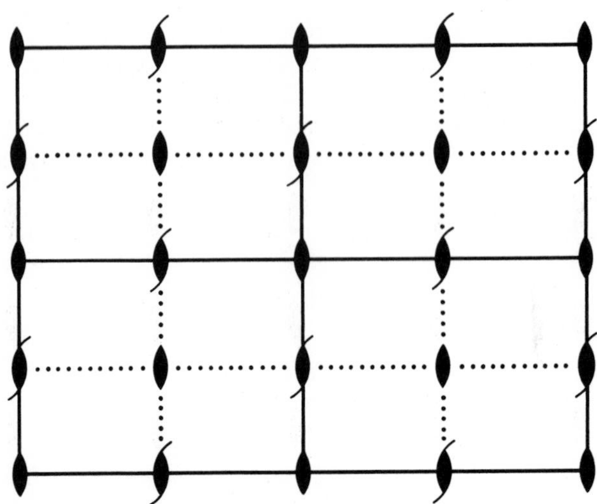

FIG. 46. *Fmm*2.

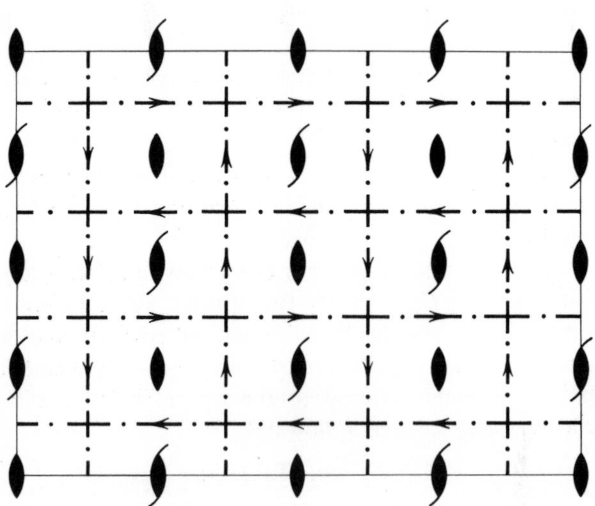

FIG. 47. *Fdd*2. The arrows on the glide planes mean that the translation component can be described as rising in the direction of the arrow.

$$F2 \cdot {}^{s}d\text{: (Table 6),}$$

$$\left.\begin{aligned} {}^{00}2 \cdot {}^{s}d^{+} &= {}^{s}d^{+}, \\ {}^{\frac{1}{4}\frac{1}{4}}2\ {}^{s}d^{-} &= {}^{s}d^{-}, \\ {}^{\frac{1}{4}0}2_1\ {}^{s}d^{+} &= {}^{s}d^{-}, \\ {}^{0\frac{1}{4}}2_1\ {}^{s}d^{+} &= {}^{s}d^{-}. \end{aligned}\right\} \begin{array}{c}\text{Space group } Fdd2, \\ \text{Fig. 47.}\end{array}$$

The designation d^+ means translation component $b/4 + c/4$ for planes parallel to A and $a/4 + c/4$ for planes parallel to B. Such translation components can be described as *rising* in the *positive* direction of $b/4$ or $a/4$ as seen from above, and in Fig. 47 the rising direction is indicated by an arrow. The d^- planes of Fig. 47 result from transformation of the d^+ planes by the 2-fold rotations and screws.

Résumé of space groups isogonal with mm2. The space groups of *mm*2 derived in this section are as follows:

*Pmm*2	*Imm*2	*Cmm*2	*Amm*2	*Fmm*2
*Pcc*2	*Iba*2	*Ccc*2	*Abm*2	*Fdd*2
*Pbm*2	*Ibm*2	$Cmc2_1$	*Ama*2	
*Pnc*2			*Aba*2	
*Pba*2				
*Pnn*2				
$Pmc2_1$				
$Pbc2_1$				
$Pnm2_1$				
$Pbn2_1$				
10 +	3 +	3 +	4 +	2 = 22

Point group $\frac{2}{m}\frac{2}{m}\frac{2}{m}$. Point group $2/m\ 2/m\ 2/m$ contains three mutually orthogonal reflection planes intersecting in three mutually orthogonal 2-fold rotation axes, and an inversion center. The point group can be derived by starting with the axial frame 222 and adding the operation of an inversion center. The combination of the inversion with each rotation produces a reflection in a plane perpendicular to the rotation axis. In a similar way, the space groups isogonal with point group $2/m\ 2/m\ 2/m$ can be deduced by adding an inversion center to the several axial frames isogonal with 222 (listed on page 243) in all distinct locations such that the center transforms the axial frame into itself. The locations and characteristics of the glide planes which result can be readily found by comparing the location of the center for each of the three orthogonal screws with Figs. 6, 7, 8, and 9.

An inversion center which transforms an axial frame into itself must be on an axis or halfway between similar axes. Since similar axes are spaced at distances of half a cell edge the centers in question can be found in an appropriate octant of the cell at one or more of the eight locations 000, $\frac{1}{4}00$, $0\frac{1}{4}0$, $00\frac{1}{4}$, $\frac{1}{4}\frac{1}{4}0$, $\frac{1}{4}0\frac{1}{4}$, $0\frac{1}{4}\frac{1}{4}$, $\frac{1}{4}\frac{1}{4}\frac{1}{4}$.

In each of the lattices to be discussed, an octant is shown with its symmetry elements, together with possible locations of inversion centers. Some pairs of

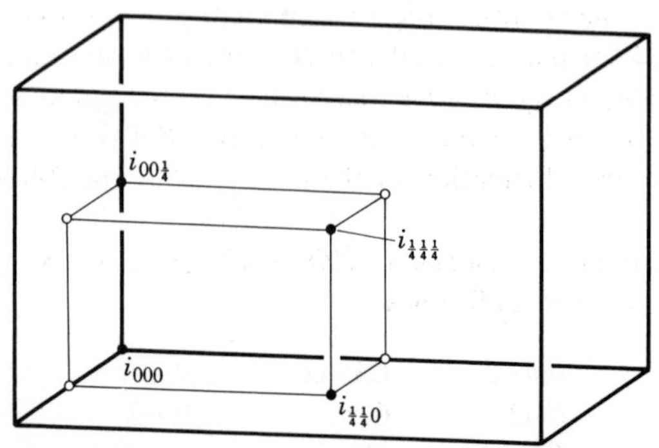

FIG. 48. Octant of $P222$ cell. Heavy lines are 2-fold axes. The black dots show characteristically different locations for inversion centers which transform $P222$ into itself. Open circles have 'similar situations to black dots. For example, the open circle at $\frac{1}{4}\,0\,\frac{1}{4}$ is in the center of a rectangle outlined by 2-fold axes, and therefore has a similar situation to the black dot at $\frac{1}{4}\,\frac{1}{4}\,0$.

the centers are related by a diagonal translation. For example, in C, $\vec{a} + \vec{b}$ is a lattice translation, T_{110}. If a center at 000 is chosen and represented by i_{000}, then this combines with the translation as follows:

$$i_{000} \cdot T_{110} = i_{\frac{1}{4}\frac{1}{4}0}. \tag{26}$$

Thus, if i_{000} is selected, it implies $i_{\frac{1}{4}\frac{1}{4}0}$. Symmetry elements so related by any translation are called *translation mates*. Both of these need not be considered. In the following deductions, one is represented by a circle, the other by a cross.

Of the centers th t are not translation mates, certain different locations have a similar situation with regard to the symmetry elements. These need not all be considered since if a center were placed at one location it would generate the same new symmetry elements as if it were placed at the other, but with a possible difference in origin and interchange of axes. In such sets one is shown as a solid circle and similar situations which need not be considered are shown in open circles.

Lattice P. For space groups isogonal with $2/m\ 2/m\ 2/m$, the axial frames of P are $P222$, $P222_1$, $P2_12_12$, and $P2_12_12_1$.

The centers which transform $P222$ into itself are shown in Fig. 48. When combined with $P222$, the four distinct centers produce four space groups, as follows:

$$P222 \cdot i_{000} \rightarrow P\frac{2}{m}\frac{2}{m}\frac{2}{m}, \qquad \text{Fig. 49,}$$

$$P222 \cdot i_{\frac{1}{4}\frac{1}{4}\frac{1}{4}} \rightarrow P\frac{2}{n}\frac{2}{n}\frac{2}{n}, \qquad \text{Fig. 50,}$$

$$P222 \cdot i_{00\frac{1}{4}} \rightarrow P\frac{2}{c}\frac{2}{c}\frac{2}{m}, \qquad \text{Fig. 51,}$$

$$P222 \cdot i_{\frac{1}{4}\frac{1}{4}0} \rightarrow P\frac{2}{b}\frac{2}{a}\frac{2}{n}, \qquad \text{Fig. 52.}$$

The centers which transform $P222_1$ into itself are shown in Fig. 53. When combined with $P222_1$, the four distinct centers produce four space groups, as follows:

$$P222_1 \cdot i_{000} \rightarrow P\frac{2}{m}\frac{2}{c}\frac{2_1}{m}, \qquad \text{Fig. 54,}$$

$$P222_1 \cdot i_{\frac{1}{4}\frac{1}{4}\frac{1}{4}} \rightarrow P\frac{2}{n}\frac{2}{a}\frac{2_1}{n}, \qquad \text{Fig. 55,}$$

$$P222_1 \cdot i_{\frac{1}{4}00} \rightarrow P\frac{2}{m}\frac{2}{n}\frac{2_1}{a}, \qquad \text{Fig. 56,}$$

$$P222_1 \cdot i_{0\frac{1}{4}0} \rightarrow P\frac{2}{b}\frac{2}{c}\frac{2_1}{b}, \qquad \text{Fig. 57.}$$

The centers which transform $P2_12_12$ into itself are shown in Fig. 58. The six distinct centers, when combined with $P2_12_12$, produce six space groups, as follows:

$$P2_12_12 \cdot i_{000} \rightarrow P\frac{2_1}{b}\frac{2_1}{a}\frac{2}{m}, \qquad \text{Fig. 59,}$$

$$P2_12_12 \cdot i_{\frac{1}{4}\frac{1}{4}\frac{1}{4}} \rightarrow P\frac{2_1}{c}\frac{2_1}{c}\frac{2}{n}, \qquad \text{Fig. 60,}$$

$$P2_12_12 \cdot i_{\frac{1}{4}00} \rightarrow P\frac{2_1}{b}\frac{2_1}{m}\frac{2}{a}, \qquad \text{Fig. 61,}$$

$$P2_12_12 \cdot i_{00\frac{1}{4}} \rightarrow P\frac{2_1}{n}\frac{2_1}{n}\frac{2}{m}, \qquad \text{Fig. 62,}$$

$$P2_12_12 \cdot i_{\frac{1}{4}\frac{1}{4}0} \rightarrow P\frac{2_1}{m}\frac{2_1}{m}\frac{2}{n}, \qquad \text{Fig. 63,}$$

$$P2_12_12 \cdot i_{\frac{1}{4}0\frac{1}{4}} \rightarrow P\frac{2_1}{n}\frac{2_1}{c}\frac{2}{a}, \qquad \text{Fig. 64.}$$

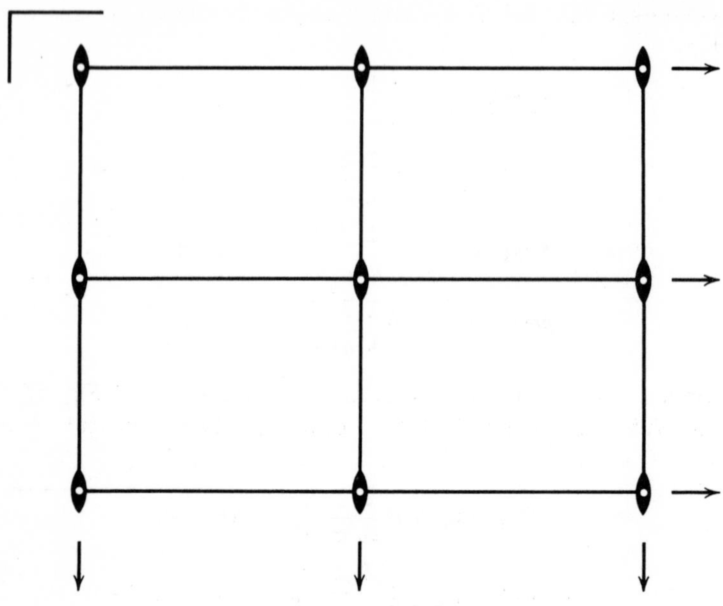

FIG. 49. $P\frac{2}{m}\frac{2}{m}\frac{2}{m}$.

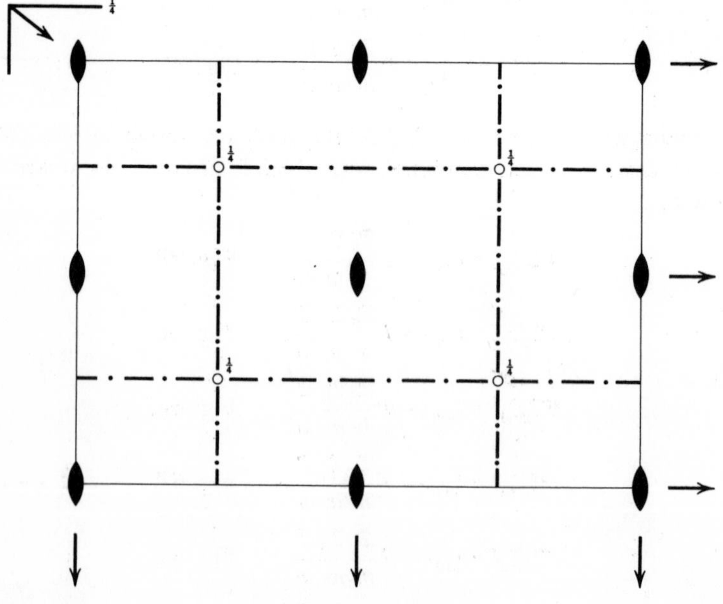

FIG. 50. $P\frac{2}{n}\frac{2}{n}\frac{2}{n}$.

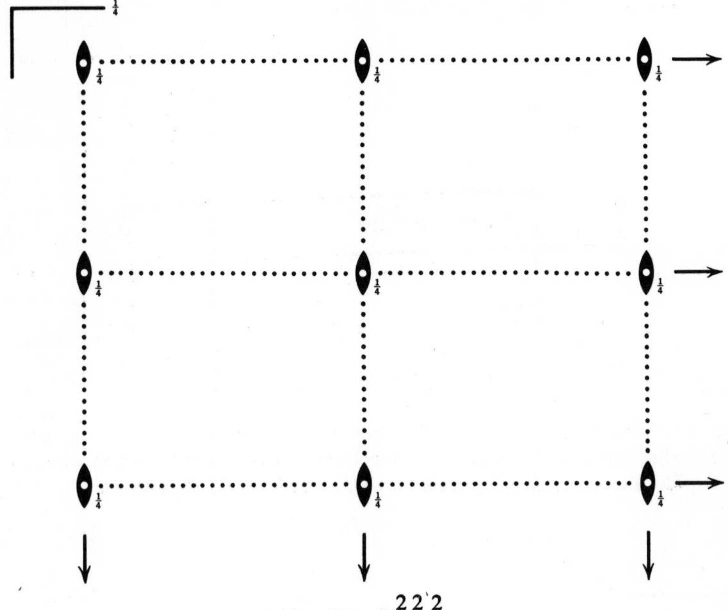

FIG. 51. $P\frac{2}{c}\frac{2}{c}\frac{2}{m}$.

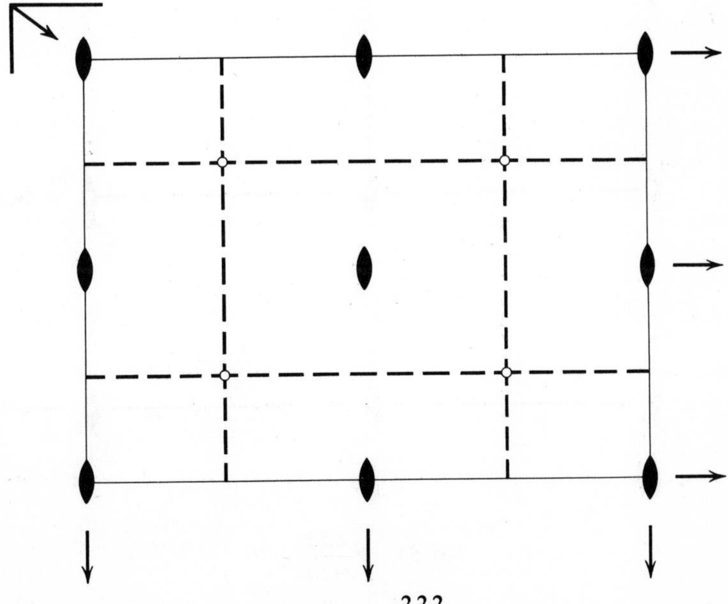

FIG. 52. $P\frac{2}{b}\frac{2}{a}\frac{2}{n}$.

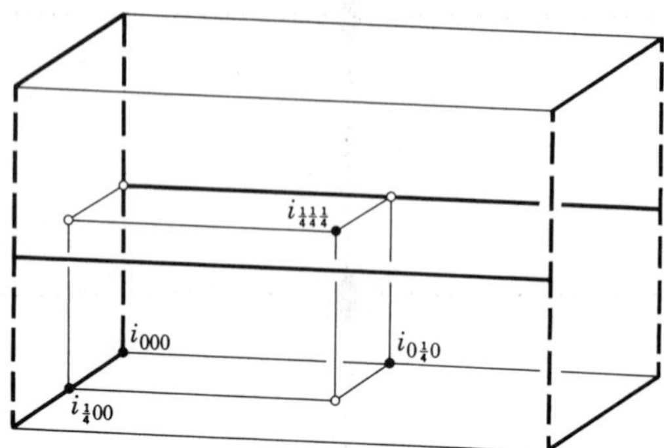

FIG. 53. Octant of $P222_1$ cell. The heavy full lines are 2-fold axes; the heavy broken lines are 2-fold screws. The black dots show characteristically different locations for inversion centers which transform $P222_1$ into itself.

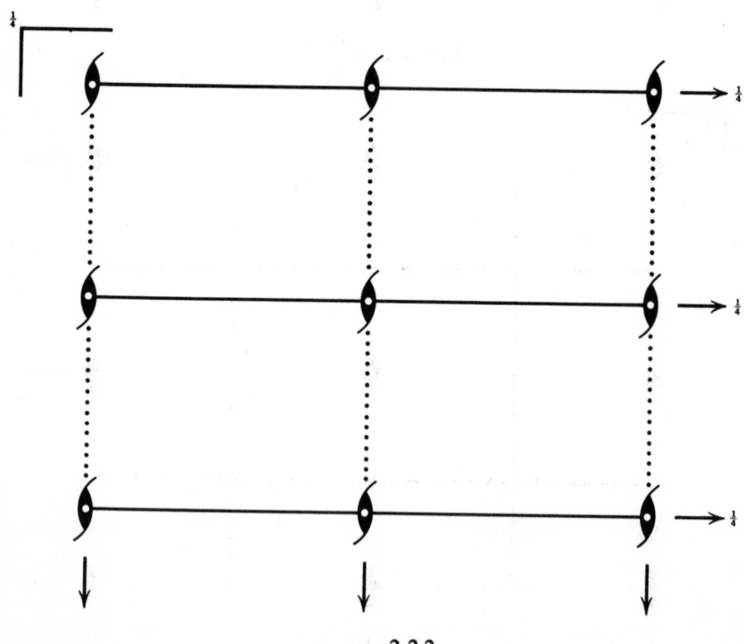

FIG. 54. $P\frac{2}{m}\frac{2}{c}\frac{2_1}{m}$.

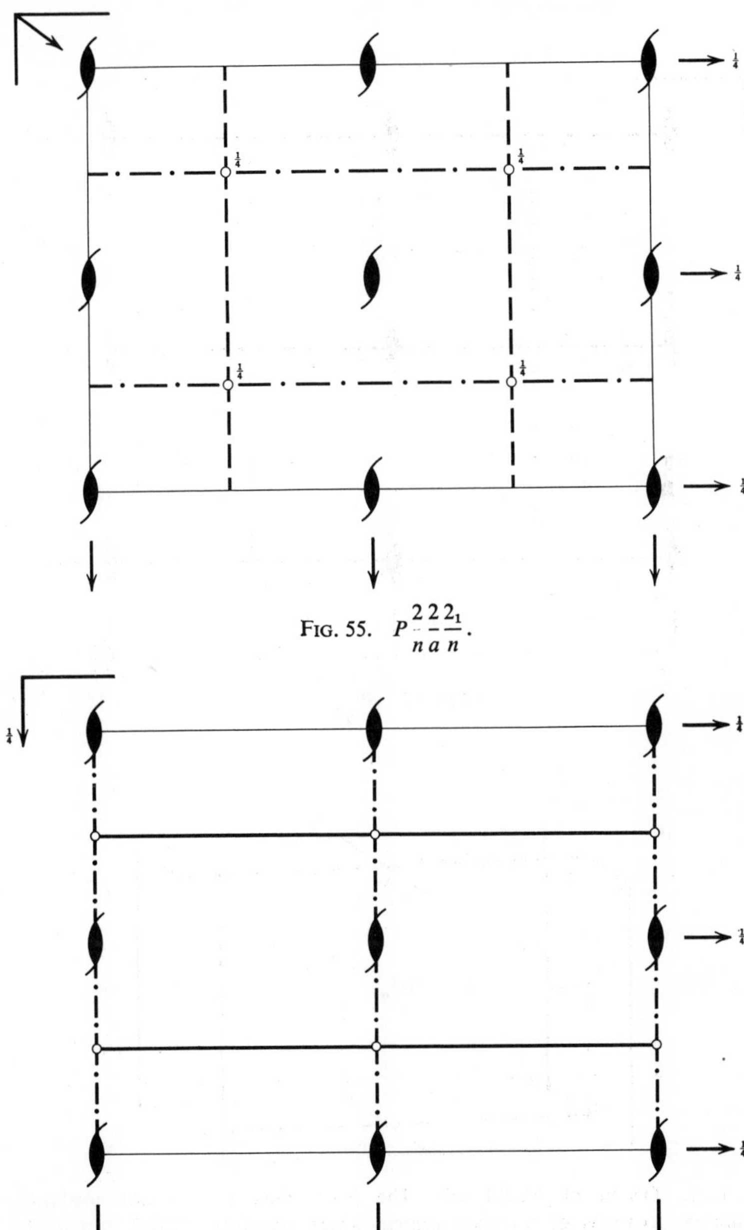

FIG. 55. $P\frac{2}{n}\frac{2}{a}\frac{2_1}{n}$.

FIG. 56. $P\frac{2}{m}\frac{2}{n}\frac{2_1}{a}$.

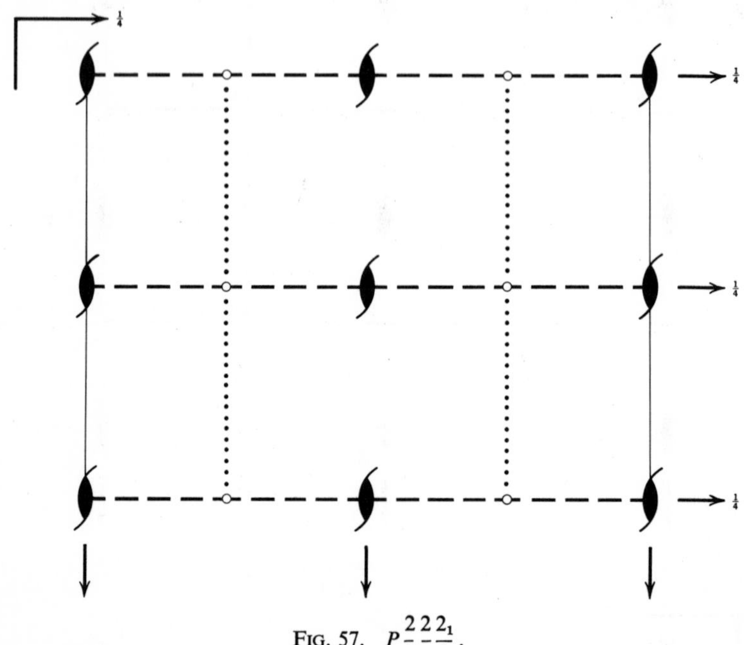

FIG. 57. $P\frac{2}{b}\frac{2}{c}\frac{2_1}{b}$.

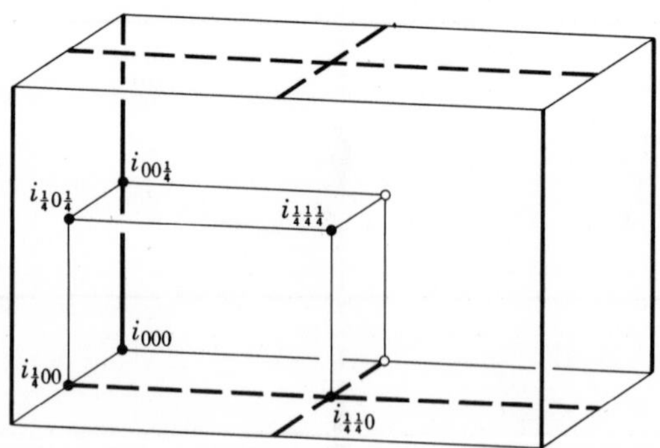

FIG. 58. Octant of $P2_12_12$ cell. The black dots show characteristically different locations of inversion centers which transform $P2_12_12$ into itself.

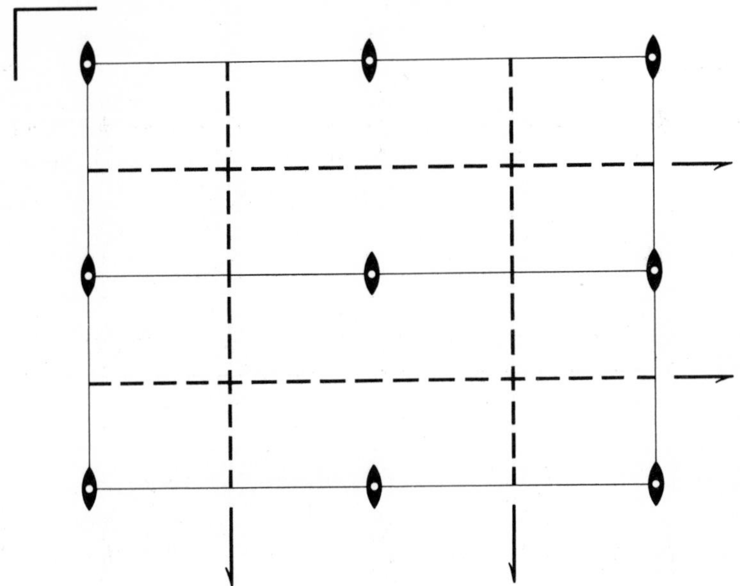

FIG. 59. $P\frac{2_1}{b}\frac{2_1}{a}\frac{2}{m}$.

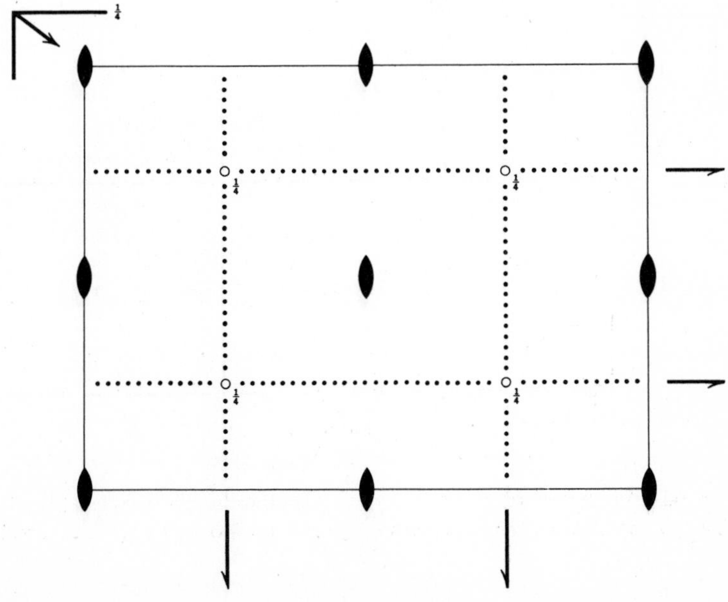

FIG. 60. $P\frac{2_1}{c}\frac{2_1}{c}\frac{2}{n}$.

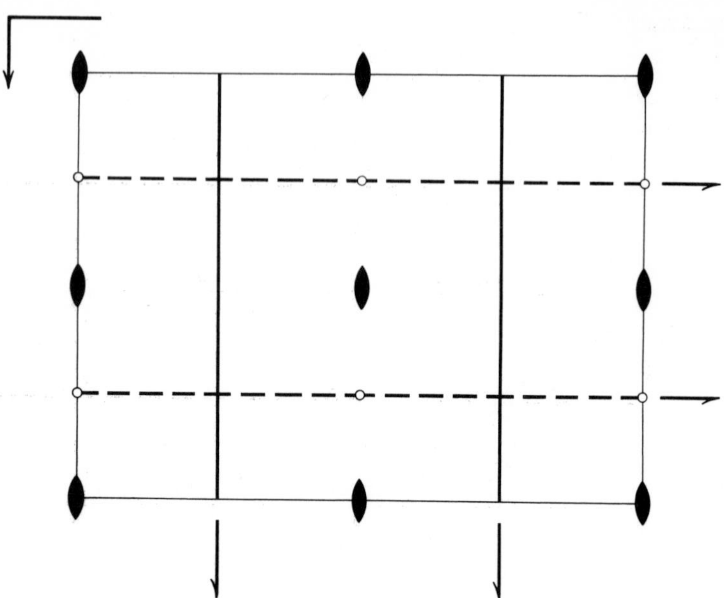

FIG. 61. $P\frac{2_1}{b}\frac{2_1}{m}\frac{2}{a}$.

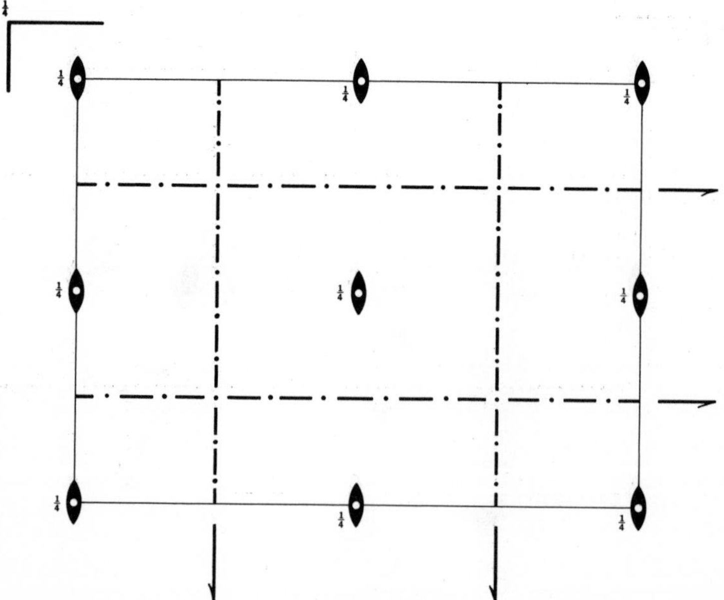

FIG. 62. $P\frac{2_1}{n}\frac{2_1}{n}\frac{2}{m}$.

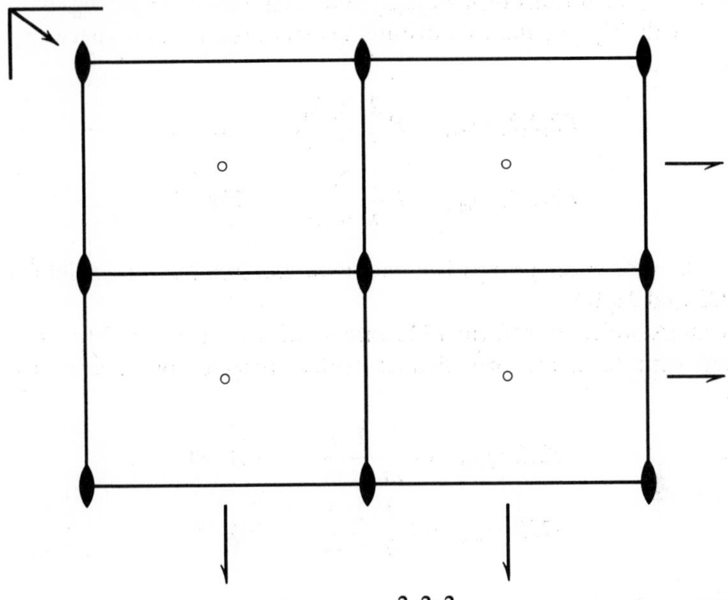

FIG. 63. $P\dfrac{2_1}{m}\dfrac{2_1}{m}\dfrac{2}{n}$.

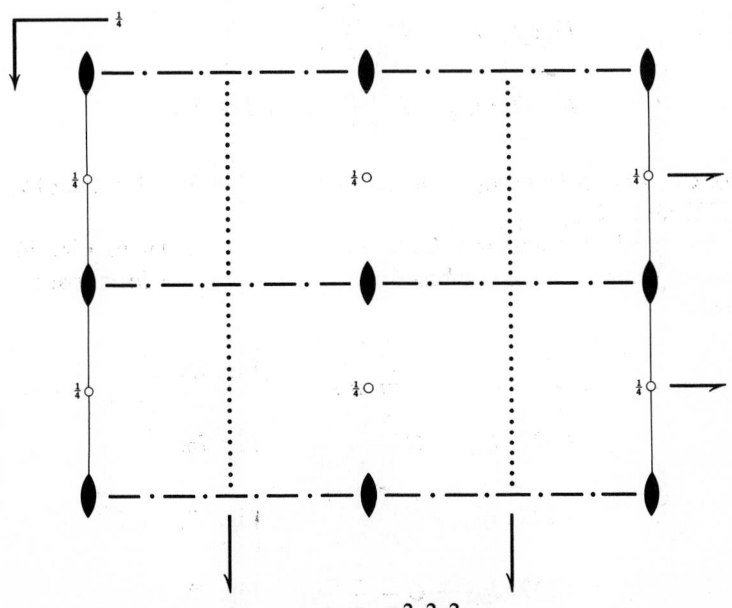

FIG. 64. $P\dfrac{2_1}{n}\dfrac{2_1}{c}\dfrac{2}{a}$.

The centers which transform $P2_12_12_1$ into itself are shown in Fig. 65. When combined with $P2_12_12_1$, the two distinct centers produce two space groups, as follows:

$$P2_12_12_1 \cdot i_{000} \rightarrow P\frac{2_1}{b}\frac{2_1}{c}\frac{2_1}{a}, \qquad \text{Fig. 66,}$$

$$P2_12_12_1 \cdot i_{00\frac{1}{4}} \rightarrow P\frac{2_1}{n}\frac{2_1}{m}\frac{2_1}{a}, \qquad \text{Fig. 67.}$$

Lattice I. For space groups isogonal with $2/m\ 2/m\ 2/m$, the axial frames of I are $I222$ and $I2_12_12_1$.

The centers which transform $I222$ into itself are shown in Fig. 68. When combined with $I222$, the two distinct centers produce two space groups, as follows:

$$I222 \cdot i_{000} \rightarrow I\frac{2}{m}\frac{2}{m}\frac{2}{m}, \qquad \text{Fig. 69,}$$

$$I222 \cdot i_{00\frac{1}{4}} \rightarrow I\frac{2}{b}\frac{2}{a}\frac{2}{m}, \qquad \text{Fig. 70.}$$

The centers which transform $I2_12_12_1$ into itself are shown in Fig. 71. When combined with $I2_12_12_1$, the two distinct centers produce two space groups, as follows:

$$I2_12_12_1 \cdot i_{\frac{1}{4}0\frac{1}{4}} \rightarrow I\frac{2_1}{b}\frac{2_1}{c}\frac{2_1}{a}, \qquad \text{Fig. 72,}$$

$$I2_12_12_1 \cdot i_{\frac{1}{4}00} \rightarrow I\frac{2_1}{m}\frac{2_1}{m}\frac{2_1}{a}, \qquad \text{Fig. 73.}$$

Lattice C. For space groups isogonal with $2/m\ 2/m\ 2/m$, the axial frames of C are $C222$ and $C222_1$.

The centers which transform $C222$ into itself are shown in Fig. 74. The four distinct centers, when combined with $C222$, produce four space groups, as follows:

$$C222 \cdot i_{000} \rightarrow C\frac{2}{m}\frac{2}{m}\frac{2}{m}, \qquad \text{Fig. 75,}$$

$$C222 \cdot i_{00\frac{1}{4}} \rightarrow C\frac{2}{c}\frac{2}{c}\frac{2}{m}, \qquad \text{Fig. 76,}$$

$$C222 \cdot i_{\frac{1}{4}00} \rightarrow C\frac{2}{m}\frac{2}{m}\frac{2}{a}, \qquad \text{Fig. 77,}$$

$$C222 \cdot i_{\frac{1}{4}0\frac{1}{4}} \rightarrow C\frac{2}{c}\frac{2}{c}\frac{2}{a}, \qquad \text{Fig. 78.}$$

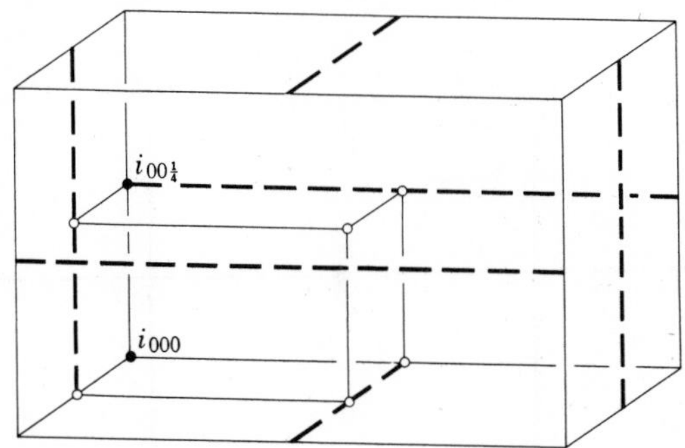

FIG. 65. Octant of $P2_12_12_1$ cell. The black dots show characteristically different locations of inversion centers which transform $P2_12_12_1$ into itself.

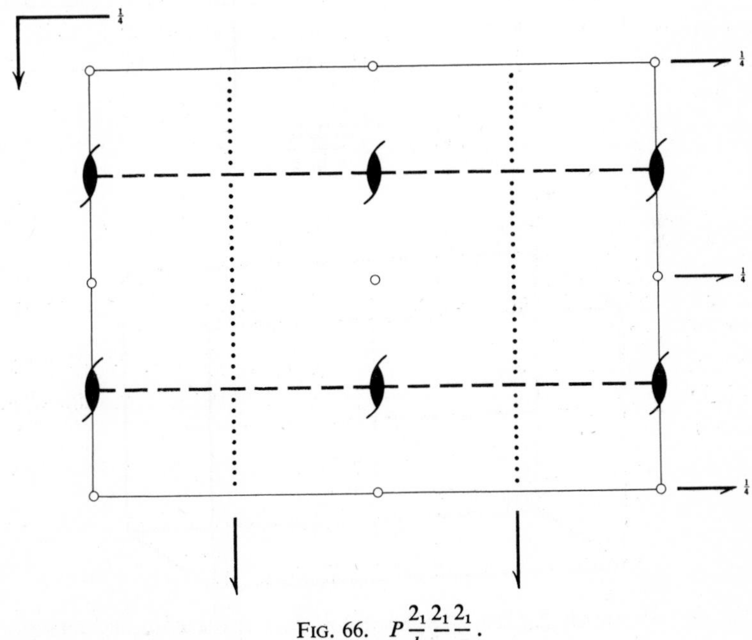

FIG. 66. $P\frac{2_1}{b}\frac{2_1}{c}\frac{2_1}{a}$.

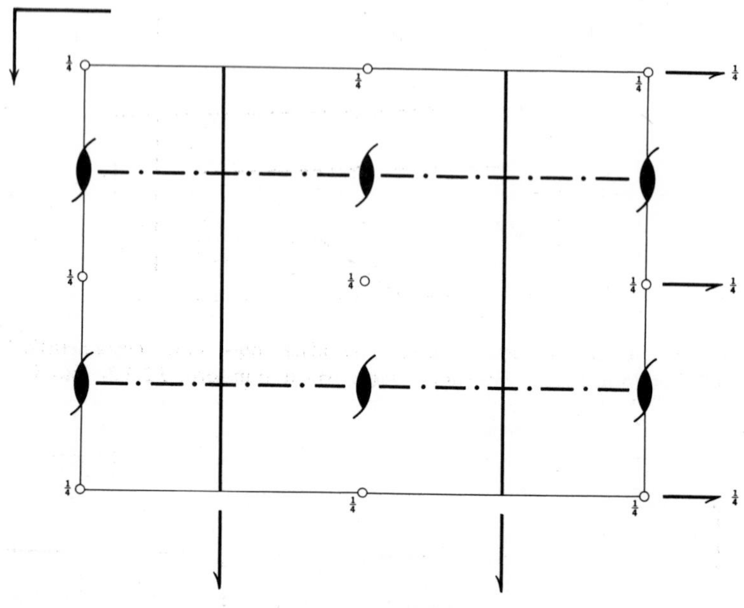

FIG. 67. $P\frac{2_1}{n}\frac{2_1}{m}\frac{2_1}{a}$.

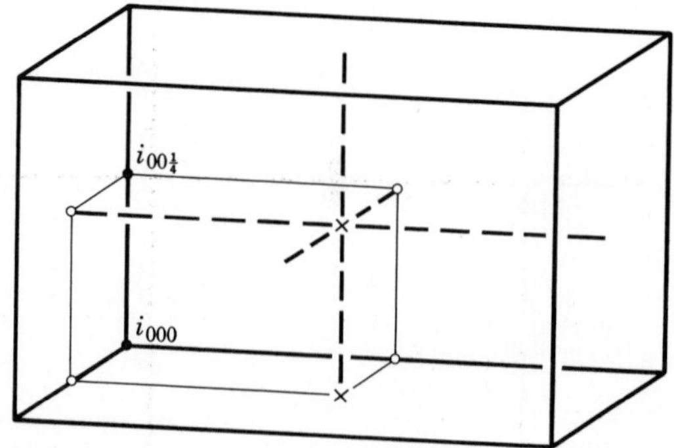

FIG. 68. Octant of *I*222 cell. The black dots show characteristically different locations of inversion centers which transform *I*222 into itself. The crosses are translation-mate inversion-center locations.

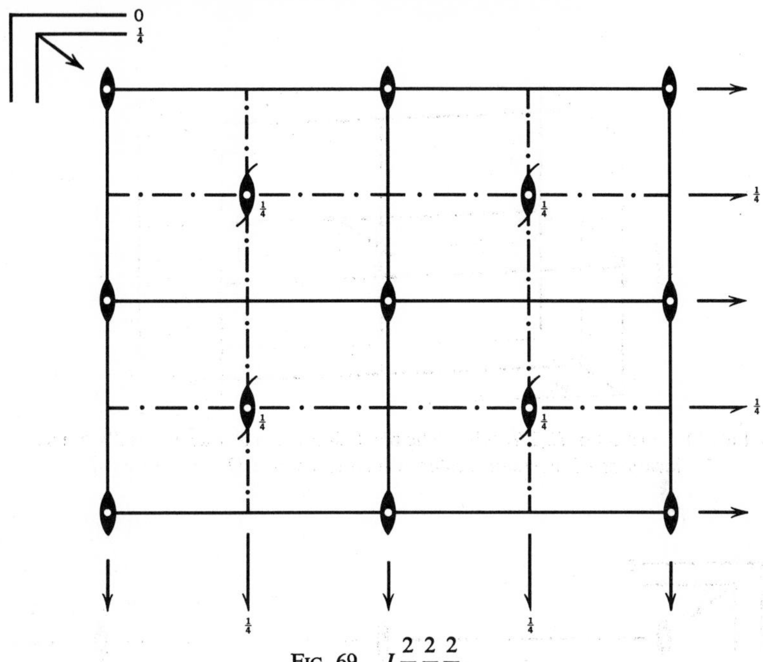

FIG. 69. $I\frac{2}{m}\frac{2}{m}\frac{2}{m}$.

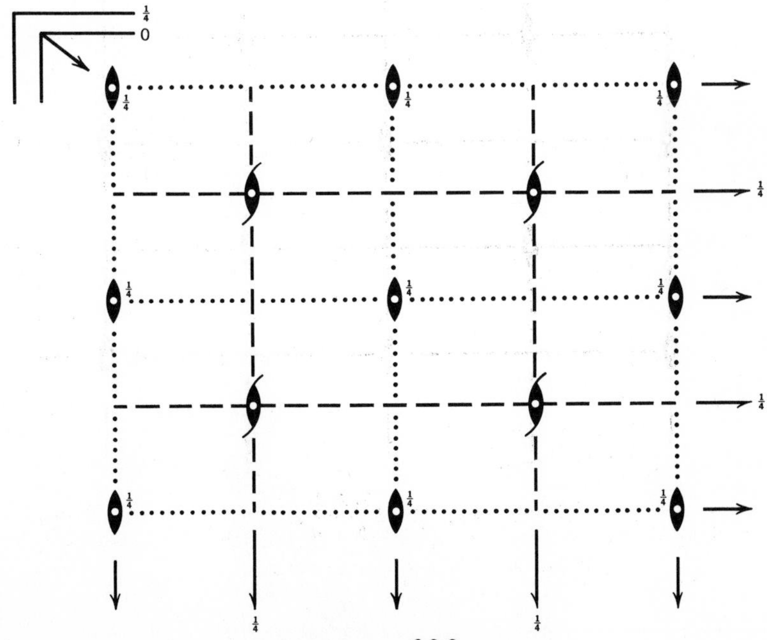

FIG. 70. $I\frac{2}{b}\frac{2}{a}\frac{2}{m}$.

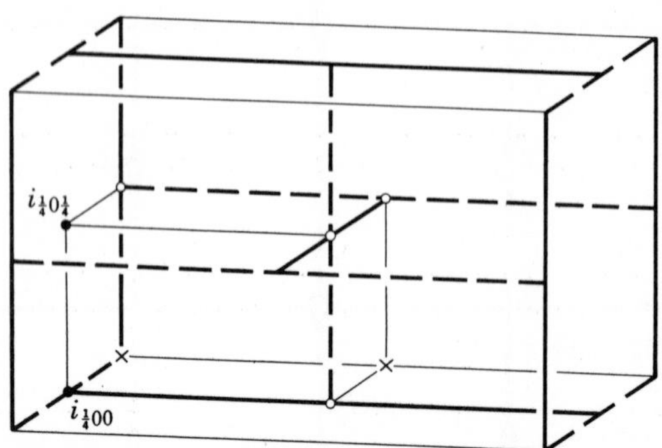

FIG. 71. Octant of $I2_12_12_1$ cell. The black dots show characteristically different locations of inversion centers which transform $I2_12_12_1$ into itself.

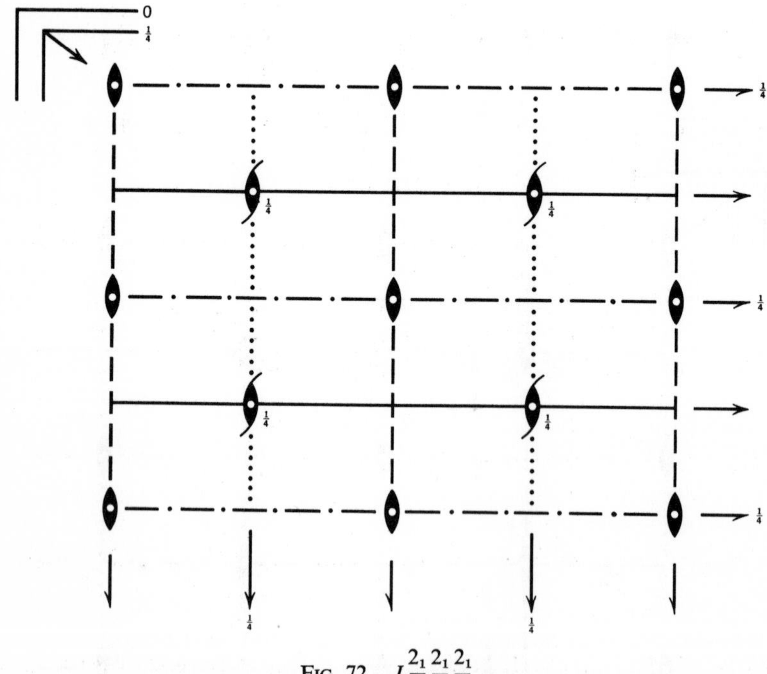

FIG. 72. $I\frac{2_1}{b}\frac{2_1}{c}\frac{2_1}{a}$.

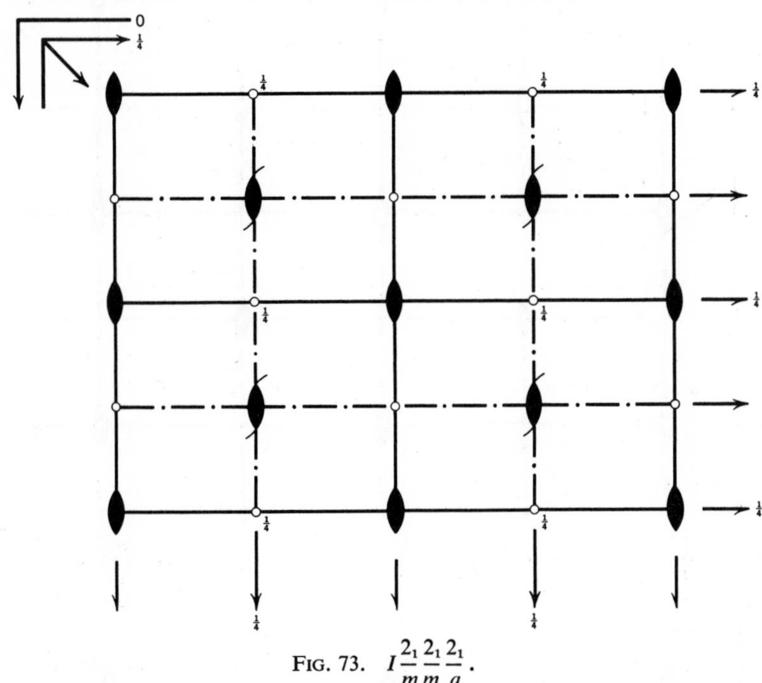

FIG. 73. $I\frac{2_1}{m}\frac{2_1}{m}\frac{2_1}{a}$.

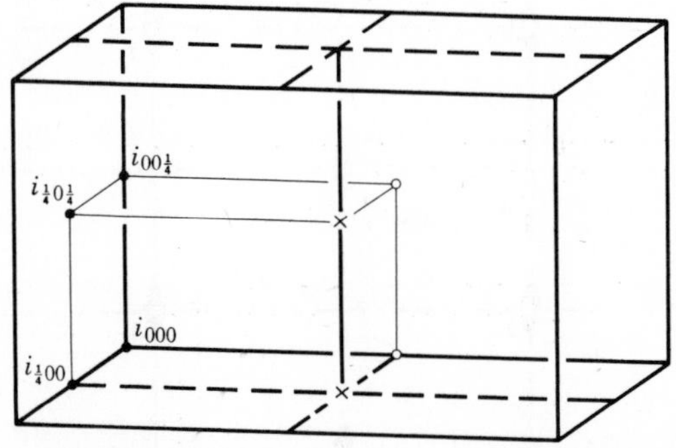

FIG. 74. Octant of $C222$ cell. The black dots show characteristically different locations of inversion centers which transform $C222$ into itself.

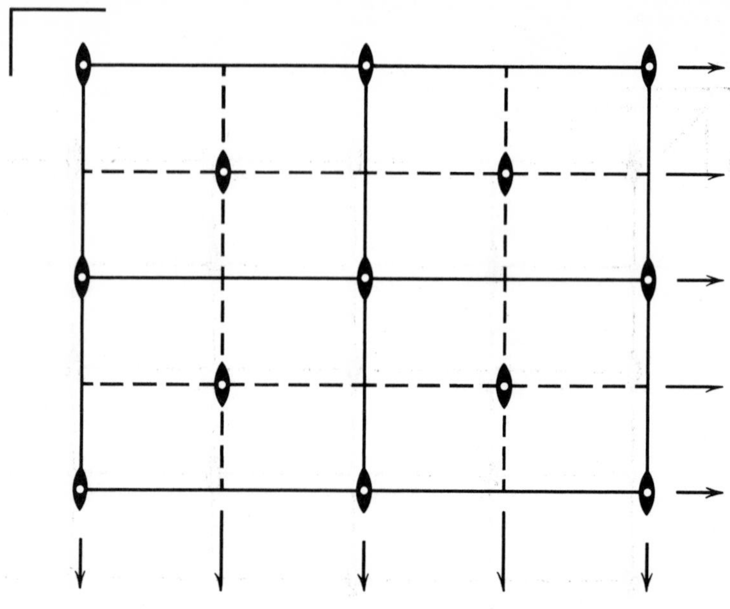

FIG. 75. $C\frac{2}{m}\frac{2}{m}\frac{2}{m}$.

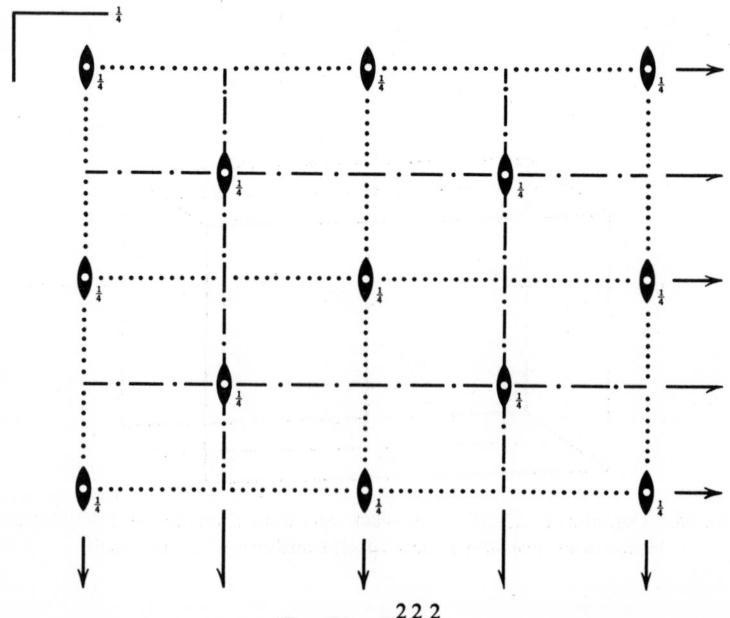

FIG. 76. $C\frac{2}{c}\frac{2}{c}\frac{2}{m}$.

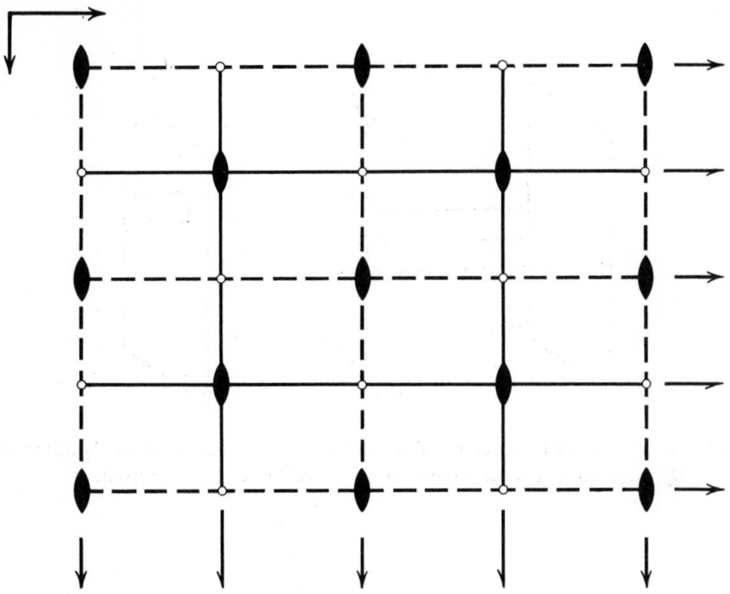

FIG. 77. $C\frac{2}{m}\frac{2}{m}\frac{2}{a}$.

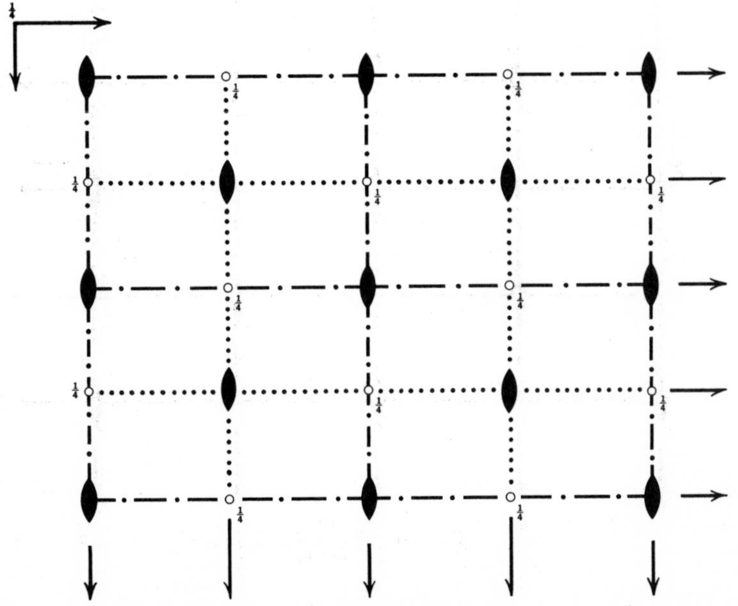

FIG. 78. $C\frac{2}{c}\frac{2}{c}\frac{2}{a}$.

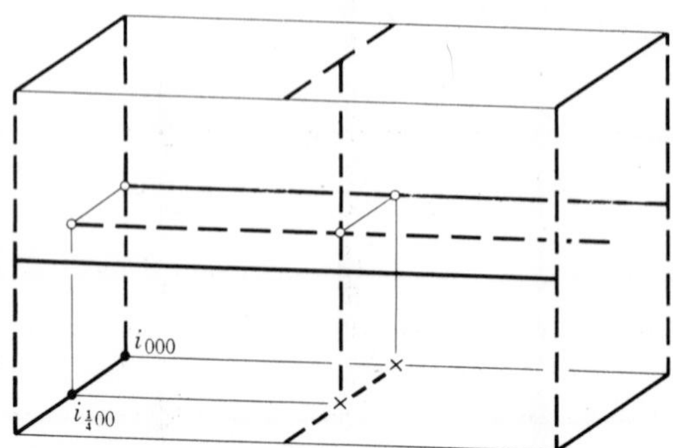

FIG. 79. Octant of $C222_1$ cell. The black dots show characteristically different locations of inversion centers which transform $C222_1$ into itself.

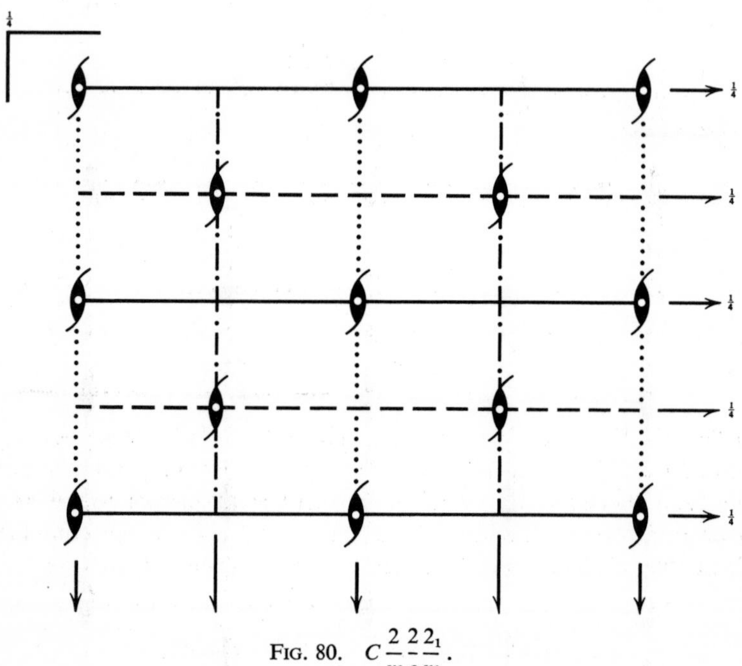

FIG. 80. $C\dfrac{2}{m}\dfrac{2}{c}\dfrac{2_1}{m}$.

The centers which transform $C222_1$ into itself are shown in Fig. 79. The two distinct centers, when combined with $C222_1$, produce two space groups, as follows:

$$C222_1 \cdot i_{000} \rightarrow C\frac{2}{m}\frac{2}{c}\frac{2_1}{m}, \qquad \text{Fig. 80,}$$

$$C222_1 \cdot i_{\frac{1}{4}00} \rightarrow C\frac{2}{m}\frac{2}{c}\frac{2_1}{a}, \qquad \text{Fig. 81.}$$

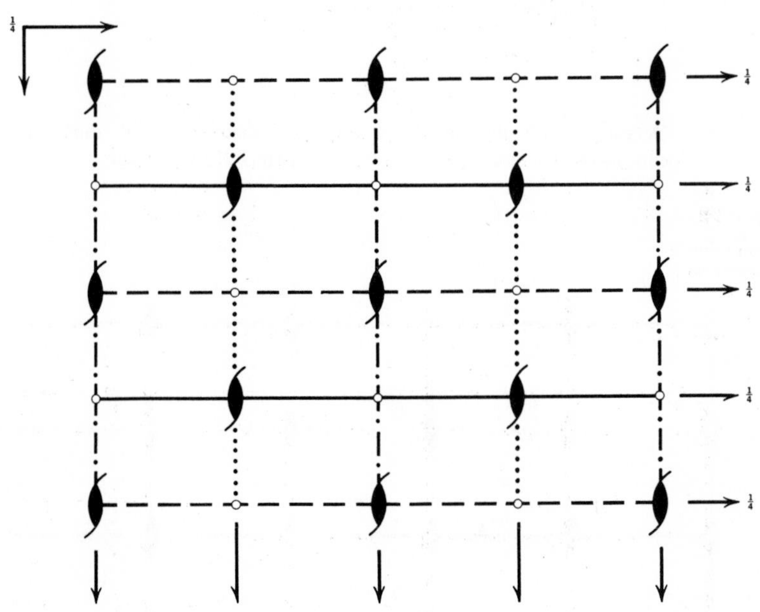

FIG. 81. $C\frac{2}{m}\frac{2}{c}\frac{2_1}{a}$.

Lattice F. For space groups isogonal with $2/m\,2/m\,2/m$, the only axial frame of F is $F222$. The centers which transform this frame into itself are shown in Fig. 82. The axial frame $F222$ is unusual in that its high symmetry permits it to be transformed into itself by a center at $\frac{1}{8}\frac{1}{8}\frac{1}{8}$. When combined with $F222$, the two distinct centers produce two space groups, as follows:

$$F222 \cdot i_{000} \rightarrow F\frac{2}{m}\frac{2}{m}\frac{2}{m}, \qquad \text{Fig. 83,}$$

$$F222 \cdot i_{\frac{1}{8}\frac{1}{8}\frac{1}{8}} \rightarrow F\frac{2}{d}\frac{2}{d}\frac{2}{d}, \qquad \text{Fig. 84.}$$

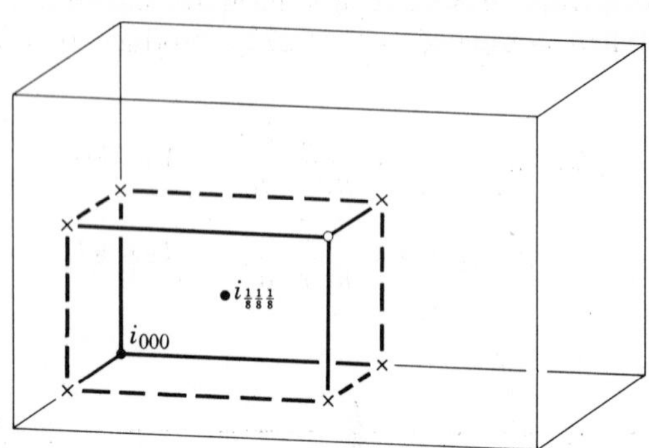

FIG. 82. Octant of *F*222 cell. The black dots show characteristically different locations of inversion centers which transform *F*222 into itself.

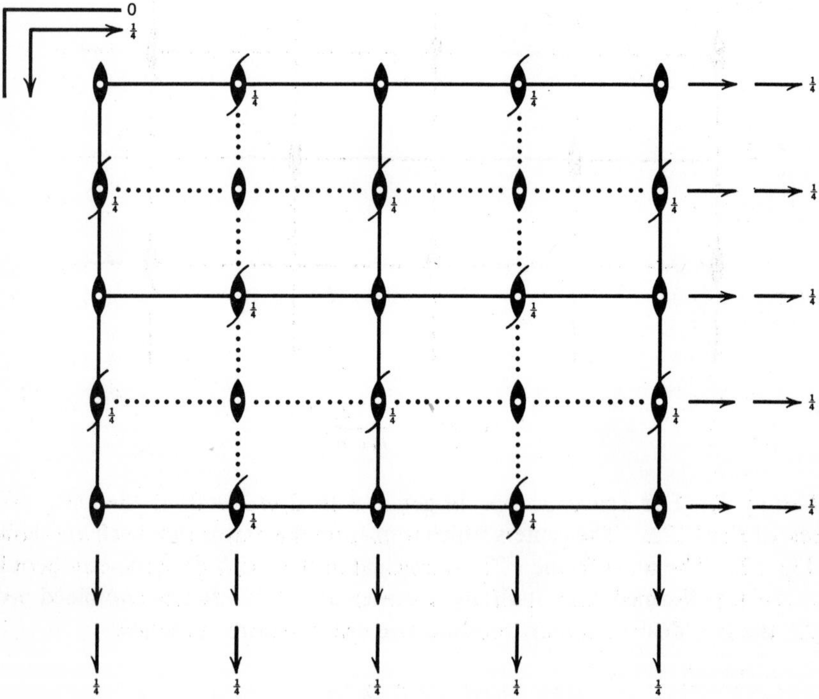

FIG. 83. $F\dfrac{2}{m}\dfrac{2}{m}\dfrac{2}{m}$.

Résumé of space groups isogonal with $2/m\ 2/m\ 2/m$. The space groups of $2/m\ 2/m\ 2/m$ derived in this section are

$P\frac{2}{m}\frac{2}{m}\frac{2}{m}$	$I\frac{2}{m}\frac{2}{m}\frac{2}{m}$	$C\frac{2}{m}\frac{2}{m}\frac{2}{m}$	$F\frac{2}{m}\frac{2}{m}\frac{2}{m}$
$P\frac{2}{n}\frac{2}{n}\frac{2}{n}$	$I\frac{2}{b}\frac{2}{a}\frac{2}{m}$	$C\frac{2}{c}\frac{2}{c}\frac{2}{m}$	$F\frac{2}{d}\frac{2}{d}\frac{2}{d}$
$P\frac{2}{c}\frac{2}{c}\frac{2}{m}$	$I\frac{2_1}{b}\frac{2_1}{c}\frac{2_1}{a}$	$C\frac{2}{m}\frac{2}{m}\frac{2}{a}$	
$P\frac{2}{b}\frac{2}{a}\frac{2}{n}$	$I\frac{2_1}{m}\frac{2_1}{m}\frac{2_1}{a}$	$C\frac{2}{c}\frac{2}{c}\frac{2}{a}$	
$P\frac{2}{m}\frac{2}{c}\frac{2_1}{m}$		$C\frac{2}{m}\frac{2}{c}\frac{2_1}{m}$	
$P\frac{2}{n}\frac{2}{a}\frac{2_1}{n}$		$C\frac{2}{m}\frac{2}{c}\frac{2_1}{a}$	
$P\frac{2}{m}\frac{2}{n}\frac{2_1}{a}$			
$P\frac{2}{b}\frac{2}{c}\frac{2_1}{b}$			
$P\frac{2_1}{b}\frac{2_1}{a}\frac{2}{m}$			
$P\frac{2_1}{c}\frac{2_1}{c}\frac{2}{n}$			
$P\frac{2_1}{b}\frac{2_1}{m}\frac{2}{a}$			
$P\frac{2_1}{n}\frac{2_1}{n}\frac{2}{m}$			
$P\frac{2_1}{m}\frac{2_1}{m}\frac{2}{n}$			
$P\frac{2_1}{n}\frac{2_1}{c}\frac{2}{a}$			
$P\frac{2_1}{b}\frac{2_1}{c}\frac{2_1}{a}$			
$P\frac{2_1}{b}\frac{2_1}{m}\frac{2_1}{a}$			
16 +	4 +	6 +	2 = 28

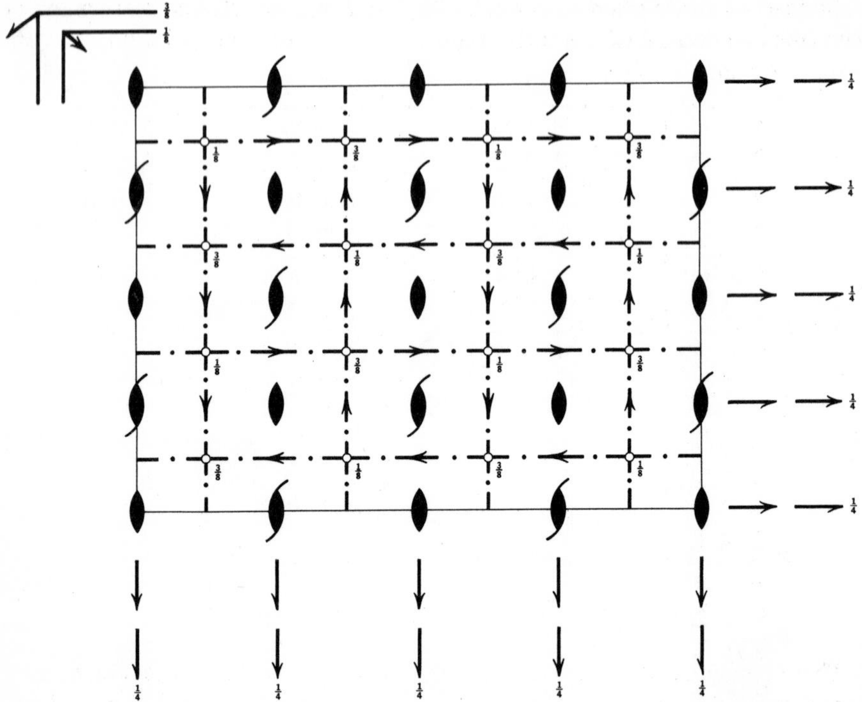

FIG. 84. $F\frac{2}{d}\frac{2}{d}\frac{2}{d}$. The arrows on the glide planes mean that the translation component can be described as rising in the direction of the arrow.

Tetragonal space groups

Point group $\bar{4}$. The space groups isogonal with $\bar{4}$ can be derived by the straightforward methods of Chapter 13 by combining the operations of $\bar{4}$ with the translations of lattice *P* or *C*. First consider the combination with *P*. The first power of the rotoreflection axis $\tilde{4}$ is $A_{\pi/2,m}$, where *m* means a reflection in a plane whose level is $z = 0$. These several powers of *A* combine with translations shown in Fig. 85 as follows:

$$\begin{aligned} A&: \quad A_{\pi/2,m} \cdot T_1 = B_{\pi/2,m}, \\ A^2&: \quad A_{\pi} \cdot T_2 = B_{\pi}, \\ A^3&: \quad A_{-\pi/2,m} \cdot T_3 = B_{-\pi/2,m}. \end{aligned} \tag{27}$$

Therefore a $\bar{4}$ axis occurs at *B* at the same level as the one at *A*.

The second power combines with T_1 as follows:

$$A_{\pi} \cdot T_1 = C_{\pi}. \tag{28}$$

Therefore 2-fold rotation axes occur at *C*. This exhausts the combinations with nonequivalent horizontal translations, as the more detailed kind of treatment of Chapter 13 would show.

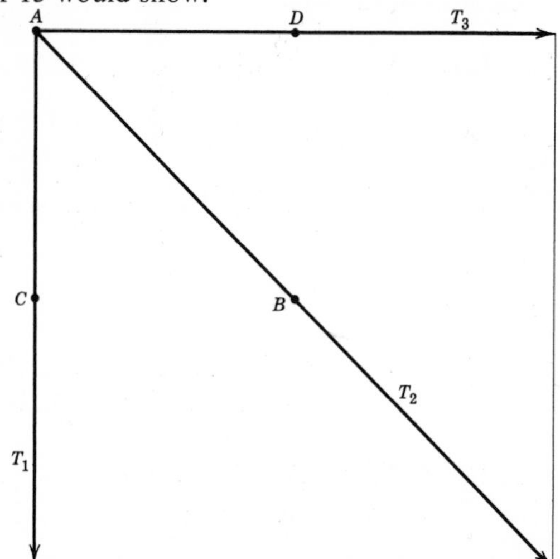

FIG. 85. The combinations of $\bar{4}$ with the translations of *P*.

There remain combinations of the $\bar{4}$ axis with the translations having vertical components. According to (12), if a rotoinversion operation occurs at level zero, it also occurs at level $\frac{1}{2}$. The resulting space group $P\bar{4}$ is as shown in Fig. 86.

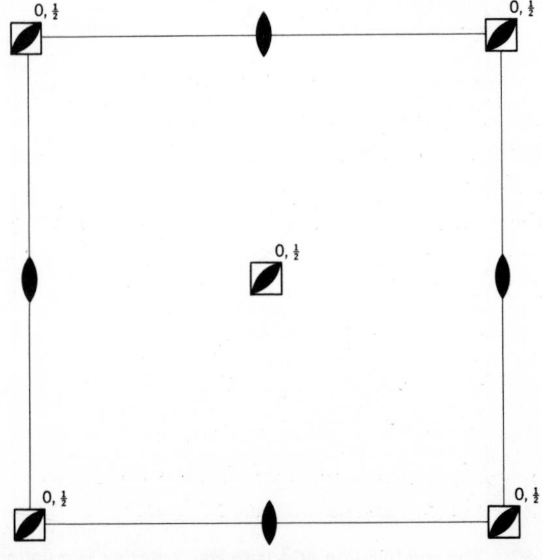

FIG. 86. $P\bar{4}$.

Lattice *I* contains the same translations as *P* plus those shown as T_4 in Fig. 87, which correspond to the lattice point at the center of the cell. The combinations of the powers of $A_{\pi/2,m}$ with this translation are

$$
\begin{aligned}
A_{\pi/2,m} \cdot T_4 &= A_{\pi/2}m \cdot T_{4,\parallel} \cdot T_{4,\perp} \\
&= A_{\pi/2}m \cdot \frac{c}{2} \cdot T_{4,\perp} \\
&= A_{\pi/2} \cdot {}^{\frac{1}{4}}m \cdot T_{4,\perp} \quad \text{(when } {}^{\frac{1}{4}}m \text{ is at level } z = c/4) \\
&= A_{\pi/2,\frac{1}{4}m} \cdot T_{4,\perp} \\
&= D_{\pi/2,\frac{1}{4}m}.
\end{aligned} \tag{29}
$$

A full investigation shows that a $\bar{4}$ axis occurs at *D* in levels $\frac{1}{4}$ and $\frac{3}{4}$. The second power of $A_{\pi/2,m}$ is A_π. This combines with T_4 as follows:

$$
\begin{aligned}
A_\pi \cdot T_4 &= A_\pi \cdot T_\parallel \cdot T_\perp \\
&= A_\pi \cdot c/2 \cdot T_\perp \\
&= A_{\pi,c/2} \cdot T_\perp \\
&= E_{\pi,c/2}.
\end{aligned} \tag{30}
$$

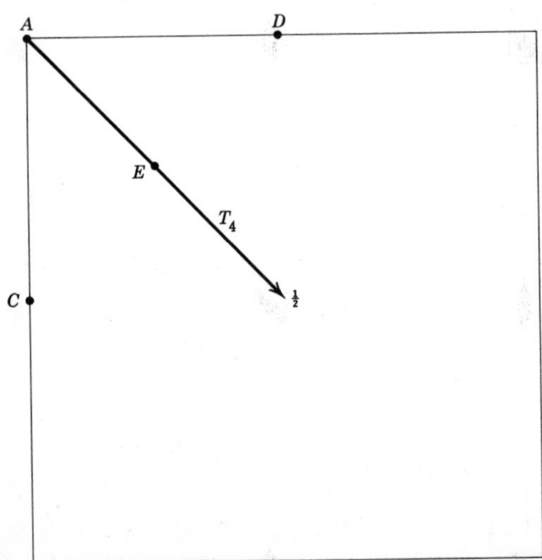

FIG. 87. The combination of $\bar{4}$ with the centering translation of *I*.

This shows that a 2-fold screw occurs at E. The complete space group $I\bar{4}$ is shown in Fig. 88.

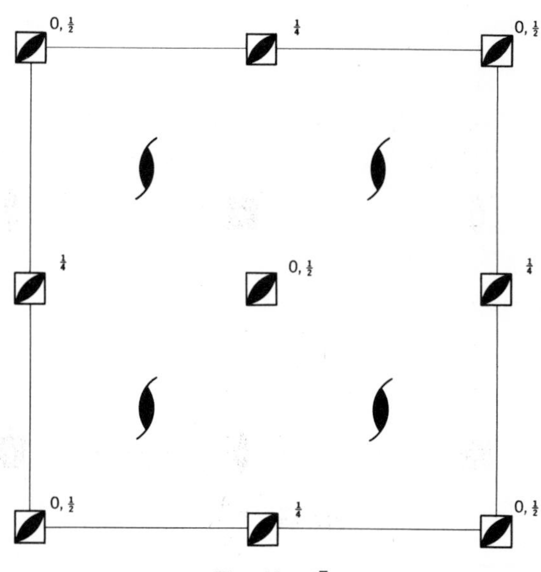

FIG. 88. $I\bar{4}$.

Point group 4/*m*. Point group $4/m$ can be derived by combining a reflection plane at right angles to a 4-fold axis. Accordingly the space groups isogonal with $4/m$ can be derived by starting with neutral axial frames isogonal with 4 and adding normal to the axes an appropriate glide plane which transforms the axes into themselves. According to Chapter 13 the neutral axial frames isogonal with 4 are $P4$, $P4_2$, $I4$, and $I4_1$.

Lattice P. The axial frame $P4$ is shown in Fig. 19 of Chapter 13. The only glides normal to the axes which transform the set of axes into itself are m and n. The two space groups based upon this frame are accordingly

$$P4 \cdot m \rightarrow P\frac{4}{m}, \qquad \text{Fig. 89,}$$

$$P4 \cdot n \rightarrow P\frac{4}{n}, \qquad \text{Fig. 90.}$$

Since a reflection normal to a 4-fold axis produces an inversion, these space groups contain inversion centers. Their locations can be found by noting that $A^2_{\pi/2} = A_\pi$, and consulting Figs. 6–9.

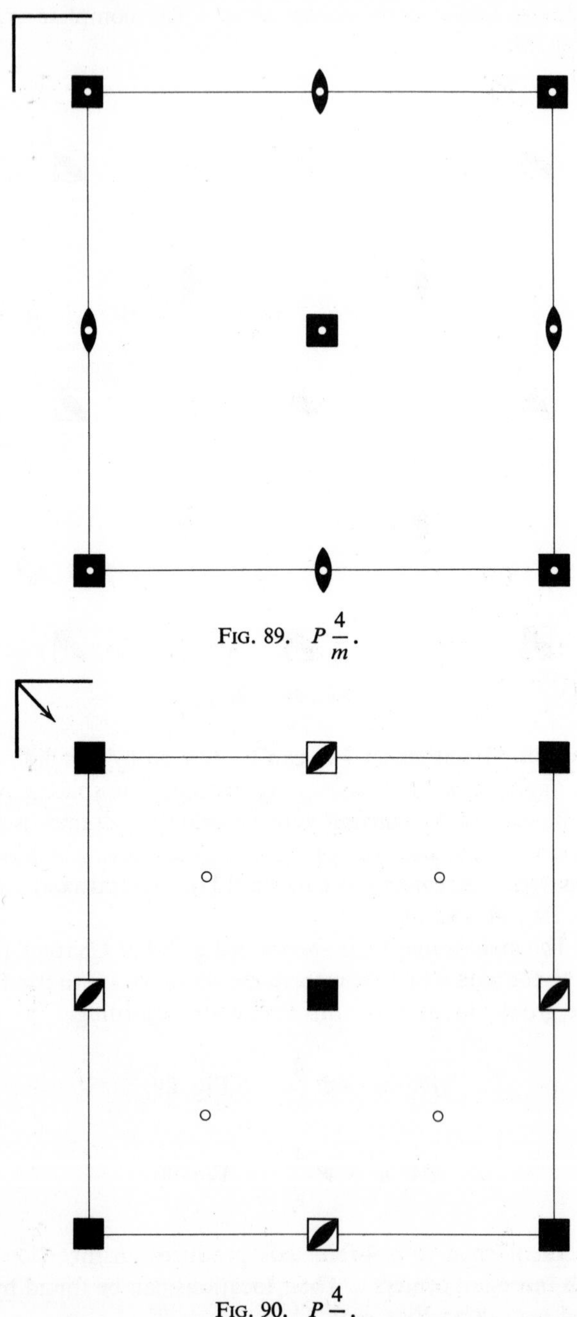

FIG. 89. $P\frac{4}{m}$.

FIG. 90. $P\frac{4}{n}$.

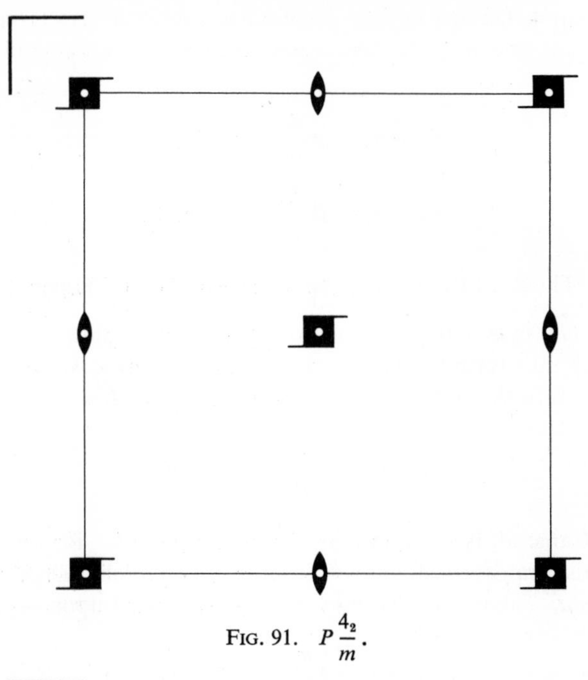

FIG. 91. $P\frac{4_2}{m}$.

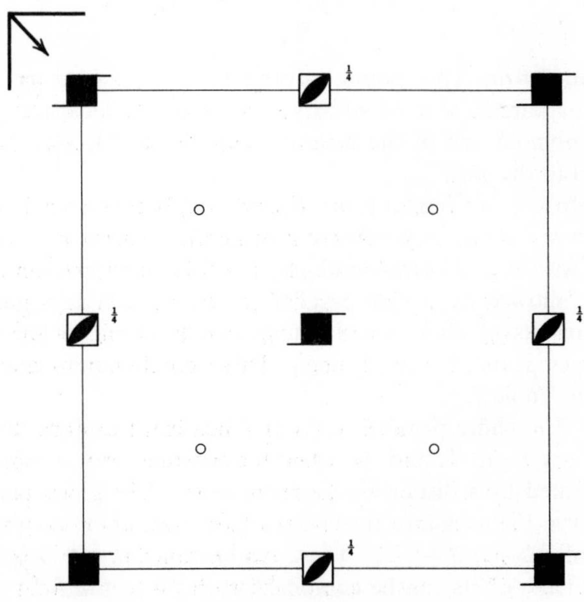

FIG. 92. $P\frac{4_2}{n}$.

Axial frame $P4_2$ (shown in Fig. 22 of Chapter 13) is also transformed into itself only by m and n. The two space groups based upon this frame are therefore

$$P4_2 \cdot m \to P\frac{4_2}{m}, \qquad \text{Fig. 91,}$$

$$P4_2 \cdot n \to P\frac{4_2}{n}, \qquad \text{Fig. 92.}$$

Lattice I. The axial frame $I4$ is shown in Fig. 24 of Chapter 13. Note that $\vec{a}/2 + \vec{b}/2 + \vec{c}/2$ is a lattice translation. The only glides perpendicular to the axes which transform this frame into itself are m and n, which are translation mates. Therefore the only space group based upon $I4$ is

$$I4 \cdot m = I\frac{4}{m}, \qquad \text{Fig. 93.}$$

The axial frame $I4_1$ is shown in Fig. 25 of Chapter 13. Bearing in mind that the plane must transform 4_1 into 4_3, the only permissible glide perpendicular to the axes is a. Therefore the only space group based upon $I4_1$ is

$$I4_1 \cdot a = I\frac{4_1}{a}, \qquad \text{Fig. 94.}$$

Point group 4*mm*. This point group can be produced by combining a reflection plane parallel to a 4-fold axis. Accordingly the space groups can be found by combining one of the neutral axial frames $P4$, $P4_2$, $I4$, or $I4_1$ with glides parallel to the axis.

According to (10) of Chapter 6, a rotation of $\pi/2$ about an axis A followed by a reflection in m_1 results in a reflection in another mirror m_2 which makes an angle of $\pi/4$ with m_1. Correspondingly, a 4-fold screw motion about an axis parallel to c followed by a glide parallel to (100) results in a glide parallel to (110). The results of these combinations can be found in the same way as those of Tables 3 and 5 were found. These combinations and their results are outlined in Table 7.

Lattice P. The glides parallel to (100) which can transform the axial frame $P4$ into itself are m, c, ${}^sb$, and ${}^sn$, when the presuperscript s indicates that the plane is separated by a distance s from the axis. The glides parallel to (110) which transform the axes into themselves have translation components 0, $c/2$, $a/2 - b/2$, and $a/2 - b/2 + c/2$. These can be called m, c, b', n', ${}^sm$, ${}^sc$, ${}^sb'$, and ${}^sn'$. Either of these sets can be combined with $P4$ to give four space groups. In the following derivation the (100) planes are used. Note that these must be combined both with the 4-fold and 2-fold axes. An alternative procedure

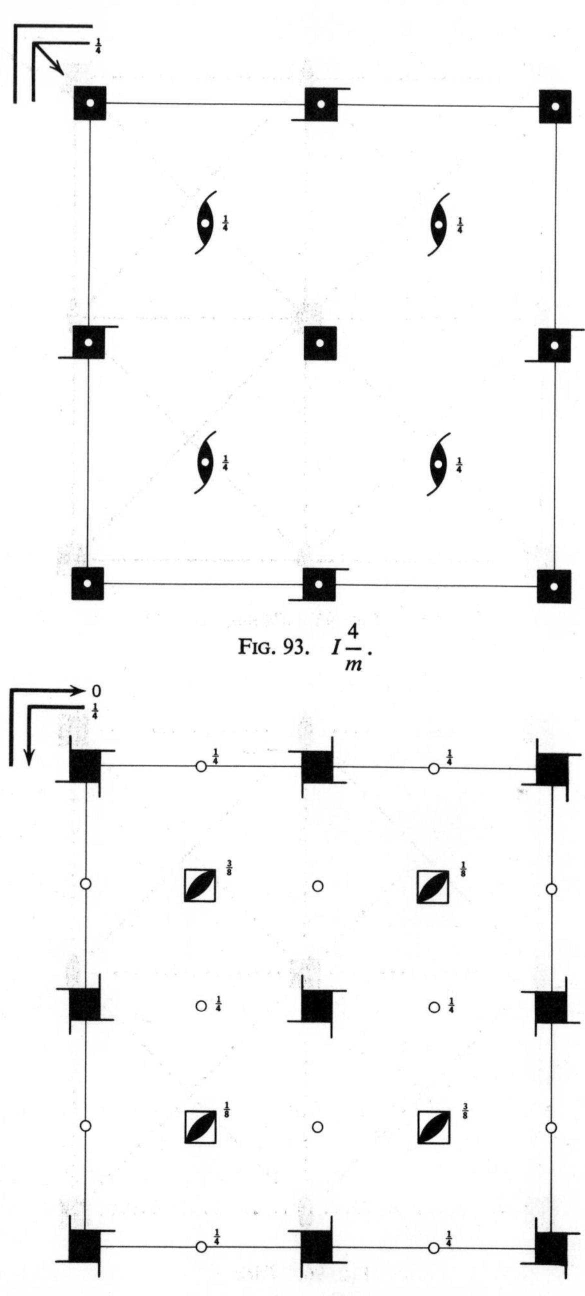

FIG. 93. $I\frac{4}{m}$.

FIG. 94. $I\frac{4_1}{a}$.

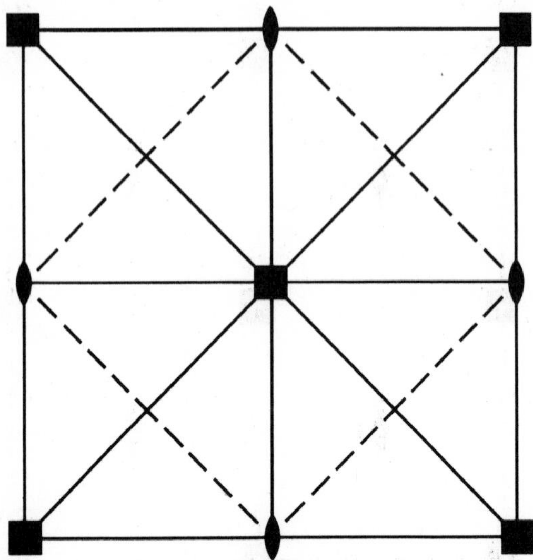

FIG. 95. *P4mm.*

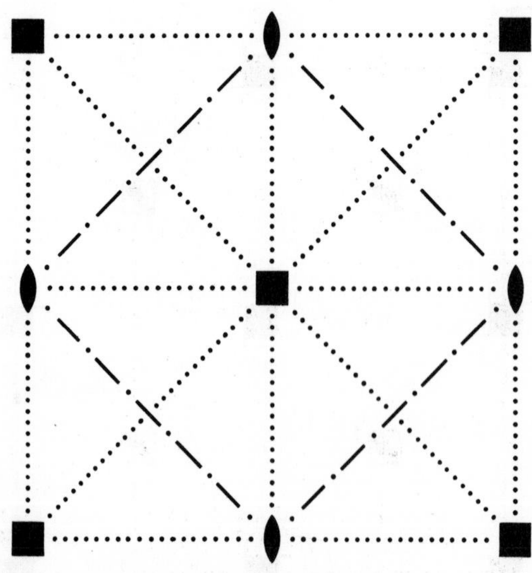

FIG. 96. *P4cc.*

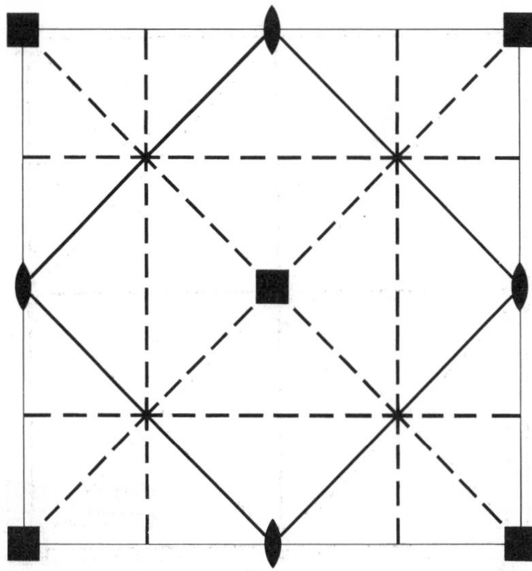

FIG. 97. *P4bm.*

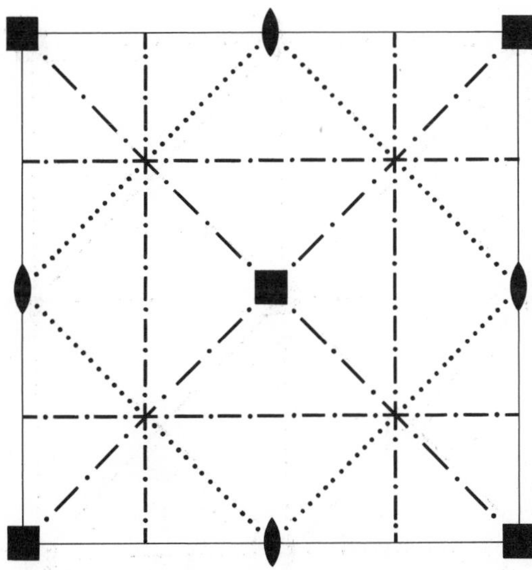

FIG. 98. *P4nc.*

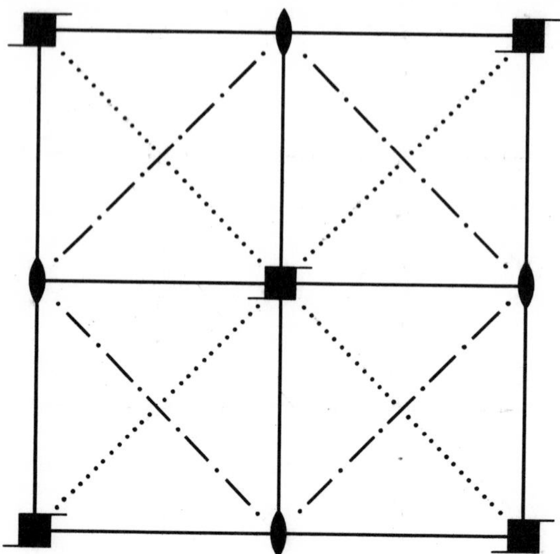

FIG. 99. $P4_2mc$.

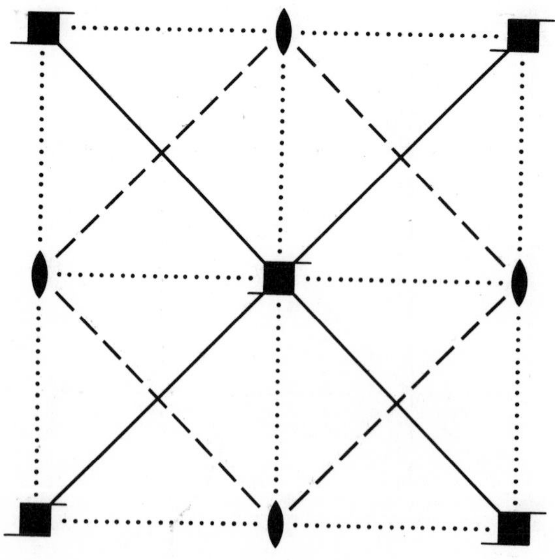

FIG. 100. $P4_2cm$.

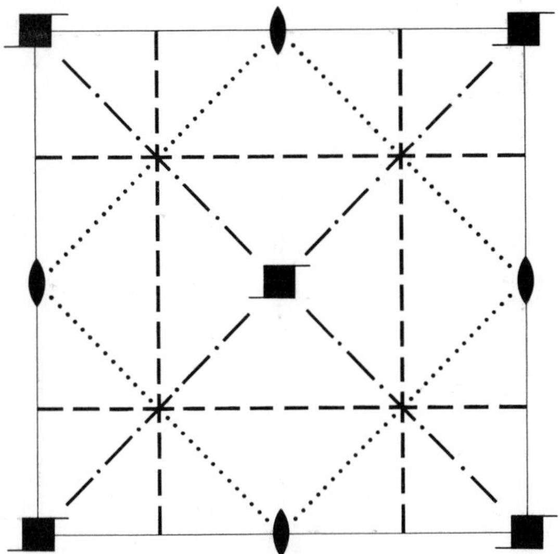

FIG. 101. $P4_2bc$.

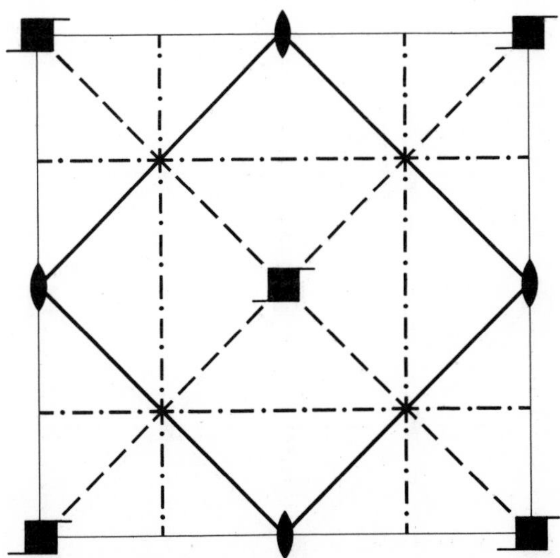

FIG. 102. $P4_2nm$.

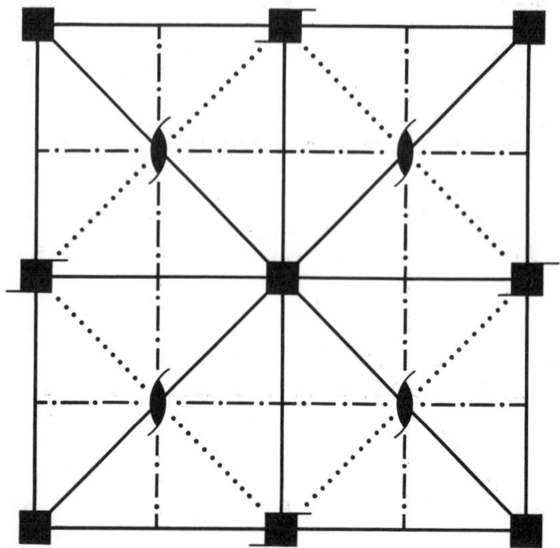

FIG. 103. *I4mm.*

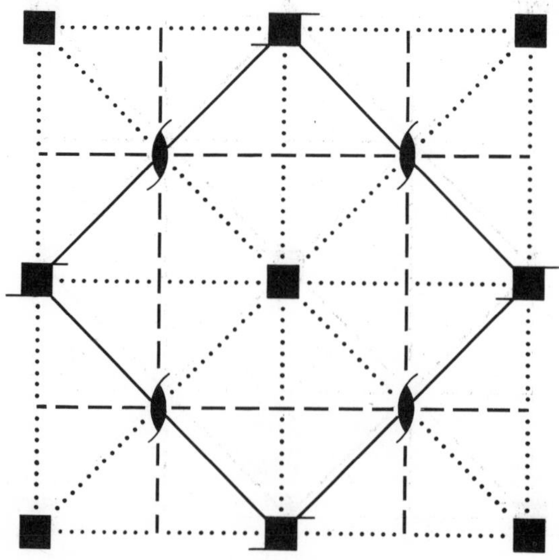

FIG. 104. *I4cm.*

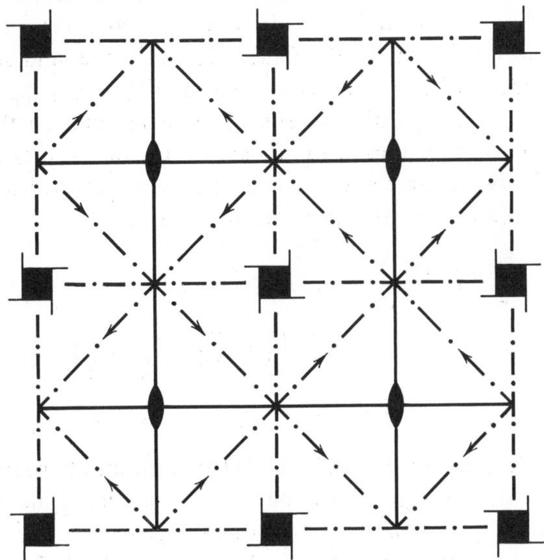

FIG. 105. $I4_1md$.

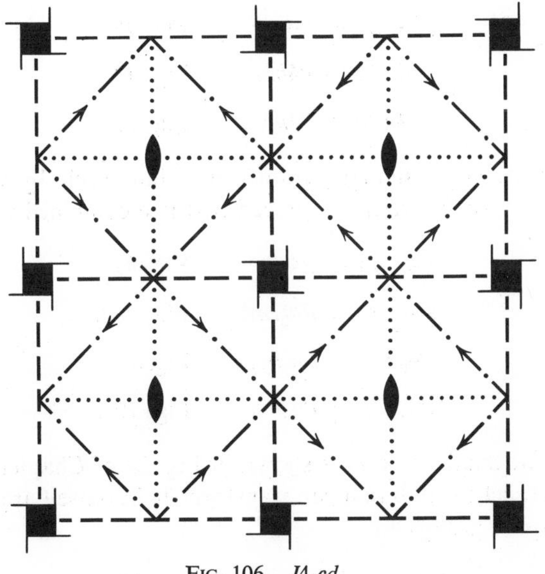

FIG. 106. $I4_1cd$.

is to combine these with the 4-fold axis only and then combine the initial plane and the resulting plane with $T_{[100]}$. In the first combination ${}^{(100)}m_\tau \cdot T_{[100]}$, the translation has no components parallel to the plane, and so the result is a sequence of similar m_τ's. In the combination ${}^{(110)}m_\tau \cdot T_{[100]}$, the translation does have a component parallel to the glide plane, and so this produces an alternating sequence of planes without, and with, this additional component. With the aid of this principle and Table 3, the space groups isogonal with $4mm$ and based upon the following combination occur

$$\begin{aligned} {}^{110}m_\tau \cdot T_{[100]} &= m_\tau \cdot T_{\|} \cdot T_{\perp} \\ &= m_\tau \cdot \overrightarrow{\left(\frac{a}{2} + \frac{b}{2}\right)}_{\|} \cdot \overrightarrow{\left(\frac{a}{2} - \frac{b}{2}\right)}_{\perp} \\ &= {}^{s}m_{\tau, a/2 - b/2}. \end{aligned} \tag{31}$$

This requires that the planes parallel to (110) form an alternating sequence of parallel planes, in which alternate planes are similar glide planes and the interleaved planes differ by a glide component $a/2 - b/2$.

With the aid of this principle, and with the aid of Table 7, the space groups based upon P are readily investigated. They are as follows:

$$\begin{aligned} &P4 \cdot m \rightarrow P4mm, && \text{Fig. 95,} \\ &P4 \cdot c \rightarrow P4cc, && \text{Fig. 96,} \\ &P4 \cdot {}^{s}b \rightarrow P4bm, && \text{Fig. 97,} \\ &P4 \cdot {}^{s}n \rightarrow P4nc, && \text{Fig. 98.} \end{aligned}$$

The axial frame $P4_2$ is similarly transformed into itself by m, c, ${}^{s}b$, and ${}^{s}n$ The four resulting space groups produced by these combined with $P4_2$ are

$$\begin{aligned} &P4_2 \cdot m \rightarrow P4_2mc, && \text{Fig. 99,} \\ &P4_2 \cdot c \rightarrow P4_2cm, && \text{Fig. 100,} \\ &P4_2 \cdot {}^{s}b \rightarrow P4_2bc, && \text{Fig. 101,} \\ &P4_2 \cdot {}^{s}n \rightarrow P4_2nm, && \text{Fig. 102.} \end{aligned}$$

Lattice I. The axial frame $I4$ is shown in Fig. 24 of Chapter 13. The only glide planes parallel to (100) that can transform $I4$ into itself are m and c. The two resulting space groups are

$$\begin{aligned} &I4 \cdot m \rightarrow I4mm, && \text{Fig. 103,} \\ &I4 \cdot c \rightarrow I4cm, && \text{Fig. 104.} \end{aligned}$$

Table 7. Combinations of

Original combination		Equivalent combination resulting from moving plane to axis			Characteristics of resulting plane				Combination designation
Designation	Separations of plane and axis	Translation of screw	New translation T, of (17)	Translation of plane	Σ translation	Separation of plane and axis	Translation of glide	Symbol of glide	
$4\,m$	0	0	0	0	0	0	0	m	$4mm$
$4\,c$	0	0	0	$\frac{c}{2}$	$\frac{c}{2}$	0	0	c	$4cc$
$4\,{}^sb$	$\frac{a}{4}$	0	$\frac{a}{2}$	$\frac{b}{2}$	$\frac{a}{2}+\frac{b}{2}$	$\begin{cases}0 \text{ or} \\ \frac{a}{4}+\frac{b}{4}\end{cases}$	$\frac{a}{2}+\frac{b}{2}$ 0	b' ${}^sm$	$4\,{}^sbm$
$4\,{}^sn$	$\frac{a}{4}$	0	$\frac{a}{2}$	$\frac{b}{2}+\frac{c}{2}$	$\frac{a}{2}+\frac{b}{2}+\frac{c}{2}$	$\begin{cases}0 \text{ or} \\ \frac{a}{4}+\frac{b}{4}\end{cases}$	$\frac{a}{2}+\frac{b}{2}+\frac{c}{2}$ $\frac{c}{2}$	n' ${}^sc$	$4\,{}^snc$
$4_2\,m$	0	$\frac{c}{2}$	0	0	$\frac{c}{2}$	0	$\frac{c}{2}$	c	$4_2\,mc$
$4_2\,c$	0	$\frac{c}{2}$	0	$\frac{c}{2}$	0	0	0	0	$4_2\,cm$
$4_2\,{}^sb$	$\frac{a}{4}$	$\frac{c}{2}$	$\frac{a}{2}$	$\frac{b}{2}$	$\frac{a}{2}+\frac{b}{2}+\frac{c}{2}$	$\begin{cases}0 \text{ or} \\ \frac{a}{4}+\frac{b}{4}\end{cases}$	$\frac{a}{2}+\frac{b}{2}+\frac{c}{2}$ $\frac{c}{2}$	n' ${}^sc$	$4_2\,bc$
$4_2\,{}^sn$	$\frac{a}{4}$	$\frac{c}{2}$	$\frac{a}{2}$	$\frac{b}{2}+\frac{c}{2}$	$\frac{a}{2}+\frac{b}{2}$	$\begin{cases}0 \text{ or} \\ \frac{a}{4}+\frac{b}{4}\end{cases}$	$\frac{a}{2}+\frac{b}{2}$ 0	b' ${}^sm$	$4_2\,nm$
$4_1\,{}^sm$	$\frac{a}{4}$	$\frac{c}{4}$	$\frac{a}{2}$	0	$\frac{a}{2}+\frac{c}{4}=$ $\left(\frac{a}{4}+\frac{b}{4}\right)+\left(\frac{a}{4}-\frac{b}{4}+\frac{c}{4}\right)$	$\frac{a}{8}+\frac{c}{8}$	$\frac{a}{4}-\frac{b}{4}+\frac{c}{4}$	d^+	$4_1\,{}^smd^+$
$4_1\,{}^sc$	$\frac{a}{4}$	$\frac{c}{4}$	$\frac{a}{2}$	$\frac{c}{2}$	$\frac{a}{2}-\frac{c}{4}=$ $\left(\frac{a}{4}+\frac{b}{4}\right)+\left(\frac{a}{4}-\frac{b}{4}-\frac{c}{4}\right)$	$\frac{a}{8}+\frac{b}{8}$	$\frac{a}{4}-\frac{b}{4}-\frac{c}{4}$	d^-	$4_1\,{}^scd^-$
$4_1\,b$	0	$\frac{c}{4}$	0	$\frac{b}{2}$	$\frac{b}{2}+\frac{c}{4}=$ $\left(\frac{a}{4}=\frac{b}{4}\right)+\left(-\frac{a}{4}+\frac{b}{4}+\frac{c}{4}\right)$	$\frac{a}{8}+\frac{b}{8}$	$-\frac{a}{4}+\frac{b}{4}+\frac{c}{4}$		$4_1\,bd^+$
$4_1\,n$	0	$\frac{c}{4}$	0	$\frac{a}{2}+\frac{c}{2}$	$\frac{a}{2}-\frac{c}{4}$ $\left(\frac{a}{4}+\frac{b}{4}\right)+\left(\frac{a}{4}-\frac{b}{4}-\frac{c}{4}\right)$	$\frac{a}{8}+\frac{c}{8}$		d^-	$4_1\,nb^-$

The details of the resulting symmetry elements can be determined with the aid of Table 7. The resolution of the lattice translations of I on (100) require that glide planes parallel to (100) be composed of an alternating sequence whose neighbors have translation components differing by $b/2 + c/2$. In a similar manner the glide planes parallel to (110) comprise a sequence whose neighbors have translation components differing by $c/2$.

The axial frame of $I4_1$ is shown in Fig. 25 of Chapter 13. The 4-fold screws are alternately 4_1 and 4_3. The only glides parallel to (100) that can transform them into each other are ${}^sm$ and ${}^sc$ halfway between axes, and b and n through axes. Reference to Table 7 shows that these, combined with $I4_1$, produce only two results, as follows:

$$I4_1 \cdot {}^sm = I4_1 \cdot n = I4_1md, \qquad \text{Fig. 105,}$$

$$I4_1 \cdot {}^sc = I4_1 \cdot b = I4_1cd, \qquad \text{Fig. 106.}$$

Résumé of space groups isogonal with 4mm. The space groups isogonal with 4*mm* derived in this section are the following:

*P*4*mm*	*I*4*mm*
*P*4*cc*	*I*4*cm*
*P*4*bm*	
*P*4*nc*	$I4_1md$
	$I4_1cd$
$P4_2mc$	
$P4_2cm$	
$P4_2bc$	
$P4_2nm$	
8	+ 4 = 12

Point group $\bar{4}2m$. The point group $\bar{4}2m$ can be formed in several ways. In Chapter 6 it was derived by starting with axial frame 222 and adding a plane through the "vertical" axis, bisecting the two horizontal axes. Corresponding to this the space groups isogonal with $\bar{4}2m$ could be derived by starting with the axial frames isogonal with 222 and adding glide planes which transform the frame into itself.

A simpler means of derivation is based upon starting with point group $\bar{4}$ and adding a 2-fold axis at right angles to it. This produces a reflection plane through the $\bar{4}$ axis and at 45° to the 2-fold axis. This follows the combination given in Chapter 5, namely,

$$\underset{45^\circ}{2 \cdot \bar{2}} = \bar{4}.$$

Corresponding to this, the space groups isogonal with $\bar{4}$ can be derived by using the isogonal space groups $P\bar{4}$ and $I\bar{4}$ as axial frames. One then finds the screw axes which transform these into themselves. The result of this combination is a glide plane at 45° to the 2-fold screw. The characteristics of this glide plane and its location can be found from the following analysis, in which C is the location of the $\bar{4}$ axis, A is the 2-fold screw axis, and the result of combining a 4-fold and orthogonal 2-fold axis is

$$C_{\pi/2} \cdot A_{\pi} = B_{\pi}. \tag{32}$$

The result of combining the $\bar{4}$ and a displaced 2-fold screw is

$$\begin{aligned} C_{\pi/2,m} \cdot {}^{s}A_{\pi,\tau} &= {}^{h}m \cdot C_{\pi/2} \cdot {}^{s}A_{\pi} \cdot \tau \\ &= {}^{h}m \cdot C_{\pi/2} \cdot A_{\pi} \cdot 2s \cdot \tau \\ &= {}^{h}m \cdot B_{\pi} \cdot 2s \cdot \tau. \end{aligned} \tag{33}$$

Now the ${}^{h}m$ is "horizontal" and contains B_{π}. This combination is equal to

$${}^{h}m \cdot B_{\pi} = m, \tag{34}$$

which is a vertical mirror at 45° from the original screw. This can be substituted into (33), giving

$$\begin{aligned} C_{\pi/2,m} \cdot {}^{s}A_{\pi,\tau} &= m \cdot 2s \cdot \tau \\ &= m_{(2s+\tau)_{\|}} \cdot (2s + \tau)_{\perp}. \end{aligned} \tag{35}$$

This sequence of combinations is carried out for all necessary screws in Table 8.

The tetragonal lattices are more symmetrical than the symmetry $\bar{4}2m$; in fact, they have 2-fold axes parallel to both [100] and [110]. Therefore the point group can be set so that the 2-fold axis is in the "axial" direction [100], or the "diagonal" direction [110]. These two permissible orientations of screw axes result in two different categories of space groups.

Lattice P. The frame $P\bar{4}$ can be transformed into itself by axial screws 2, ${}^{s}2$, ${}^{s}2_1$, and ${}^{ss}2_1$, and by the diagonal screws 2, ${}^{s}2$, ${}^{s}2_1$, and ${}^{ss}2_1$. (In studying these transformations, the $\bar{4}$ locations must be transformed into each other.) These eight combinations of $P\,\bar{4}$ with screws produce eight space groups, whose details can be found by reference to Table 8. These are as follows:

Axial screws	$P\bar{4} \cdot 2 \to P\bar{4}2m$,	Fig. 107,
	$P\bar{4} \cdot {}^{s}2 \to P\bar{4}2c$,	Fig. 108,
	$P\bar{4} \cdot {}^{s}2_1 \to P\bar{4}2_1m$,	Fig. 109,
	$P\bar{4} \cdot {}^{ss}2_1 \to P\bar{4}2_1c$,	Fig. 110;

Table 8. Combinations of a $\bar{4}$ axis and perpendicular screws

	Original combination		Equivalent combination resulting from moving 2-fold axis to $\bar{4}$		Characteristics of resulting plane				Combination designation
	Designation	Separation of 2-fold axis from $\bar{4}$	Translation of screw	New translation T of (35)	Σ translations	Separation of plane from $\bar{4}$ axis	Translation of glide plane $\parallel (1\bar{1}0)$	Designation of glide	
axial	$\bar{4}2$	0	0	0	0	0	0	m	$\bar{4}2m$
axial	$\bar{4}\,{}^{c}2$	$\frac{c}{4}$	0	$\frac{c}{2}$	$\frac{c}{2}$	0	$\frac{c}{2}$	c	$\bar{4}2c$
axial	$\bar{4}\,{}^{b}2_1$	$\frac{b}{4}$	$\frac{a}{2}$	$\frac{b}{2}$	$\frac{a}{2}+\frac{b}{2}$	$\frac{a}{4}+\frac{b}{4}$	0	${}^{s}m$	$\bar{4}2_1m$
axial	$\bar{4}\,{}^{bc}2_1$	$\frac{b}{4}+\frac{c}{4}$	$\frac{a}{2}$	$\frac{b}{2}+\frac{c}{2}$	$\frac{a}{2}+\frac{b}{2}+\frac{c}{2}$	$\frac{a}{4}+\frac{b}{4}$	$\frac{c}{2}$	${}^{s}c$	$\bar{4}2_1c$
	$\bar{4}\,{}^{bc}2$	$\frac{b}{4}+\frac{c}{8}$	0	$\frac{b}{2}+\frac{c}{4}$	$\frac{b}{2}+\frac{c}{4}=\left(\frac{a}{4}+\frac{b}{4}\right)+\left(-\frac{a}{4}+\frac{b}{4}+\frac{c}{4}\right)$	$\frac{a}{8}+\frac{b}{8}$	$-\frac{a}{4}+\frac{b}{4}+\frac{c}{4}$	${}^{s}d$	$\bar{4}2d$
diagonal	$\bar{4}2$	0	0	0	0	0	0	m	$\bar{4}m2$
diagonal	$\bar{4}\,{}^{c}2$	$\frac{c}{4}$	0	$\frac{c}{2}$	$\frac{c}{2}$	0	$\frac{c}{2}$	c	$\bar{4}c2$
diagonal	$\bar{4}2_1$	0	$\frac{a}{2}+\frac{b}{2}$	0	$\frac{a}{2}+\frac{b}{2}$	$\frac{a}{4}$	$\frac{b}{2}$	${}^{s}b$	$\bar{4}b2_1$
diagonal	$\bar{4}\,{}^{c}2_1$	$\frac{c}{4}$	$\frac{a}{2}+\frac{b}{2}$	$\frac{c}{2}$	$\frac{a}{2}+\frac{b}{2}+\frac{c}{2}$	$\frac{a}{4}$	$\frac{b}{2}+\frac{c}{2}$	${}^{s}n$	$\bar{4}n2_1$

Diagonal screws

$$\begin{cases} P\bar{4}\cdot 2 \rightarrow P\bar{4}m2, & \text{Fig. 111,} \\ P\bar{4}\cdot {}^{s}2 \rightarrow P\bar{4}c2, & \text{Fig. 112,} \\ P\bar{4}\cdot {}^{s}2_1 \rightarrow P\bar{4}b2_1, & \\ \quad \Leftrightarrow P\bar{4}b2 & \text{Fig. 113,} \\ P\bar{4}\cdot {}^{ss}2_1 \rightarrow P\bar{4}n2_1, & \\ \quad \Leftrightarrow P\bar{4}n2 & \text{Fig. 114.} \end{cases}$$

Lattice I. The axial frame $I\bar{4}$ is shown in Fig. 88. It can be transformed into itself by distinct axial screws 2, ${}^{bc}2$, and by distinct diagonal screws 2, ${}^{c}2$, where the presuperscripts give directions of displacement of the screw from location $\bar{4}$. When these are combined with $I\bar{4}$ they produce four space groups, whose details can be obtained from Table 8:

Axial screws

$$\begin{cases} I\bar{4}\cdot 2 \rightarrow I\bar{4}2m, & \text{Fig. 115,} \\ I\bar{4}\cdot {}^{s}2 \rightarrow I\bar{4}2d, & \text{Fig. 116;} \end{cases}$$

Diagonal screws

$$\begin{cases} I\bar{4}\cdot 2 \rightarrow I\bar{4}m2, & \text{Fig. 117,} \\ I\bar{4}\cdot {}^{s}2 \rightarrow I\bar{4}c2, & \text{Fig. 118.} \end{cases}$$

Résumé of space groups isogonal with $\bar{4}2m$. The space groups isogonal with $\bar{4}2m$ derived in this section are as follows:

$P\bar{4}2m$	$I\bar{4}2m$
$P\bar{4}2c$	$I\bar{4}2d$
$P\bar{4}2_1m$	$I\bar{4}m2$
$P\bar{4}2_1c$	$I\bar{4}c2$
$P\bar{4}m2$	
$P\bar{4}c2$	
$P\bar{4}b2$	
$P\bar{4}n2$	
8 +	4 = 12

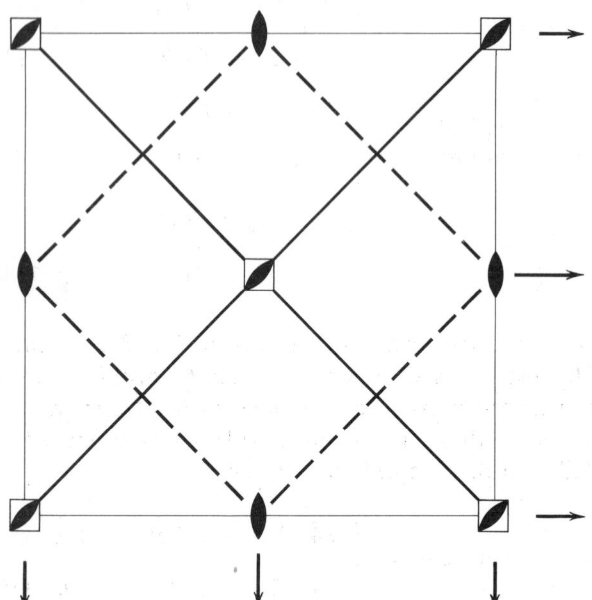

Fig. 107. $P\bar{4}2m$.

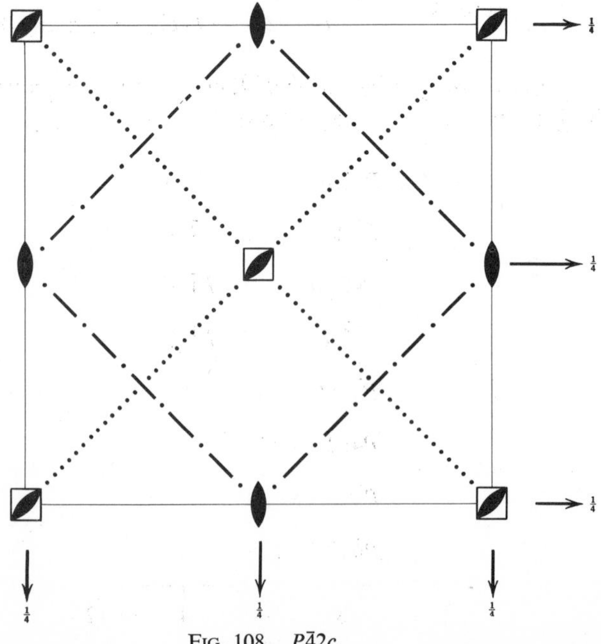

Fig. 108. $P\bar{4}2c$.

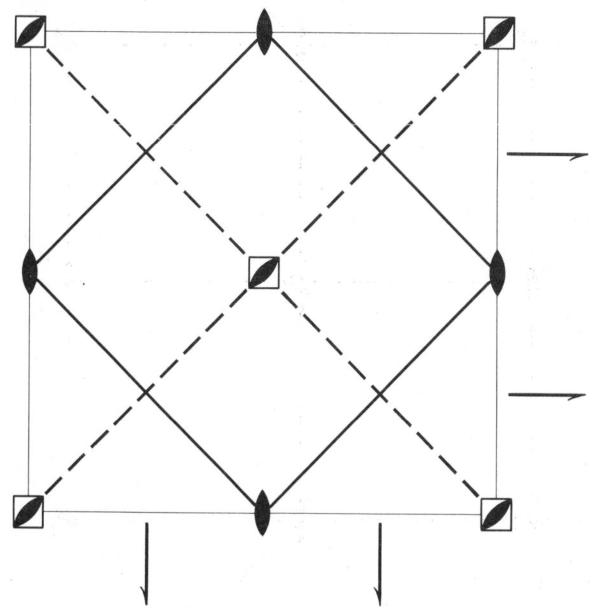

FIG. 109. $P\bar{4}2_1m$.

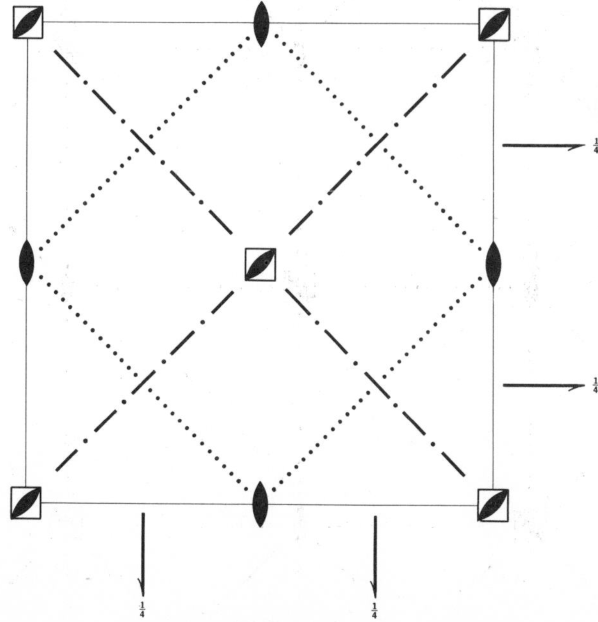

FIG. 110. $P\bar{4}2_1c$.

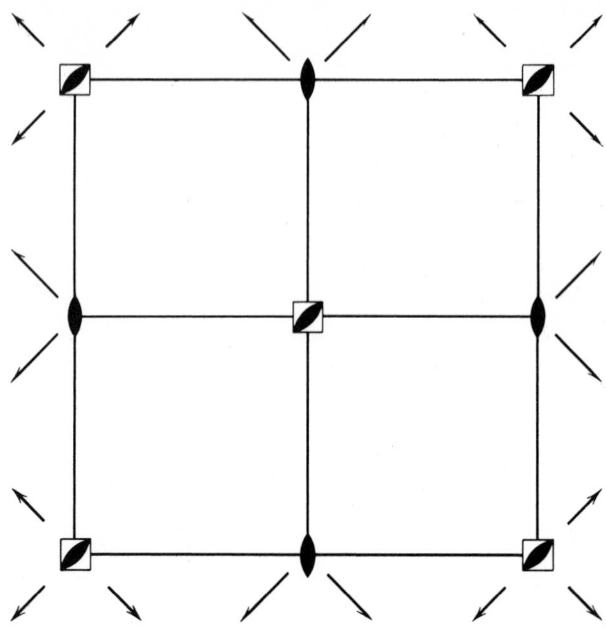

FIG. 111. $P\bar{4}m2$.

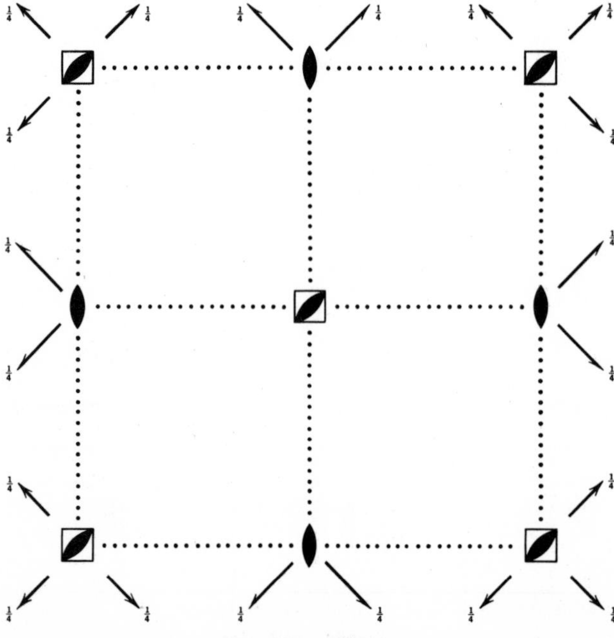

FIG. 112. $P\bar{4}c2$.

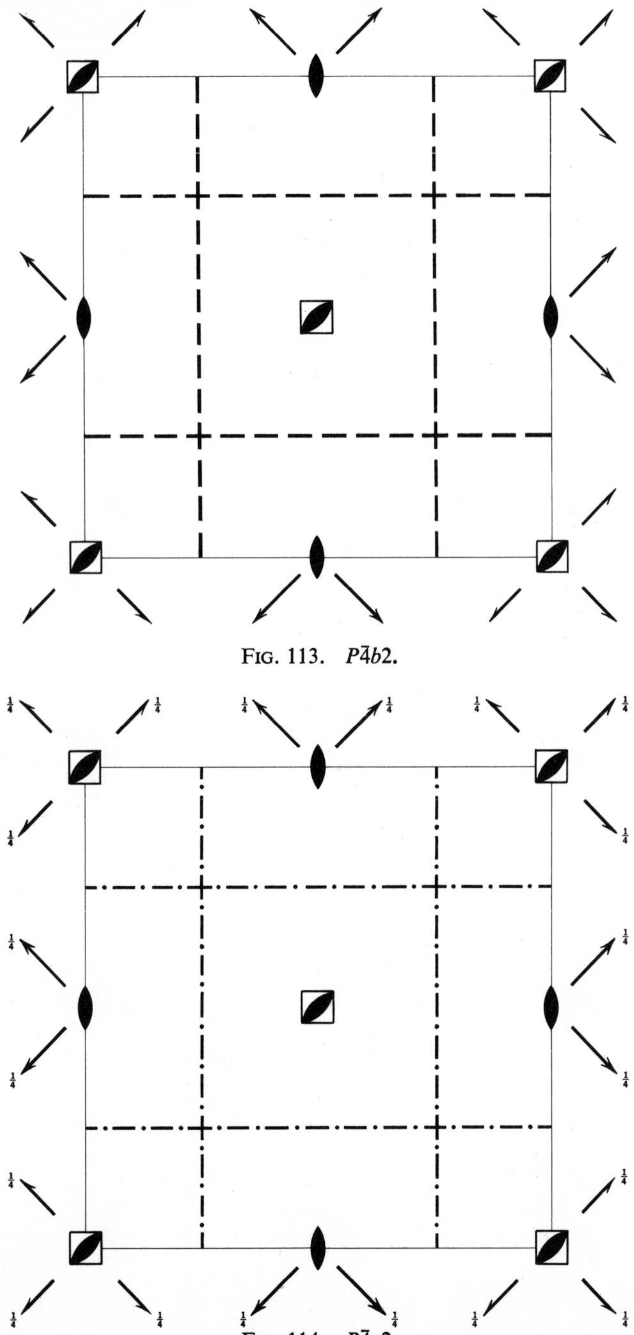

FIG. 113. $P\bar{4}b2$.

FIG. 114. $P\bar{4}n2$.

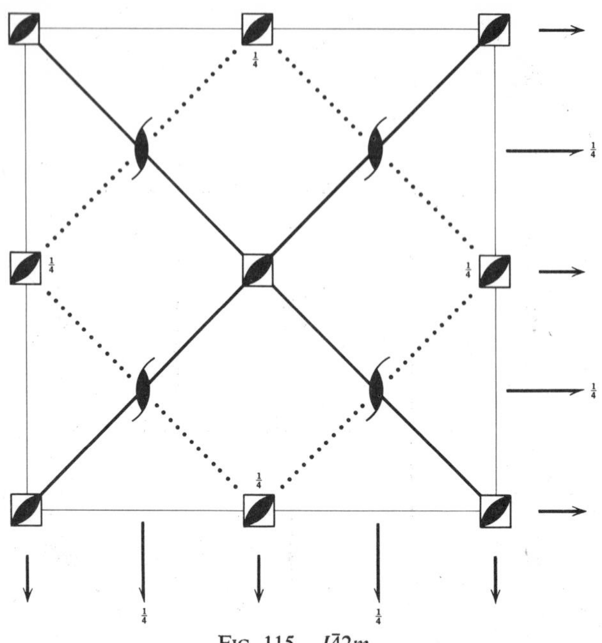

FIG. 115. $I\bar{4}2m$.

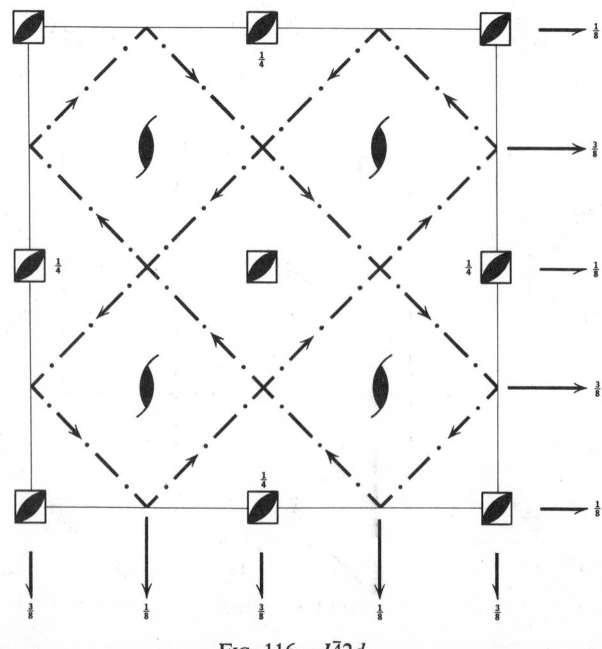

FIG. 116. $I\bar{4}2d$.

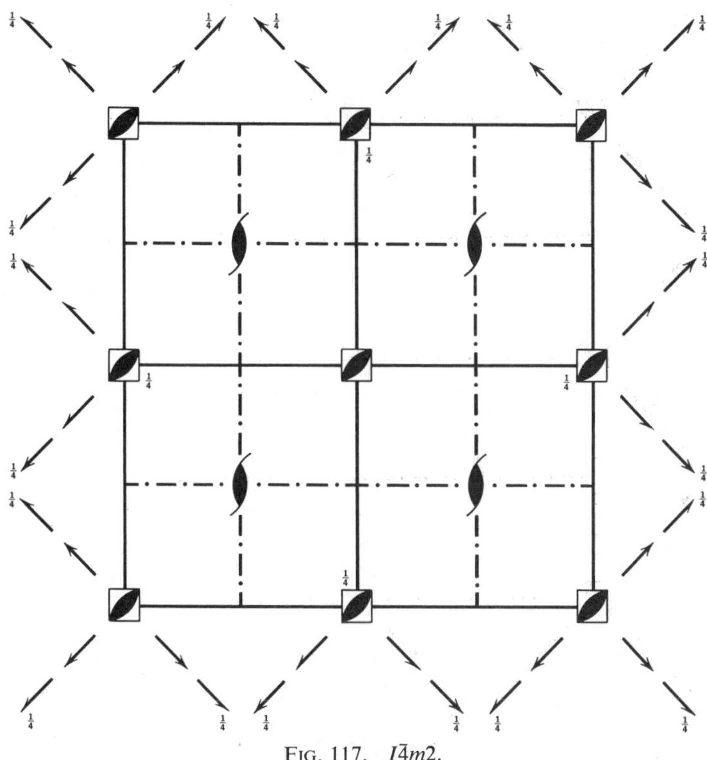

FIG. 117. $I\bar{4}m2$.

Point group $\frac{4}{m}\frac{2}{m}\frac{2}{m}$. Point group $4/m\ 2/m\ 2/m$ can be derived from 422 by adding an inversion center at the intersection of the axes. Correspondingly space groups isogonal with $4/m\ 2/m\ 2/m$ can be derived by starting with each of the neutral axial frames isogonal with 422 by adding inversions which transform the frame into itself. The neutral axial frames isogonal with 422 are $P422$, $P42_12$, $P4_222$, $P4_22_12$, $I422$, and $I4_122$.

Lattice P. Parts of an octant of the axial frames $P422$, $P42_12$, $P4_222$, and $P4_22_12$ are shown in Figs. 119–122. These frames can be transformed into themselves by inversions located on 4-fold axes or between similar 4-fold axes, and on or between 2-fold axes. These four combinations occur at 000, $00\frac{1}{4}$, $\frac{1}{4}\frac{1}{4}0$, and $\frac{1}{4}\frac{1}{4}\frac{1}{4}$. All other inversion locations constitute *translation mates* with one of these four; that is, they are related by lattice translations as the pair in (26). Only one of a pair of translation mates need be considered. Evidently

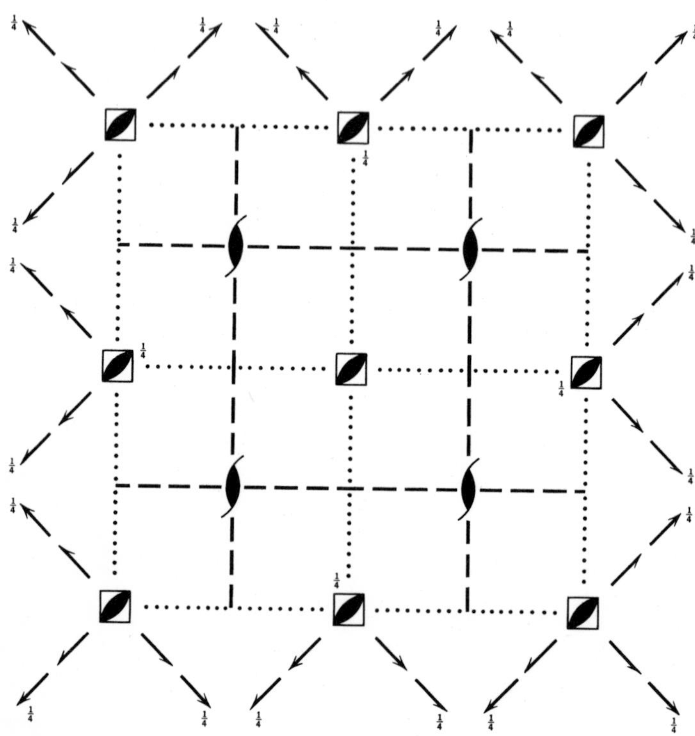

FIG. 118. $I\bar{4}c2$.

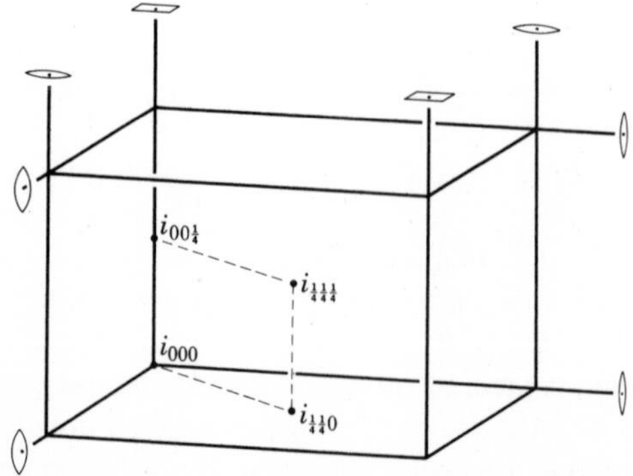

FIG. 119. Octant of $P422$ cell. The black dots show characteristically different locations of inversion centers which transform $P422$ into itself.

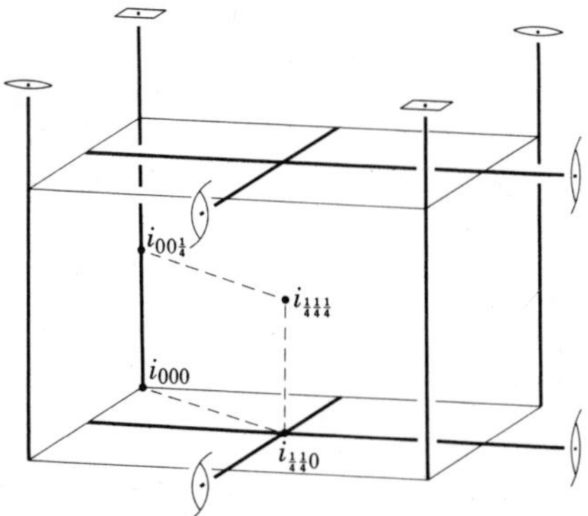

FIG. 120. Octant of $P42_12$ cell. The black dots show characteristically different locations of inversion centers which transform $P42_12$ into itself.

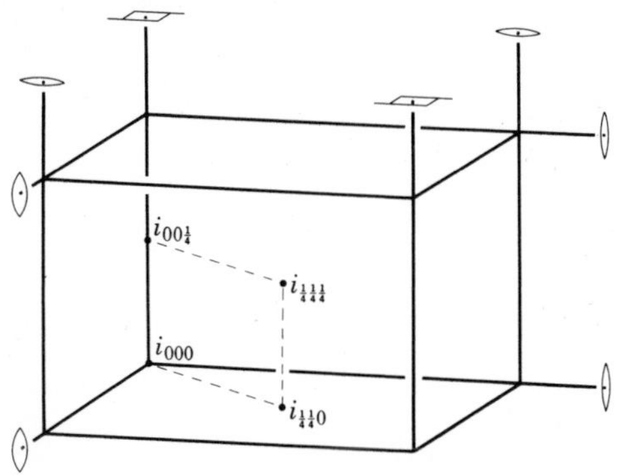

FIG. 121. Octant of $P4_222$ cell. The black dots show characteristically different locations of inversion centers which transform $P4_222$ into itself.

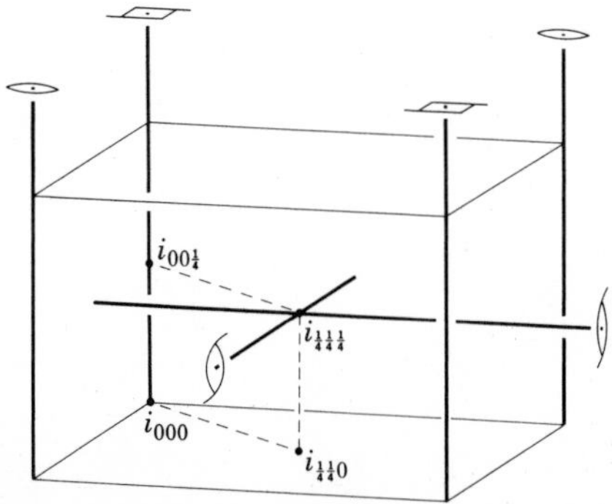

FIG. 122. Octant of $P4_22_12$ cell. The black dots show characteristically different locations of inversion centers which transform $P4_22_12$ into itself.

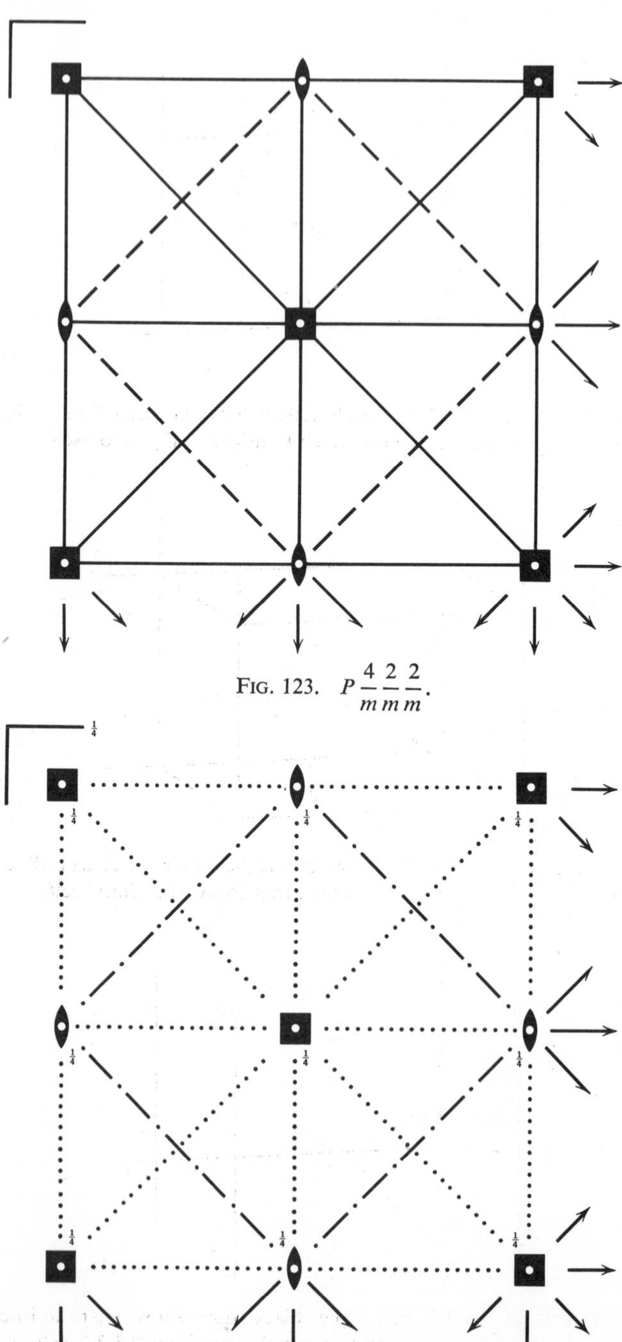

FIG. 123. $P\frac{4}{m}\frac{2}{m}\frac{2}{m}$.

FIG. 124. $P\frac{4}{m}\frac{2}{c}\frac{2}{c}$.

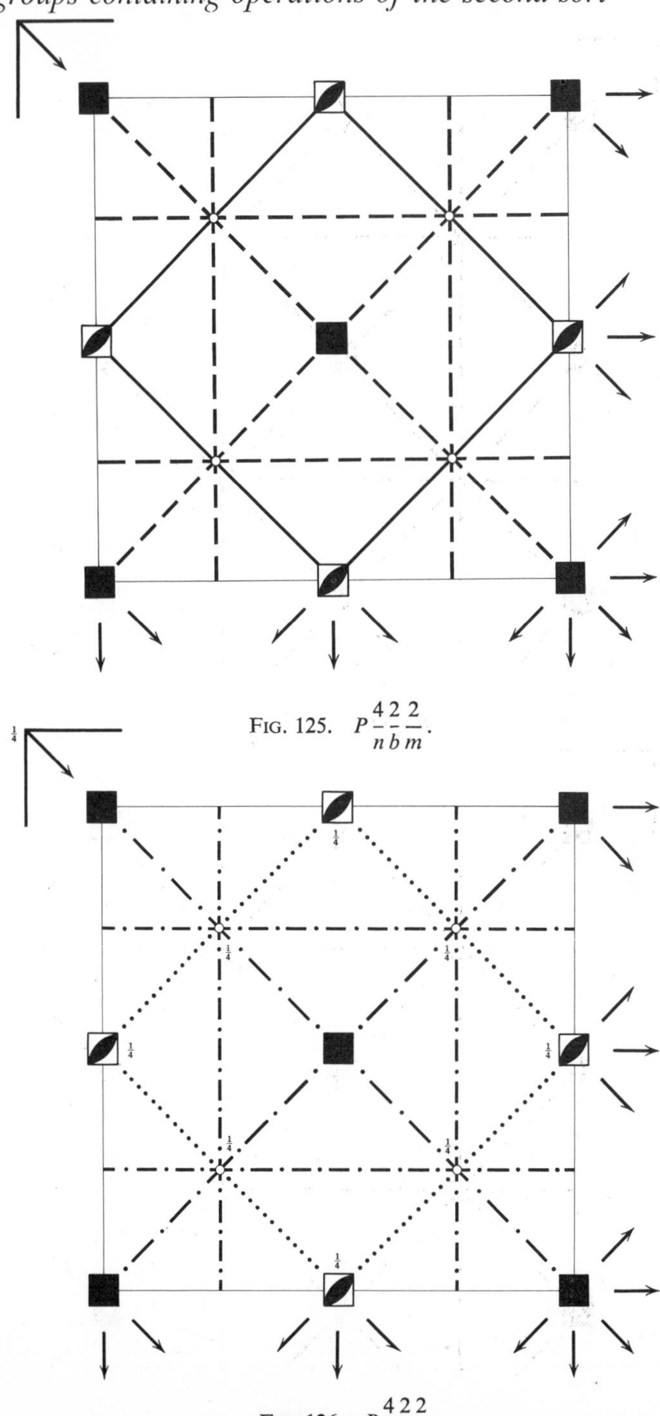

FIG. 125. $P\frac{4}{n}\frac{2}{b}\frac{2}{m}$.

FIG. 126. $P\frac{4}{n}\frac{2}{n}\frac{2}{c}$.

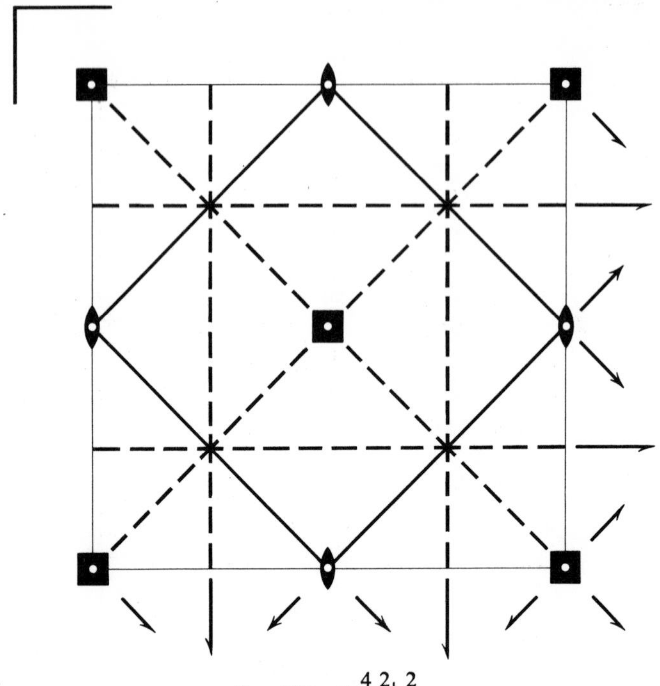

FIG. 127. $P\frac{4}{m}\frac{2_1}{b}\frac{2}{m}$.

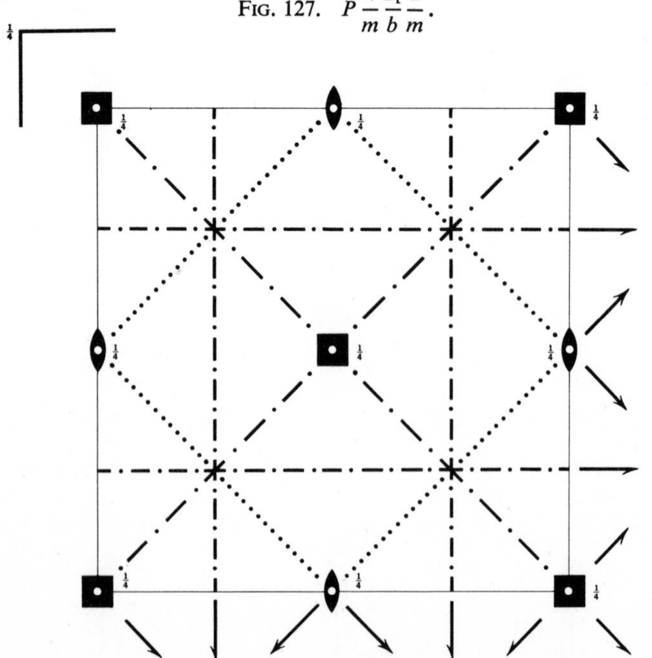

FIG. 128. $P\frac{4}{m}\frac{2_1}{n}\frac{2}{c}$.

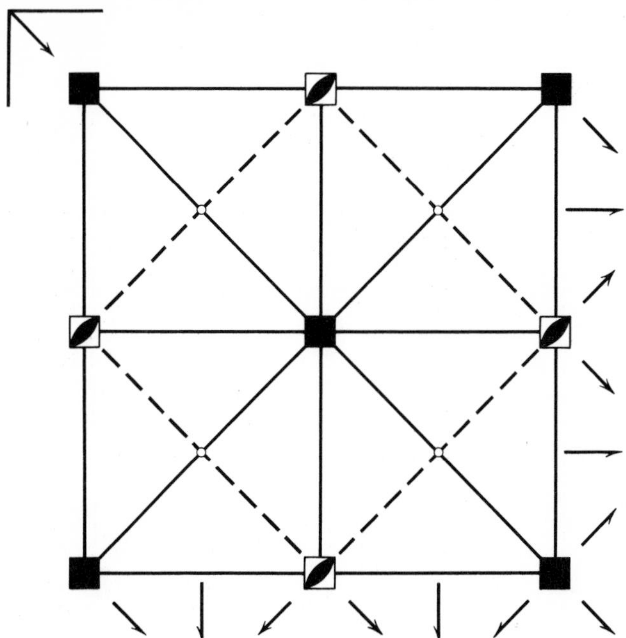

FIG. 129. $P\frac{4}{n}\frac{2_1}{m}\frac{2}{m}$.

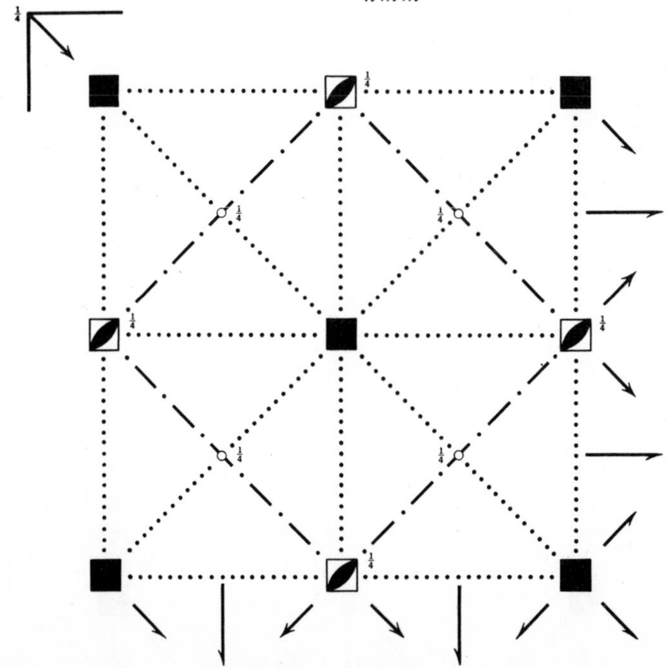

FIG. 130. $P\frac{4}{n}\frac{2_1}{c}\frac{2}{c}$.

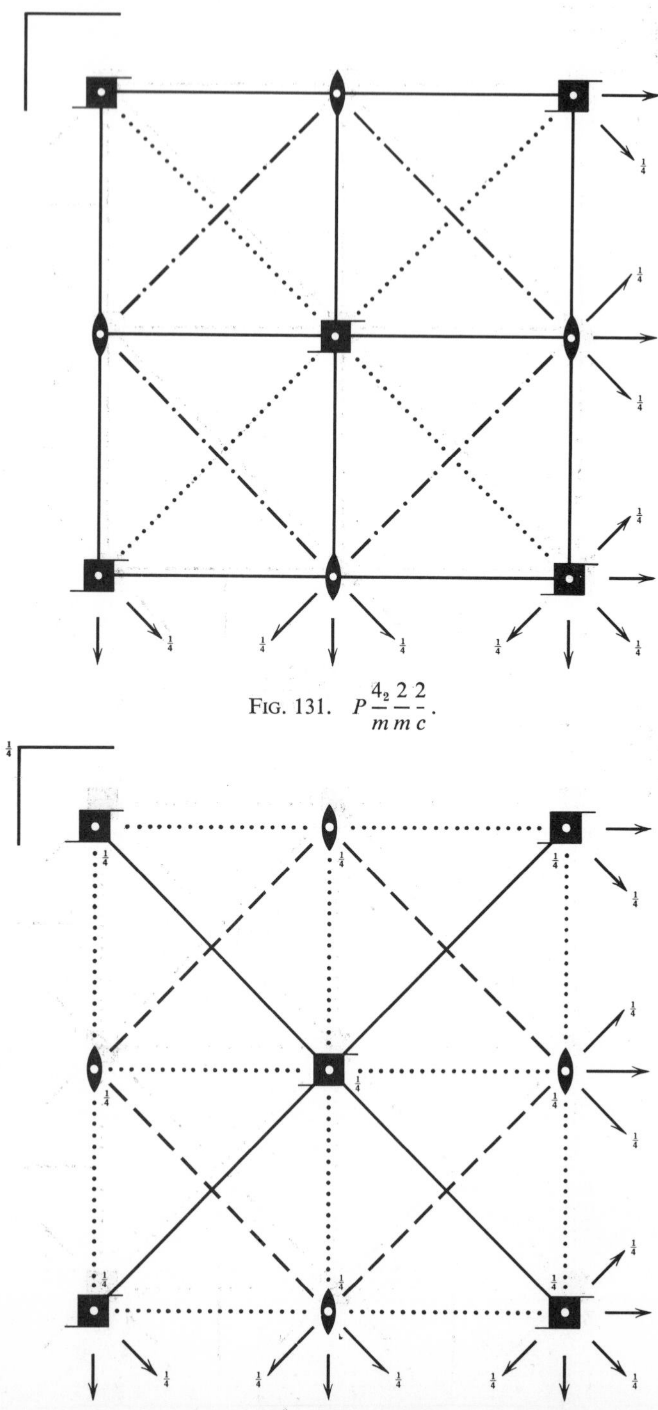

FIG. 131. $P\frac{4_2}{m}\frac{2}{m}\frac{2}{c}$.

FIG. 132. $P\,4_2\,2\,2$

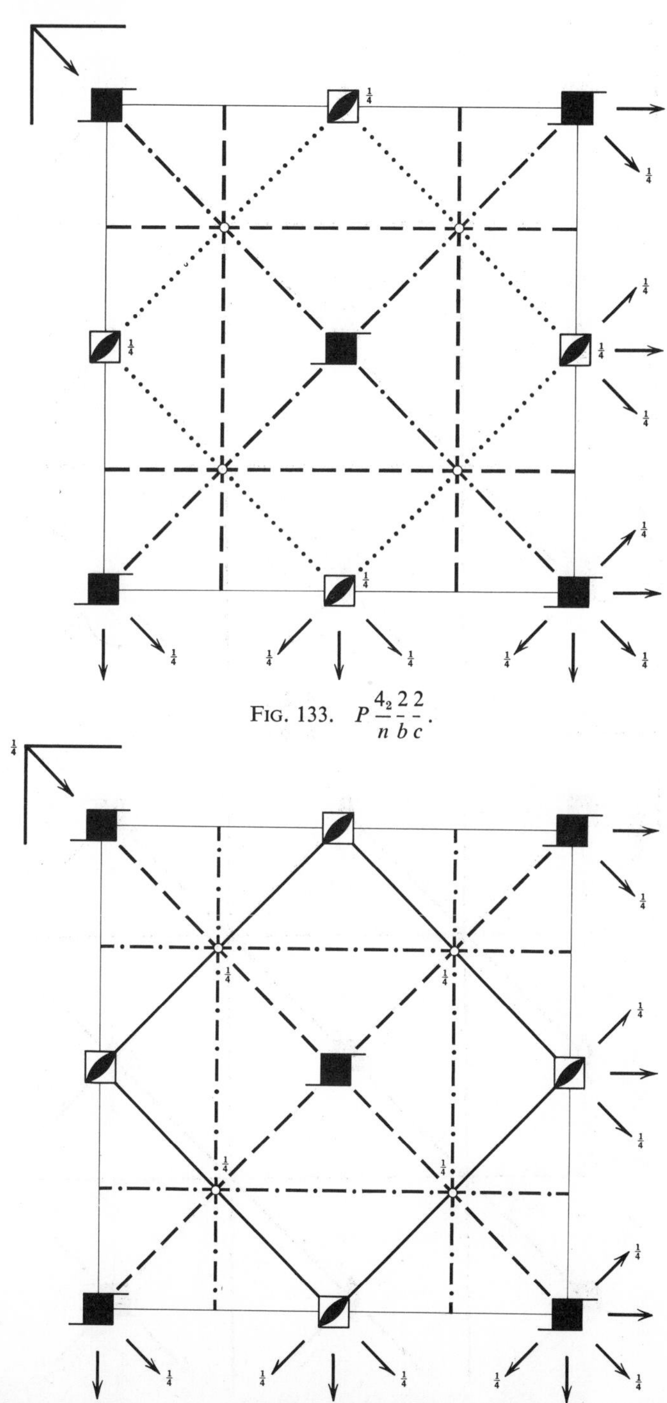

FIG. 133. $P\dfrac{4_2}{n}\dfrac{2}{b}\dfrac{2}{c}$.

FIG. 134. $P\dfrac{4_2}{}\dfrac{2}{}\dfrac{2}{}$

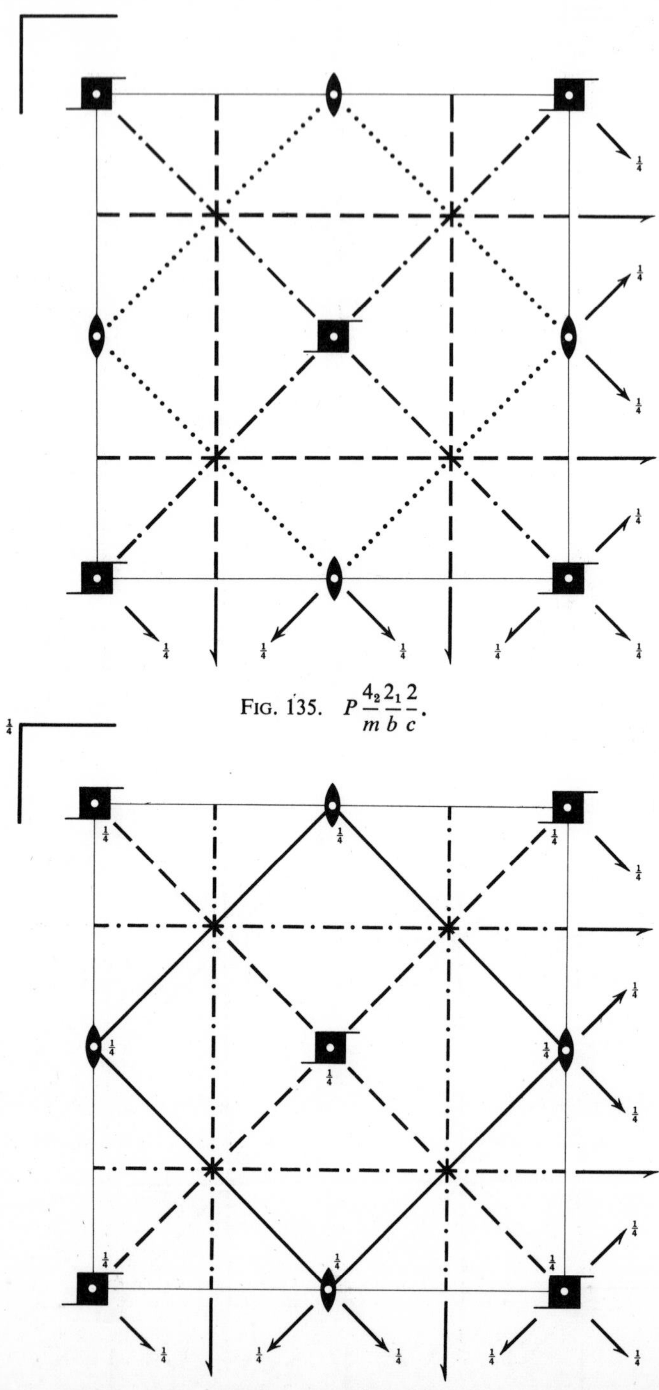

FIG. 135. $P\frac{4_2}{m}\frac{2_1}{b}\frac{2}{c}$.

FIG. 136. $P\frac{4_2}{m}\frac{2_1}{n}\frac{2}{m}$.

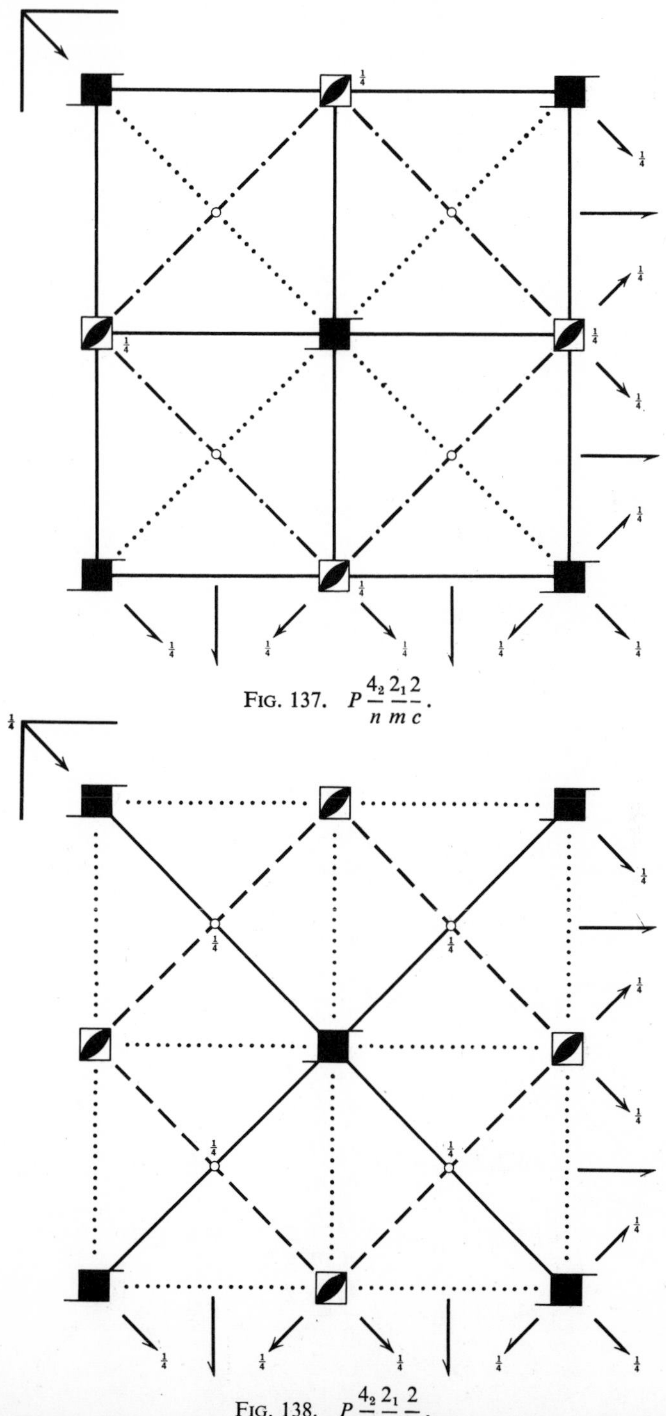

FIG. 137. $P\frac{4_2}{n}\frac{2_1}{m}\frac{2}{c}$.

FIG. 138. $P\frac{4_2}{n}\frac{2_1}{c}\frac{2}{m}$.

sixteen space groups are determined by the sixteen combinations of the four neutral axial frames and the four distinct inversions. Their detailed properties can be found by applying Figs. 6–9. The derivation of these space groups is as follows:

$$P422 \cdot i_{000} \rightarrow P\frac{4}{m}\frac{2}{m}\frac{2}{m}, \qquad \text{Fig. 123,}$$

$$P422 \cdot i_{00\frac{1}{2}} \rightarrow P\frac{4}{m}\frac{2}{c}\frac{2}{c}, \qquad \text{Fig. 124,}$$

$$P422 \cdot i_{\frac{1}{2}\frac{1}{2}0} \rightarrow P\frac{4}{n}\frac{2}{b}\frac{2}{m}, \qquad \text{Fig. 125,}$$

$$P422 \cdot i_{\frac{1}{2}\frac{1}{2}\frac{1}{2}} \rightarrow P\frac{4}{n}\frac{2}{n}\frac{2}{c}, \qquad \text{Fig. 126,}$$

$$P42_12 \cdot i_{000} \rightarrow P\frac{4}{m}\frac{2_1}{b}\frac{2}{m}, \qquad \text{Fig. 127,}$$

$$P42_12 \cdot i_{00\frac{1}{2}} \rightarrow P\frac{4}{m}\frac{2_1}{n}\frac{2}{c}, \qquad \text{Fig. 128,}$$

$$P42_12 \cdot i_{\frac{1}{2}\frac{1}{2}0} \rightarrow P\frac{4}{n}\frac{2_1}{m}\frac{2}{m}, \qquad \text{Fig. 129,}$$

$$P42_12 \cdot i_{\frac{1}{2}\frac{1}{2}\frac{1}{2}} \rightarrow P\frac{4}{n}\frac{2_1}{c}\frac{2}{c}, \qquad \text{Fig. 130,}$$

$$P4_222 \cdot i_{000} \rightarrow P\frac{4_2}{m}\frac{2}{m}\frac{2}{c}, \qquad \text{Fig. 131,}$$

$$P4_222 \cdot i_{00\frac{1}{2}} \rightarrow P\frac{4_2}{m}\frac{2}{c}\frac{2}{m}, \qquad \text{Fig. 132,}$$

$$P4_222 \cdot i_{\frac{1}{2}\frac{1}{2}0} \rightarrow P\frac{4_2}{n}\frac{2}{b}\frac{2}{c}, \qquad \text{Fig. 133,}$$

$$P4_222 \cdot i_{\frac{1}{2}\frac{1}{2}\frac{1}{2}} \rightarrow P\frac{4_2}{n}\frac{2}{n}\frac{2}{m}, \qquad \text{Fig. 134,}$$

$$P4_22_12 \cdot i_{000} \rightarrow P\frac{4_2}{m}\frac{2_1}{b}\frac{2}{c}, \qquad \text{Fig. 135,}$$

$$P4_22_12 \cdot i_{00\frac{1}{2}} \rightarrow P\frac{4_2}{m}\frac{2_1}{n}\frac{2}{m}, \qquad \text{Fig. 136,}$$

$$P4_22_12 \cdot i_{\frac{1}{2}\frac{1}{2}0} \rightarrow P\frac{4_2}{n}\frac{2_1}{m}\frac{2}{c}, \qquad \text{Fig. 137,}$$

$$P4_22_12 \cdot i_{\frac{1}{2}\frac{1}{2}\frac{1}{2}} \rightarrow P\frac{4_2}{n}\frac{2_1}{c}\frac{2}{m}, \qquad \text{Fig. 138.}$$

Lattice I. Parts of an octant of the axial frames $I422$ and $I4_122$ are shown in Fig. 139 and 142. The two 4-fold axes shown in Fig. 139 are translation equivalent, so that $I422$ can be transformed into itself only by inversions on the 4-fold axis, and these inversions are limited to locations on or between 2-fold

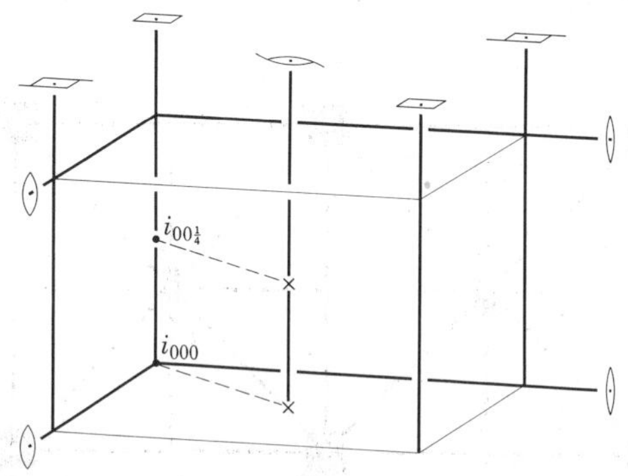

FIG. 139. Octant of $I422$ cell. The black dots show characteristically different locations of inversion centers which transform $I422$ into itself. The crosses are translation-mate inversion-center locations.

axes. All other possible inversions are translation mates with these two. Therefore there are two space groups based upon frame $I422$.

$$I422 \cdot i_{000} \rightarrow I\frac{4}{m}\frac{2}{m}\frac{2}{m}, \qquad \text{Fig. 140,}$$

$$I422 \cdot i_{00\frac{1}{4}} \rightarrow I\frac{4}{m}\frac{2}{c}\frac{2}{m}, \qquad \text{Fig. 141.}$$

Axial frame $I4_122$ contains both left- and right-handed screws. The frame can be transformed into itself only by inversion between such pairs of 4-fold screws, and on or halfway between 2-fold axes. The distinct inversions, not including translation mates, are located at $0\frac{1}{4}0$ and $0\frac{1}{4}\frac{1}{4}$, Fig. 142. The two possible space groups based upon frame $I4_122$ are therefore

$$I4_122 \cdot i_{0\frac{1}{4}\frac{1}{4}} \rightarrow I\frac{4_1}{a}\frac{2}{m}\frac{2}{d}, \qquad \text{Fig. 143,}$$

$$I4_122 \cdot i_{0\frac{1}{4}0} \rightarrow I\frac{4_1}{a}\frac{2}{c}\frac{2}{d}, \qquad \text{Fig. 144.}$$

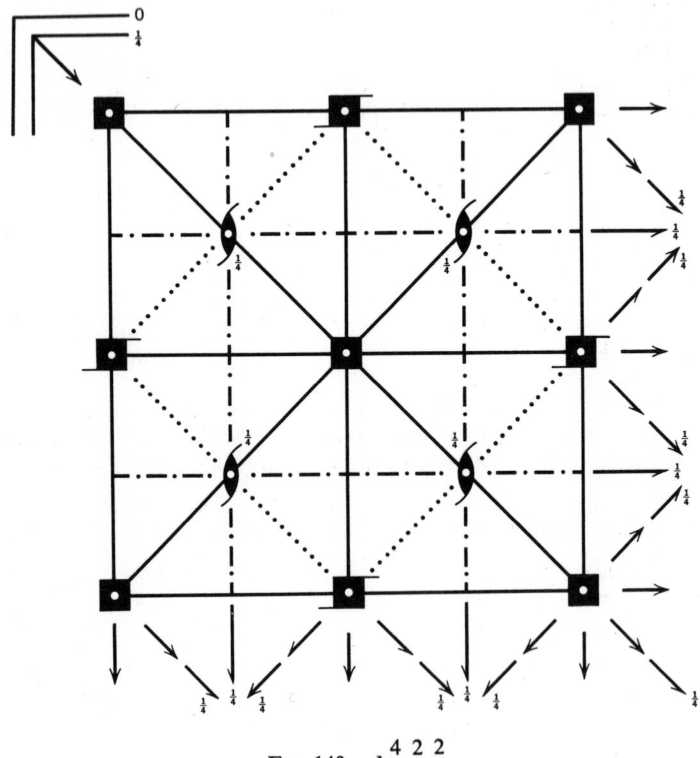

FIG. 140. $I\frac{4}{m}\frac{2}{m}\frac{2}{m}$.

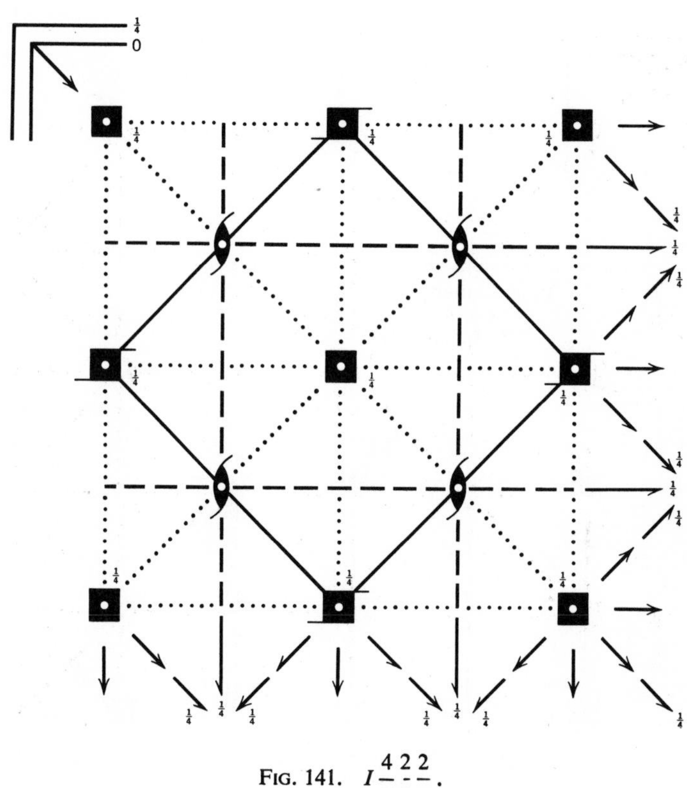

FIG. 141. $I\frac{4}{m}\frac{2}{c}\frac{2}{m}$.

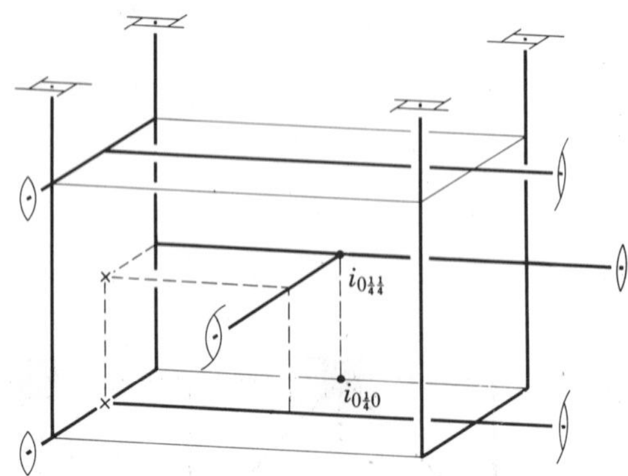

FIG. 142. Octant of $I4_122$ cell. The black dots show characteristically different locations of inversion centers which transform $I4_122$ into itself. The crosses are translation-mate inversion center locations.

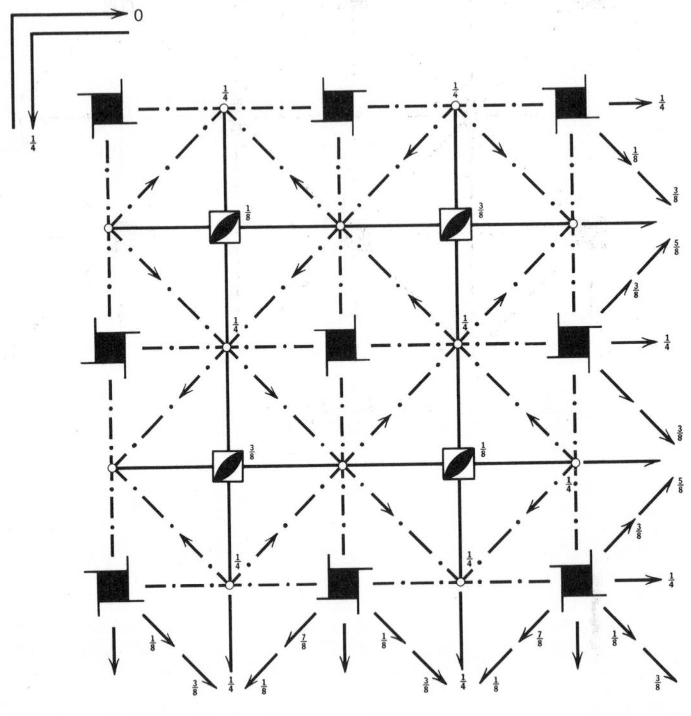

FIG. 143. $I\frac{4_1}{a}\frac{2}{m}\frac{2}{d}$.

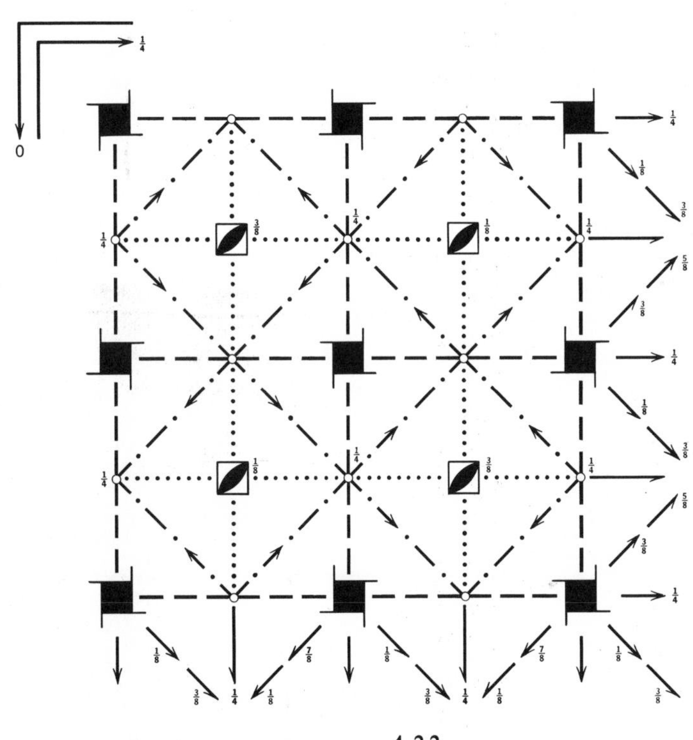

FIG. 144. $I\frac{4_1}{a}\frac{2}{c}\frac{2}{d}$.

Résumé of space groups isogonal with $4/m\ 2/m\ 2/m$. The space groups isogonal with 422 derived in this section are

$P\frac{4}{m}\frac{2}{m}\frac{2}{m}$	$I\frac{4}{m}\frac{2}{m}\frac{2}{m}$
$P\frac{4}{m}\frac{2}{c}\frac{2}{c}$	$I\frac{4}{m}\frac{2}{c}\frac{2}{m}$
$P\frac{4}{n}\frac{2}{b}\frac{2}{m}$	
$P\frac{4}{n}\frac{2}{n}\frac{2}{c}$	$I\frac{4_1}{a}\frac{2}{m}\frac{2}{d}$
	$I\frac{4_1}{a}\frac{2}{c}\frac{2}{d}$
$P\frac{4}{m}\frac{2_1}{b}\frac{2}{m}$	
$P\frac{4}{m}\frac{2_1}{n}\frac{2}{c}$	
$P\frac{4}{n}\frac{2_1}{m}\frac{2}{m}$	
$P\frac{4}{n}\frac{2_1}{c}\frac{2}{c}$	
$P\frac{4_2}{m}\frac{2}{m}\frac{2}{c}$	
$P\frac{4_2}{m}\frac{2}{c}\frac{2}{m}$	
$P\frac{4_2}{n}\frac{2}{b}\frac{2}{c}$	
$P\frac{4_2}{n}\frac{2}{n}\frac{2}{m}$	
$P\frac{4_2}{m}\frac{2_1}{b}\frac{2}{c}$	
$P\frac{4_2}{m}\frac{2_1}{n}\frac{2}{m}$	
$P\frac{4_2}{n}\frac{2_1}{m}\frac{2}{c}$	
$P\frac{4_2}{n}\frac{2_1}{c}\frac{2}{m}$	
16	+ 4 = 20

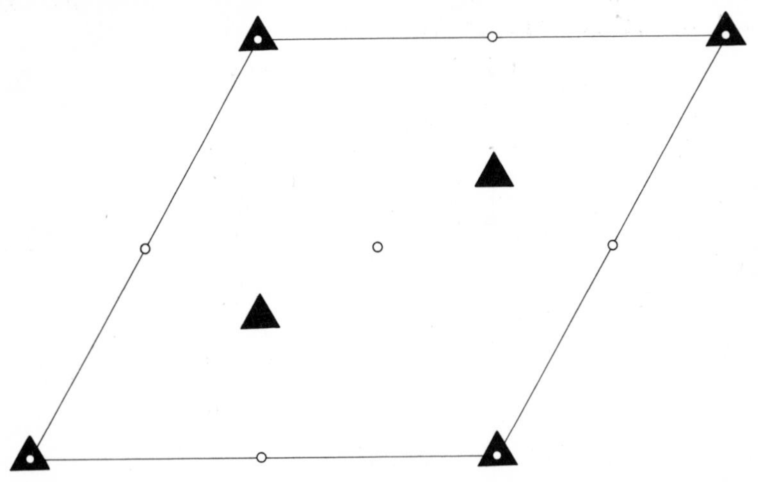

FIG. 145. $P\bar{3}$.

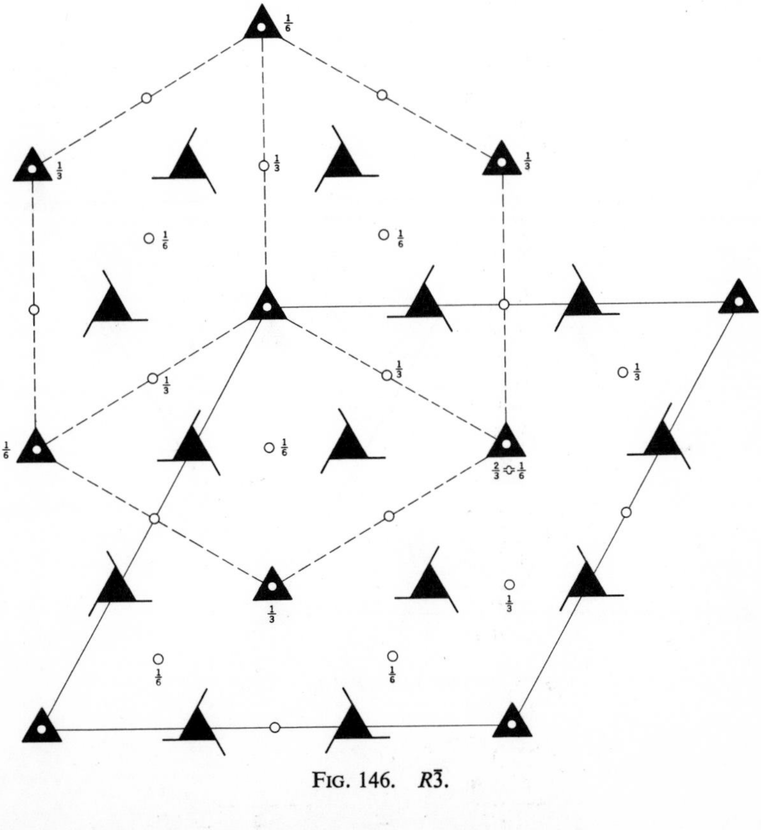

FIG. 146. $R\bar{3}$.

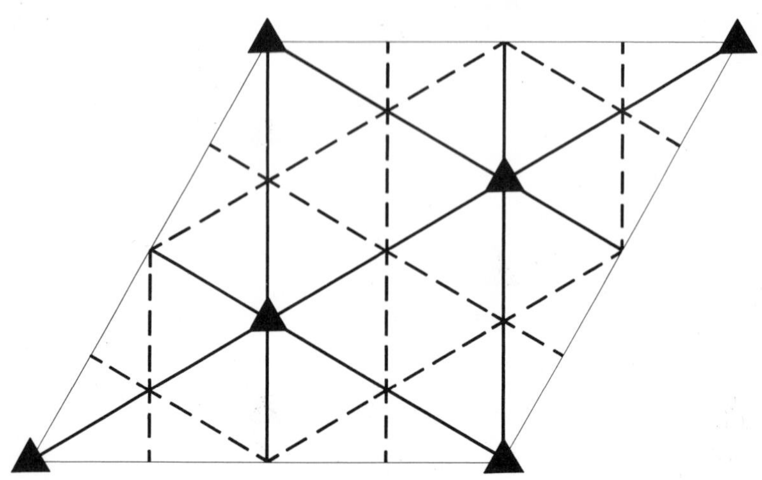

FIG. 147. *P3m1*.

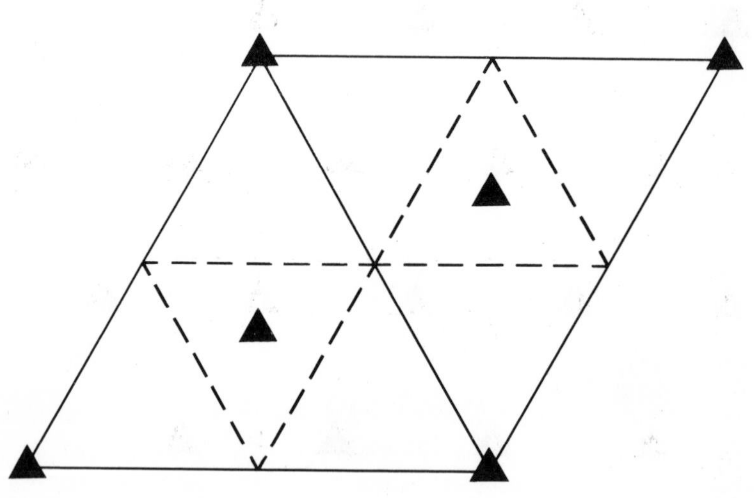

FIG. 148. *P31m*.

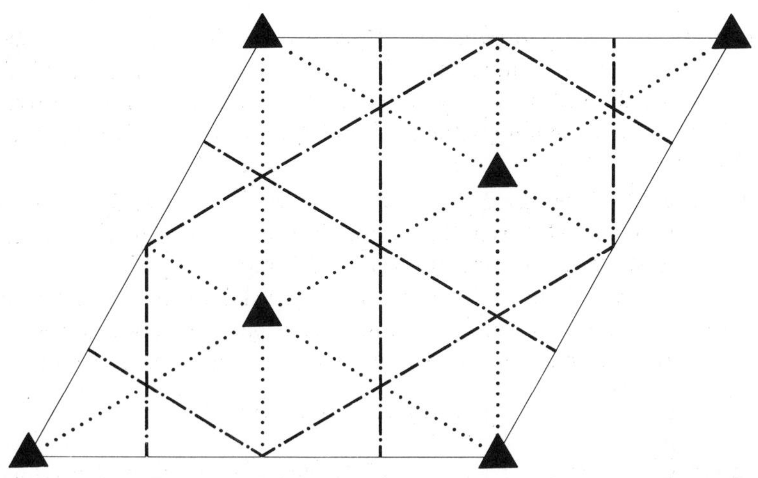

FIG. 149. *P*3*c*1.

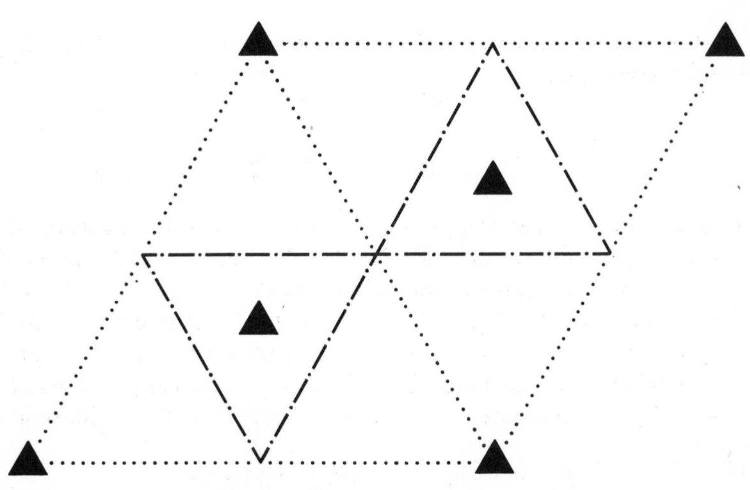

FIG. 150. *P*31*c*.

Trigonal space groups

There are five purely trigonal point groups, specifically, 3, 32, $\bar{3}$, 3*m*, and $\bar{3}$ 2/*m*. These can have either primitive or rhombohedral lattices. The point group $\bar{3}$ can be derived from 3 by adding an inversion, 3*m* can be derived from 3 by adding a plane containing the axis, and $\bar{3}$ 2/*m* can be derived by adding an inversion to 3*m*.

Point group $\bar{3}$. The space groups isogonal with $\bar{3}$ can be found by adding an inversion which transforms the neutral frames isogonal with point group 3 into themselves. These neutral frames are *P*3 and *R*3.

Lattice P. Axial frame *P*3 can be transformed into itself by an inversion, only if the inversion is located on a 3-fold axis or halfway between axes. These centers are translation mates, and so only one space group is possible:

$$P3 \cdot i \rightarrow P\bar{3}, \qquad \text{Fig. 145.}$$

(The point groups $3/m = \bar{6}$ and $3/m\,m2 = \bar{6}m2$ are classed as hexagonal and will be discussed under a subsequent heading.)

Lattice R. Axial frame *R*3 can be transformed into itself only by an inversion on or halfway between 3-fold axes. Since these are translation mates, the only space group is

$$R3 \cdot i \rightarrow R\bar{3}, \qquad \text{Fig. 146.}$$

Résumé of space groups isogonal with $\bar{3}$. The only space groups isogonal with $\bar{3}$ are, accordingly,

$P\bar{3}$		$R\bar{3}$
1	+	1 = 2

Point group 3*m*. Space groups isogonal with 3*m* can be found by starting with one of the two neutral frames *P*3 and *R*3, and adding a glide parallel to the 3-fold axis which transforms the frame into itself.

Lattice P. The axial frame *P*3, Fig. 13, Chapter 13, can be transformed into itself only by planes through the axes and perpendicular either to the primitive translation [100] or to a long diagonal of the cell. These can be pure reflection planes or can have translation components *c*/2. The four resulting space groups are

$$P3 \cdot {}^{\perp[10\cdot0]}m \rightarrow P3m1, \qquad \text{Fig. 147,}$$

$$P3 \cdot {}^{\perp[21\cdot0]}m \rightarrow P31m, \qquad \text{Fig. 148,}$$

$$P3 \cdot {}^{\perp[10\cdot0]}m_{c/2} \rightarrow P3c1, \qquad \text{Fig. 149,}$$

$$P3 \cdot {}^{\perp[21\cdot0]}m_{c/2} \rightarrow P31c, \qquad \text{Fig. 150.}$$

Lattice R. The neutral axial frame $R3$ can be transformed into itself by a pure reflection or c glide only normal to $[10 \cdot 0]$. The two resulting space groups are

$$R3 \cdot m \rightarrow R3m, \qquad \text{Fig. 151,}$$
$$R3 \cdot c \rightarrow R3c, \qquad \text{Fig. 152.}$$

Résumé of space groups isogonal with 3*m*. The space groups isogonal with $3m$ are, accordingly,

$P3m1$	$R3m$
$P3c1$	$R3c$
$P31m$	
$P31c$	
4 +	2 = 6

Point group $\bar{3}\,\dfrac{2}{m}$. The space groups isogonal with $\bar{3}\ 2/m$ can be derived by adding to the space groups isogonal with $\bar{3}m$, inversion centers which transform these space groups into themselves. It has been shown already that the only distinct inversion which can be added to the frame $P\bar{3}$ is on a 3-fold axis, and this holds good for space groups containing this frame. In the case of space groups isogonal with $\bar{3}\ 2/m$, the addition of the inversion on the 3-fold axis also places it on the mirror or c glide, and consequently 2-fold rotation axes develop perpendicular to the reflection planes in a location determined by Figs. 9 and 8.

The six space groups determined by adding inversions to the six space groups isogonal with $3m$ are

$$P3m1 \cdot i \rightarrow P\bar{3}\frac{2}{m}1, \qquad \text{Fig. 153,}$$
$$P31m \cdot i \rightarrow P\bar{3}1\frac{2}{m}, \qquad \text{Fig. 154,}$$
$$P3c1 \cdot i \rightarrow P\bar{3}\frac{2}{c}1, \qquad \text{Fig. 155,}$$
$$P31c \cdot i \rightarrow P\bar{3}1\frac{2}{c}, \qquad \text{Fig. 156,}$$
$$R3m \cdot i \rightarrow R\bar{3}\frac{2}{m}, \qquad \text{Fig. 157,}$$
$$R3c \cdot i \rightarrow R\bar{3}\frac{2}{c}, \qquad \text{Fig. 158.}$$

6

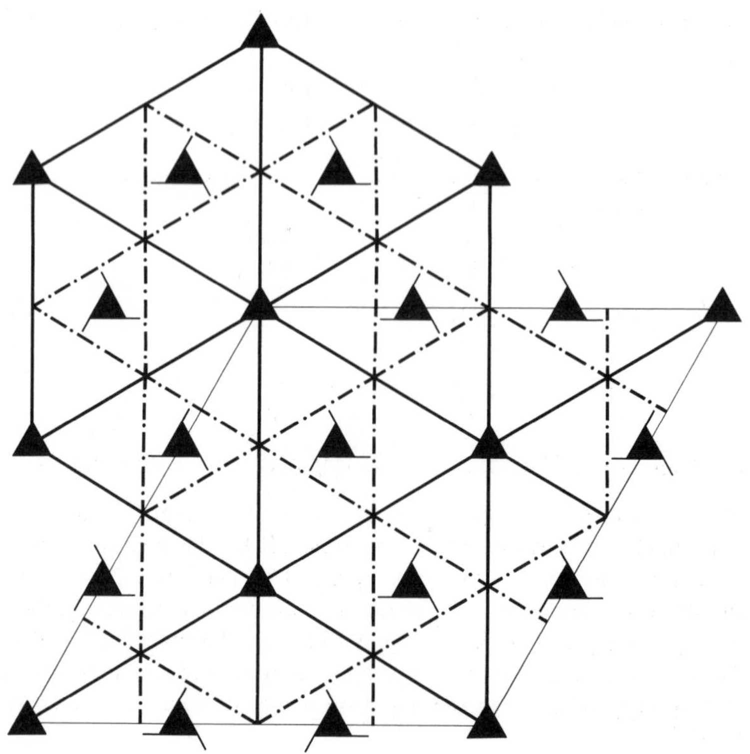

FIG. 151. *R*3*m*. Both hexagonal and rhombohedral cells are outlined.

Hexagonal space groups

The hexagonal point groups containing operations of the second sort are $\bar{6}$ (= 3/*m*), $\bar{6}m2$ (= 3/*m m*2), 6/*m*, 6*mm*, and 6/*m* 2/*m* 2/*m*. *These point groups can have only a primitive lattice.*

Point group $\bar{6} = \dfrac{3}{m}$. Point group $\bar{6}$ can be derived by adding a mirror at right angles to a 3-fold axis. The space groups isogonal with it can be derived by starting with the only neutral frame having a primitive lattice, namely *P*3, and adding a reflection plane normal to the 3-fold axis. Since no translation of half a cell edge, or half a cell diagonal, transforms one 3-fold axis into another nonequivalent one, the only translation component this glide can have is zero. There is therefore only one space group in this class, namely,

$$P3 \cdot {}^{\perp}m \rightarrow P\frac{3}{m} \equiv P\bar{6}, \qquad \text{Fig. 159.}$$

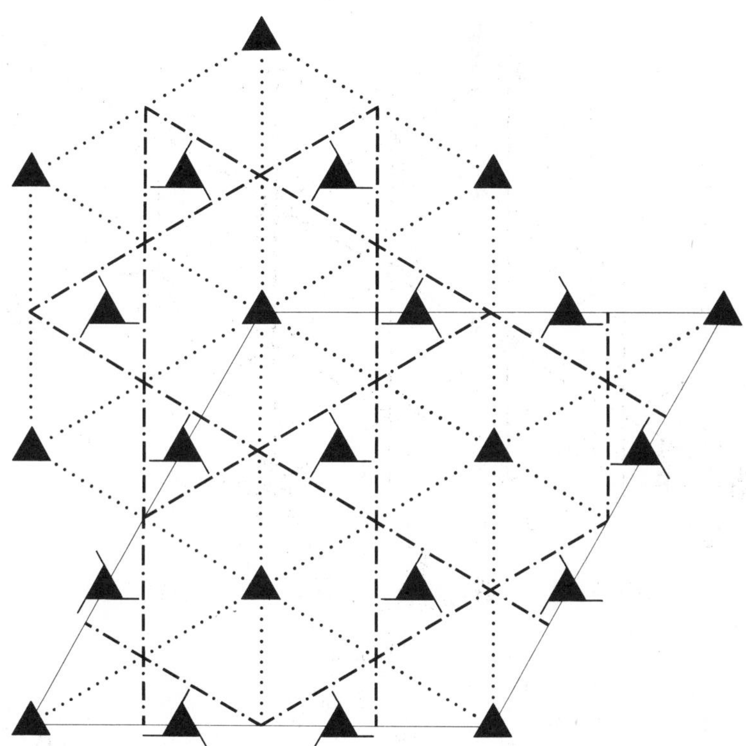

FIG. 152. *R3c*. Both hexagonal and rhombohedral cells are outlined.

Point group $\bar{6}m2 = \dfrac{3}{m}\,m\,2$. Point group $\bar{6}m2$ can be derived by starting with point group $\bar{6}$ and adding either a mirror parallel to the $\bar{6}$ axis or a 2-fold axis perpendicular to the $\bar{6}$ axis. In a corresponding fashion space groups isogonal with it can be derived by adding to $P\bar{6}$, glides parallel to the $\bar{6}$ axes, or adding 2-fold screws perpendicular to them in such a way that $P\bar{6}$ is transformed into itself. The following derivation makes use of added glides. The only possible glides are *m* and *c* through the $\bar{6}$ axes (and their translation mates, which are horizontal and diagonal glides, between $\bar{6}$ axes) perpendicular to [10·0], and also *m* and *c* perpendicular to [21·0] through the $\bar{6}$ axes (and their translation mates *a* and *n* between $\bar{6}$ axes). These four space groups are as follows:

$$P\bar{6}\cdot{}^{\perp[10\cdot0]}m = P\bar{6}m2, \qquad \text{Fig. 160,}$$
$$P\bar{6}\cdot{}^{\perp[10\cdot0]}c = P\bar{6}c2, \qquad \text{Fig. 161,}$$
$$P\bar{6}\cdot{}^{\perp[21\cdot0]}m = P\bar{6}2m, \qquad \text{Fig. 162,}$$
$$P\bar{6}\cdot{}^{\perp[21\cdot0]}c = P\bar{6}2c, \qquad \text{Fig. 163.}$$

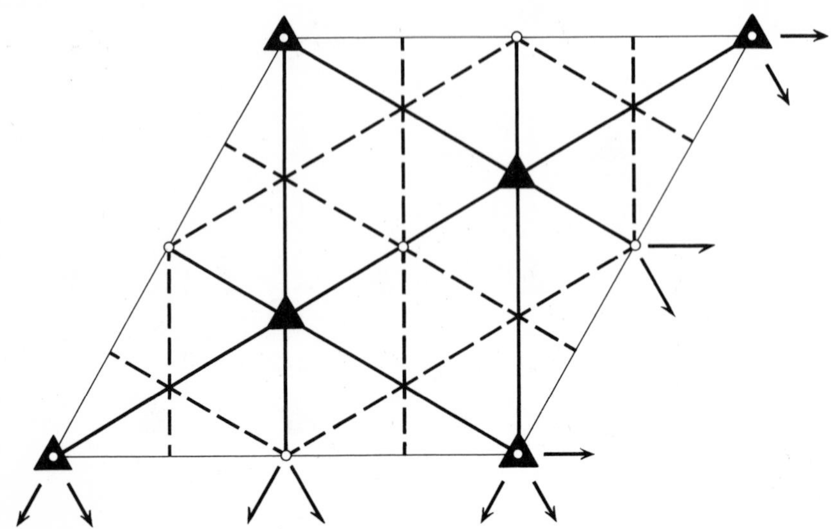

FIG. 153. $P\bar{3}\frac{2}{m}1$.

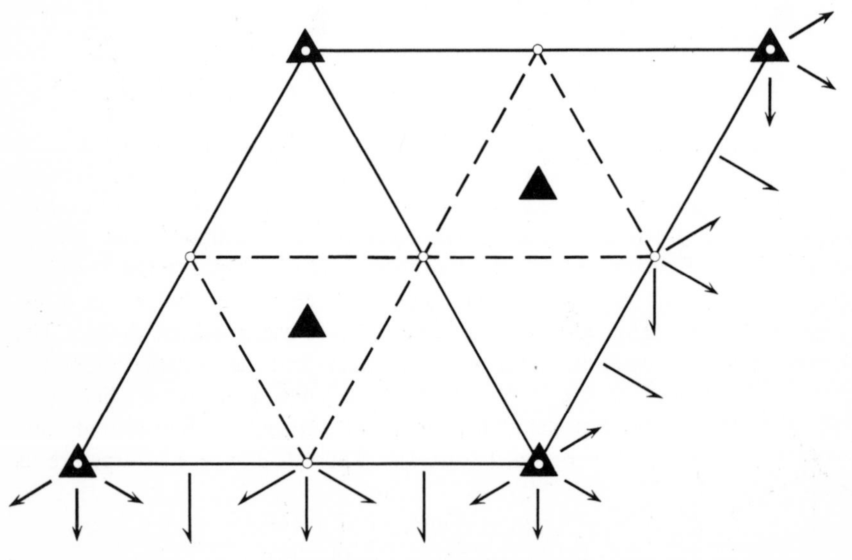

FIG. 154. $P\bar{3}1\frac{2}{m}$.

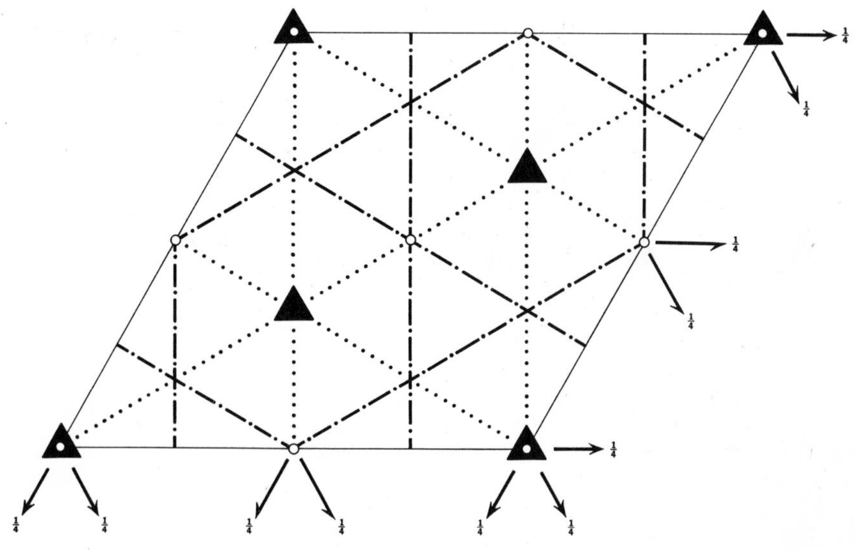

FIG. 155. $P\bar{3}\frac{2}{c}1$.

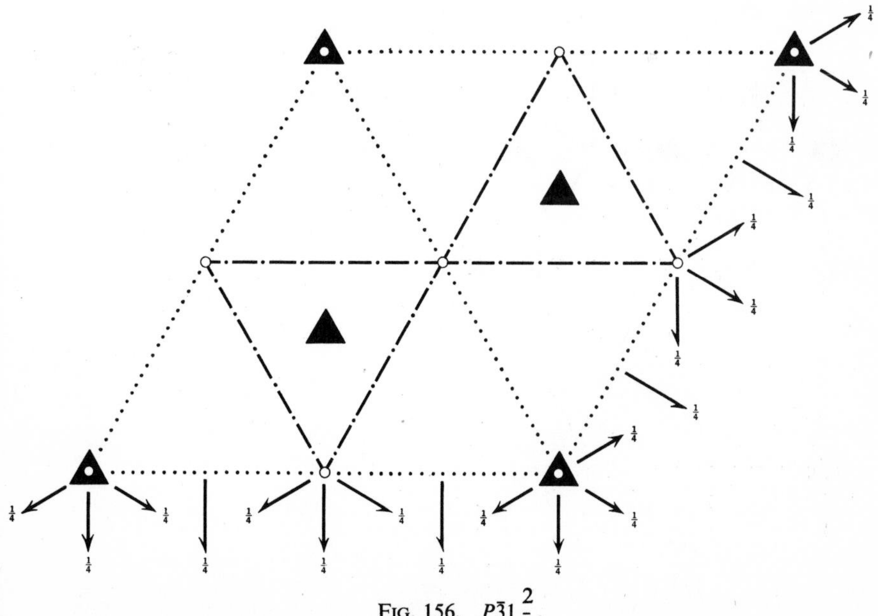

FIG. 156. $P\bar{3}1\frac{2}{c}$.

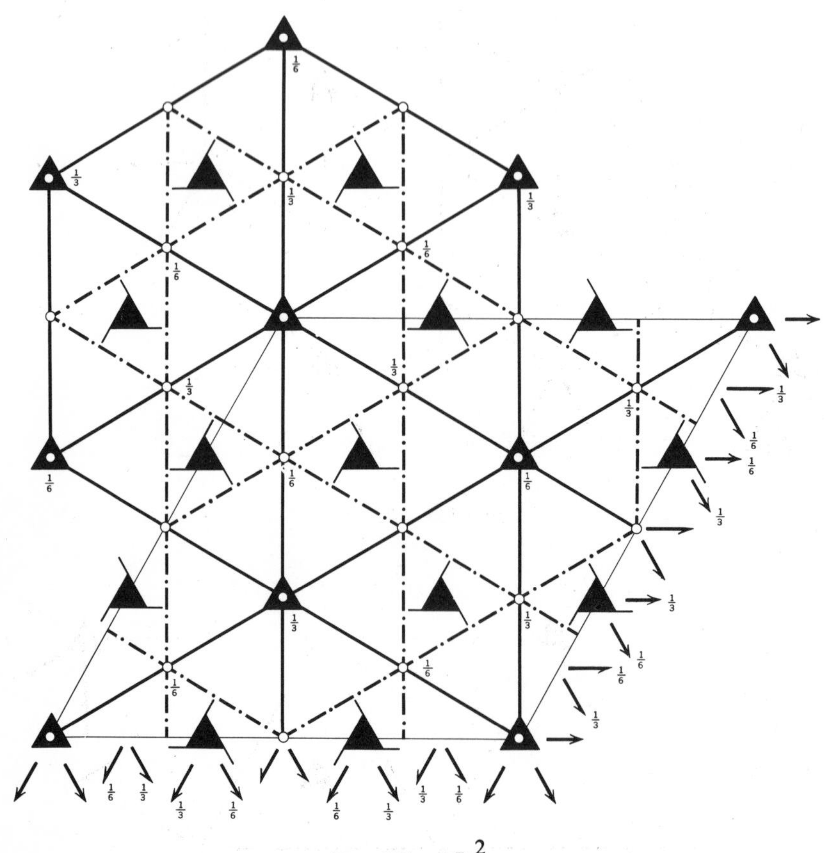

FIG. 157. $R\bar{3}\dfrac{2}{m}$.

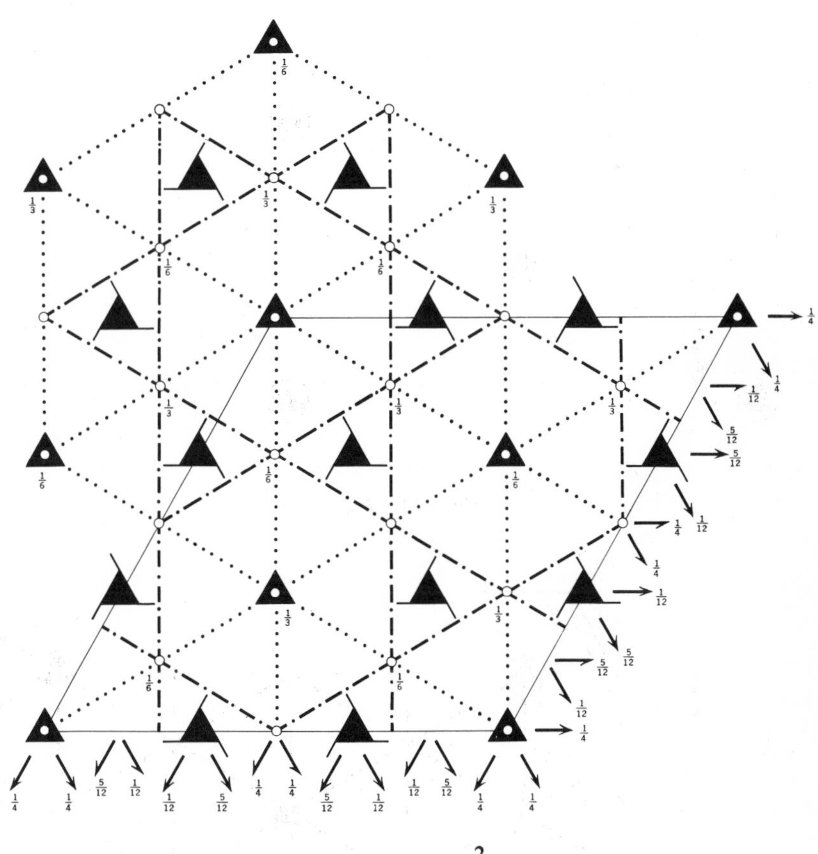

FIG. 158. $R\bar{3}\,\frac{2}{c}$.

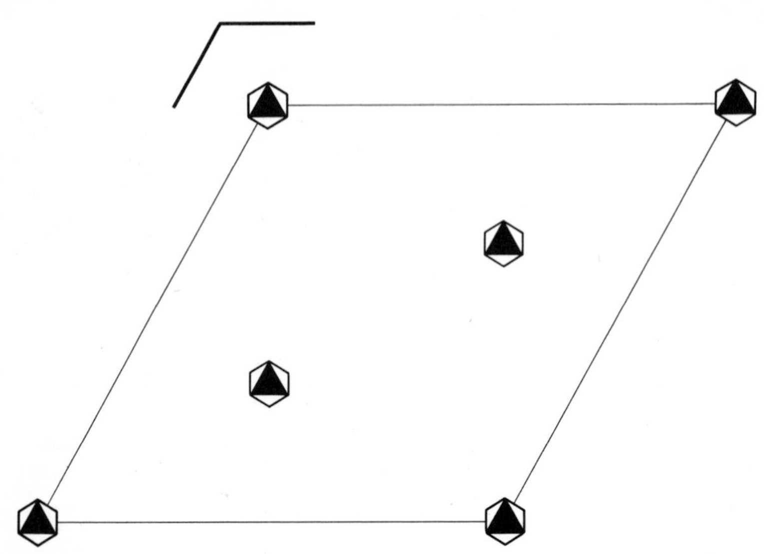

FIG. 159. $P\bar{6}$.

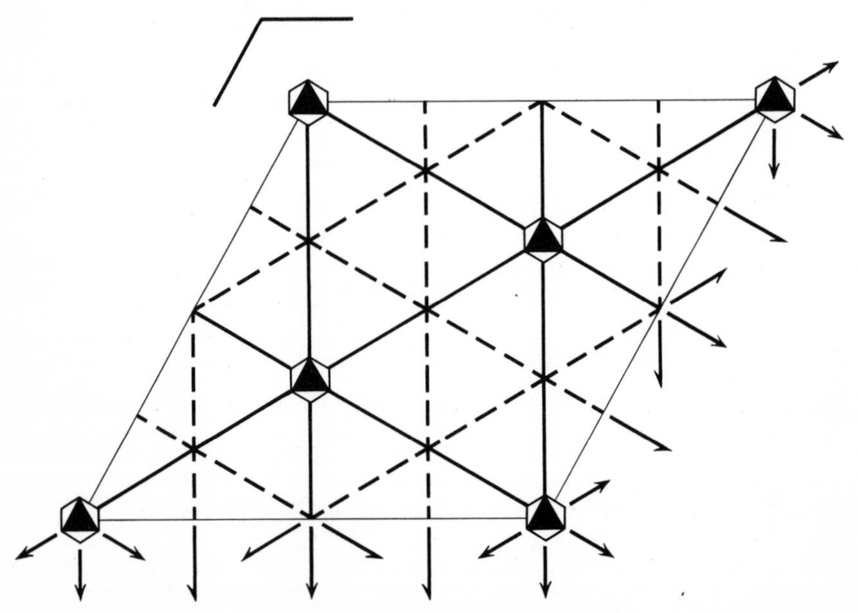

FIG. 160. $P\bar{6}m2$.

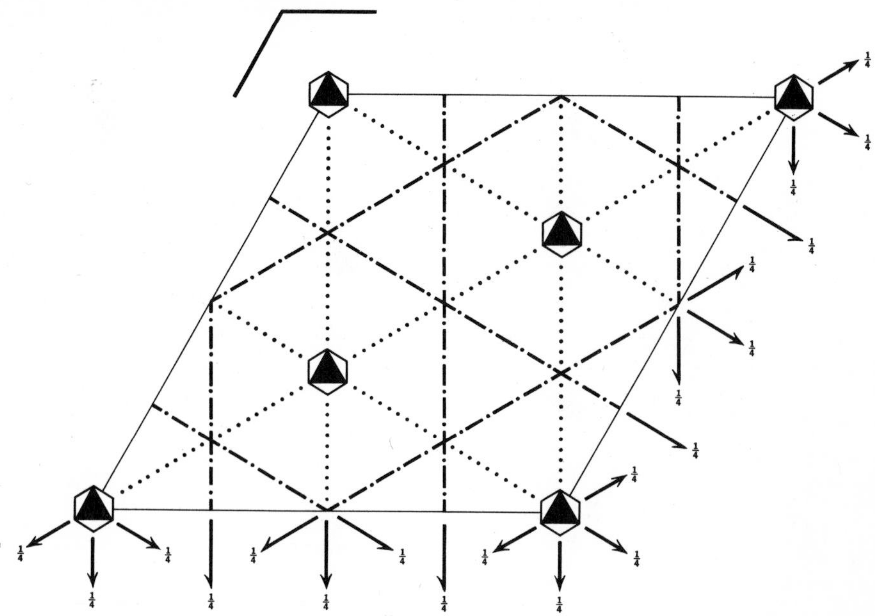

FIG. 161. $P\bar{6}c2$.

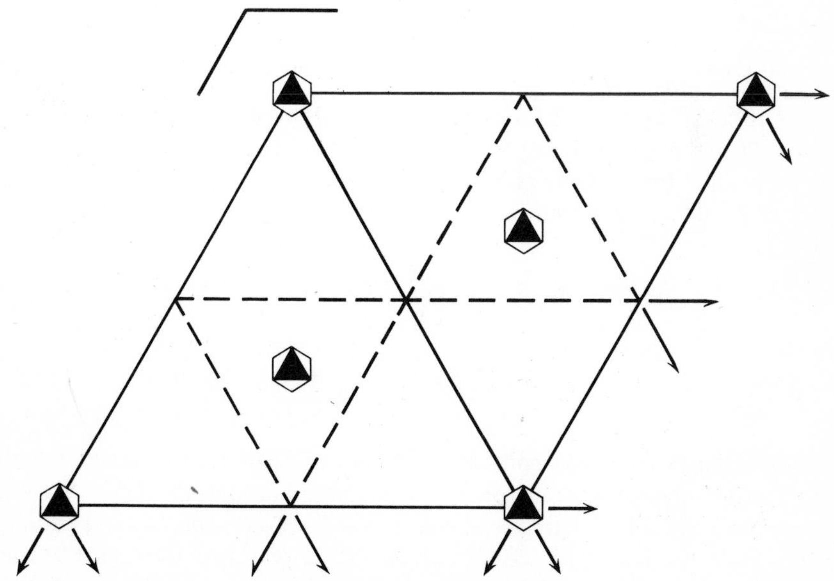

FIG. 162. $P\bar{6}2m$.

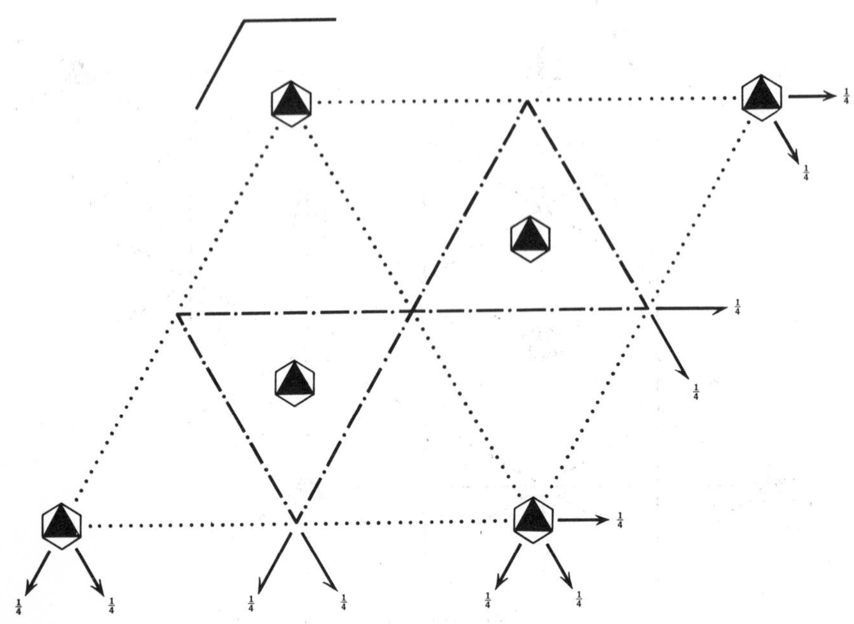

FIG. 163. $P\bar{6}2c$.

Point group $\frac{6}{m}$. This point group can be derived by adding a mirror at right angles to a 6-fold axis. Its space groups are derived by starting with neutral frames $P6$ and $P6_3$ and adding to each any perpendicular glide which transforms the frame into itself. Only glides with translation component zero can do this, since all 6-fold axes are translation-equivalent. The two possible space groups are therefore

$$P6 \cdot {}^{\perp}m = P\frac{6}{m}, \quad \text{Fig. 164,}$$

$$P6_3 \cdot {}^{\perp}m = P\frac{6_3}{m}, \quad \text{Fig. 165.}$$

Point group 6*mm*. The point group 6*mm* can be derived by starting with a 6-fold axis and adding a mirror in a position containing the axis. Its space groups are derived by starting with the neutral frames $P6$ and $P6_3$ and adding to each a glide parallel to the 6-fold axis in such a way that the frame is transformed into itself. Only a mirror and vertical glide perpendicular to [10·0] or [21·0], plus their translation mates, perform this function. Four distinct

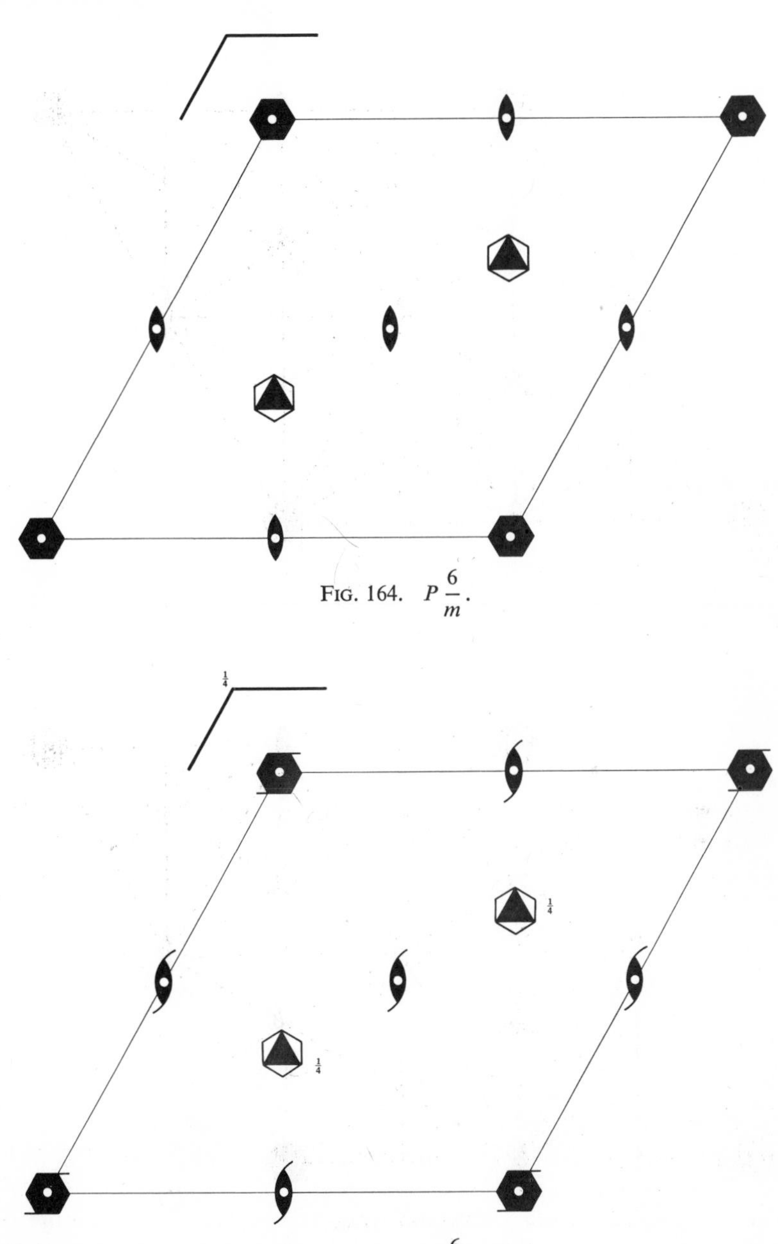

FIG. 164. $P\frac{6}{m}$.

FIG. 165. $P\frac{6_3}{m}$.

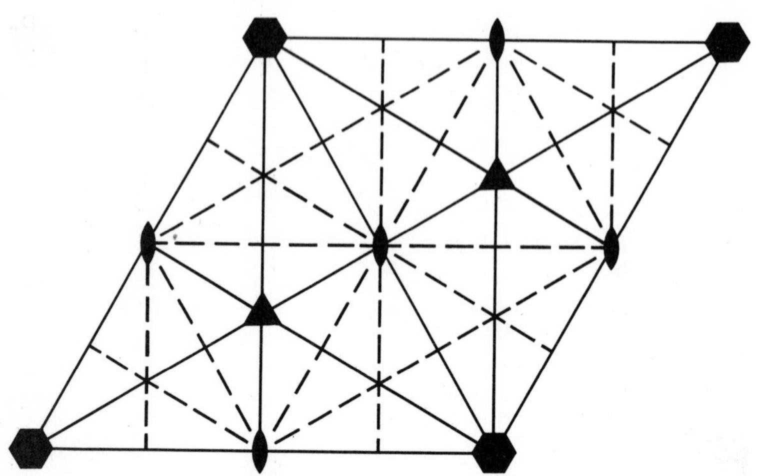

FIG. 166. *P6mm.*

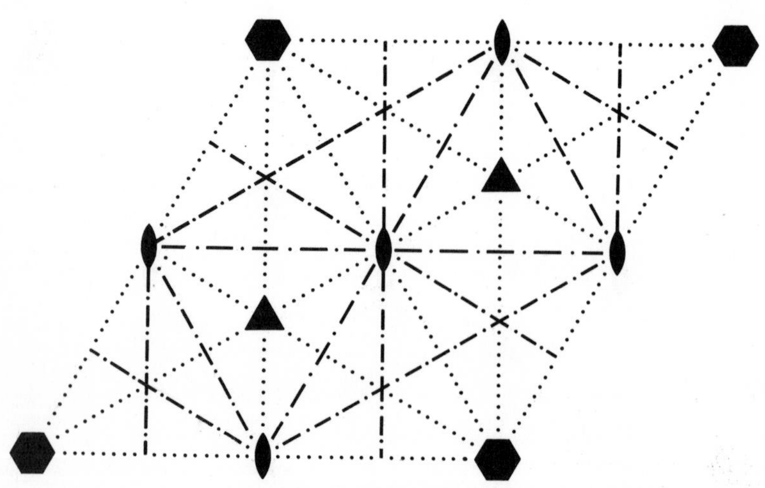

FIG. 167. *P6cc.*

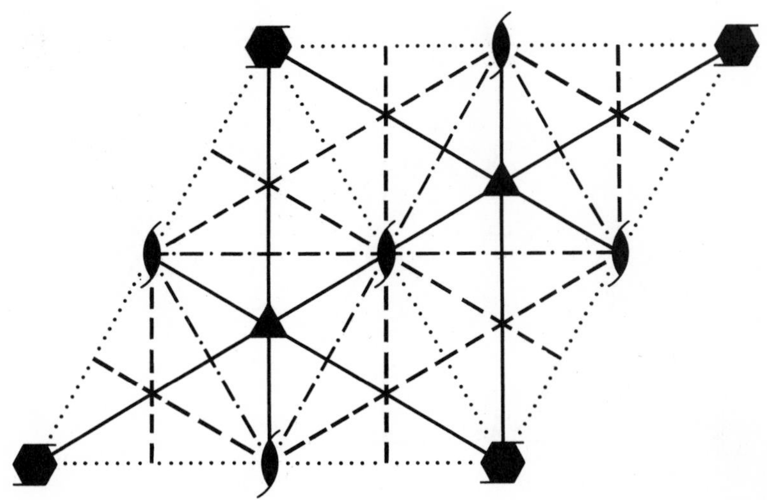

FIG. 168. $P6_3mc$.

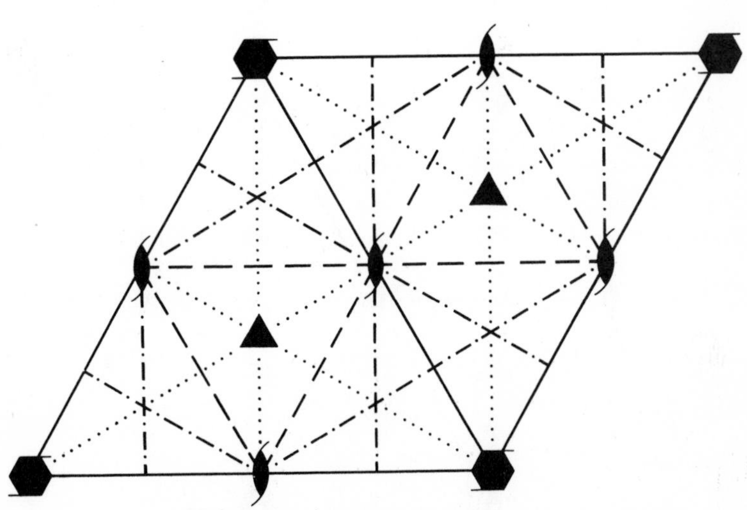

FIG. 169. $P6_3cm$.

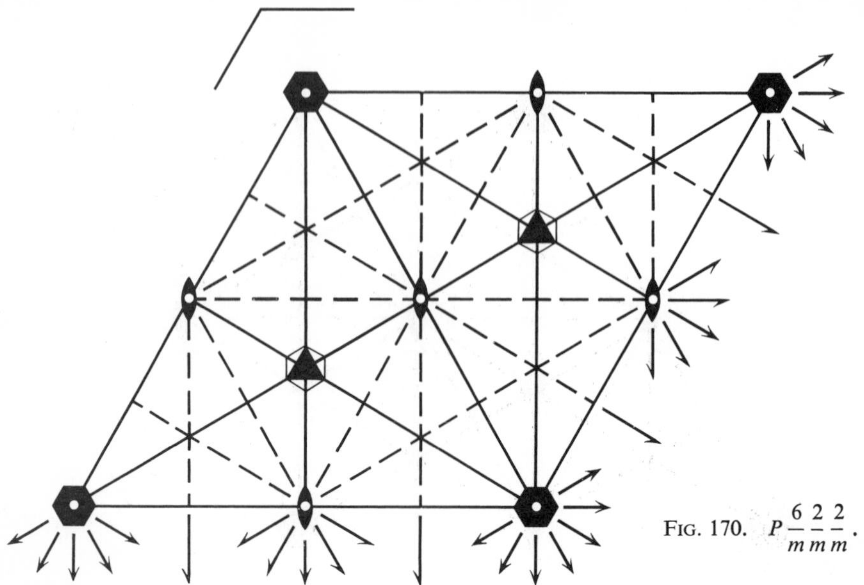

FIG. 170. $P\frac{6}{m}\frac{2}{m}\frac{2}{m}$.

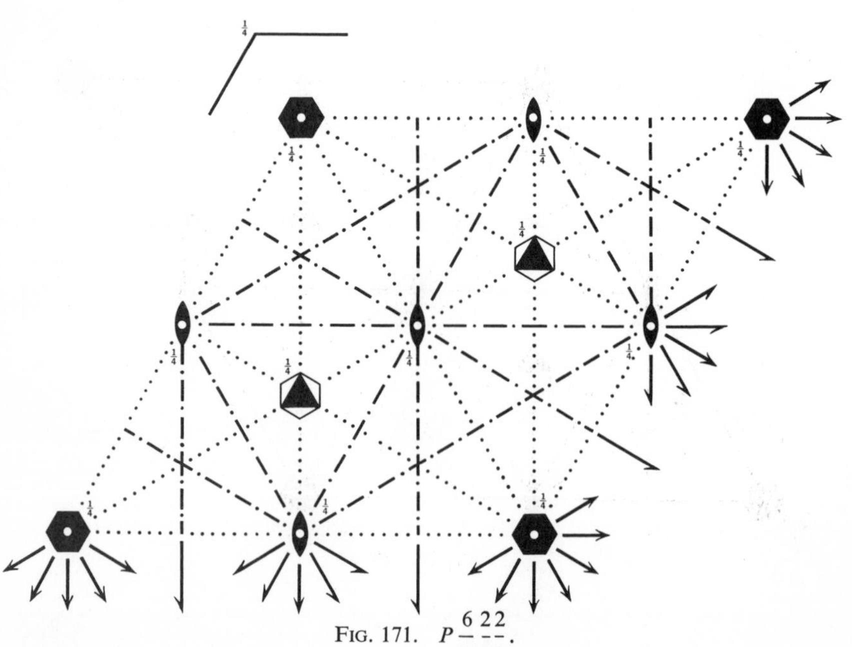

FIG. 171. $P\frac{6}{m}\frac{2}{c}\frac{2}{c}$.

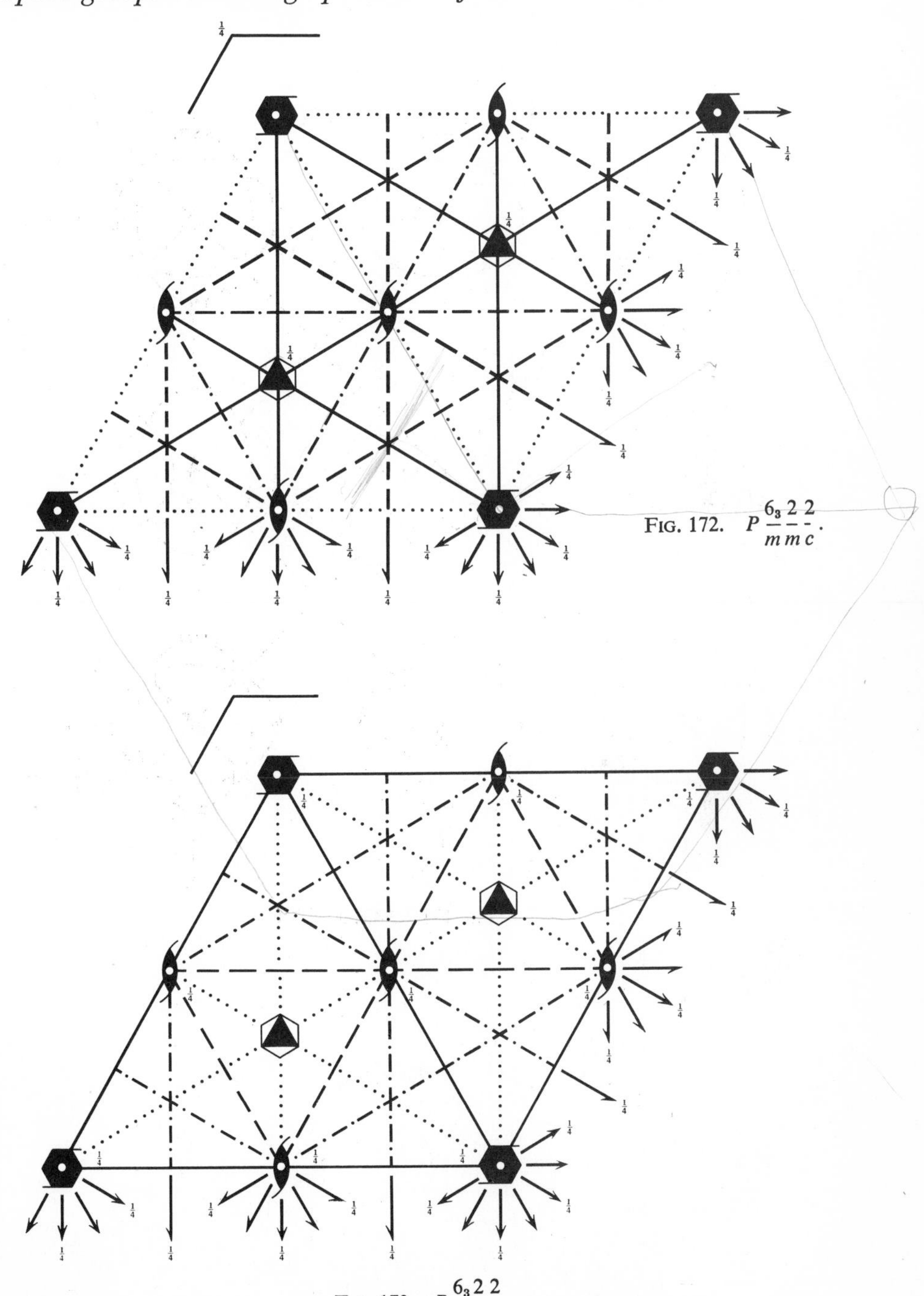

FIG. 172. $P\frac{6_3}{m}\frac{2}{m}\frac{2}{c}$.

FIG. 173. $P\frac{6_3}{m}\frac{2}{c}\frac{2}{m}$.

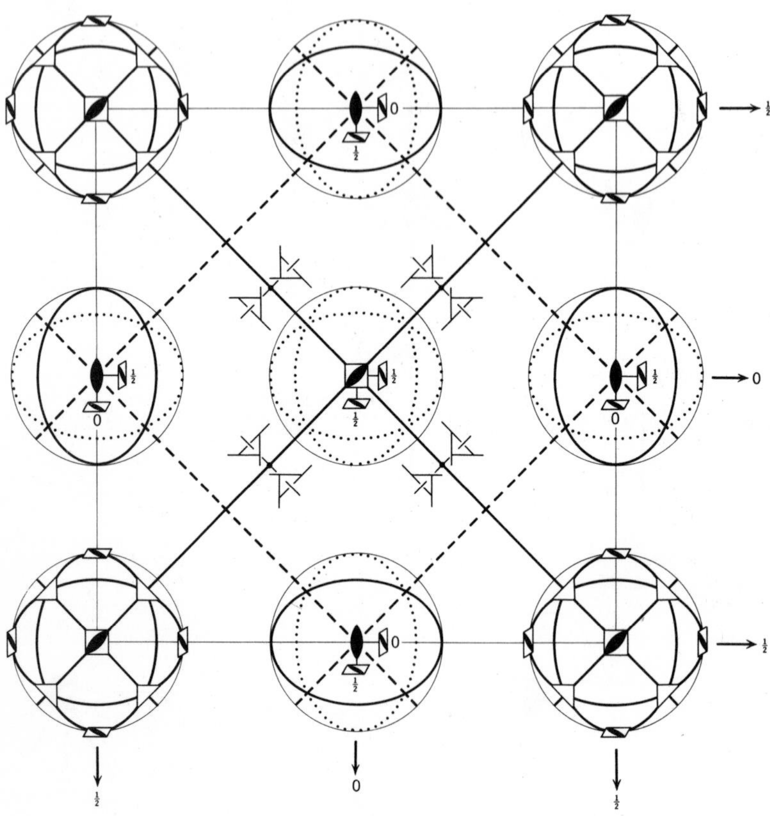

FIG. 174. $P\bar{4}3m$.

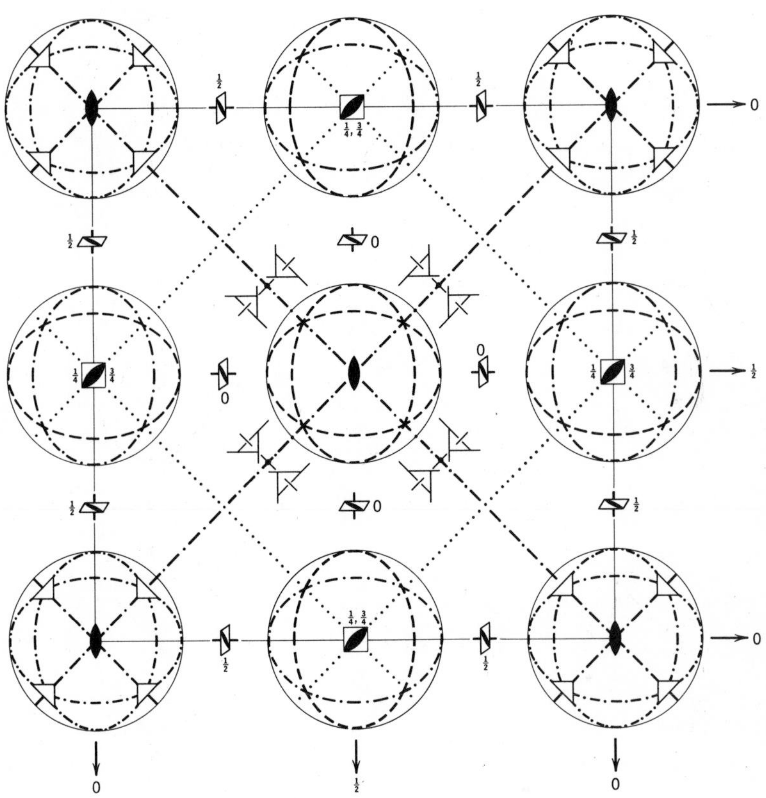

FIG. 175. $P\bar{4}3n$.

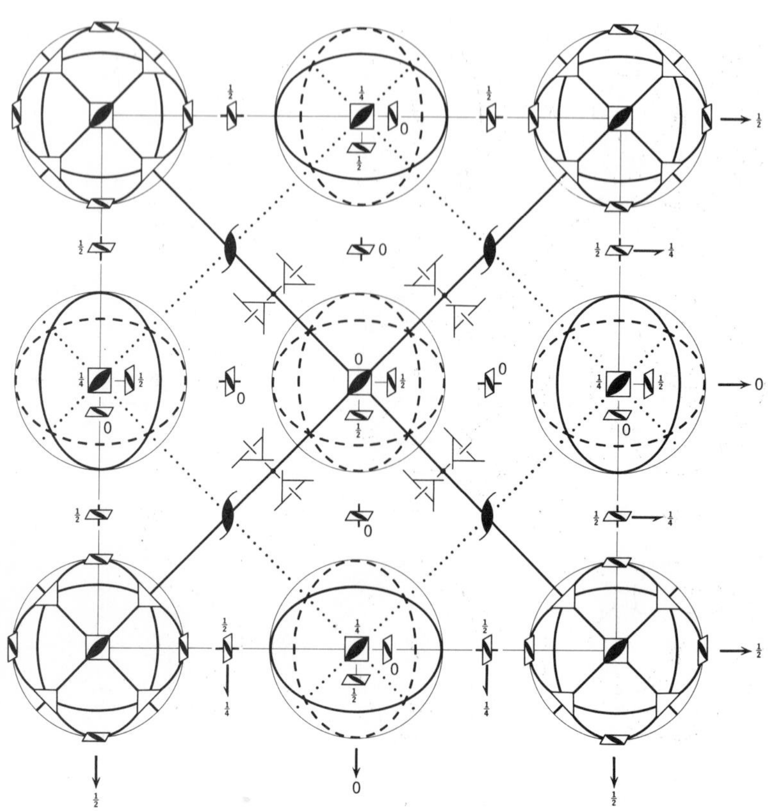

FIG. 176. $I\bar{4}3m$.

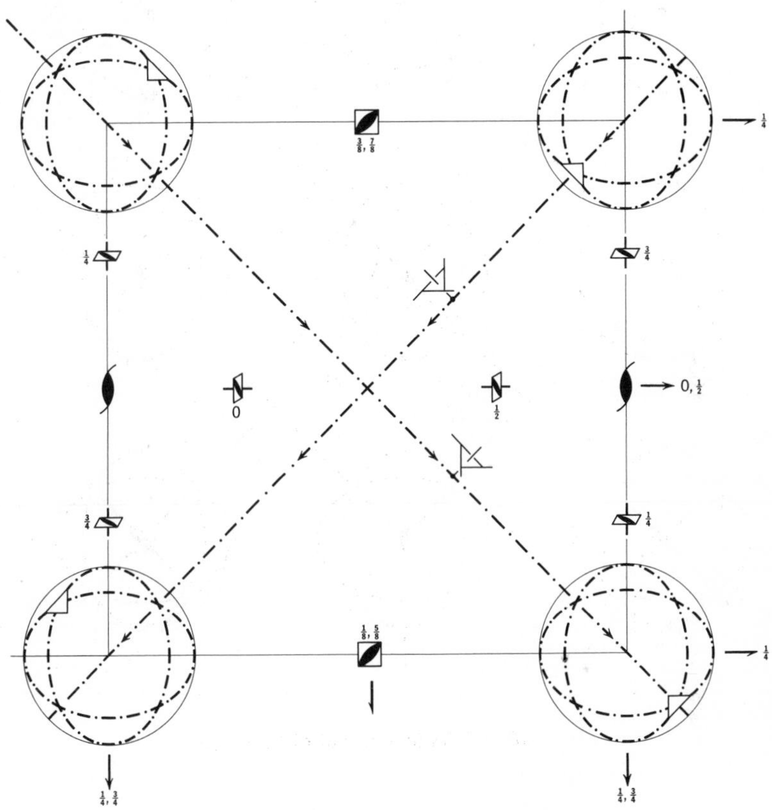

FIG. 177. $I\bar{4}3d$. (one octant of the cell).

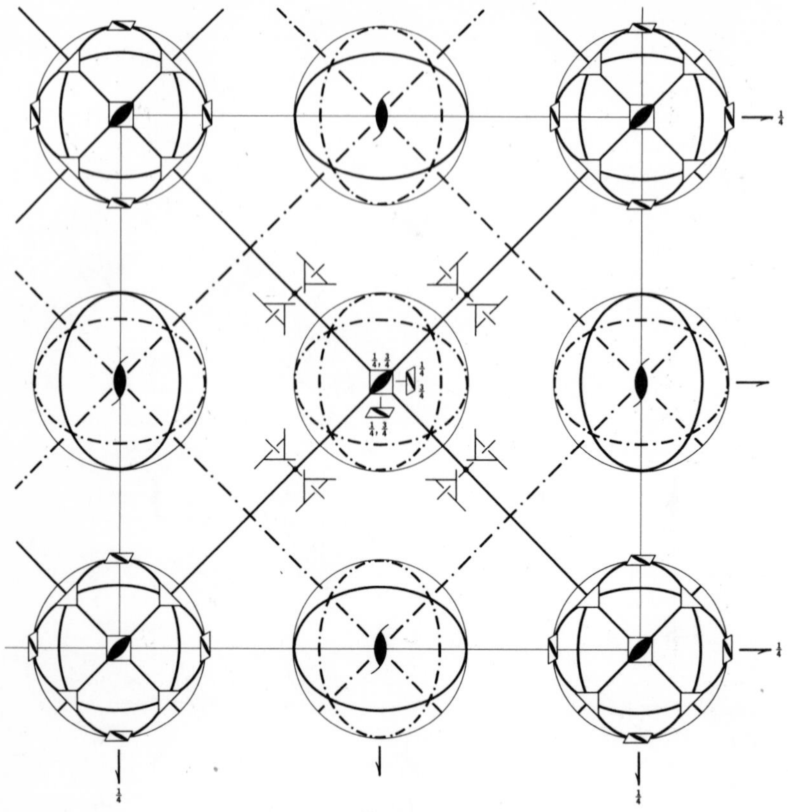

FIG. 178. $F\bar{4}3m$ (one octant of the cell).

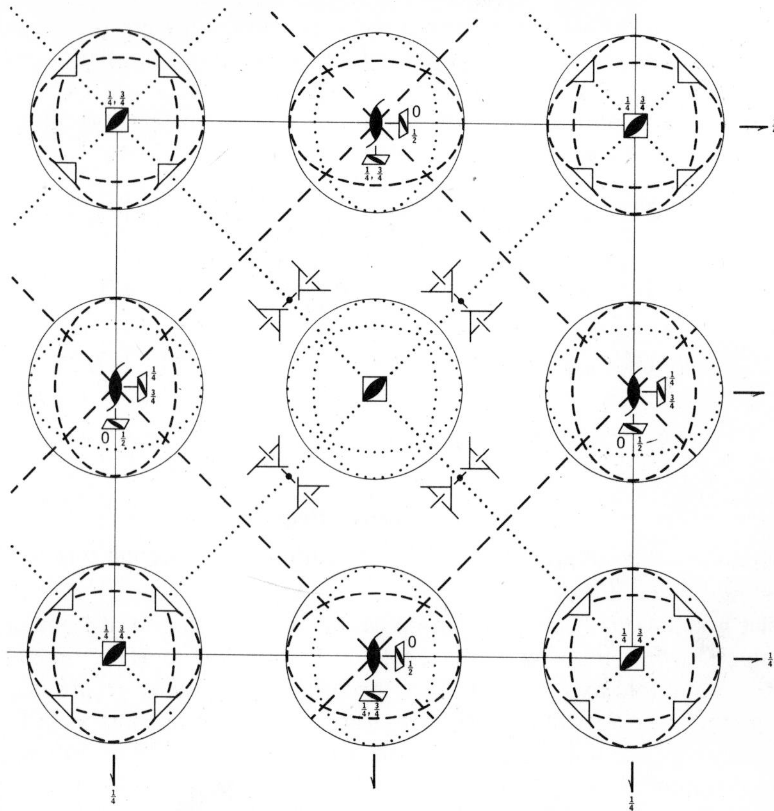

FIG. 179. $F\bar{4}3c$ (one octant of the cell).

space groups are produced by these combinations, as follows (where presuperscript *d* indicates that the plane is parallel to the diagonal [21·0]:

$$P6 \cdot m \quad \rightarrow P6mm, \qquad \text{Fig. 166,}$$
$$P6 \cdot c \quad \rightarrow P6cc, \qquad \text{Fig. 167,}$$
$$P6_3 \cdot m \;= P6_3 \cdot {}^{d}c \rightarrow P6_3mc, \qquad \text{Fig. 168,}$$
$$P6_3 \cdot c \;= P6_3 \cdot {}^{d}m \rightarrow P6_3cm, \qquad \text{Fig. 169.}$$

Point group $\frac{6}{m}\frac{2}{m}\frac{2}{m}$. This point group can be derived in several ways. One is to add an inversion to axial frame 622. Another is to add a mirror perpendicular to the 6-fold axis in 6*mm*. Space groups isogonal with $\frac{6}{m}\frac{2}{m}\frac{2}{m}$ can therefore be derived by starting with the two neutral axial frames *P*622 and $P6_322$ and adding inversion centers which transform the frames into themselves. The only locations for these inversions are on the 6-fold axes and also on, or halfway between, 2-fold axes (or their translation mates). Alternatively, the space groups isogonal with $6mm$ can be transformed into themselves by a mirror perpendicular to the 6-fold axes. By either procedure the four following space groups result:

$$P622 \cdot i_{000} \quad \text{or} \quad P6mm \cdot m \rightarrow P\frac{6}{m}\frac{2}{m}\frac{2}{m}, \qquad \text{Fig. 170,}$$

$$P622 \cdot i_{00\frac{1}{4}} \quad \text{or} \quad P6cc \cdot m \rightarrow P\frac{6}{m}\frac{2}{c}\frac{2}{c}, \qquad \text{Fig. 171,}$$

$$P6_322 \cdot i_{000} \quad \text{or} \quad P6_3mc \cdot m \rightarrow P\frac{6_3}{m}\frac{2}{m}\frac{2}{c}, \qquad \text{Fig. 172,}$$

$$P6_322 \cdot i_{00\frac{1}{4}} \quad \text{or} \quad P6_3cm \cdot m \rightarrow P\frac{6_3}{m}\frac{2}{c}\frac{2}{m}, \qquad \text{Fig. 173.}$$

Isometric space groups

The isometric point groups containing operations of the second sort are $\bar{4}3m$, $2/m\ \bar{3}$, and $4/m\ \bar{3}\ 2/m$.

Point group $\bar{4}3m$. This point group can be derived from axial frame 23 by adding a mirror containing both a 2-fold and a 3-fold axis. The combination converts the 2-fold axis into a $\bar{4}$ axis. Accordingly, the space groups isogonal with point group 23 can be derived by starting with permissible axial frames isogonal with 23 and adding a reflection parallel to ($\bar{1}10$). This converts the 2-fold axis into a $\bar{4}$ axis. Now, the second power of the fundamental operation of this axis is A_π, which corresponds to a 2-fold rotation axis. Since axial frame $P2_13$ contains no pure 2-fold rotations, it cannot be used as an axial frame for space groups isogonal with $\bar{4}3m$. The permissible frames are therefore $P23$, $I23$, $I2_13$, and $F23$. These can all be transformed only by glides through the 2-fold axis or their translation mates. There is a curious restriction on these glides. Since, viewed along a 3-fold axis, the axial frame is rhombohedral, only glides that transform $R3$ into itself are possible. In $R3$ orientation these glides are m and c. The rhombohedral c becomes n for the P lattice, d for the I lattice, and c for the F lattice. The only glides that transform the frames into themselves are therefore those of the following combinations:

$$P23 \cdot m \rightarrow P\bar{4}3m, \qquad \text{Fig. 174,}$$

$$P23 \cdot n \rightarrow P\bar{4}3n, \qquad \text{Fig. 175,}$$

$$I23 \cdot m \rightarrow I\bar{4}3m, \qquad \text{Fig. 176,}$$

$$I2_13 \cdot d \rightarrow I\bar{4}3d, \qquad \text{Fig. 177,}$$

$$F23 \cdot m \rightarrow F\bar{4}3m, \qquad \text{Fig. 178,}$$

$$F23 \cdot c \rightarrow F\bar{4}3c, \qquad \text{Fig. 179.}$$

In these space groups the relative elevation of the $\bar{4}$ and the horizontal 2-fold axes can be readily found by consulting the combinations listed at the right of Table 8 together with the illustrations of the corresponding tetragonal space groups isogonal with $\bar{4}2m$.

Point group $\frac{2}{m}\bar{3}$. Point group $2/m\ \bar{3}$ can be derived from axial frame 23 by adding an inversion. The space groups isogonal with $2/m\ \bar{3}$ can therefore be derived by starting with each of the five axial frames $P23$, $P2_13$, $I23$, $I2_13$, and $F23$, and adding inversions in locations that transform the frames into themselves. Again, these frames are rhombohedral as seen along the 3-fold axis, so that the same conditions obtain which are required to convert $R3$ to $R\bar{3}$, namely that the inversion can be added only on the 3-fold axis. The permissible locations along the 3-fold axis are such as to transform the 2-fold screws into similar screws. These locations are

for $P23$: 000 and $\frac{1}{4}\frac{1}{4}\frac{1}{4}$
for $P2_13$: 000 ($\frac{1}{4}\frac{1}{4}\frac{1}{4}$ is an indistinguishable location)
for $I23$: 000 ($\frac{1}{4}\frac{1}{4}\frac{1}{4}$ is a translation mate)
for $I2_13$: 000 ($\frac{1}{4}\frac{1}{4}\frac{1}{4}$ is a translation mate)
for $F23$: 000 and $\frac{1}{4}\frac{1}{4}\frac{1}{4}$.

The space groups obtained by adding inversions at these points to the axial frames are as follows:

$$P23 \cdot i_{000} \rightarrow P\frac{2}{m}\bar{3}, \qquad \text{Fig. 180,}$$

$$P23 \cdot i_{\frac{1}{4}\frac{1}{4}\frac{1}{4}} \rightarrow P\frac{2}{n}\bar{3}, \qquad \text{Fig. 181,}$$

$$P2_13 \cdot i_{000} \rightarrow P\frac{2_1}{a}\bar{3}, \qquad \text{Fig. 182,}$$

$$I23 \cdot i_{000} \rightarrow I\frac{2}{m}\bar{3}, \qquad \text{Fig. 183,}$$

$$I2_13 \cdot i_{000} \rightarrow I\frac{2_1}{a}\bar{3}, \qquad \text{Fig. 184,}$$

$$F23 \cdot i_{000} \rightarrow F\frac{2}{m}\bar{3}, \qquad \text{Fig. 185,}$$

$$F23 \cdot i_{\frac{1}{4}\frac{1}{4}\frac{1}{4}} \rightarrow F\frac{2}{d}\bar{3}, \qquad \text{Fig. 186.}$$

The characteristics of the reflections from the combinations of the inversions and 2-fold screws can be determined with the aid of Figs. 6–9.

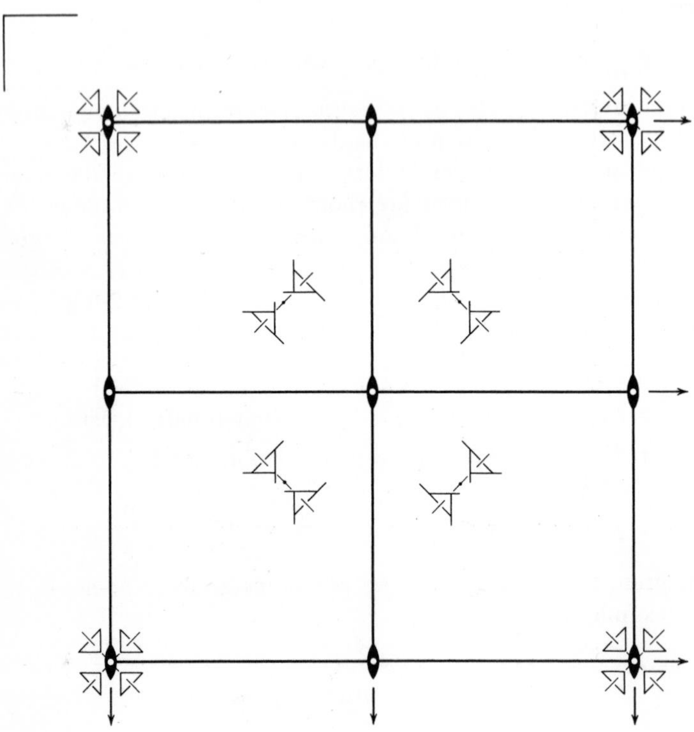

FIG. 180. $P\frac{2}{m}\bar{3}$.

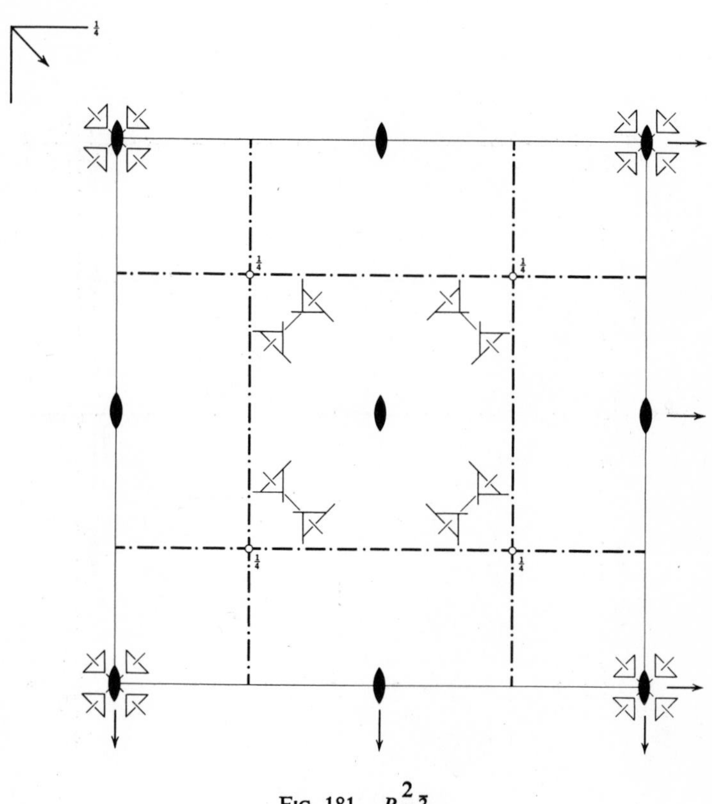

FIG. 181. $P\frac{2}{n}\bar{3}$.

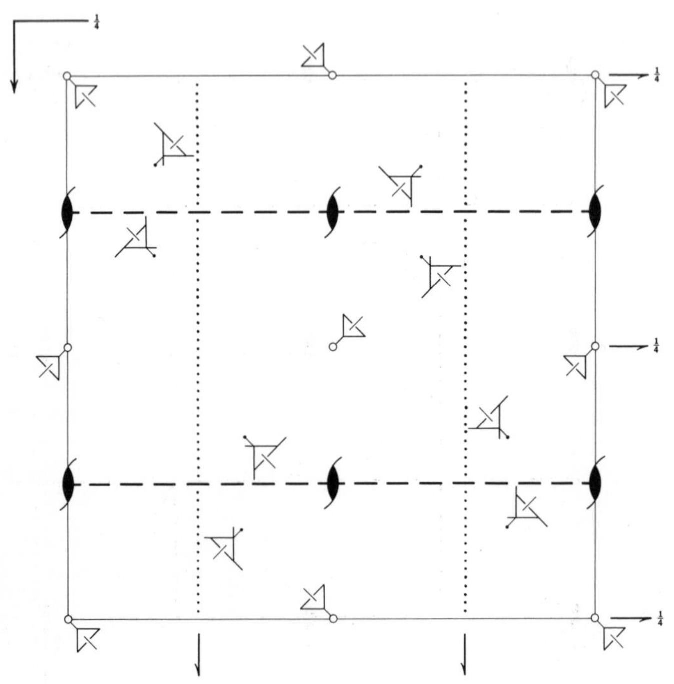

FIG. 182. $P\frac{2_1}{a}\bar{3}$.

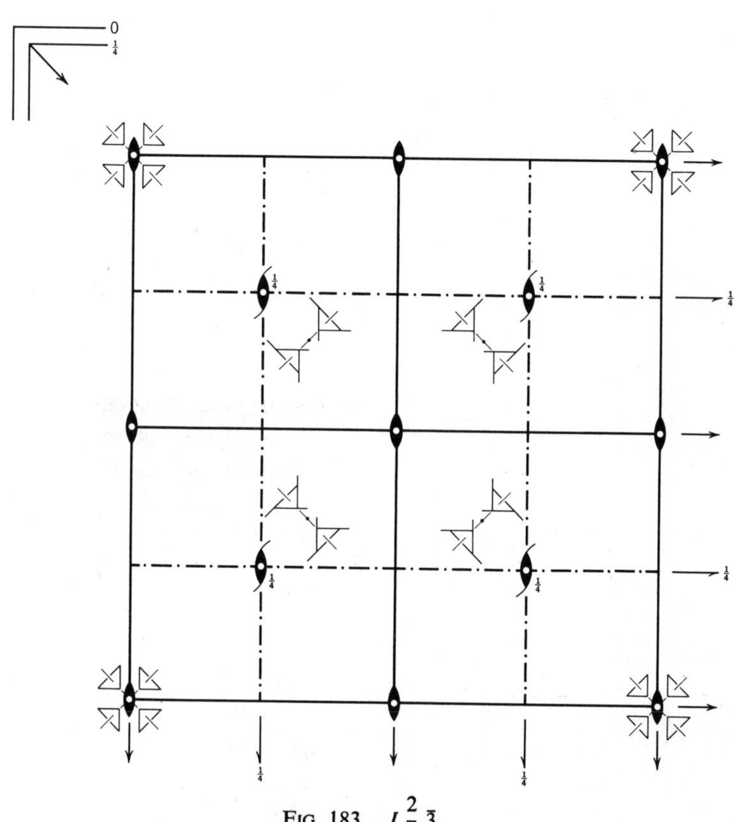

FIG. 183. $I\frac{2}{m}\bar{3}$.

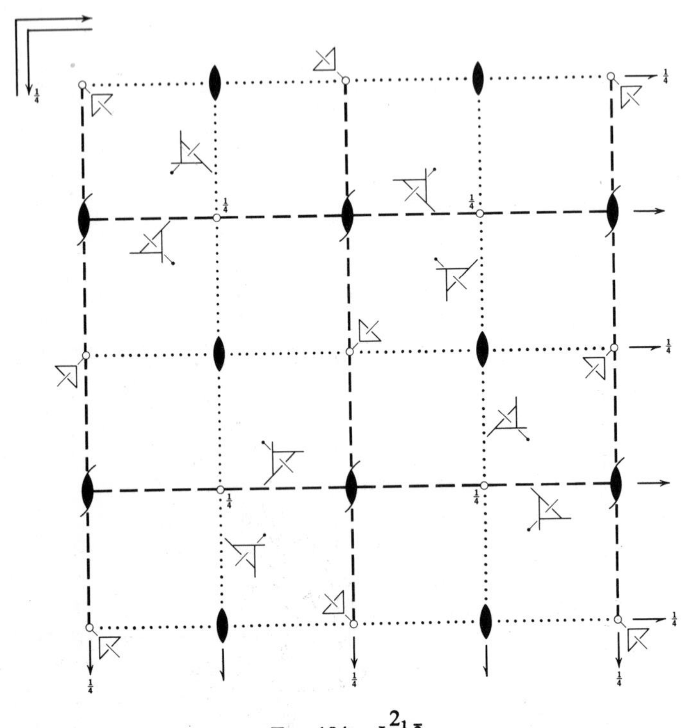

FIG. 184. $I\frac{2_1}{a}\bar{3}$.

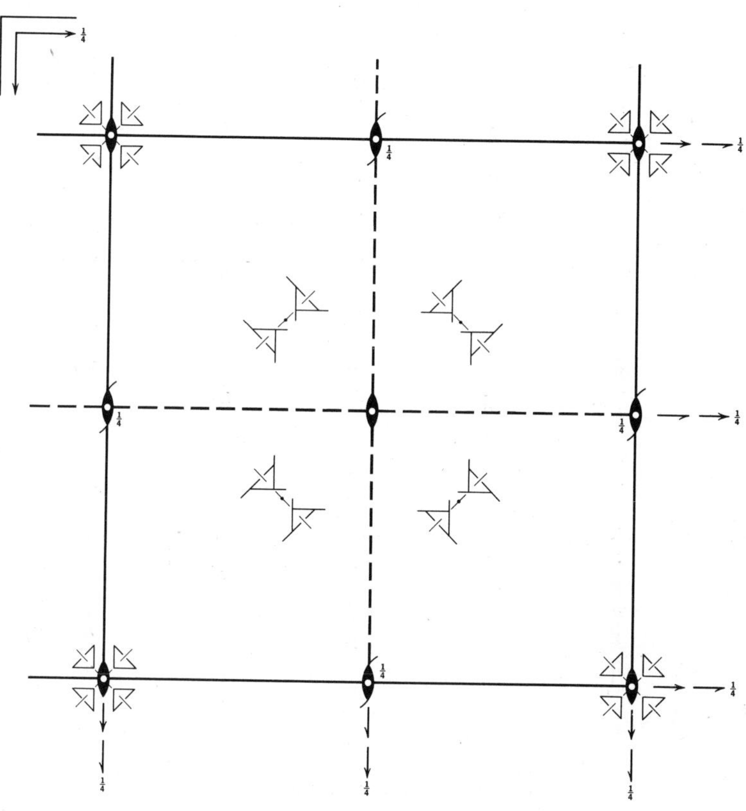

FIG. 185. $F\frac{2}{m}\bar{3}$ (one octant of the cell).

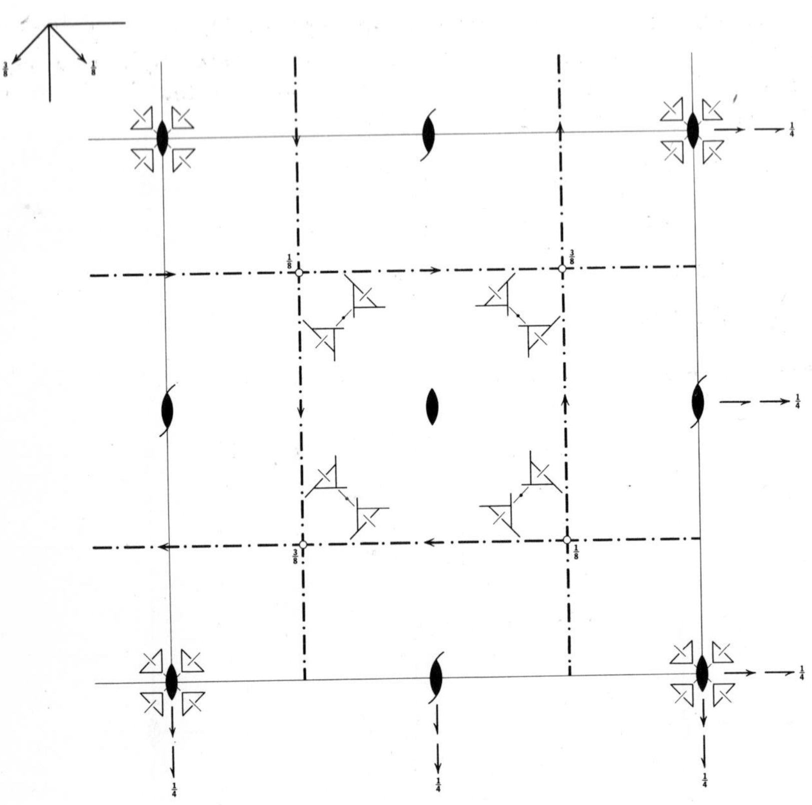

FIG. 186. $F\frac{2}{d}\overline{3}$ (one octant of the cell).

Point group $\frac{4}{m}\bar{3}\frac{2}{m}$. This symmetry can be derived by adding an inversion to the axial frame 432. Accordingly the space groups isogonal with $4/m\,\bar{3}\,2/m$ can be derived by starting with neutral axial frames $P432$, $P4_232$, $I432$, $I4_132$, $F432$, and $F4_132$, and adding inversions which transform the axial frame into itself. These inversions are located as follows:

for $P432$, $P4_232$:	000 and $\frac{1}{4}\frac{1}{4}\frac{1}{4}$
for $I432$ and $I4_132$:	000 ($\frac{1}{4}\frac{1}{4}\frac{1}{4}$ is a translation mate)
for $F432$:	000 and $\frac{1}{4}\frac{1}{4}\frac{1}{4}$
for $F4_132$:	$\frac{1}{8}\frac{1}{8}\frac{1}{8}$ and $\frac{1}{8}\frac{1}{8}\frac{3}{8}$

The space groups which result from these combinations are as follows:

$$P432 \cdot i_{000} \rightarrow P\frac{4}{m}\bar{3}\frac{2}{m}, \qquad \text{Fig. 187,}$$

$$P432 \cdot i_{\frac{1}{4}\frac{1}{4}\frac{1}{4}} \rightarrow P\frac{4}{n}\bar{3}\frac{2}{n}, \qquad \text{Fig. 188,}$$

$$P4_232 \cdot i_{000} \rightarrow P\frac{4_2}{m}\bar{3}\frac{2}{n}, \qquad \text{Fig. 189,}$$

$$P4_232 \cdot i_{\frac{1}{4}\frac{1}{4}\frac{1}{4}} \rightarrow P\frac{4_2}{n}\bar{3}\frac{2}{m}, \qquad \text{Fig. 190,}$$

$$I432 \cdot i_{000} \rightarrow I\frac{4}{m}\bar{3}\frac{2}{m}, \qquad \text{Fig. 191,}$$

$$I4_132 \cdot i_{000} \rightarrow I\frac{4_1}{a}\bar{3}\frac{2}{d}, \qquad \text{Fig. 192,}$$

$$F432 \cdot i_{000} \rightarrow F\frac{4}{m}\bar{3}\frac{2}{m}, \qquad \text{Fig. 193,}$$

$$F432 \cdot i_{\frac{1}{4}\frac{1}{4}\frac{1}{4}} \rightarrow F\frac{4}{m}\bar{3}\frac{2}{c}, \qquad \text{Fig. 194,}$$

$$F4_132 \cdot i_{\frac{1}{8}\frac{1}{8}\frac{1}{8}} \rightarrow F\frac{4_1}{d}\bar{3}\frac{2}{m}, \qquad \text{Fig. 195,}$$

$$F4_132 \cdot i_{\frac{1}{8}\frac{1}{8}\frac{3}{8}} \rightarrow F\frac{4_1}{d}\bar{3}\frac{2}{c}, \qquad \text{Fig. 196.}$$

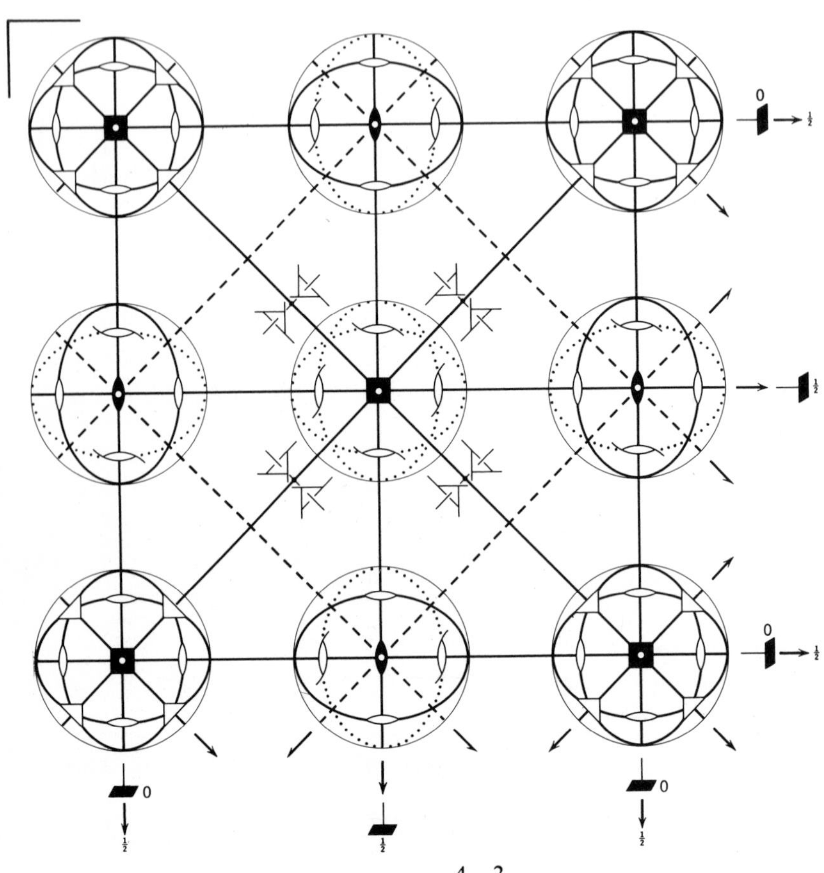

FIG. 187. $P\,\frac{4}{m}\,\bar{3}\,\frac{2}{m}$.

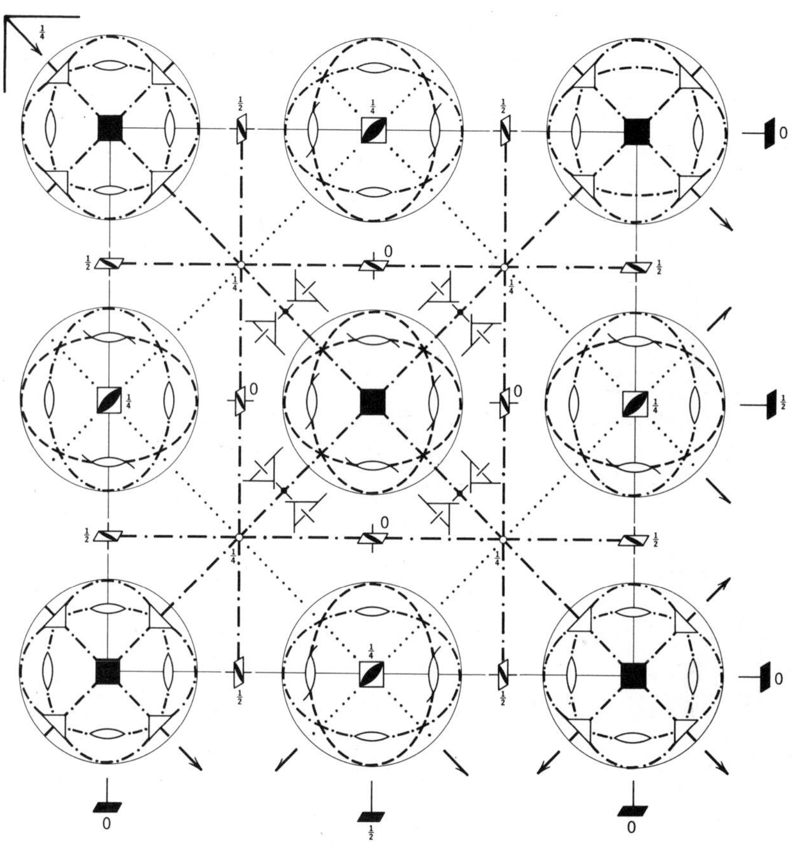

FIG. 188. $P\frac{4}{n}\bar{3}\frac{2}{n}$.

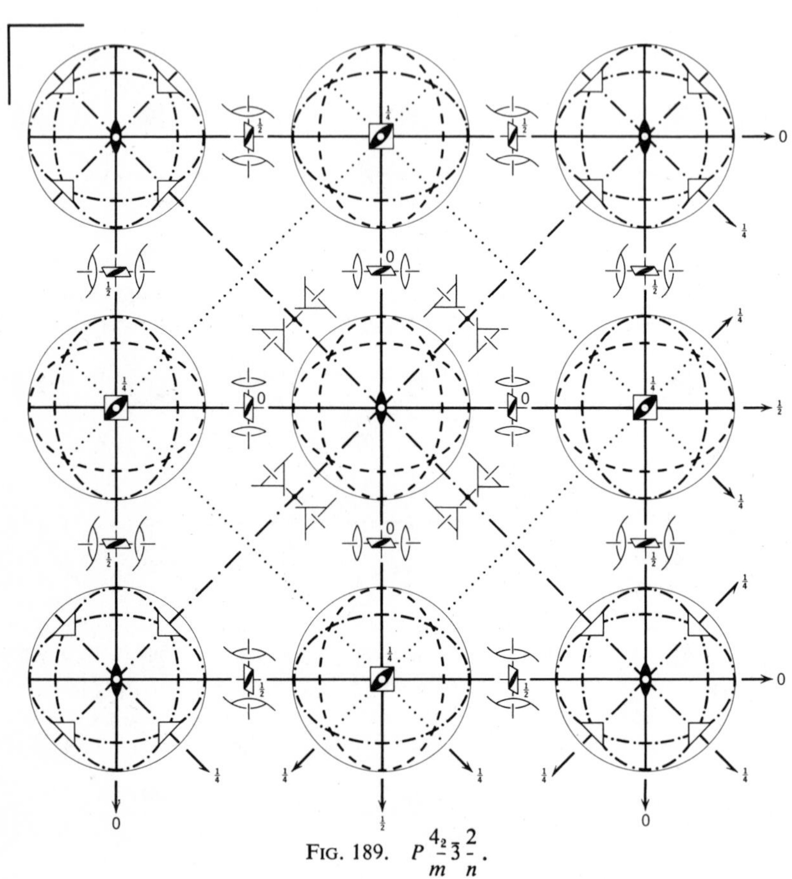

FIG. 189. $P\frac{4_2}{m}\bar{3}\frac{2}{n}$.

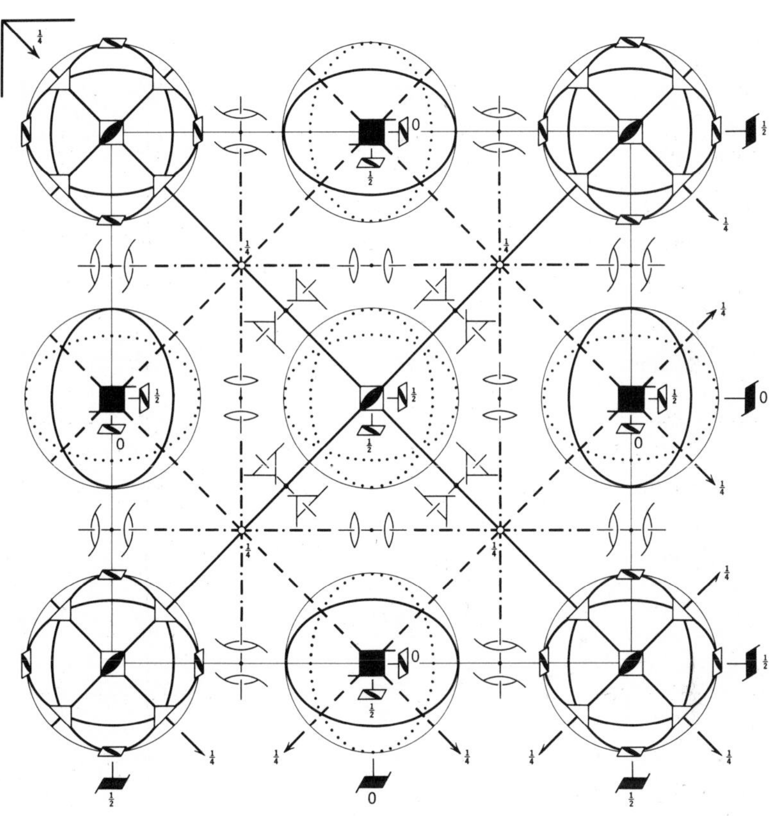

FIG. 190. $P\frac{4_2}{n}\bar{3}\frac{2}{m}$.

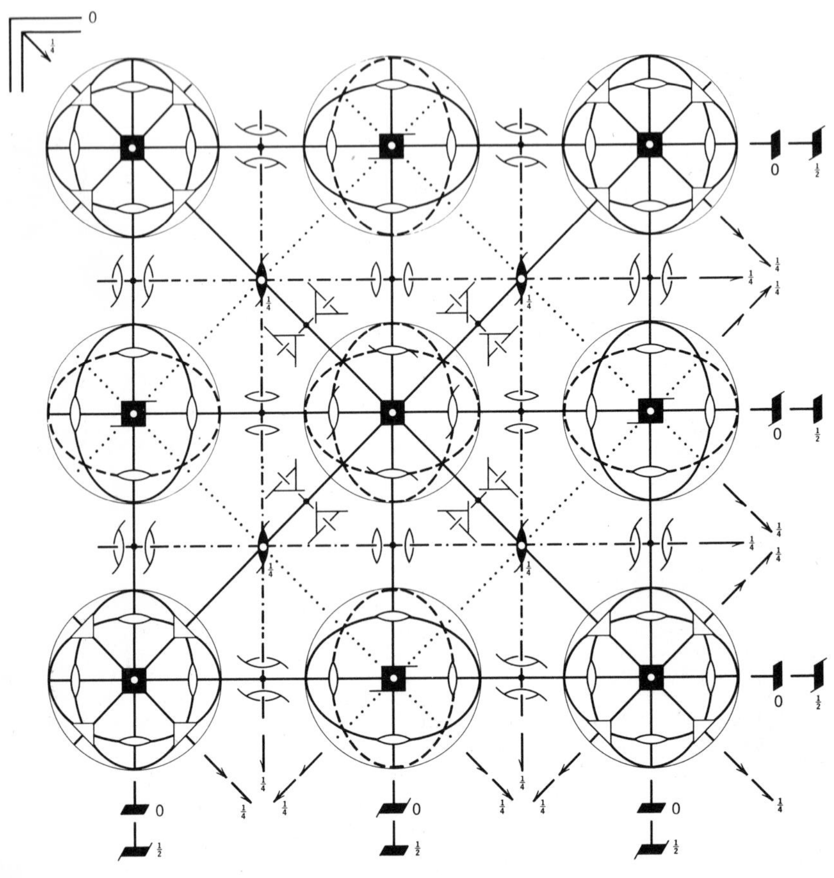

FIG. 191. $I\frac{4}{m}\bar{3}\frac{2}{m}$.

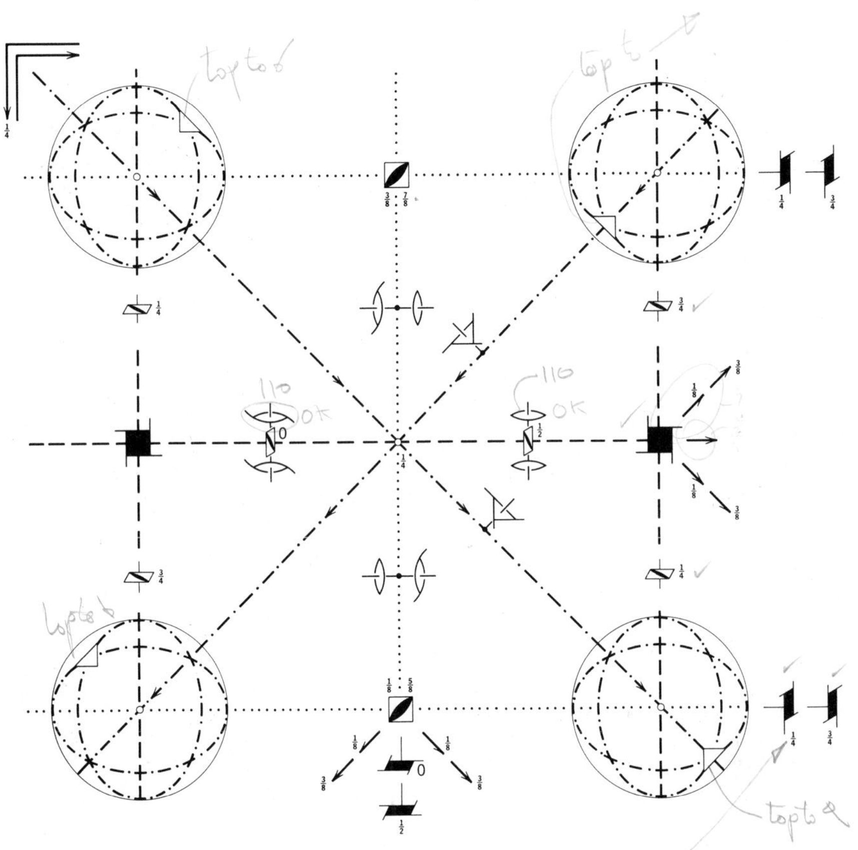

FIG. 192. $I\frac{4_1}{a}\bar{3}\frac{2}{d}$ (one octant of the cell).

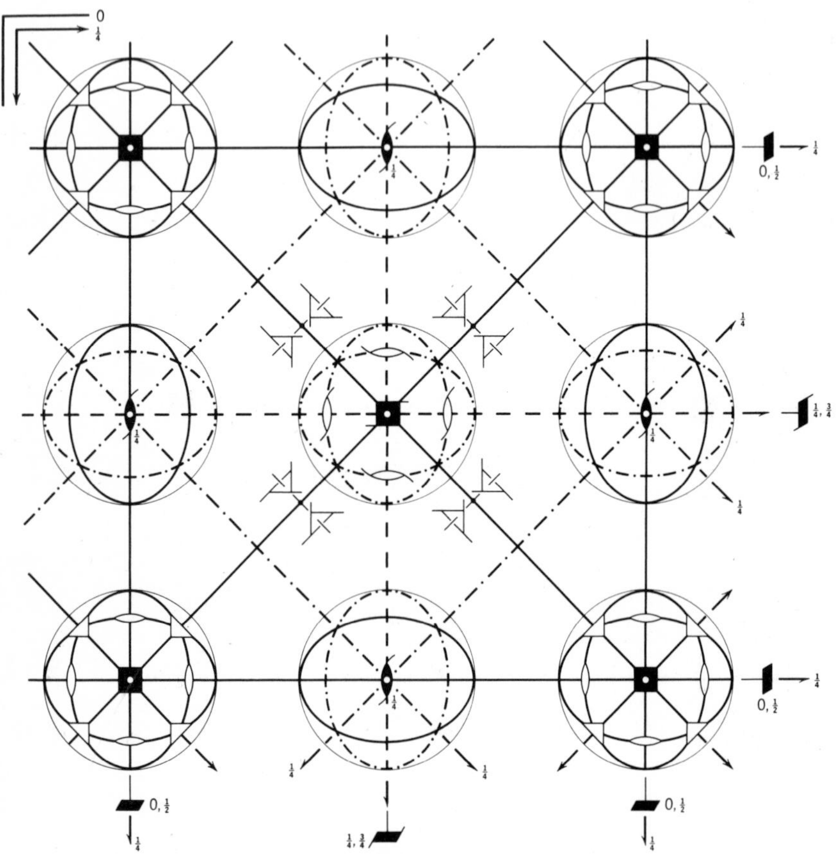

FIG. 193. $F\frac{4}{m}\bar{3}\frac{2}{m}$ (one octant of the cell).

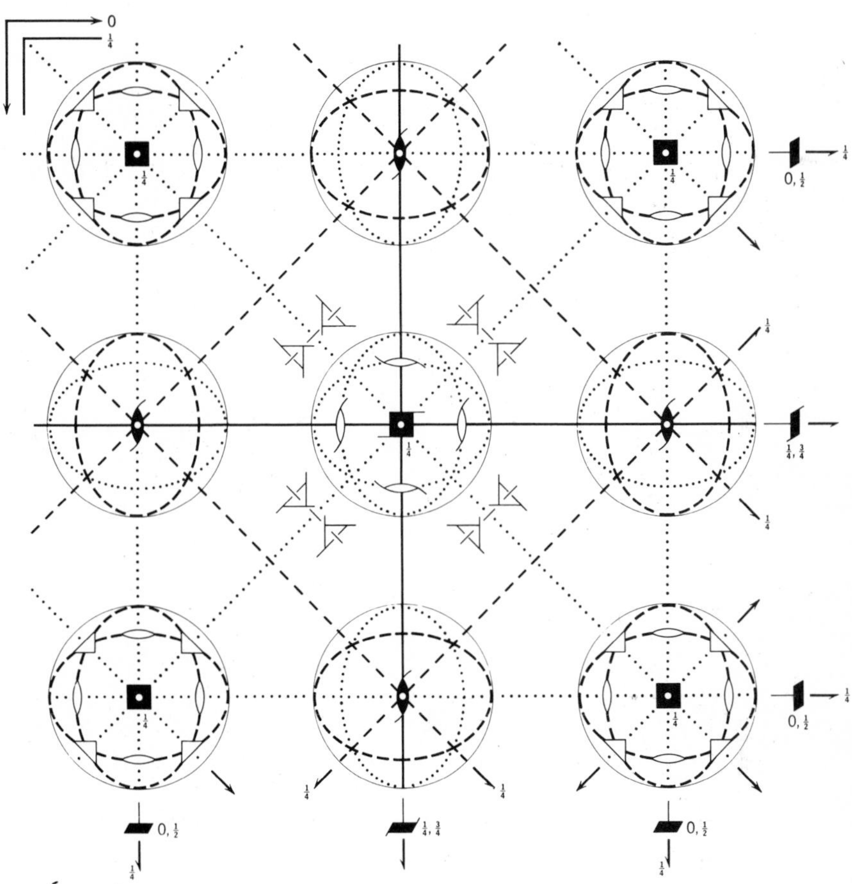

FIG. 194. $F\frac{4}{m}\bar{3}\frac{2}{c}$ (one octant of the cell).

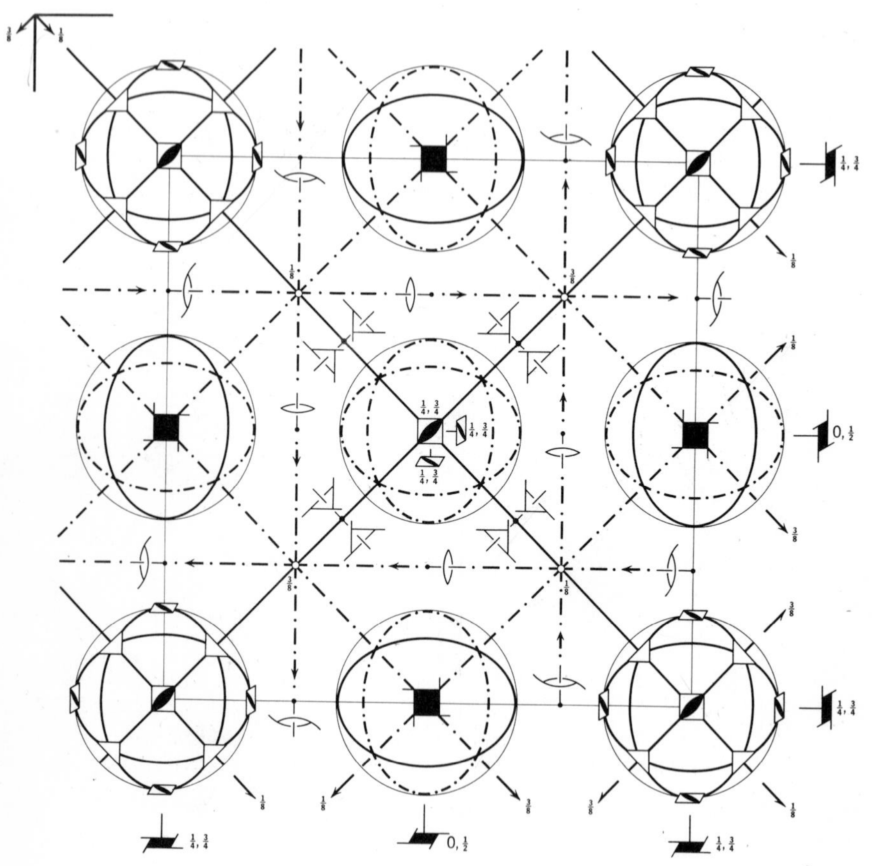

FIG. 195. $F\frac{4_1}{d}\bar{3}\frac{2}{m}$ (one octant of the cell).

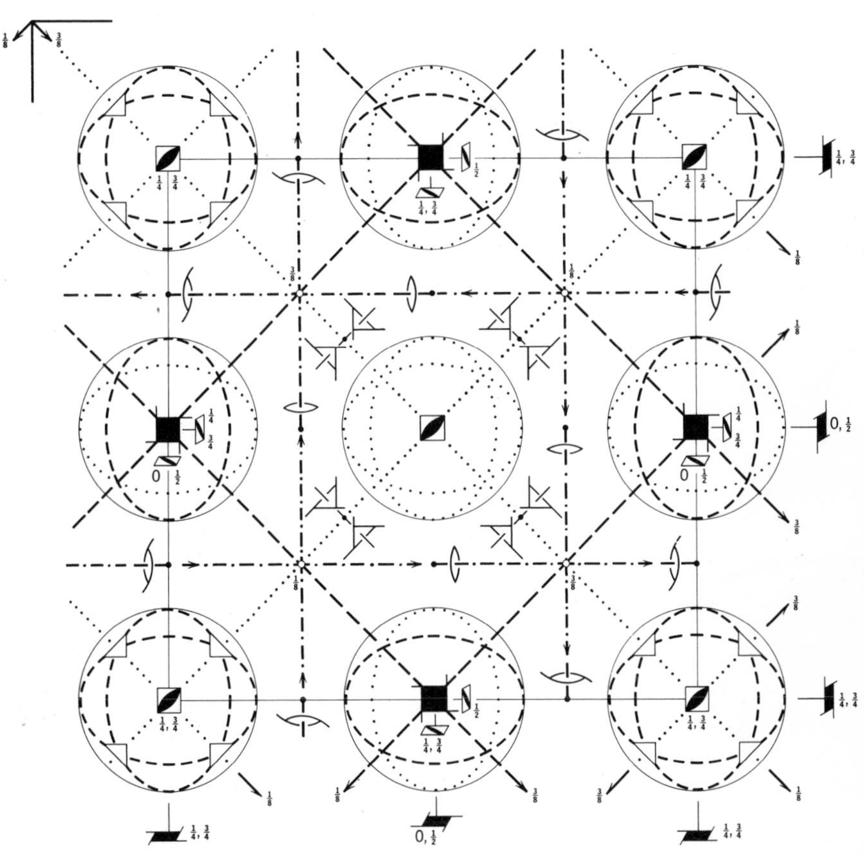

FIG. 196. $F\frac{4_1}{d}\bar{3}\frac{2}{c}$ (one octant of the cell).

17 · Résumé of space groups and their derivation

In the last four chapters the possible space symmetries (commonly called space groups) have been derived. Although the systematic derivation of all these symmetries has not been difficult, it has been a lengthy affair, and it is important that the student look back and see the matter in some perspective. In this chapter the general features of space-group derivation are considered again, and some of the properties of space symmetries are discussed.

A look back at space-group derivation

It is worth while to look back at the derivation of the space symmetries from a somewhat more mature viewpoint. To discover in what ways space may be symmetrical one must first find operations which transform a periodic structure into itself. The most general kind of operation of the first sort which has this property is a screw motion. A requirement of such an operation is that n repetitions of the operation must restore the periodic structure to itself in parallel orientation. This implies that n such operations must rotate the structure to parallel position. The n operations define a screw axis, a special case of which is a pure rotation axis. It turns out that n is limited to 1, 2, 3, 4, or 6. In a similar way the most general operation of the second sort is a combination of an n-fold rotation of the second sort with a translation. Unless n is divisible by 4, the general symmetry element corresponding to this is a glide plane. When n is divisible by 4, the general symmetry element is a 4-fold rotoinversion axis.

The derivation of space groups consists in combining these symmetry elements in all permissible ways with one another. The result is all the specific ways in which periodic structures in space can have symmetry.

Although the combination of symmetry elements can be handled in words, it is convenient to use a shorthand for these words, which may be called the *algebra of operations* (discussed in Chapter 12). By either device, it becomes apparent that the combination of space-group symmetry elements takes place in such a way that it can always be split into two parts. One part comprises the translations, and the other part comprises a set of translation-free rotational operations. The latter are identical with one of the point-group symmetry combinations. Usually several space-group symmetry combinations have the same point-group symmetry component. These several space groups are said to be *isogonal* with this point-group combination, since all the angular relations involved are the same as in that point group.

This has interesting consequences. In the first place it implies that the translation-free residue of any space group is a point group. Phenomenologically, this means that, if the translations are ignored, any space group appears to be a point group. Hence, if the translations are too small to be detected, a space group appears as a point group. As the symmetry of a crystal is examined by megascopic means, then, it is the point group of the crystal that is apparent, not the space group.

The relation between point group and space group has another use. If the simpler point groups are first derived the more complicated space groups can be derived by adding permissible translations to operations of the point group. This was, in fact, the method followed in the previous chapters.

In this book, use was made of the theory of symmetrical space lattice in deriving space groups. This approach need not be adopted, however. For example, in constructing space groups isogonal with crystal class m, one can reason that the symmetry elements consist of some kind of stacks of symmetry planes isogonal with m. The sequence in the stack can be $m, m, \cdots, b, b, \cdots$, or $m, b, \cdots$. It immediately follows that the space-lattice types are P, P, and A, respectively. In other words, the space-lattice type need not be assumed, as it is in this book, but can become a result derived from a permissible combination of isogonal symmetry elements.

All space groups could be derived by the long method of substituting, for each symmetry element in the point group, permissible isogonal symmetry elements in the space group. This straightforward procedure is tedious except for the simplest space groups. Fortunately there are methods for handling symmetry elements in bulk. A specific method of doing this is to develop first all the simplest space groups. A particular simple space group can then be transformed into one (or more) more complex space group (or groups), of which it is known to be a part, by adding a symmetry element that transforms the simple space group into the more complex one. The requirement for this is that the added symmetry element must bring the set of orignal symmetry elements to coincide with itself. This method of finding complex space groups is the chief method used in this book.

Tabulation of the space symmetries

The space symmetries derived in the last four chapters are brought together in a single list in Table 1. The right-hand column of the table indicates where the illustration of the space group may be found. Before discussing some of the matters brought out by the table, some aspects of the space-group symbols are first reviewed.

Table 1. Résumé of the space groups

Crystal system	Crystal class	Space group	Illustration of space group		
			Page	Fig.	Chapter
Triclinic	1	$P1$	210	6	13
	$\bar{1}$	$P\bar{1}$	299	10	16
Monoclinic	2	$P2$	211	8	13
		$P2_1$	211	9	13
		$I2, A2, B2$	212	11	13
	m	Pm	301	11	16
		Pa, Pb, Pn	301	12	16
		Im, Am, Bm	303	13	16
		Ia, Aa, Bb	303	14	16
	$\frac{2}{m}$	$P\frac{2}{m}$	304	15	16
		$P\frac{2}{a}, P\frac{2}{b}, P\frac{2}{n}$	304	16	16
		$P\frac{2_1}{m}$	305	17	16
		$P\frac{2_1}{a}, P\frac{2_1}{b}, P\frac{2_1}{n}$	305	18	16
		$I\frac{2}{m}, A\frac{2}{m}, B\frac{2}{m}$	306	19	16
		$I\frac{2}{a}, A\frac{2}{a}, B\frac{2}{b}$	306	20	16

Table 1 (*continued*)

Crystal system	Crystal class	Space group	Illustration of space group		
			Page	Fig.	Chapter
Ortho-rhombic	222	$P222$	238	5	14
		$P222_1$, $P2_122$, $P22_12$	238	6	14
		$P2_12_12$, $P22_12_1$, $P2_122_1$	239	7	14
		$P2_12_12_1$	239	8	14
		$C222$, $A222$, $B222$	241	10	14
		$C222_1$, $A2_122$, $B22_12$	241	11	14
		$I222$	242	12	14
		$I2_12_12_1$	242	13	14
		$F222$	243	14	14

Table 1 (*continued*)

Crystal system	Crystal class	Space group	Illustration of space group		
			Page	Fig.	Chapter
Ortho-rhombic (cont.)	$mm2$	$Pmm2$, $P2mm$, $Pm2m$	311	21	16
		$Pcc2$, $P2aa$, $Pb2b$	311	22	16
		$Pbm2$, $Pma2$, $P2cm$, $P2mb$, $Pm2a$, $Pc2m$	312	23	16
		$Pnc2$, $Pcn2$, $P2na$, $P2an$, $Pb2n$, $Pn2b$	312	24	16
		$Pba2$, $P2cb$, $Pc2a$	313	25	16
		$Pnn2$, $P2nn$, $Pn2n$	313	26	16
		$Pmc2_1$, $Pcm2_1$, $P2_1ma$, $P2_1am$, $Pb2_1m$, $Pm2_1b$	314	27	16
		$Pbc2_1$, $Pca2_1$, $P2_1ca$, $P2_1ab$, $Pb2_1a$, $Pc2_1b$	314	28	16
		$Pnm2_1$, $Pmn2_1$, $P2_1nm$, $P2_1mn$, $Pm2_1n$, $Pn2_1m$	315	29	16
		$Pbn2_1$, $Pna2_1$, $P2_1cn$, $P2_1nb$, $Pn2_1a$, $Pc2_1n$	315	30	16
		$Imm2$, $I2mm$, $Im2m$	316	32	16
		$Iba2$, $I2cb$, $Ic2a$	318	33	16
		$Ibm2$, $Ima2$, $I2cm$, $I2mb$, $Im2a$, $Ic2m$	318	34	16
		$Cmm2$, $A2mm$, $Bm2m$	320	37	16
		$Ccc2$, $A2aa$, $Bb2b$	320	38	16
		$Cmc2_1$, $Ccm2_1$, $A2_1ma$, $A2_1am$, $Bb2_1m$, $Bm2_1b$	321	39	16
		$Amm2$, $Bmm2$, $B2mm$, $C2mm$, $Cm2m$, $Am2m$	324	41	16
		$Abm2$, $Bma2$, $B2cm$, $C2mb$, $Cm2a$, $Ac2m$	324	42	16
		$Ama2$, $Bbm2$, $B2mb$, $C2cm$, $Cc2m$, $Am2a$	325	43	16
		$Aba2$, $Bba2$, $B2cb$, $C2cb$, $Cc2a$, $Ac2a$	325	44	16
		$Fmm2$, $F2mm$, $Fm2m$	328	46	16
		$Fdd2$, $F2dd$, $Fd2d$	328	47	16

Table 1 (*continued*)

Crystal system	Crystal class	Space group	Illustration of space group		
			Page	Fig.	Chapter
Orthorhombic (cont.)	$\frac{2}{m}\frac{2}{m}\frac{2}{m}$	$P\frac{2}{m}\frac{2}{m}\frac{2}{m}$	332	49	16
		$P\frac{2}{n}\frac{2}{n}\frac{2}{n}$	332	50	16
		$P\frac{2}{c}\frac{2}{c}\frac{2}{m}$, $P\frac{2}{b}\frac{2}{m}\frac{2}{b}$, $P\frac{2}{m}\frac{2}{a}\frac{2}{a}$	333	51	16
		$P\frac{2}{b}\frac{2}{a}\frac{2}{n}$, $P\frac{2}{c}\frac{2}{n}\frac{2}{a}$, $P\frac{2}{n}\frac{2}{c}\frac{2}{b}$	333	52	16
		$P\frac{2}{m}\frac{2}{c}\frac{2_1}{m}$, $P\frac{2}{c}\frac{2}{m}\frac{2_1}{m}$, $P\frac{2_1}{m}\frac{2}{m}\frac{2}{a}$, $P\frac{2_1}{m}\frac{2}{a}\frac{2}{m}$, $P\frac{2}{b}\frac{2_1}{m}\frac{2}{m}$, $P\frac{2}{m}\frac{2_1}{m}\frac{2}{b}$	334	54	16
		$P\frac{2}{n}\frac{2}{a}\frac{2_1}{n}$, $P\frac{2}{b}\frac{2}{n}\frac{2_1}{n}$, $P\frac{2_1}{n}\frac{2}{n}\frac{2}{b}$, $P\frac{2_1}{n}\frac{2}{c}\frac{2}{n}$, $P\frac{2}{c}\frac{2_1}{n}\frac{2}{n}$, $P\frac{2}{n}\frac{2_1}{n}\frac{2}{a}$	335	55	16
		$P\frac{2}{m}\frac{2}{n}\frac{2_1}{a}$, $P\frac{2}{n}\frac{2}{m}\frac{2_1}{b}$, $P\frac{2_1}{b}\frac{2}{m}\frac{2}{n}$, $P\frac{2_1}{c}\frac{2}{n}\frac{2}{m}$, $P\frac{2}{n}\frac{2_1}{c}\frac{2}{m}$, $P\frac{2}{m}\frac{2_1}{a}\frac{2}{n}$	335	56	16
		$P\frac{2}{b}\frac{2}{c}\frac{2_1}{b}$, $P\frac{2}{c}\frac{2}{a}\frac{2_1}{a}$, $P\frac{2_1}{c}\frac{2}{c}\frac{2}{a}$, $P\frac{2_1}{b}\frac{2}{a}\frac{2}{b}$, $P\frac{2}{b}\frac{2_1}{a}\frac{2}{a}$, $P\frac{2}{c}\frac{2_1}{c}\frac{2}{b}$	336	57	16
		$P\frac{2_1}{b}\frac{2_1}{a}\frac{2}{m}$, $P\frac{2}{m}\frac{2_1}{c}\frac{2_1}{b}$, $P\frac{2_1}{c}\frac{2}{m}\frac{2_1}{a}$	337	59	16
		$P\frac{2_1}{c}\frac{2_1}{c}\frac{2}{n}$, $P\frac{2}{n}\frac{2_1}{a}\frac{2_1}{a}$, $P\frac{2_1}{b}\frac{2}{n}\frac{2_1}{b}$	337	60	16
		$P\frac{2_1}{b}\frac{2_1}{m}\frac{2}{a}$, $P\frac{2_1}{m}\frac{2_1}{a}\frac{2}{b}$, $P\frac{2}{b}\frac{2_1}{c}\frac{2_1}{m}$, $P\frac{2}{c}\frac{2_1}{m}\frac{2_1}{b}$, $P\frac{2_1}{m}\frac{2}{c}\frac{2_1}{a}$, $P\frac{2_1}{c}\frac{2}{a}\frac{2_1}{m}$	338	61	16
		$P\frac{2_1}{n}\frac{2_1}{n}\frac{2}{m}$, $P\frac{2}{m}\frac{2_1}{n}\frac{2_1}{n}$, $P\frac{2_1}{n}\frac{2}{m}\frac{2_1}{n}$	338	62	16
		$P\frac{2_1}{m}\frac{2_1}{m}\frac{2}{n}$, $P\frac{2}{n}\frac{2_1}{m}\frac{2_1}{m}$, $P\frac{2_1}{m}\frac{2}{n}\frac{2_1}{m}$	339	63	16
		$P\frac{2_1}{n}\frac{2_1}{c}\frac{2}{a}$, $P\frac{2_1}{c}\frac{2_1}{n}\frac{2}{b}$, $P\frac{2}{b}\frac{2_1}{n}\frac{2_1}{a}$, $P\frac{2}{c}\frac{2_1}{a}\frac{2_1}{n}$, $P\frac{2_1}{b}\frac{2}{c}\frac{2_1}{n}$, $P\frac{2_1}{n}\frac{2}{a}\frac{2_1}{b}$	339	64	16
		$P\frac{2_1}{b}\frac{2_1}{c}\frac{2_1}{a}$, $P\frac{2_1}{c}\frac{2_1}{a}\frac{2_1}{b}$	341	66	16
		$P\frac{2_1}{n}\frac{2_1}{m}\frac{2_1}{a}$, $P\frac{2_1}{m}\frac{2_1}{n}\frac{2_1}{b}$, $P\frac{2_1}{b}\frac{2_1}{n}\frac{2_1}{m}$, $P\frac{2_1}{c}\frac{2_1}{m}\frac{2_1}{n}$, $P\frac{2_1}{m}\frac{2_1}{c}\frac{2_1}{n}$, $P\frac{2_1}{n}\frac{2_1}{a}\frac{2_1}{m}$	342	67	16

Table 1 (*continued*)

Crystal system	Crystal class	Space group	Illustration of space group		
			Page	Fig.	Chapter
Ortho-rhombic (cont.)	$\frac{2}{m}\frac{2}{m}\frac{2}{m}$ (cont.)	$I\frac{2}{m}\frac{2}{m}\frac{2}{m}$	343	69	16
		$I\frac{2}{b}\frac{2}{a}\frac{2}{m}$, $I\frac{2}{m}\frac{2}{c}\frac{2}{b}$, $I\frac{2}{c}\frac{2}{m}\frac{2}{a}$	343	70	16
		$I\frac{2_1}{b}\frac{2_1}{c}\frac{2_1}{a}$, $I\frac{2_1}{c}\frac{2_1}{a}\frac{2_1}{b}$	344	72	16
		$I\frac{2_1}{m}\frac{2_1}{m}\frac{2_1}{a}$, $I\frac{2_1}{b}\frac{2_1}{m}\frac{2_1}{m}$, $I\frac{2_1}{m}\frac{2_1}{c}\frac{2_1}{m}$	345	73	16
		$C\frac{2}{m}\frac{2}{m}\frac{2}{m}$, $A\frac{2}{m}\frac{2}{m}\frac{2}{m}$, $B\frac{2}{m}\frac{2}{m}\frac{2}{m}$	346	75	16
		$C\frac{2}{c}\frac{2}{c}\frac{2}{m}$, $A\frac{2}{m}\frac{2}{a}\frac{2}{a}$, $B\frac{2}{b}\frac{2}{m}\frac{2}{b}$	346	76	16
		$C\frac{2}{m}\frac{2}{m}\frac{2}{a}$, $C\frac{2}{m}\frac{2}{m}\frac{2}{b}$, $A\frac{2}{b}\frac{2}{m}\frac{2}{m}$, $A\frac{2}{c}\frac{2}{m}\frac{2}{m}$, $B\frac{2}{m}\frac{2}{c}\frac{2}{m}$, $B\frac{2}{m}\frac{2}{a}\frac{2}{m}$	347	77	16
		$C\frac{2}{c}\frac{2}{c}\frac{2}{a}$, $C\frac{2}{c}\frac{2}{c}\frac{2}{b}$, $A\frac{2}{b}\frac{2}{a}\frac{2}{a}$, $A\frac{2}{c}\frac{2}{a}\frac{2}{a}$, $B\frac{2}{b}\frac{2}{c}\frac{2}{b}$, $B\frac{2}{b}\frac{2}{a}\frac{2}{b}$	347	78	16
		$C\frac{2}{m}\frac{2}{c}\frac{2_1}{m}$, $C\frac{2}{c}\frac{2}{m}\frac{2_1}{m}$, $A\frac{2_1}{m}\frac{2}{m}\frac{2}{a}$, $A\frac{2_1}{m}\frac{2}{a}\frac{2}{m}$, $B\frac{2}{b}\frac{2_1}{m}\frac{2}{m}$, $B\frac{2}{m}\frac{2_1}{m}\frac{2}{b}$	348	80	16
		$C\frac{2}{m}\frac{2}{c}\frac{2_1}{a}$, $C\frac{2}{c}\frac{2}{m}\frac{2_1}{b}$, $A\frac{2_1}{b}\frac{2}{m}\frac{2}{a}$, $A\frac{2_1}{c}\frac{2}{a}\frac{2}{m}$, $B\frac{2}{b}\frac{2_1}{c}\frac{2}{m}$, $B\frac{2}{m}\frac{2_1}{a}\frac{2}{b}$	349	81	16
		$F\frac{2}{m}\frac{2}{m}\frac{2}{m}$	350	83	16
		$F\frac{2}{d}\frac{2}{d}\frac{2}{d}$	352	84	16

Table 1 (*continued*)

Crystal system	Crystal class	Space group	Illustration of space group		
			Page	Fig.	Chapter
Tetragonal	4	*P*4	220	19	13
		{ $P4_1$	220	20	13
		{ $P4_3$	221	21	13
		$P4_2$	221	22	13
		*I*4	223	24	13
		$I4_1$	223	25	13
	422	*P*422	253	30	14
		{ $P4_122$	254	31	14
		{ $P4_322$	255	32	14
		$P4_222$	256	33	14
		$P42_12$	258	35	14
		{ $P4_12_12$	259	36	14
		{ $P4_32_12$	260	37	14
		$P4_22_12$	261	38	14
		*I*422	263	40	14
		$I4_122$	264	41	14
	$\bar{4}$	$P\bar{4}$	353	86	16
		$I\bar{4}$	355	88	16

Table 1 (*continued*)

Crystal system	Crystal class	Space group	Illustration of space group		
			Page	Fig.	Chapter
Tetragonal (cont.)	$\frac{4}{m}$	$P\frac{4}{m}$	356	89	16
		$P\frac{4}{n}$	356	90	16
		$P\frac{4_2}{m}$	357	91	16
		$P\frac{4_2}{n}$	357	92	16
		$I\frac{4}{m}$	359	93	16
		$I\frac{4_1}{a}$	359	94	16
	$4mm$	$P4mm$	360	95	16
		$P4cc$	360	96	16
		$P4bm$	361	97	16
		$P4nc$	361	98	16
		$P4_2mc$	362	99	16
		$P4_2cm$	362	100	16
		$P4_2bc$	363	101	16
		$P4_2nm$	363	102	16
		$I4mm$	364	103	16
		$I4cm$	364	104	16
		$I4_1md$	365	105	16
		$I4_1cd$	365	106	16

Table 1 (*continued*)

Crystal system	Crystal class	Space group	Illustration of space group		
			Page	Fig.	Chapter
Tetragonal (cont.)	$\bar{4}2m$	$P\bar{4}2m$	372	107	16
		$P\bar{4}2c$	372	108	16
		$P\bar{4}2_1m$	373	109	16
		$P\bar{4}2_1c$	373	110	16
		$P\bar{4}m2$	374	111	16
		$P\bar{4}c2$	374	112	16
		$P\bar{4}b2$	375	113	16
		$P\bar{4}n2$	375	114	16
		$I\bar{4}2m$	376	115	16
		$I\bar{4}2d$	376	116	16
		$I\bar{4}m2$	377	117	16
		$I\bar{4}c2$	377	118	16
	$\frac{4}{m}\frac{2}{m}\frac{2}{m}$	$P\frac{4}{m}\frac{2}{m}\frac{2}{m}$	380	123	16
		$P\frac{4}{m}\frac{2}{c}\frac{2}{c}$	380	124	16
		$P\frac{4}{n}\frac{2}{b}\frac{2}{m}$	381	125	16
		$P\frac{4}{n}\frac{2}{n}\frac{2}{c}$	381	126	16
		$P\frac{4}{m}\frac{2_1}{b}\frac{2}{m}$	382	127	16
		$P\frac{4}{m}\frac{2_1}{n}\frac{2}{c}$	382	128	16

Table 1 (*continued*)

Crystal system	Crystal class	Space group	Illustration of space group		
			Page	Fig.	Chapter
Tetragonal (cont.)	$\frac{4}{m}\frac{2}{m}\frac{2}{m}$ (cont.)	$P\frac{4}{n}\frac{2_1}{m}\frac{2}{m}$	383	129	16
		$P\frac{4}{n}\frac{2_1}{c}\frac{2}{c}$	383	130	16
		$P\frac{4_2}{m}\frac{2}{m}\frac{2}{c}$	384	131	16
		$P\frac{4_2}{m}\frac{2}{c}\frac{2}{m}$	384	132	16
		$P\frac{4_2}{n}\frac{2}{b}\frac{2}{c}$	385	133	16
		$P\frac{4_2}{n}\frac{2}{n}\frac{2}{m}$	385	134	16
		$P\frac{4_2}{m}\frac{2_1}{b}\frac{2}{c}$	386	135	16
		$P\frac{4_2}{m}\frac{2_1}{n}\frac{2}{m}$	386	136	16
		$P\frac{4_2}{n}\frac{2_1}{m}\frac{2}{c}$	387	137	16
		$P\frac{4_2}{n}\frac{2_1}{c}\frac{2}{m}$	387	138	16
		$I\frac{4}{m}\frac{2}{m}\frac{2}{m}$	390	140	16
		$I\frac{4}{m}\frac{2}{c}\frac{2}{m}$	391	141	16
		$I\frac{4_1}{a}\frac{2}{m}\frac{2}{d}$	392	143	16
		$I\frac{4_1}{a}\frac{2}{c}\frac{2}{d}$	393	144	16

Table 1 (*continued*)

Crystal system	Crystal class	Space group	Illustration of space group		
			Page	Fig.	Chapter
Hexagonal	3	$P3$	214	13	13
		$P3_1$	215	14	13
		$P3_2$	215	15	13
		$R3$	217	17	13
	32	$P321$	246	18	14
		$P3_121$	247	19	14
		$P3_221$	247	20	14
		$P312$	248	22	14
		$P3_112$	249	23	14
		$P3_212$	249	24	14
		$R32$	251	26	14
	$\bar{3}$	$P\bar{3}$	395	145	16
		$R\bar{3}$	395	146	16
	$3m$	$P3m1$	396	147	16
		$P31m$	396	148	16
		$P3c1$	397	149	16
		$P31c$	397	150	16
		$R3m$	400	151	16
		$R3c$	401	152	16

Table 1 (*continued*)

Crystal system	Crystal class	Space group	Illustration of space group		
			Page	Fig.	Chapter
Hexagonal (cont.)	$\bar{3}\frac{2}{m}$	$P\bar{3}\frac{2}{m}1$	402	153	16
		$P\bar{3}1\frac{2}{m}$	402	154	16
		$P\bar{3}\frac{2}{c}1$	403	155	16
		$P\bar{3}1\frac{2}{c}$	403	156	16
		$R\bar{3}\frac{2}{m}$	404	157	16
		$R\bar{3}\frac{2}{c}$	405	158	16
	6	$P6$	226	27	13
		{ $P6_1$	226	28	13
		{ $P6_5$	227	29	13
		{ $P6_2$	227	30	13
		{ $P6_4$	228	31	13
		$P6_3$	228	32	13
	622	$P622$	226	44	14
		{ $P6_122$	267	46	14
		{ $P6_522$	267	47	14
		{ $P6_222$	268	48	14
		{ $P6_422$	268	49	14
		$P6_322$	266	45	14

Table 1 *(continued)*

Crystal system	Crystal class	Space group	Illustration of space group: Page	Fig.	Chapter
Hexagonal (cont.)	$\frac{6}{m}$	$P\frac{6}{m}$	409	164	16
		$P\frac{6_3}{m}$	409	165	16
	$6mm$	$P6mm$	410	166	16
		$P6cc$	410	167	16
		$P6_3mc$	411	168	16
		$P6_3cm$	411	169	16
	$\bar{6} = \frac{3}{m}$	$P\bar{6}$ $(= P\frac{3}{m})$	406	159	16
	$\bar{6}m2 = \frac{3}{m}m2$	$P\bar{6}m2$ $(= P\frac{3}{m}m2)$	406	160	16
		$P\bar{6}c2$ $(= P\frac{3}{m}c2)$	407	161	16
		$P\bar{6}2m$ $(= P\frac{3}{m}2m)$	407	162	16
		$P\bar{6}2c$ $(= P\frac{3}{m}2c)$	408	163	16
	$\frac{6}{m}\frac{2}{m}\frac{2}{m}$	$P\frac{6}{m}\frac{2}{m}\frac{2}{m}$	412	170	16
		$P\frac{6}{m}\frac{2}{c}\frac{2}{c}$	412	171	16
		$P\frac{6_3}{m}\frac{2}{m}\frac{2}{c}$	413	172	16
		$P\frac{6_3}{m}\frac{2}{c}\frac{2}{m}$	413	173	16

Table 1 (*continued*)

Crystal system	Crystal class	Space group	Illustration of space group		
			Page	Fig.	Chapter
Iso-metric	23	$P23$	274	10	15
		$P2_13$	274	11	15
		$I23$	275	12	15
		$I2_13$	275	13	15
		$F23$	276	14	15
	432	$P432$	280	24	15
		$P4_132$	287	32	15
		$P4_332$	287	33	15
		$P4_232$	284	28	15
		$I432$	281	25	15
		$I4_132$	288	34	15
		$F432$	282	26	15
		$F4_132$	285	29	15
	$\frac{2}{m}\bar{3}$	$P\frac{2}{m}\bar{3}$	422	180	16
		$P\frac{2}{n}\bar{3}$	423	181	16
		$P\frac{2_1}{a}\bar{3}$	424	182	16
		$I\frac{2}{m}\bar{3}$	425	183	16
		$I\frac{2_1}{a}\bar{3}$	426	184	16
		$F\frac{2}{m}\bar{3}$	427	185	16
		$F\frac{2}{d}\bar{3}$	428	186	16

Table 1 (*continued*)

Crystal system	Crystal class	Space group	Illustration of space group		
			Page	Fig.	Chapter
Iso-metric (cont.)	$\bar{4}3m$	$P\bar{4}3m$	414	174	16
		$P\bar{4}3n$	415	175	16
		$I\bar{4}3m$	416	176	16
		$I\bar{4}3d$	417	177	16
		$F\bar{4}3m$	418	178	16
		$F\bar{4}3c$	419	179	16
	$\frac{4}{m}\bar{3}\frac{2}{m}$	$P\frac{4}{m}\bar{3}\frac{2}{m}$	430	187	16
		$P\frac{4}{n}\bar{3}\frac{2}{n}$	431	188	16
		$P\frac{4_2}{m}\bar{3}\frac{2}{n}$	432	189	16
		$P\frac{4_2}{n}\bar{3}\frac{2}{m}$	433	190	16
		$I\frac{4}{m}\bar{3}\frac{2}{m}$	434	191	16
		$I\frac{4_1}{a}\bar{3}\frac{2}{d}$	435	192	16
		$F\frac{4}{m}\bar{3}\frac{2}{m}$	436	193	16
		$F\frac{4}{m}\bar{3}\frac{2}{c}$	437	194	16
		$F\frac{4_1}{d}\bar{3}\frac{2}{m}$	438	195	16
		$F\frac{4_1}{d}\bar{3}\frac{2}{c}$	439	196	16

Symbols for the various symmetries. A particular space symmetry can sometimes be expressed by alternative symbols. The alternative possibilities arise through three different causes. The first cause resembles a change of origin. Thus, in Chapter 13 it was shown that if I is combined with 2 the same space group results as when I is combined with 2_1. If the origin is regarded as a lattice point, and if 2 is placed at a lattice point, then 2_1 axes arise at $\frac{1}{4}\frac{1}{4}0$, and vice versa. Therefore $I2 = I2_1$. In such instances an arbitrary choice must be made between symbols with identical meanings. Usually the simplest or most symmetrical symbol is chosen, in this case $I2$. To this extent the symbols are somewhat arbitrary.

A somewhat similar situation occurs with respect to symbolizing the glide planes associated with certain multiple cells. Thus, the combinations Ia and Ib are identical. This is because, with lattice I, if a glide plane with translation component $a/2$ is placed at level zero, another glide plane occurs halfway along the centering translation $\vec{a}/2 + \vec{b}/2 + \vec{c}/2$. This glide plane, which occurs at level $c/4$, has translation components $a/2 + a/2 + b/2 = a + b/2 \simeq b/2$. A reciprocal relation is discovered if a glide plane with translation component $b/2$ is placed at level zero. Therefore $Ia = Ib$, the relation resembling a change of origin. In all such instances Table 1 shows only one of the several possible symbols.

A different type of alternative symbol arises as a result of choice of cell. It was shown in Chapter 16 (p. 300) that if, as in monoclinic cells, symmetry does not fix the choice of cell, a glide plane can have its translation component in the direction of any translation parallel to the glide plane. These directions include the two cell edges and the cell diagonal. These three arrangements have the same symmetry. Consequently Pa, Pb, and Pn are regarded as the same space group. In Table 1, this is indicated by entering all three possibilities as a single space group separated by commas. Given any specific crystal with its lattice defined by the structure, different primitive cells could be chosen to describe the lattice. The possible choices cause the glide to be parallel to a cell edge (which could be labeled either a or b) or to a cell diagonal. With these three permissible choices of cell, the space group would be labeled Pa, Pb, or Pn, respectively. But it is usual to select a reduced cell; this means that a and b are the shortest translations in the plane. Furthermore, according to convention, the two edges are selected so that $a < b$. Thus, for a particular crystal when the cell is selected according to rules based upon cell dimensions, the crystal is automatically placed in one of the categories Pa, Pb, or Pn. *But without the conventions of cell choice all these amount to merely* Pg, where g is a glide plane. In this case, then, these alternative symbols serve to reveal the relation between glide direction and cell edges chosen.

In the third place, certain sets of space-group symbols are the same by an interchange of X, Y, and Z reference axes. The simplest example of this occurs in crystal class $mm2 \Leftrightarrow \bar{2}\bar{2}2$. In this class the axis 2 is unique and may be chosen as the crystallographic c axis. But the two $\bar{2}$ axes, which, in general, correspond to different perpendicular glide planes in the space symmetries, can be perpendicular to either a or b. As a consequence, when these glides are not the same, two different symbols result, depending on which is placed perpendicular to a. In this manner the space-group symbol may vary, depending on which of the axes of the space group are a, b, and c. There are six possible symbols for the general case in the orthorhombic system. (In some instances these six degenerate to three symbols or to one symbol.) All possible symbols for a particular space group are listed on a single line in Table 1. The first symbol is the one as derived in the text; the remaining symbols are found by placing the Z axis (as derived) first in the a direction, and then in the b direction, and in each instance taking the two possible permutations of the other two labels.

If the labels of the axes of a particular crystal are chosen according to some convention based upon their relative lengths, then the space group may turn out to be designated by any one of the several symbols on the same line. On the other hand, in class $mm2$ it is possible to adopt the convention that, since the axis 2 is unique, it may be accepted as the c axis. If this is done the last four symbols in a line of six (or the last two in a line of three) may be disregarded.

Another, alternative convention that reduces the number of possible symbols is always to orient a crystal based upon an end-centered lattice so that the lattice symbol is C. With this convention, there are only two alternative symbols for a space group based upon an end-centered lattice.

The total number of space symmetries and their distribution. In Table 2, the number of space groups in each crystal class and in each crystal system is noted. The total number of possible space symmetries is seen to be 230. These are distributed in an interesting way. The least symmetrical crystal systems and crystal classes contain the fewest space groups. The crystal systems and crystal classes of intermediate symmetry content contain the greatest number of space groups. The tetragonal system contains more space groups than any other, and the orthorhombic class $2/m\ 2/m\ 2/m$ contains more space groups than any other class. Only a moderate number of space groups belong to the most symmetrical crystal system, the isometric.

The enantiomorphic pairs. Table 1 shows 11 pairs of space groups connected by braces. These are the enantiomorphic pairs. Such pairs can occur only in the classes lacking operations of the second sort, that is, in the axial classes. Furthermore, the possibility of enantiomorphous pairs requires at least one axis of the space group to be nonneutral. Since only axes for which $n > 2$ can be nonneutral, such space groups cannot belong to the triclinic, monoclinic, or orthorhombic systems, but are found only in the tetragonal, hexagonal, and isometric systems.

Table 2. Distribution of the space symmetries

Crystal system		Crystal class	Number of space groups in crystal class		Number of space groups in crystal system
Triclinic		1	1		2
		$\bar{1}$	1		
Monoclinic		2	3		13
		m	4		
		$\frac{2}{m}$	6		
Orthorhombic		222	9		59
		$mm2$	22		
		$\frac{2}{m}\frac{2}{m}\frac{2}{m}$	28		
Tetragonal		4	6		68
		422	10		
		$\bar{4}$	2		
		$\frac{4}{m}$	6		
		$4mm$	12		
		$\bar{4}2m$	12		
		$\frac{4}{m}\frac{2}{m}\frac{2}{m}$	20		
Hexagonal	3-fold symmetry	3	4	25	52
		32	7		
		$\bar{3}$	2		
		$3m$	6		
		$3\frac{2}{m}$	6		
	6-fold symmetry	6	6	27	
		622	6		
		$\frac{6}{m}$	2		
		$6mm$	4		
		$\bar{6} = \frac{3}{m}$	1		
		$\bar{6}m2 = \frac{3}{m}m2$	4		
		$\frac{6}{m}\frac{2}{m}\frac{2}{m}$	4		

Table 2 (*continued*)

Crystal system	Crystal class	Number of space groups in crystal class	Number of space groups in crystal system
Isometric	23	5	36
	432	8	
	$\frac{2}{m}\bar{3}$	7	
	$\bar{4}3m$	6	
	$\frac{4}{m}\bar{3}\frac{2}{m}$	10	
		230	230

The enantiomorphic space groups are peculiar in that the members of a pair are not distinguishable from one another by any known means. It will be seen in Chapter 19 that all other space groups are distinguishable.

18 · Equivalent positions in space groups

In discussing crystal forms in Chapter 10 it was shown that, if the normal to a face occupies certain special positions, the number of faces in the form degenerates to a submultiple of the number of faces in the general form. A corresponding situation exists with regard to the location of points in a space group. The theory of this degeneracy is useful in finding the location of atoms in crystals.

Sets of equivalent positions

If a point is placed among the symmetry elements of a space group, each of the symmetry operations can be regarded as repeating this point to another point. The resulting set of points conforms to the symmetry of the space group. Such a set of points is known as a set of *equivalent positions.* A set of equivalent positions can be defined as the set of all points equivalent by the space-group symmetry to a given point.

The number of operations in a space group is infinite. The number of operations per unit cell, however, is a small, finite number. Since each point of the set of equivalent positions can be regarded as a repetition of a representative point by a particular one of the operations of the space group, the number of equivalent positions per cell is also a small, finite number, called the *rank of the equipoint.* (Temporarily, the word "equipoint can be regarded as a short expression for "the set of equivalent positions in a cell." An added meaning will be given shortly.) In crystal structures, the number of atoms per cell is controlled by this equipoint rank.

Space group *Pmm*2. Figure 1 shows the space group *Pmm*2. The operations of this space group may be listed as the identical operation, the lattice translations, a reflection in m_1, a reflection in m_2, and a rotation of π about A. Let these operations be called 1, Γ, m_1, m_2, and A_π, respectively.

Suppose that the origin is taken at the center of the cell on the 2-fold axis. Let an arbitrary point P having general coordinates xyz be placed in the cell. Then the operations of the cell are those of the space group other than the lattice translations, namely 1, m_1, m_2, and A_π. These operations repeat the point at xyz, namely P_{xyz}, as follows:

$$\begin{aligned} P_{xyz} \cdot 1 &= P_{xyz}, \\ P_{xyz} \cdot m_1 &= P_{\bar{x}yz}, \\ P_{xyz} \cdot A_\pi &= P_{\bar{x}\bar{y}z}, \\ P_{xyz} \cdot m_2 &= P_{x\bar{y}z}. \end{aligned} \tag{1}$$

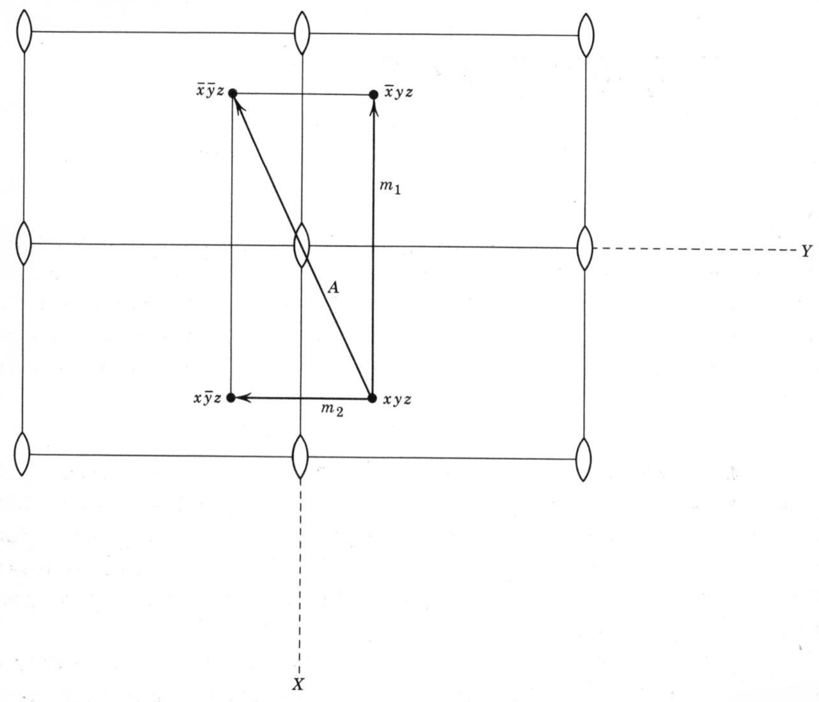

FIG. 1. Space group *Pmm*2, showing the repetition of a point at xyz by the operations in the cell.

The set of points at the right of (1) constitutes that portion of the set of equivalent positions of space group *Pmm*2 which is contained within the cell. The further operations of the space group not considered in (1), namely the lattice translations, Γ, repeat the set of points on the right of (1) to form a pattern extending infinitely in three dimensions. In a strict sense this larger set of points constitutes the equivalent set. For convenience, however, the limited set of points within the cell—those on the right of (1)—are usually referred to as the set of equivalent positions of the space group. In particular, the set of points at the right of (1) constitutes an equivalent set of points of the space group *Pmm*2.

Point P_{xyz} was chosen as a representative point, but any of the points on the right of (1) could be chosen as a representative point. Whichever one is chosen, the same set of points results from the operations of the space group.

Space group *P*4. Figure 2 shows a second example of a set of equivalent positions, namely those of the space group *P*4. The operations of this space group consist of the identical operation, the lattice translations, and the powers of the rotation of $\pi/2$ about *A*. Let these operations be called 1, Γ, $A_{\pi/2}$, $A^2_{\pi/2}$, and $A^3_{\pi/2}$. The operations per cell are 1, $A_{\pi/2}$, $A^2_{\pi/2}$, and $A^3_{\pi/2}$. Each

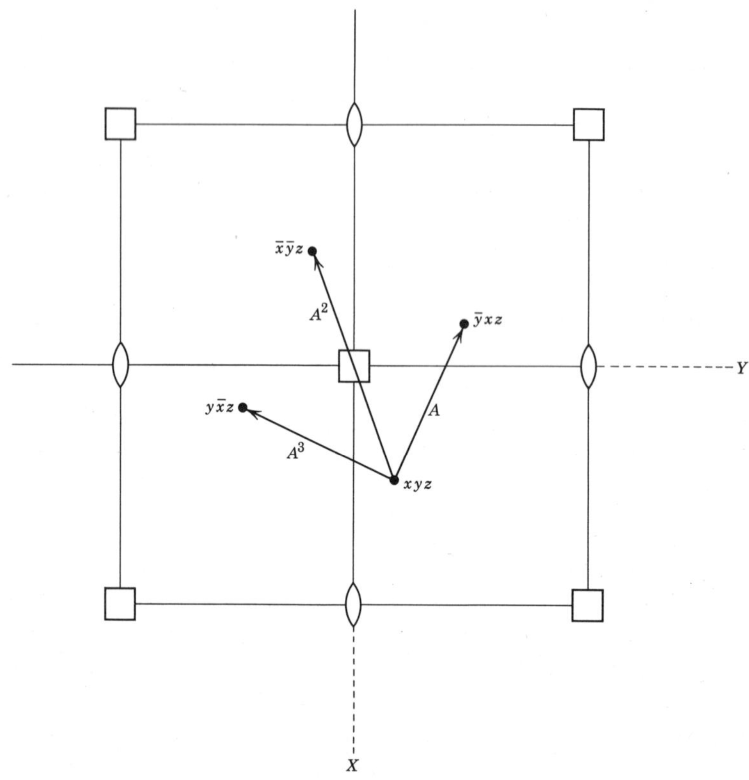

FIG. 2. Space group $P4$, showing the repetition of a point at xyz by the operations in the cell.

of these operations repeats an arbitrary point having coordinates xyz. If the origin of coordinates is chosen at the center of the cell on the 4-fold axis, then the operations of the cell repeat the point at xyz, namely P_{xyz}, as follows:

$$\begin{aligned} P_{xyz} \cdot 1 \quad &= P_{xyz}, \\ P_{xyz} \cdot A_{\pi/2} &= P_{\bar{y}xz}, \\ P_{xyz} \cdot A^2_{\pi/2} &= P_{\bar{x}\bar{y}z}, \\ P_{xyz} \cdot A^3_{\pi/2} &= P_{y\bar{x}z}. \end{aligned} \tag{2}$$

The set of points on the right of (2) constitutes the set of equivalent positions of space group $P4$.

General positions and special positions

If the representative point of a set of equivalent positions is given unspecialized coordinates xyz, the equivalent position is called a *general position* of the space group. The number of points in the general position (i.e., its rank) is equal to the number of operations in a cell of the space group.

If the coordinates xyz are specialized so that the representative point comes to lie on a symmetry element of the space group which lacks a translation component, and in some cases even if it has a translation component, certain pairs (or sets) of points of the set of equivalent positions are caused to coalesce, and the rank of the equipoint becomes a submultiple of the rank of the general position. Such a specialized location is called a *special position* of the space group.

There are usually several different special positions in a space group. They may have the same or different ranks. The collections of the special positions and the general position are sometimes referred to as the *equipoints* of a space group. In the following sections some examples of equipoints are discussed.

Space group *Pmm*2. Figure 3 shows space groups *Pmm*2 again, together with a set of points in the general position epitomized by the point at xyz. If this point is moved so that its x coordinate decreases, the points at xyz and $\bar{x}yz$ approach one another and finally coalesce in the reflection plane m_1. This location therefore reduces the rank of the equivalent set from 4 to 2. Therefore, reflection plane m_1 is a special position having coordinates epitomized by $0yz$. In the same way, if the x coordinate of the point in the general position is increased, the point at xyz approaches another point in the next cell below, located at $1 - x$, yz, and the two points eventually coalesce on the reflection plane m_3. Therefore, this is a special position of rank 2 and having coordinates epitomized by $\frac{1}{2}yz$. In a similar way m_2 and m_4 are special positions of rank 2.

If both x and y coordinates of the point at xyz are decreased so that the point approaches the 2-fold axis at the origin, all four points of the general position approach one another and eventually coalesce on the 2-fold axis. This reduction of rank is from a 4-fold general position to a 1-fold special position. In a similar way the other nonequivalent 2-fold axes are 1-fold special positions.

The various equipoints of a space group are customarily designated by a number followed by a letter. The number gives the rank of the equipoint, and the letter offers a specific (but arbitrary) designation which incidentally differentiates the several equipoints of the space group that have equal rank. The lettering advances through the alphabet toward equipoints of higher rank.

As a result of the discussion just given the equipoints of space group *Pmm*2 can be listed as shown in Table 1.

Space group *P*4. Figure 4 shows space group *P*4. A discussion analogous to that given in the last section shows that, if a point of the 4-fold general position is moved to the 4-fold axis at the origin, a condensation of four points into one point occurs. A similar condensation occurs on the 4-fold axis at $\frac{1}{2}\frac{1}{2}z$. The two 4-fold axes are therefore two different 1-fold equipoints.

A condensation of four points to two points occurs on the 2-fold axis at

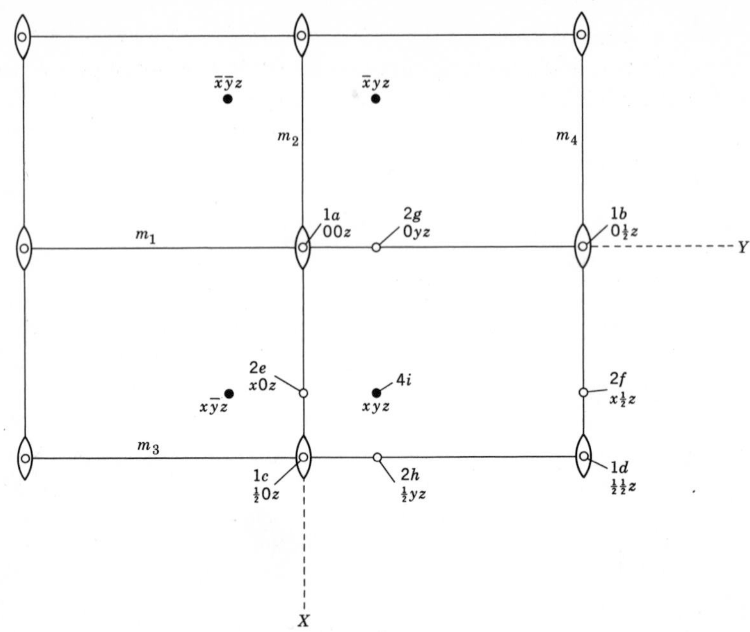

FIG. 3. The special positions of space group *Pmm*2.

Table 1. Equipoints of space group *Pmm*2 (Fig. 3)

Equipoint designation	Location	Symmetry of location	Coordinates of equivalent points
1*a*	2-fold axis at $00z$	*mm*2	$00z$
1*b*	,, ,, ,, $0\frac{1}{2}z$	*mm*2	$0\frac{1}{2}z$
1*c*	,, ,, ,, $\frac{1}{2}0z$	*mm*2	$\frac{1}{2}0z$
1*d*	,, ,, ,, $\frac{1}{2}\frac{1}{2}z$	*mm*2	$\frac{1}{2}\frac{1}{2}z$
2*e*	Reflection plane at $0yz$	*m*	$0yz$, $0\bar{y}z$
2*f*	,, ,, ,, $\frac{1}{2}yz$	*m*	$\frac{1}{2}yz$, $\frac{1}{2}\bar{y}z$
2*g*	,, ,, ,, $x0z$	*m*	$x0z$, $\bar{x}0z$
2*h*	,, ,, ,, $x\frac{1}{2}z$	*m*	$x\frac{1}{2}z$, $\bar{x}\frac{1}{2}z$
4*i*	General position	1	xyz, $\bar{x}yz$, $\bar{x}\bar{y}z$, $x\bar{y}z$

$0\frac{1}{2}z$. Since the 2-fold axes at $0\frac{1}{2}z$ and $\frac{1}{2}0z$ are equivalent by the 4-fold rotation, these two different 2-fold axes do not constitute separate equipoints but are part of the same 2-fold equipoint.

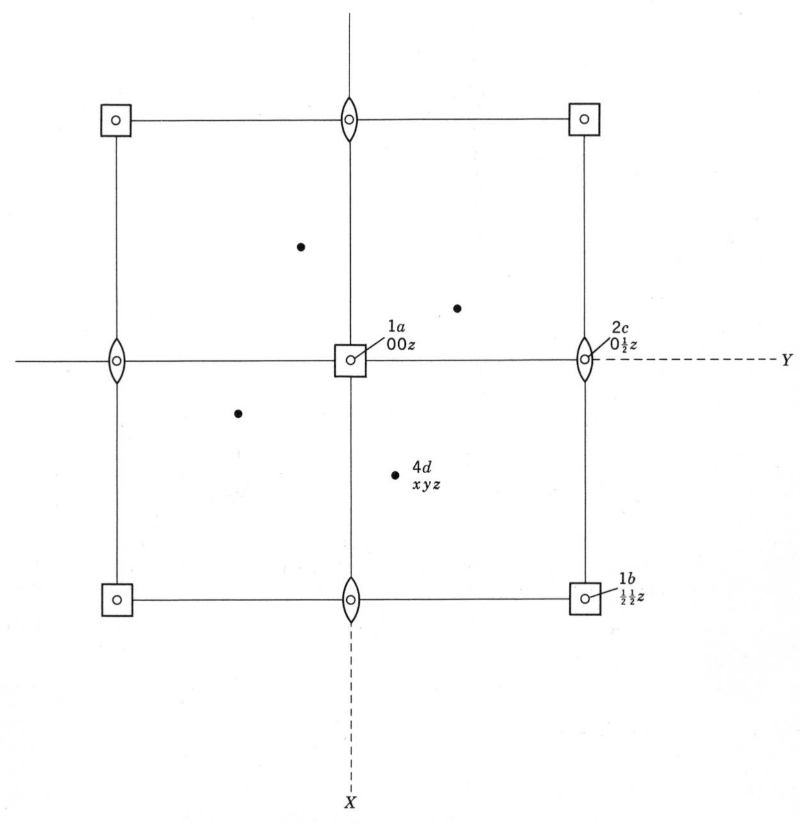

FIG. 4. The special positions of space group *P*4.

Table 2. Equipoints of space group *P*4 (Fig. 4)

Equipoint designation	Location	Symmetry of location	Coordinates of equivalent points
1*a*	4-fold axis at $00z$	4	$00z$
1*b*	,, ,, ,, $\frac{1}{2}\frac{1}{2}z$	4	$\frac{1}{2}\frac{1}{2}z$
2*c*	2-fold axis at $0\frac{1}{2}z$	2	$0\frac{1}{2}z$, $\frac{1}{2}0z$
4*d*	General position	1	xyz, $\bar{y}xz$, $\bar{x}\bar{y}z$, $y\bar{x}z$

The equipoints of $P4$ are listed in Table 2.

Space group $P4_1$. The several space groups isogonal with a point group do not, in general, have the same set of equipoints or even the same number of equipoints. To illustrate this, consider space group $P4_1$. Both $P4$, discussed in the last section, and $P4_1$, Fig. 5, are isogonal with point group 4. $P4$ has the four equipoints listed in Table 2, whereas $P4_1$ has only one equipoint as described in Table 3. The sole equipoint is the general position, and there are no special

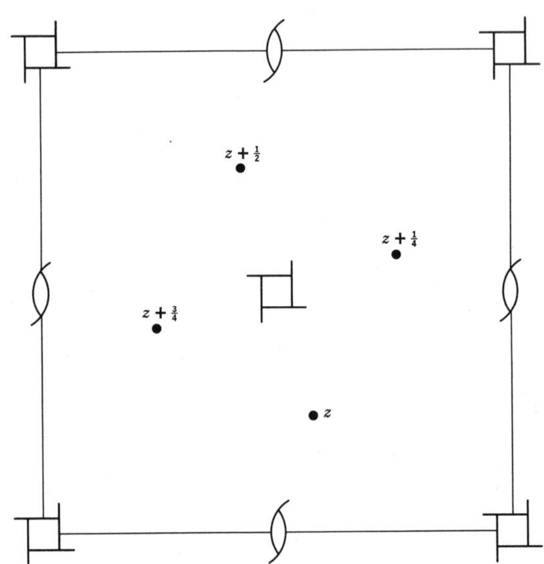

FIG. 5. The general position of space group $P4_1$.

Table 3. Equipoints of space group $P4_1$ (Fig. 5)

Equipoint designation	Location	Symmetry of location	Coordinates of equivalent points
4*a*	General position	1	$xyz,\quad \bar{y}x,\tfrac{1}{4}+z,\quad \bar{x}\bar{y},\tfrac{1}{2}+z,\quad y,\bar{x},\tfrac{3}{4}+z$

positions. This is because, if a point in the general position is moved to the only symmetry elements, which are screw axes, the points do not coalesce, but are separated by intervals of $z = \frac{1}{4}$ for the 4_1 axes, or $z = \frac{1}{2}$ for the 2_1 axes.

In a similar way, special positions do not occur on symmetry elements with

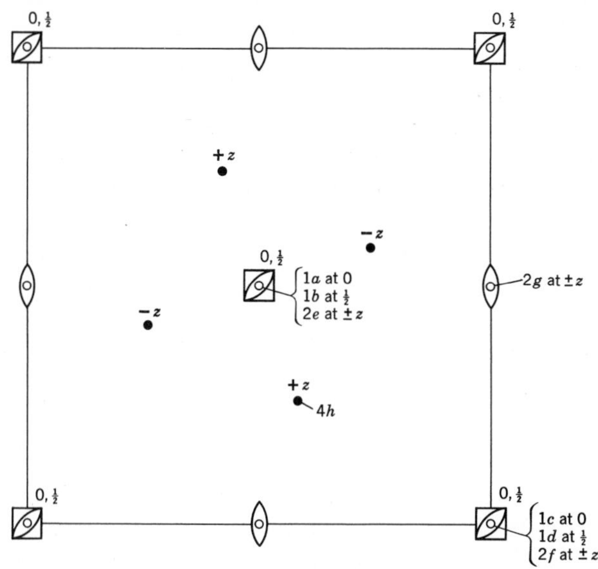

FIG. 6. The special positions of space group $P\bar{4}$.

Table 4. Equipoints of space group $P\bar{4}$ (Fig. 6)

Equipoint designation	Location	Symmetry of location	Coordinates of equivalent points
1*a*	On $\bar{4}$ axis at 000	$\bar{4}$	000
1*b*	,, ,, ,, $00\frac{1}{2}$	$\bar{4}$	$00\frac{1}{2}$
1*c*	,, ,, ,, ,, $\frac{1}{2}\frac{1}{2}0$	$\bar{4}$	$\frac{1}{2}\frac{1}{2}0$
1*d*	,, ,, ,, ,, $\frac{1}{2}\frac{1}{2}\frac{1}{2}$	$\bar{4}$	$\frac{1}{2}\frac{1}{2}\frac{1}{2}$
2*e*	,, ,, ,, ,, $00z$	2	$00z$, $00\bar{z}$
2*f*	,, ,, ,, ,, $\frac{1}{2}\frac{1}{2}z$	2	$\frac{1}{2}\frac{1}{2}z$, $\frac{1}{2}\frac{1}{2}\bar{z}$
2*g*	On 2-fold axis at $0\frac{1}{2}z$	2	$0\frac{1}{2}z$, $\frac{1}{2}0\bar{z}$
4*h*	General position	1	xyz, $\bar{y}x\bar{z}$, $\bar{x}\bar{y}z$, $y\bar{x}\bar{z}$

most general glide components. These include all glide planes and the screws 2_1, 3_1, 3_2, 4_1, 4_3, 6_1, and 6_5. Special positions do, however, occur on screw axes whose pitch subscript and order, n, contain a common factor, specifically 4_2, 6_2, 6_3 6_4.

Space group $P\bar{4}$. Another aspect of special positions is illustrated by those of $P\bar{4}$, Fig. 6. The characteristics of the equipoints of this space group are listed in Table 4. It can be seen that the equipoints $1a$, $1b$, $1c$, and $1d$ are different from those discussed previously in that the coordinates contain no variables. The equipoint positions are consequently without degrees of freedom. On the other hand the equipoints $2e$, $2f$, and $2g$ contain all the variable z and consequently all have one degree of freedom. The general position $4h$ has all three degrees of freedom.

Utilization of equipoint information

Tabulation of equipoint information. The ranks of the equipoints of each space group constitute important information for the investigation of the arrangements of atoms in crystals, that is, for the science of crystal-structure analysis. A standard reference work which supplies this information for each space group, together with diagrams showing the space-group symmetry and the distribution of points in the general position, is the following:

International Tables for X-Ray Crystallography, Vol. I (Kynoch Press, Birmingham, England, 1952).

Determination of the number of molecules per unit cell. Equipoint information often supplies the first hint concerning the arrangement of atoms in crystals, and in any event it supplies a valuable check on the certain other information which is available. The basis for this is that it is an easy matter to measure the dimensions of the unit cell with the aid of x-ray diffraction.* This means that the absolute volume V of the unit cell can be readily computed.

The density, G, of the cell is

$$G_{\text{cell}} = \frac{\text{cell mass}}{V_{\text{cell}}}, \tag{3}$$

From a chemical point of view, this mass of material in the cell comprises N chemical molecules, or formula weights, each of mass M, so that (3) can be written

$$G_{\text{cell}} = \frac{NM}{V}. \tag{4}$$

* See, for example, M. J. Buerger, *X-Ray Crystallography* (John Wiley & Sons, New York, 1942).

In the usual case, the chemical nature of the material comprising the crystal is known so that M is readily found by adding the masses of the individual chemical atoms in the formula. The density of the cell is the same as the density of the entire crystal, and this can be experimentally determined by standard methods, such as the pycnometer or Berman-type Jolly balance. Therefore, all quantities but N in (4) are known. If the other quantities are expressed in comparable units, (4) can be solved for N as follows:

$$N = \frac{GV}{M}. \tag{5}$$

To express this in *cgs* units, the following should be used:

$$N = \frac{G(\text{grams/cm}^3) \times V(\text{cm}^3)}{M\ (\text{grams})}. \tag{6}$$

The usual list of atomic "weights" is based upon oxygen = 16 chemical weight units. This can be converted to grams by multiplying by 1.660×10^{-24}. The cell is measured in Ångström units, each of which is equal to 10^{-24} cm. The units of (6) can therefore be supplied from available data as follows:

$$N = \frac{G(\text{grams/cm}^3) \times V(\text{Ångström units})^3 \times 10^{-24}}{M(\text{atomic weight units}) \times 1.660 \times 10^{-24}}. \tag{7}$$

Now, the whole story of space groups, especially when looked at from a point of view of repetition theory, requires this number N (the number of molecules, or formula weights, in a cell) to be an integer. Furthermore, it must be an integer compatible with the ranks of the equipoints in the space group.

Limitation on the locations of molecules. Suppose that the space group of a crystal had been determined as $P\bar{4}$, and suppose further that the cell investigation discussed above had shown that the cell contained only one molecule. Table 4 shows that space group $P\bar{4}$ has 4-fold, 2-fold, and 1-fold equipoints. It is evident that the molecule could be placed only in a 1-fold equipoint, but there would be a choice of placing it in 1*a*, 1*b*, 1*c*, or 1*d*. Actually, if the molecule is placed in any of these, the resulting structures are identical for this simple example. This is because each structure can be transformed into the other by a simple translation. For example, 1*b*, 1*c*, and 1*d* transform to 1*a* as follows:

$$00\tfrac{1}{2}(\text{i.e., } 1b) - 00\tfrac{1}{2} = 000 \quad (\text{i.e., } 1a),$$

$$\tfrac{1}{2}\tfrac{1}{2}0(\text{i.e., } 1c) - \tfrac{1}{2}\tfrac{1}{2}0 = 000 \quad (\text{i.e., } 1a),$$

$$\tfrac{1}{2}\tfrac{1}{2}\tfrac{1}{2}(\text{i.e., } 1d) - \tfrac{1}{2}\tfrac{1}{2}\tfrac{1}{2} = 000 \quad (\text{i.e., } 1a).$$

In this case the arrangement of atoms in the crystal is completely determined from a knowledge of the number of molecules per cell, assuming that the molecule is one of known shape. If the shape is not known, then this analysis determines only the center of the molecule, and the details of its shape must be determined by further crystal-structure analysis study.

On the other hand, if there are two molecules per cell, they can be accommodated *either* in any one of the 2-fold equipoints *or* in any two of the 1-fold equipoints.

If there are four molecules per cell, the situation is more complicated. Since there are 4-fold, 2-fold, and 1-fold equipoints, the 4 molecules per cell can be made up by selecting from these as follows:

$$4 = 4,$$
$$4 = 2 + 2,$$
$$4 = 2 + 1 + 1,$$
$$4 = 1 + 1 + 1 + 1.$$

Note that there are several possible ways of selecting equipoints for the two middle possibilities, since there are three kinds of 2-fold equipoints.

19 · The determination of space groups and the utilization of space-group information

The background for space-group determination

The theory of crystal symmetry was essentially complete before the opening of the twentieth century. Although many had contributed to it, the final steps in showing that there are 230 space groups were shared by three scientists of different nationalities, Artur Schoenflies (a German mathematician), E. S. Fedorov (a Russian crystallographer), and William Barlow (an English crystallographer).

For almost a generation these results stood as a purely theoretical development without confirmation and without any indication that they did, indeed, apply to crystals. In 1912 a fortuitous gathering of scientists, which was destined to change this situation, occurred in Munich. These included the crystallographer, von Groth, and a number of physicists interested in the recently discovered x-rays. As a result of discussions by members of this group, it occurred to Laue that, if crystals were truly the periodic arrangements of molecules that crystallographers claimed, and if x-rays were radiation transmitted by waves of molecular dimensions, then crystals might be expected to act as diffraction gratings to x-rays. Laue's assistants quickly followed this conjecture with experimental work that proved beyond doubt both that x-rays were waves and that crystals were periodic arrangements of matter with patterns of molecular dimensions. These experiments marked a turning point for science in general, and for crystallography in particular, because it put at the disposal of the crystallographer a powerful tool for testing the patterns of crystals.

The theory and practice of studying crystals by x-ray diffraction were quickly simplified and perfected. In a short time the detailed nature of the arrangements of atoms in some of the simpler crystals, such as the alkali halides, pyrite, and calcite, was deduced. The earliest crystal-structure investigations were performed by physicists. As they apparently made no explicit use of space-group theory it is probable that they were either unaware of it or did not know how to put it to use.

It remained for the great Swiss crystallographer Paul Niggli to show how x-ray diffraction could be used as a tool for space-group investigation. From that time onward, it became a routine procedure to first determine the space group of a crystal (within limits to be discussed) before proceeding further with the crystal-structure investigation. Niggli's contribution was important not only because it placed this tool at the disposal of the crystallographer but also because its use incidentally, over a short period of years, established the correctness of the results of a long line of theorizers about crystal symmetry. In brief, space-group theory became gradually but certainly established as the general geometrical frame into which crystals must fit.

Space-group determination

Determination by abnormal spacings. Space-group determination is partly concerned with the technique of producing and recording x-ray diffraction from crystals. For a full account of this the reader is referred to another book.* In this place only the theoretical basis for space-group determination is suggested.

X-ray diffraction experiments fortunately provide two different kinds of information about a crystal. In the first place the translations of a crystal in any rational direction are easily measured. From this kind of information not only are the absolute dimensions of the cell easily found but also the presence of any lattice points other than those at the cell corners is readily established. This kind of information, therefore, provides the Bravais lattice type, and hence the first symbol of the space group, as well as the dimensions of the cell corresponding to the general symmetry observed in the crystal.

The general, but not the detailed, nature of the next three symbols is revealed by the symmetry of the x-ray diffraction effects. This was discussed in Chapter 11. In general, the symmetry of the diffraction effects yields the crystal class multiplied by an inversion center (if not already present in the crystal class). Accordingly there remains the ambiguity that the crystal class lies between two, three, or four possibilities, as outlined in Table 7, Chapter 11. *If it were not for this ambiguity every space group (except enantiomorphous pairs) could be distinguished quite simply.* But the ambiguity in crystal class, as it can be tested by the symmetry of x-ray diffraction effects, gives rise to ambiguities between some (but not all) sets of space groups which can be resolved only by certain advanced quantitative tests.

For the purpose of understanding the simplest method of space-group determination, ignore this ambiguity temporarily. Then the detailed nature of the part of the space-group symbol which follows the lattice symbol is determined if the characteristics of the screw axes and glide planes can be determined. Fortunately these can be found from the second kind of information that diffraction experiments supply. This second kind of information is the spacings between

* M. J. Buerger, *X-Ray Crystallography* (John Wiley & Sons, New York, 1942).

equivalent planes. Screw axes (as compared with pure rotation axes of the same n) and glide planes (as compared with pure reflection planes) require certain planes to have submultiple spacings. In fact, the set of spacings is characteristic of the screw or glide.

To see how this occurs, consider a crystal with a 4-fold axis parallel to c in the point group. This 4-fold axis can be represented by a 4, 4_1, 4_2, or 4_3 axis in the space group. If the space group has axis 4, the spacing of the (001) planes is the ordinary translation c of the lattice. But if the space group contains axis 4_1, then the $c/4$ translation component of the screw reproduces these planes at a spacing $c/4$. If the screw is 4_2, the translation component of the screw reproduces these planes at a spacing of $c/2$. If the screw is 4_3, the $3c/4 = -c/4$ translation component of the screw again reproduces these planes

Table 1. Determination of the nature of the screw axis isogonal with a 4-fold axis of the point group

Observed spacing of (001) planes	Inferred translation component of screw	Inferred axis isogonal with 4-fold axis of point group
c	0	4
$\frac{c}{2}$	$\pm\frac{c}{2}$	4_2
$\frac{c}{4}$	$\pm\frac{c}{4}$	4_1 or 4_3

at a spacing of $c/4$. Thus, if it is *known* from point-group symmetry information that there is a 4-fold axis parallel to c, the nature of the screw is revealed by the abnormal spacings of the planes normal to the axis, namely the (001) planes. The matter is outlined in Table 1.

It is evident that the spacings of certain planes can act as detectors of translations in the space group which are submultiples of the lattice translations. The class of plane whose spacing reveals the submultiple translations of a screw axis is the stack of planes at right angles to the axis. Thus, if the axis is parallel to [001], its submultiple translations are revealed by spacings of the planes (001). Similarly the submultiple translations of a glide plane are revealed by the spacings of all stacks of planes at right angles to the glide plane. Accordingly, if the glide plane is parallel to (100), its submultiple translations are revealed by the spacings of the planes ($0kl$).

Ambiguities in the subnormal-spacing method. It will be observed that the pure rotation axis and the pure reflection plane do not require any spacings of planes which are different from those required by the bare lattice itself. This means that a pure rotation axis or a pure reflection plane does not reveal itself except in its general effect on the symmetry of the x-ray reflections. But the symmetry of this effect always contains an inversion center. Therefore a pure rotation axis A_π and a pure reflection plane m must effect the reflection symmetry as $A_\pi \cdot i = m$ and $m \cdot i = A_\pi$ respectively. For this reason the diffraction symmetries due to m, to 2, and to $2/m$ cannot be distinguished in any way. Sets of space groups that give the same effect in diffraction symmetry and the same effect in spacing constitute a *diffraction group.*

The space groups within a diffraction group cannot be distinguished by simple qualitative means, that is, by a simple inspection of the diffraction record. There are 122 diffraction groups.* Some diffraction groups contain but one space group. Such space groups are uniquely distinguishable. There are 160 such uniquely determinable space groups.

Quantitative methods. About 1945 it began to be evident that, even though some sets of space groups could not be distinguished by simply inspecting the x-ray record, there were quantitative means by which the x-ray record could be made to yield the space group. Since these means invoke advanced crystal-structure-analysis theory, they cannot be discussed with profit here. It will suffice to note that the three-dimensional Patterson synthesis of the x-ray diffraction intensities of a crystal contains characteristics which reveal the space group of the crystal.

The importance of space-group study

When any aspect of a crystal is to be investigated nowadays, knowledge of its space group is an essential preliminary to further investigation. Not only is knowledge of the space group essential for investigation of the crystal pattern itself, but it is essential also for the investigation of any characteristic of a crystal which depends upon the pattern. For example, crystal morphology is a function of space group.

Until very recently, a majority of the crystallographers have ignored space-group theory. The reason for this is that they were occupied with crystal morphology and did not realize that space-group theory had any bearing on the subject. But it is now patently clear that no branch of crystallography can ignore space-group theory, and it is evident that space-group study is just as essential for the student as form study, which is the limit of much of the teaching of present-day crystallography.

* These are listed in M. J. Buerger, *X-Ray Crystallography* (John Wiley & Sons, New York, 1942), pp. 511–516. The count of 121 given there is incorrect for two reasons. In the first place there are 23 isometric diffraction groups instead of 24, as stated. In the second place the enantiomorphous pairs of hexagonal space groups $\{C3_112, C3_212\}$ can be distinguished from the pair $\{C3_121, C3_221\}$. Also $C3m1$ can be distinguished from $C31m$, and $C\bar{3}m1$ can be distinguished from $C\bar{3}1m$. The net result of these corrections is that there are 122 diffraction groups.

20 · Group theory

The operations of symmetry of a symmetry system can be elegantly formulated with the aid of a branch of mathematics known as the *theory of groups*. The application of this theory is by no means restricted to the study of symmetry but can be applied to many situations involving closed systems. Group theory is an extensive subject. Only enough of the elementary part of the theory is presented here to illustrate its application to the derivation of groups of symmetry operations.

Fundamental ideas about groups

Preliminary ideas. Group theory deals with combinations, particularly combinations in closed systems. The meaning of "combination" is unrestricted, but, applied to crystallography, it refers to the combination of symmetry operations. For example, a rotation through angle α about axis A can be combined with a rotation through angle β about the same axis, to give the resulting rotation of $\alpha + \beta$ about axis A. Or a rotation of π about axis A can be combined with a reflection in a plane m perpendicular to A, to give a result which is an inversion through the point of intersection of A and m. These are ordinary crystallographic examples of combinations.

In the last example, let the operations of rotation, reflection, and inversion be denoted by the symbols A_π, m, and i. It was shown in (20), (21), and (22) of Chapter 6 that the combinations of these operations, two at a time, are

$$A_\pi \cdot m = i, \tag{1}$$

$$m \cdot i = A_\pi, \tag{2}$$

$$i \cdot A_\pi = m. \tag{3}$$

Thus, when any two of these operations are combined, the result is the remaining operation. The gist of the idea of groups is here, namely that if a set of operations is properly selected they form a closed system.

The group postulates. To truly constitute a group, a set of *elements* (these are operations in the crystallographic application) must conform to three *group postulates*.

Postulate 1. *The combination of any two elements, including an element with itself, is also an element of the set.*

The elements are customarily represented by letters, like A and B, and the combination of A and B is represented as the product $A \cdot B$, or AB. In crystallographic applications the "elements" are symmetry operations.

Postulate 1*a*. *The combination of elements is associative.*

This merely means that the combination of A with BC has the same result as the combination of AB with C. In short,

$$A(BC) = (AB)C = ABC. \tag{4}$$

Postulate 2. *The set contains a single element, known as "the identity," which has the property that, when it is combined with any element, the result is that same element.*

The "identity" is usually designated I, sometimes E. This postulate can be formulated in two combinations:

$$AI = A, \tag{5}$$

$$IA = A. \tag{6}$$

In some simpler applications, the identity corresponds to the operation of doing nothing, and is then often symbolized by 1. This is not true in some of the more general applications of group theory.

Postulate 3. *For each element, A, of the set, there exists a unique element A', called the inverse of A, such that the combination of A and A' is the identity.*

This postulate can be formulated

$$AA' = I, \tag{7}$$

and

$$A'A = I. \tag{8}$$

In simple crystallographic applications, the inverse is symbolized by A^{-1}, so that (7) and (8) are written $AA^{-1} = I$ and $A^{-1}A = I$.

If these postulates are applied to the set of operations A_π, m, and I of equations (1)–(3) it is evident that this set does not constitute a group, since they do not include the identity. The set 1, A_π, m, and i, however, does form a group. This can be verified by showing that the three group postulates are obeyed: Equations (1), (2), and (3), plus

$$\left.\begin{aligned} A_\pi \cdot 1 &= A_\pi, \\ m \cdot 1 &= m, \\ i \cdot 1 &= i, \end{aligned}\right\} \tag{9}$$

show that postulate 1 is obeyed. That postulate 2 is obeyed is also shown by (9). Postulate 3 is obeyed since each of the operations A_π, m, and i is its own inverse; i.e.,

$$\left.\begin{aligned} A_\pi \cdot A_\pi &= A_\pi{}^2 = A_{2\pi} = 1, \\ m \cdot m &= 1, \\ i \cdot i &= 1. \end{aligned}\right\} \tag{10}$$

The multiplication table of a group. A convenient device for formulating all the possible products of operations in a group is the *multiplication table* of the group. For the group just considered, the operations of the group are 1, A_π, m, and i. All possible products are given by the square array

	1	A_π	m	i
1	1	A_π	m	i
A_π	A_π	1	i	m
m	m	i	1	A_π
i	i	m	A_π	1

(11)

This is the multiplication table of the particular group whose elements are 1, A_π, m, and i.

To show that group properties are not confined to geometrical operations, consider the four numbers $+1, -1, +\sqrt{-1}, -\sqrt{-1}$. All possible products of this set are given by the square array

	$+1$	-1	$+\sqrt{-1}$	$-\sqrt{-1}$
$+1$	$+1$	-1	$\sqrt{-1}$	$-\sqrt{-1}$
-1	-1	$+1$	$-\sqrt{-1}$	$\sqrt{-1}$
$+\sqrt{-1}$	$\sqrt{-1}$	$-\sqrt{-1}$	$+1$	$+1$
$-\sqrt{-1}$	$-\sqrt{-1}$	$+\sqrt{-1}$	$+1$	$+1.$

(12)

From this multiplication table it is evident that all products are contained in the original set of numbers, so that postulate 1 is obeyed. It is also evident that any number combined with $+1$ produces the same number. Therefore there is an identity, I, namely $+1$; hence postulate 2 is obeyed. Finally, for each number there exists another unique number with which it can be combined to produce I, that is, to give $+1$, so that postulate 3 is obeyed. The set of numbers $+1, -1, +\sqrt{-1}$, and $-\sqrt{-1}$ therefore constitutes a group, the rule of combination being multiplication.

Powers of operations. Since postulate 1, and also its representation in the multiplication table, provides that any element A can be combined with itself, the combination AA is an element of the group. But postulate 1 requires that a combination of A and AA is also an element of the group. This implies that the combinations in the following infinite series of combinations must be members of the group:

$$A \quad AA \quad AAA \quad AAAA \quad \cdots \quad . \tag{13}$$

Since these are thought of as products, they are usually represented as

$$A \quad A^2 \quad A^3 \quad A^4 \quad \cdots \quad . \tag{14}$$

The number of distinct operations of a group is called its *order*. This may be finite, as in the case of point groups, or infinite, as in the case of space groups. Now, consider the collection of powers of each operation, given in (14). This is an infinite series, and yet, for a finite group, it must be finite. The only way that this can be true is that not all terms are distinct. Accordingly certain sets of elements of (14) which appear to be different are actually the same. Let the pth and qth powers be the same, that is,

$$A^p = A^q, \tag{15}$$

and let $p > q$. If the symbol A^{-q} is adopted for the inverse A^q, postulate 2 provides

$$A^q A^{-q} = I. \tag{16}$$

Now, if both sides of (15) are postmultiplied by the inverse A^{-q}, there results

$$\begin{aligned} A^p A^{-q} &= A^q A^{-q} \\ &= I. \end{aligned} \tag{17}$$

But this is the same as

$$A^{p-q} = I. \tag{18}$$

This shows that some power of A is the identity. The lowest such power, other than zero, is called the order of A. Let this lowest order be n, so that

$$A^n = I. \tag{19}$$

If two operations A^n are combined there results

$$A^n \cdot A^n = I \cdot I = I. \tag{20}$$

Therefore cyclically recurring powers of A are equal to I, namely $A^n, A^{2n}, A^{3n}, \cdots$.

This cyclic recurrence of powers is well illustrated by a group of rotations about an axis A. For example, consider a rotation of $\pi/2$ about A, and its powers. Four such rotations are $4 \cdot \pi/2 = 2\pi$, so that A^4 brings the system to its original condition. All the powers of A can be arranged in cycles of four as follows:

$$\begin{array}{cccc} A^0 & A^1 & A^2 & A^3, \\ A^4 & A^5 & A^6 & A^7, \\ A^8 & A^9 & A^{10} & A^{11}, \\ A^{12} & A^{13} & A^{14} & A^{15}, \\ \cdot & \cdot & \cdot & \cdot \\ \cdot & \cdot & \cdot & \cdot \\ \cdot & \cdot & \cdot & \cdot \end{array} \tag{21}$$

Any cycle has the four operations

$$A^{4N} \quad A^{4N+1} \quad A^{4N+2} \quad A^{4N+3}, \tag{22}$$

where N is an integer. Since $A^{4N} = I$, it follows that powers greater than $4N$ can be reduced. For example, $A^{4N+3} = A^{4N}A^3 = IA^3 = A^3$. This means that all the elements in each vertical column of (21) are the same, so that only the first cycle of (21) is distinct, all other cycles being other representations of the first cycle.

Some groups are composed of only a cycle of powers of one element. Such groups are called *cyclical groups*. In Chapter 6 some cyclical groups were encountered. The Schoenflies designation C_n stands for a "cyclical group of order n" and applies specifically to groups of rotations. The Schoenflies designation C_s stands for a group of reflections, and C_i stands for a group of inversions. Both the last groups are cyclical groups of order 2.

Groups which are not cyclical are noncyclical. Postulate 1 provides that, for each element A, the power A^2 is a member of the group. In some cases, such as C_s and C_i, $A^2 = I$. But only for the unique element I can the first power be I. In general, therefore, $A \neq I$. For this reason every noncyclical group contains within itself two or more cyclical groups of order 2 or greater.

Permutability

Conjugate products. In general, if the order of two elements in a product is reversed, the new product is not the same as the original. In other words, in general

$$AB \neq BA. \tag{23}$$

Although these two products are not generally the same, they are related in a manner to be discussed. They are called *conjugate products*. BA is said to be *conjugate to* AB, or to be *the conjugate of* AB.

Transforms. To see how BA is related to AB, it can be manipulated to involve AB, as follows:

$$\begin{aligned} BA &= (BA) \\ &= A^{-1}A(BA) \\ &= A^{-1}(AB)A. \end{aligned} \tag{24}$$

Similarly, starting with AB, it can be manipulated:

$$\begin{aligned} AB &= (AB) \\ &= B^{-1}B(AB) \\ &= B^{-1}(BA)B. \end{aligned} \tag{25}$$

Equations (24) and (25) have the form

$$Y = R^{-1}XR. \tag{26}$$

This is recognized from the discussion of Chapter 12 as the element X as transformed by R. Therefore the relations in (24) and (25) can be described as follows:

Theorem: The transform of a product by its first element is the conjugate product.

This theorem provides one view of the relation of a product to its conjugate product. Another view of the relation can be seen as follows: Consider the transformation of element B by A, and call the transformed element B' to emphasize the relation between B and its transform. Thus

$$A^{-1}BA = B'. \tag{27}$$

If both sides are premultiplied by A, there results

$$BA = AB'. \tag{28}$$

In a like manner, consider the transformation of A by B^{-1}. This is

$$BAB^{-1} = A'', \tag{29}$$

so that

$$BA = A''B. \tag{30}$$

This provides another meaning to a reversed product BA, which can be expressed as follows:

Theorem: A product can be reformulated as a permuted product whose first term is unchanged but whose last term is the transform of the other by the first (or whose second term is unchanged but whose first term is the transform by the inverse of the other).

Condition of permutability. Now consider the special case where a product and its permuted equivalent are the same. This can be written

$$BA = AB. \tag{31}$$

If both sides are premultiplied by A^{-1}, the result is

$$A^{-1}BA = B. \tag{32}$$

Alternatively, if both sides are premultiplied by B^{-1}, the result is

$$A = B^{-1}AB. \tag{33}$$

The results of (32) and (33) can be formulated as follows:

Theorem: The condition for permutability of two elements in a product is that each element transforms the other into itself.

Abelian groups. When all the elements of a group are permutable with one another, the group is called a *commutative group*, or an *Abelian group*. According to the last theorem, each operation of such a group must transform the other operations into themselves. Any power of an operation transforms the operation into itself. This is readily shown as follows:

$$X^{-n}XX^{n} = X^{-n+1+n}$$
$$= X. \tag{34}$$

Since a cyclical group is composed only of powers of one operation, any cyclical group is Abelian.

In particular, rotations are transformed into themselves by other rotations about the same axis. Therefore groups of rotations about the same axis are Abelian groups.

Conjugates

Conjugate elements. Equations (24) and (25) show that conjugate products are transforms of one another. The word *conjugate* is also extended to include any two elements that are transformed into each other. If any element, A, transforms an element X into another element Y, that is, if

$$Y = A^{-1}XA, \tag{35}$$

then X and $A^{-1}XA$ are conjugate elements. The relation is usually expressed by saying that "*$A^{-1}XA$ is conjugate to X*," or that "*$A^{-1}XA$ is the conjugate of X*."

Theorem: Any element is conjugate to itself.

This is because any element transforms itself into itself, since

$$A^{-1}(A)A = A. \tag{36}$$

Sets of conjugate elements. The collection of all conjugates of an element with respect to all elements of the group is called a *complete set of conjugates* of that element. It is also known as the *class* of that element. For example, in the symmetry 322, the operations of the 3-fold axis are 1, $A_{2\pi/3}$, $A^2_{2\pi/3}$. These three operations transform a 2-fold rotation (about an axis perpendicular to the 3-fold axis) into 2-fold rotations about three axes separated by 120°. These three 2-fold rotations comprise a complete set of conjugates of the original 2-fold rotation. These elements are also known as a class of 2-fold rotations.

Each element of a complete conjugate set has the same complete conjugate set. It is obvious that two different conjugate sets cannot have an element in common, for then they would constitute a single complete conjugate set. This makes it possible to enumerate the total number of elements of a group as the sum of the separate elements of the several complete conjugate sets.

Invariant elements. When every element of a group transforms a particular element into itself, that element is said to be a *self-conjugate* or *invariant* element of the group. This implies, of course, that this element is permutable with every element of the group.

A crystallographic example of an invariant element is afforded by one of the rotations of the principal axis of a group n/m. For example, in $6/m$, the 6-fold rotation is transformed into itself by all of its powers and also by the perpendicular reflection. Since these operations, their products, and the identity exhaust the group, the 6-fold operation is an invariant element of $6/m$. On the other hand, in the group 622, a 2-fold rotation about an axis perpendicular to the 6-fold axis transforms the 6-fold rotation $A_{2\pi/6}$ into $A_{2\pi/6}^{-1} = A_{-2\pi/6}$. In the group 622, therefore, the 6-fold rotation is not an invariant element of the group.

Subgroups

Basic ideas. A group may contain among its elements a smaller collection of elements which by themselves constitute a group. This smaller collection is called a *subgroup*. As a first example, consider the group defined by (12). It can be seen that the terms +1 and −1 constitute a subgroup whose multiplication table is

	+1	−1
+1	+1	−1
−1	−1	+1 .

(37)

As a second example, the group defined by (11) contains three obvious subgroups, whose elements are 1, A_π; 1, m; 1, i; and whose multiplication tables are

	1	A_π
1	1	A_π
A_π	A_π	1 ,

(38)

	1	m
1	1	m
m	m	1 ,

(39)

	1	i
1	1	i
i	i	1 .

(40)

In addition, every group contains two *trivial* subgroups. One of these is the group whose only element is the identity. It is usually also convenient to call the group itself one of its own subgroups. These two trivial subgroups are called *improper* subgroups. Those groups that are distinct from these two trivial subgroups are designated as *proper* subgroups. To illustrate this distinction, the subgroups of (11) are 1, (38), (39), (40), and (11). Of these, 1 and (11) are improper and (38), (39), and (40) are proper subgroups.

In subsequent discussions the group itself will usually be designated by G and one of its subgroups by g. Just as g is a subgroup of G, it can be said that G is a supergroup of g. A considerable part of the application of group theory to crystallography consists of first devising simple groups g, and then finding supergroups G based upon g by adding appropriate operations to g. In this way complicated groups are constructed from simple ones.

Cosets. A group may be regarded as composed of some particular subgroup and other elements not in that subgroup. The set of products of one outside element (called a *representative*) with the elements of the subgroup is called a *coset*. To illustrate this, let the subgroup g consist of the elements a_1, a_2, and $a_3, \ldots$, and let B be an element not in the subgroup. Then collection of elements Ba_1, Ba_2, $Ba_3 \ldots$ is a coset of g, and can be abbreviated Bg. In particular it is a left coset of g since g is multiplied on the left by B. The corresponding right coset gB is the set a_1B, a_2B, $a_3B \ldots$.

The following notation of cosets is convenient. If the subgroup is written as the set of its distinct elements:

$$g = a_1, \quad a_2, \quad a_3, \quad \cdots,$$

then $\quad gB = a_1B, \quad a_2B, \quad a_3B, \quad \cdots$ represents a right coset,

and $\quad Bg = Ba_1, \quad Ba_2, \quad Ba_3, \quad \cdots$ represents a left coset.

The right and left cosets of g are, in general, different collections, although under certain conditions they may be the same collection.

The order of a subgroup. A fundamental property of subgroups is stated by the *Theorem of Lagrange;*

Theorem: The order of a subgroup is a factor of the order of the group.

To prove this, the elements of the group G are tabulated as cosets of the subgroup g. Let the r distinct elements of the subgroup g be

$$g = \quad a_1(=I) \qquad a_2, \qquad a_3, \quad \cdots, \qquad a_r. \tag{41}$$

Let the elements of group G not contained in subgroup g be designated by B's with various subscripts. Select one of these, designate it as B_2, and form its cosets (say, left cosets) of g, as follows:

$$B_2g = B_2a_1, \qquad B_2a_2, \qquad B_2a_3, \quad \cdots, \quad B_2a_r. \tag{42}$$

The various terms in (42) are other B's. If this tabulation does not exhaust the B's, select another, designate it as B_3, and form its cosets of g as follows:

$$B_3g = B_3a_1, \qquad B_3a_2, \qquad B_3a_3, \quad \cdots, \quad B_3a_r. \tag{43}$$

If this does not use up all the B's, continue the process until the remaining B's are exhausted. The total number of elements in the group are now displayed as the group g and its cosets, as follows:

$$\left.\begin{array}{llllll} g = & a_1(=I), & a_2, & a_3, & \cdots, & a_r \\ B_2g = & B_2a_1, & B_2a_2, & B_2a_3, & \cdots, & B_2a_r \\ B_3g = & B_3a_1, & B_3a_2, & B_3a_3, & \cdots, & B_3a_r \\ \cdot & \cdot & \cdot & \cdot & \cdots, & B_3a_r \\ \cdot & \cdot & \cdot & \cdot & \cdots, & \cdot \\ \cdot & \cdot & \cdot & \cdot & \cdots, & \cdot \\ B_qg = & B_qa_1, & B_qa_2, & B_qa_3, & \cdots, & B_qa_r \end{array}\right\} \tag{44}$$

This tabulation is called the expansion of the group G in left cosets of g. It is obvious that the table contains qr elements. Since r is the order of subgroup g, it is evident that this is a submultiple of order qr of group G. The number, r, of cosets in the expansion is known as the *index of the subgroup.*

To prove Lagrange's theorem it must be shown that no two terms of the tabulation (44) are different representations of the same term, and that therefore the tabulation is a true list of the elements in the group G. This can be done in two stages.

First, no coset B_ng has any term in common with the subgroup g. If it did, then, suppose that the terms which are equal are

$$B_na_k = a_j. \tag{45}$$

This can be rearranged to

$$B_n = a_ja_k^{-1}. \tag{46}$$

But the left-hand side of this is a B term and therefore not in the subgroup, whereas the right-hand side is an a term and therefore in the subgroup. Since this conclusion contradicts the hypotheses, no term in any coset has a term in common with the subgroup.

Secondly, no two elements in a row are different representations of the same term. If they were, then suppose that the equal terms are

$$B_ma_i = B_ma_j. \tag{47}$$

The common term can be removed from both sides, so that this implies

$$a_i = a_j, \tag{48}$$

which means that two distinct terms of the subgroup g are equal. Since this is contrary to the hypotheses, (47) is false.

These two steps show that all terms in (44) are distinct. Since the tabulation exhausts the group, the order of the group is qr. The order of the subgroup is r, which is a factor of qr. Therefore the order of the subgroup is a factor of the order of the group.

The *index* of a subgroup is the factor r.

Conjugate subgroups. If A is an element of G, the operator $A^{-1}(\ )A$ transforms an entire subgroup g into another, similar subgroup h. This can be represented as

$$h = A^{-1}gA.$$

To prove this, let the subgroup g contain the elements

$$g \quad = a_1(=I), \quad a_2, \quad\quad a_3, \quad \cdots, \quad\quad a_r. \tag{49}$$

Then the operation A transforms each of the operations of subgroup (49) as follows:

$$A^{-1}gA = A^{-1}a_1A, \quad A^{-1}a_2A, \quad A^{-1}a_3A, \quad \cdots, \quad A^{-1}a_rA. \tag{50}$$

That this collection is a group similar to (49) can be shown as follows: The product of each transform in (50) is the transform of the corresponding product in (49), for

$$A^{-1}a_pA \cdot A^{-1}a_qA = A^{-1}a_pa_qA. \tag{51}$$

Therefore (51) is a closed collection and conforms to postulate 1. Also

$$A^{-1}a_1A = A^{-1}IA = I, \tag{52}$$

so that $A^{-1}IA$ is the identity. Also, since

$$A^{-1}a_pA \cdot A^{-1}a_p{}^{-1}A = A^{-1}a_pa_p{}^{-1}A = I, \tag{53}$$

each element has an inverse. Therefore h is a group which is similar, term for term, to g. Since it is composed of elements of G, it is also a subgroup of G. The subgroups g and $A^{-1}gA$ are called *conjugate subgroups*. $A^{-1}gA$ is said to be *conjugate to* g, or the *conjugate of* g.

The set of all conjugates of a subgroup, g, with respect to the various elements of the group G is called the *complete set of conjugate subgroups of* g in G. An example of a complete set of conjugate subgroups is afforded by the groups of 3-fold rotations in the isometric groups. For example, in point group $23 = T$, the operations of the 2-fold axes relate the groups of operations of the 3-fold axes in pairs. The group of operations of each 3-fold axis is conjugate to the groups of operations of one other 3-fold axis through transformations by A_π. The operations of all the 2-fold axes therefore serve to relate all the 3-fold axes. The operations of the four 3-fold axes consequently constitute a complete set of conjugate subgroups of any of the 3-fold axes.

Each subgroup of a complete set of conjugate subgroups has the same complete set of conjugates. No two complete sets of conjugate subgroups can have a subgroup in common; otherwise, the two sets would be the same set.

Invariant subgroups. If every element of group G transforms a subgroup into itself, that subgroup is called a *self-conjugate*, or *invariant*, subgroup. This requires that, for every element B of group G,

$$B^{-1}gB = g. \tag{54}$$

It therefore follows that

$$gB = Bg. \tag{55}$$

The terms in the two sides of (55) are right and left cosets of g, specifically,

$$gB = a_1B, \quad a_2B, \quad a_3B, \quad \cdots. \tag{56}$$

$$Bg = Ba_1, \quad Ba_2, \quad Ba_3, \quad \cdots. \tag{57}$$

Relation (55) implies that collections (56) and (57) are identical, although the order of terms may be different. If g is an invariant subgroup of G, then its right and left cosets are identical for all elements B of group G.

Every subgroup of index 2 *is an invariant subgroup.* In this case the expansion of the group in right and left cosets is

$$G = g, \quad gB$$

$$G = g, \quad Bg$$

Since g is common to these two collections, it is evident that (55) holds. This implies (54), so that g is an invariant subgroup.

Group products

When some simple groups are discovered there are a number of ways of incorporating them into more complex groups in such a way that the simple group becomes a subgroup of a more complex group. These methods have direct application to the construction of complicated crystallographic groups from simpler crystallographic groups. They will be discussed in several stages of increasing generality.

Let the simpler group be designated g, and let it contain the operations a_1, $a_2, a_3, \cdots, a_r$. Let B be an element not in the simple group g.

Theorem: If an element B of order 2 *transforms a group g into itself, then the elements of g, together with the products of B with g, form a group.*

The collection of elements under consideration is

$$\begin{matrix} g = a_1\,(=I), & a_2, & a_3, & a_4, & \cdots, & a_r, \\ Bg = Ba_1, & Ba_2, & Ba_3, & Ba_4, & \cdots, & Ba_r, \end{matrix} \tag{58}$$

and the conditions are

$$Bg = gB. \tag{59}$$

Collection (58) is now examined for conformity to the group postulates:

1. Since g is a group,

$$a_i a_j = a_k \tag{60}$$

holds for any product formed from elements in the first line of (58). For products found from an element of the first line and an element of the second line, the general form is Ba_1a_j. But according to (60),

$$Ba_i a_j = Ba_k, \tag{61}$$

which is in the second line. For products formed from two elements of the second line, the general form is Ba_iBa_j. Now, according to (28) and the corresponding theorem, the product Ba_i can be reformulated as a permuted product involving a transformed element. In this particular case, consider the transform of a_i by B^{-1}. This is

$$a_i' = Ba_iB^{-1}, \tag{62}$$

and so

$$a_i'B = Ba_i. \tag{63}$$

Therefore the product Ba_iBa_j can be reduced to

$$Ba_iBa_j = a_i'BBa_j. \tag{64}$$

Since B is of order 2,

$$BB = I, \tag{65}$$

so that (64) becomes

$$Ba_iBa_j = a_i'a_j. \tag{66}$$

Since B transforms the group g into itself, the term a_i' (that is a_i transformed by B) is simply another element of the first row of (58). Thus the products of elements of (58) comprise a closed set.

2. The identity is the identity of g, namely $a_1 = I$.

3. The inverse of any element a_n in the first line of (58) is a_n^{-1} and occurs in that line because g is a group. The inverse of any element in the second line is $(Ba_n)^{-1}$. According to Chapter 12 this is $a_n^{-1}B^{-1}$, and this is the same as $B^{-1}(a_n^{-1})'$, where the prime again denotes the element a_n^{-1} transformed by B^{-1}. Since the order of B is 2, $B^{-1} = B$, so that $B^{-1}(a_n^{-1})' = B(a_n^{-1})'$, which is in the second line.

Thus the collection (58) is a group. This is one of the simplest ways of finding somewhat more complex groups from simple ones, and its application in crystallography will be illustrated shortly.

This method of forming groups can be readily generalized to apply to an operation of order n:

Theorem: If B is an element of order n which transforms a group g into itself, the set of products with g of the powers of B comprise a group.

For example, let B generate a cyclical group of order 3 whose elements are 1, B, and B^2. The products with the elements of g are

$$\begin{array}{cccccc} a_1(=I) & a_2, & a_3 & a_4, & \cdots, & a_r, \\ B & Ba_2, & Ba_3, & Ba_4, & \cdots, & Ba_r, \\ B^2 & B^2a_2, & B^2a_3 & B^2a_4, & \cdots, & B^2a_r. \end{array} \qquad (67)$$

That the products of elements of this collection are closed is indicated briefly as follows:

(*a*) Any product $a_ia_j = a_k$ is in the set.

(*b*) Any product $Ba_ia_j = Ba_k$ is in the set.

(*c*) Any product $Ba_iBa_j = BBa_i'a_j = B^2a_i'a_j$ is in the set.

(*d*) Any product $Ba_iB^2a_j = a_i'BB^2a_j = a_i'Ia_j = a_i'a_j$ is in the set.

(*e*) Any product $B^2a_iB^2a_j = a_i'B^2B^2a_j = a_i'Ba_j = B'a_i'a_j$ is in the set.

The identity is $a_1 = I$, and it can be proved, as in the last demonstration, that each element has an inverse.

The method of forming groups just discussed can be described as taking the products of the terms of a cyclical group h with the terms of another group g, with the restriction that the group g is transformed into itself by an operation in h. The new group is represented by the symbol $h \cdot g$. This method of forming the product of two groups can be generalized so that group h is not necessarily cyclic:

Theorem: If g and h are two groups having no common element except the identity, and if each of the elements of group h transforms group g into itself, the set of products of the elements of the two groups constitutes a group. The new group is called a group product, $g \cdot h$.

Let the elements of g be

$$a_1(=I), \quad a_2, \quad a_3 \quad a_4, \quad \cdots, \quad a_r,$$

and let the elements of h be

$$b_1(=I), \quad b_2, \quad b_3 \quad b_4, \quad \cdots, \quad b_s$$

Then the set of products of the elements of the two groups is

$$\left.\begin{array}{cccccc} I & a_2, & a_3, & a_4, & \cdots, & a_r \\ b_2a_1, & b_2a_2, & b_2a_3, & b_2a_4, & \cdots, & b_2a_r \\ b_3a_1, & b_3a_2, & b_3a_3, & b_3a_4, & \cdots, & b_3a_r \\ b_4a_1, & b_4a_2, & b_4a_3, & b_4a_4, & \cdots, & b_4a_r \\ \cdot & \cdot & \cdot & \cdot & \cdots, & \cdot \\ \cdot & \cdot & \cdot & \cdot & \cdots, & \cdot \\ \cdot & \cdot & \cdot & \cdot & \cdots, & \cdot \\ b_sa_1, & b_sa_2, & b_sa_3, & b_sa_4, & \cdots, & b_sa_r \end{array}\right\} \qquad (68)$$

The important condition is that any b transforms the first line of (68) into itself, i.e., that

$$b_n^{-1}a_x b_n = a_y \tag{69}$$

so that

$$a_x b_n = b_n a_y, \tag{70}$$

where both a_x and a_y are in g, i.e., in the first line of (68).

The general form of a product of two elements of array (68) is $b_q a_p \cdot b_n a_m$. By virtue of (70), pairs of elements of this product can be transposed by changing the subscript of the a; for example,

$$b_q a_p \cdot b_n a_m = a_u b_q b_n a_m \tag{71}$$

$$= a_u b_v a_m. \tag{72}$$

Note that, since h is a group, $b_q b_n = b_v$ is in the group. Again, an ab pair can be permuted by changing the subscript of the a. Therefore the right side of (72) can be written

$$= b_v a_w a_m. \tag{73}$$

Note that $a_w a_m = a_z$ (say) is a member of group g, so that (73) can be written

$$= b_v a_z \tag{74}$$

This last product is a member of set (68), and so the set of products is closed.

The identity is the only common term $a_1 = I = b_1$, because $b_n a_m \cdot I = b_n(a_m \cdot I) = b_n a_m$. An inverse exists for any term $b_n a_m$, namely $a_m^{-1} b_n^{-1}$, since $b_n a_m a_m^{-1} b_n^{-1} = I$. This inverse $a_m^{-1} b_n^{-1}$ is in the set, since a_m^{-1} and b_n^{-1} are in groups g and h respectively. Thus the terms in array (68) conform to the group postulates.

Each term of (68) is distinct. If not, suppose that

$$b_n a_m = b_q a_p. \tag{75}$$

This implies that

$$b_q^{-1} b_n a_m = a_p$$

and

$$b_q^{-1} b_n = a_p a_m^{-1}. \tag{76}$$

But this requires the two groups to have a common element. Since this is contrary to hypothesis, unless the two sides of (76) are both the identity, all elements in (68) are distinct. Therefore the order of the product $h \cdot g$ is the product of the orders of the groups h and g.

Isomorphic groups

Simple isomorphism. Two (or more) groups whose elements have different meanings may have certain formal features the same. The relationship is described by saying that the groups are *isomorphic*, that is, that they have the same form. Specifically, two groups G and G' are said to be *isomorphic* (sometimes specifically described as *simply isomorphic*) if, to every element X of G, there corresponds a unique element X' of G', and if, to the product X_1X_2 of G, there corresponds the product $X_1'X_2'$ of G'. This amounts to saying that two groups are simply isomorphic if they have the same kind of multiplication table. In other words, if no significance is attached to the symbols in the multiplication table, two simply isomorphic groups have *abstractly identical* multiplication tables.

To illustrate this in simplest form, consider the multiplication table for a group whose elements are I and X; namely,

$$\begin{array}{c|cc} & I & X \\ \hline I & I & X \\ X & X & I. \end{array} \tag{77}$$

No significance has yet been attached to the symbol X, so that (77) represents an *abstract group*. The important feature of the group is that it contains only two elements I and X, so that X^2 must equal I. Now this is also true of a group of 2-fold rotations, or of a group of reflections, or of a group of inversions. The multiplication tables of these specific groups are respectively:

2-fold rotation

$$\begin{array}{c|cc} & 1 & A_\pi \\ \hline 1 & 1 & A_\pi \\ A_\pi & A_\pi & 1 \end{array}; \tag{78}$$

reflection

$$\begin{array}{c|cc} & 1 & m \\ \hline 1 & 1 & m \\ m & m & 1 \end{array}; \tag{79}$$

inversion

$$\begin{array}{c|cc} & 1 & i \\ \hline 1 & 1 & i \\ i & i & 1 \end{array}. \tag{80}$$

Since these tables are abstractly identical, these three groups are isomorphic.

Consider some slightly more complicated examples: The point groups 222 and $mm2$ are simply isomorphic. Let the different axes and directions normal to planes be distinguished by priming. Then the multiplication tables of these groups are

222: (81)

	1	A'	A''	A'''
1	1	A'	A''	A'''
A'	A'	1	A'''	A''
A''	A''	A'''	1	A'
A'''	A'''	A''	A'	1 ;

*mm*2: (82)

	1	m'	m''	A'''
1	1	m'	m''	A'''
m'	m'	1	A'''	m''
m''	m''	A'''	1	m'
A'''	A'''	m''	m'	1. .

These two multiplication tables are similar in that

1 corresponds to 1,
m' ,, ,, A',
m'' ,, ,, A'',
and A''' ,, ,, A'''.

The two groups 222 and *mm*2 are therefore isomorphic.

But it does not follow that any two groups of order 4 are isomorphic. The isomorphism of the groups just considered is founded on the characteristics that $m^2 = 1$ and $A^2 = 1$. Other groups of order 4 can be devised for which this is not true. Consider the group of rotations of the crystal class $\bar{4}$, for example. Here the operations are 1, $A_{\pi/2,i}$, $A^2_{\pi/2,i}$, $A^3_{\pi/2,i}$, so that this is a cyclical group with $A^4 = 1$. Its multiplication table is

$\bar{4}$: (83)

	1	A	A^2	A^3
1	1	A	A^2	A^3
A	A	A^2	A^3	1
A^2	A^2	A^3	1	A
A^3	A^3	1	A	A^2

Since the elements in (83) cannot be made to correspond with (81), the point groups $\bar{4}$ and 222 are not isomorphic.

General isomorphism. The relation of "simple" isomorphism of groups has just been discussed. There exists also a more general kind of isomorphism known as *homomorphism*. This will be introduced in connection with space groups.

The transform of a group by its own elements

In the multiplication tables just given, each element of the group appears once in each column and once in each row. This is a consequence of group property; that is, if any element of the group is combined with another element of the group, the result is an element of the group. Furthermore, if an element X is combined with each element $B_1, B_2, \cdots$, of the group, the various products are distinct. If two were the same, say XB_i and XB_j, then

$$XB_i = XB_j \tag{84}$$

so that

$$B_i = B_j, \tag{85}$$

which implies that two elements of the group are not distinct, which is contrary to the listing of group elements. Therefore each row and column of the multiplication table contains only the n distinct elements of the group in some order.

In this way each element X of the group G transforms the group into itself. The analytical expression of this is

$$XG = G. \tag{86}$$

Since this is true for all elements, X, of the group, it can also be said that the group transforms itself into itself. A representation of this is

$$GG = G. \tag{87}$$

21 · Group theory applied to point symmetries

The point symmetries can be derived by showing first that certain simple symmetries can be formulated as groups of symmetry operations, and then creating supergroups based upon these simple ones. An outline of how this is done is contained in this chapter.

Groups of rotations about an axis

General aspects of groups of rotations. Different rotations about an axis can be combined by the algebraic addition of the angles of rotation. Combinations of rotations are therefore associative and conform to group postulate 1*a*.

Rotations about the same axis which are multiples of the same angular displacement form a closed set, and therefore conform to group postulate 1. If negative, zero, and positive multiples are included in the set, then it also conforms to group postulates 2 and 3. This group of rotations is, in general, infinite, and is isomorphic with the group of all integers combined by addition.

A simplification occurs if the fundamental rotation, α, is an aliquot part, $1/n$, of 2π, for then n rotations equal 2π, which is the same as no displacement. This group has only the n distinct operations,

$$A_\alpha, \quad A_\alpha^2, \quad A_\alpha^3, \quad \cdots, \quad A_\alpha^n \, (= 1). \tag{1}$$

This set of rotations evidently comprises a cyclical group of order n. It is designated in Schoenflies notation as C_n, and in the symbols employed in this book by $\{n\}$. In these groups each rotation transforms all other rotations of the group into themselves, so that they are all mutually permutable and the groups are Abelian.

It should be observed that nothing has been said so far about crystallographic groups. For example, C_5, C_7, C_{10}, etc., are perfectly possible groups of rotations.

The multiplication table of a cyclical group follows the pattern of (83) of the last chapter. A characteristic of this table is that any line has a sequence of operations the same as the preceding line except that it is shifted one position to the left. This shift occurs because the multiplying element of the line is one power greater than that of the preceding line.

The groups of improper rotations. The groups of improper rotations offer some interesting complications. One peculiarity is that in some groups the "order" of the axis is not the same as the order of the group. Another is that in some groups the cyclical group can be decomposed into group products involving rotations or inversions.

To discuss these groups, let n be the order of the axis and η be the order of the group. The operations of such a group are

$$A_{\alpha,i}, \quad A^2_{\alpha,i}, \quad A^3_{\alpha,i}, \quad A^4_{\alpha,i}, \quad \cdots, \quad A^{\eta}_{\alpha,i} \, (= 1) \tag{2}$$

This can be rewritten in such a way that the rotation and inversion are separated:

$$A_\alpha \cdot i, \quad (A_\alpha \cdot i)^2, \quad (A_\alpha \cdot i)^3, \quad (A_\alpha \cdot i)^4, \quad \cdots, \quad (A_\alpha i)^{\eta} \, (= 1). \tag{3}$$

This is the same as

$$A_\alpha i, \quad A_\alpha{}^2 i^2, \quad A_\alpha{}^3 i^3, \quad A_\alpha{}^4 i^4, \quad \cdots, \quad A_\alpha{}^{\eta} i^{\eta} \, (= 1). \tag{4}$$

Since $i^2 = 1$, as shown in (40) of Chapter 20, the even-powered terms of (4) can be simplified, so that it reduces to

$$A_\alpha i, \quad A_\alpha{}^2, \quad A_\alpha{}^3 i, \quad A_\alpha{}^4, \quad \cdots, \quad A_\alpha{}^{\eta} \, (= 1) \tag{5}$$

It is evident from this that the *order of an improper cyclical rotation group must always be even*; otherwise, i^{η} could not vanish in (4) and the last term in (5) could not be identity. Consequently, when n is even, the nth term of (5) is identity, but when n is odd, it takes $2n$ terms of (5) to reach identity. Therefore when n is even, $\eta = n$, but when n is odd, $\eta = 2n$.

It is evident that the category of n is important. Consider the following categories:

n odd (i.e., $n = 4N \pm 1$). The simplest group of this category other than $\bar{1}$ itself is that of the rotations of the $\bar{3}$ axis. (This and $\bar{1}$ are also the only crystallographic examples.) For clearness consider this simple case. Its operations are:

$$A_\alpha i, \quad A_\alpha{}^2, \quad A_\alpha{}^3 i, \quad A_\alpha{}^4, \quad A_\alpha{}^5 i, \quad A_\alpha{}^6 \, (= 1). \tag{6}$$

But, in view of the fact that n is odd, the sequence A^4, A^5, A^6 is the same as A, A^2, A^3, so that (6) can be reduced to

$$A_\alpha i, \quad A_\alpha{}^2, \quad A_\alpha{}^3 i, \quad A_\alpha, \quad A_\alpha{}^2 i, \quad A_\alpha{}^3 \, (= 1). \tag{7}$$

Now it is clear that there is a sequence of powers of A_α and a sequence of the same powers multiplied by i. They can be arranged as follows:

$$\begin{matrix} 1 & A_\alpha & A_\alpha{}^2 \\ i & A_\alpha i & A_\alpha{}^2 i \end{matrix} \tag{8}$$

This arrangement can be described as the subgroup 1, A_α, $A_\alpha{}^2$ and its coset with respect to i. It can also be described as the product of the subgroups $\{1, A_\alpha, A_\alpha{}^2\}$ and $\{1, i\}$. If these subgroups are abbreviated as $\{3\}$, and $\{\bar{1}\}$ while the full group is represented by $\{\bar{3}\}$, then the relation can be written

$$\{\bar{3}\} = \{3\}\{\bar{1}\}$$

or

$$\{\bar{3}\} = \{3\}\{i\}. \tag{9}$$

In a similar way any improper rotation group $\{\bar{n}\}$ in this category can be written as a product of $\{n\}$ and $\{\bar{1}\}$. Its subgroups are evidently $\{n\}$, $\{\bar{1}\}$, any factors of n, and the two trivial groups $\{\bar{n}\}$ and $\{1\}$.

n even, n/2 odd (i.e., $n = 4N + 2$). The simplest groups of this category are those of the rotations of the $\bar{2}$ and $\bar{6}$ axes, which are also the only crystallographic examples. Since $\bar{2}$ shows certain trivial features, the group of rotations of the $\bar{6}$ axis may be taken as a type case. The operations of this group are

$$A_\alpha i,\quad A_\alpha{}^2 i^2,\quad A_\alpha{}^3 i^3,\quad A_\alpha{}^4 i^4,\quad A_\alpha{}^5 i^5,\quad A_\alpha{}^6 i^6\,(=1), \tag{10}$$

and, since even orders of i are identity, this is the same as

$$A_\alpha i,\quad A_\alpha{}^2,\quad A_\alpha{}^3 i,\quad A_\alpha{}^4,\quad A_\alpha{}^5 i,\quad A_\alpha{}^6\,(=1) \tag{11}$$

Since n is even in this category, the nth element is $A_{2\pi}$ and the rotational part of the $(n/2)$th term is A_π. Since

$$A_\pi \cdot i = m, \tag{12}$$

it is convenient to express the rotational parts of the elements containing i in such a way as to include a factor A_π, if possible. This can be done by making use of the relations (for the particular case of $\bar{6}$)

$$\begin{aligned} A_\alpha{}^3 &= A_\pi \\ A_\alpha{}^5 &= A_\alpha{}^2 A_\alpha{}^3 = A^2 A_\pi \\ A_\alpha &= A_\alpha{}^{-2} A_\alpha{}^3 = A_\alpha{}^4 A_\pi \end{aligned} \tag{13}$$

When these substitutions are made in (11) it takes the form

$$A_\alpha{}^4 A_\pi i,\quad A_\alpha{}^2,\quad A_\pi i,\quad A_\alpha{}^4,\quad A_\alpha{}^2 A_\pi i,\quad 1. \tag{14}$$

By virtue of (12) this can be converted to

$$A_\alpha{}^4 m \quad A_\alpha{}^2 \quad m \quad A_\alpha{}^4 \quad A_\alpha{}^2 m \quad 1 \tag{15}$$

This can be arranged in a form similar to (8), namely,

$$\begin{matrix} 1 & A_\alpha{}^2 & A_\alpha{}^4 \\ m & A_\alpha{}^2 m & A_\alpha{}^4 m. \end{matrix} \tag{16}$$

This arrangement shows that this group is the product of the groups $\{1, A_\alpha^2, A_\alpha^4\}$ and $\{1, m\}$. The relation can be written

$$\{\bar{6}\} = \{6/2\}\{\bar{2}\}$$

or

$$\{\bar{6}\} = \{3\}\{m\}. \tag{17}$$

In a similar way any improper rotation group in this category can be written as the product of the proper rotation group of half the order and the group $\{m\}$.

n even, n/2 even (i.e., $n = 4N$). The simplest nontrivial group of this category is that of the rotations of the $\bar{4}$ axis, which is also the only crystallographic example. For clearness, consider this simplest case. Its operations are

$$A_\alpha i, \quad A_\alpha^2, \quad A_\alpha^3 i, \quad A_\alpha^4 (= 1) \tag{18}$$

Since n is even in this category, the nth term is $A_{2\pi}$ and the $(n/2)$th element is A_π. These two operations always constitute a subgroup $\{1, A_\pi\} \equiv \{2\}$. There is no further way to relate the elements that do not contain the factor i with those that do. Therefore this category cannot be decomposed into products involving $\{i\}$ or $\{m\}$.

Subgroups of the cyclical groups of proper rotations. The subgroups of a cyclical group are generated by powers of its elements. If a group of proper rotations is generated by a rotation A_α, then its subgroups are generated by $A_\alpha^p = A_{p\alpha}$. Since $\alpha = 2\pi/n$, $p\alpha = 2\pi/(n/p)$. This implies that, if $\{n\}$ is a group, its subgroups are $\{n/p\}$. Both n and p are integers. Therefore, to find the subgroups of $\{n\}$, one simply writes down the results of dividing n by its factors; this result is simply a list of factors of n. The subgroups of the crystallographic cyclical groups of proper rotations are given in Table 1.

Table 1. Subgroups of the crystallographic cyclical groups of proper rotations

Group	Subgroups				
{1}	{1}				
{2}	{1}	{2}			
{3}	{1}		{3}		
{4}	{1}	{2}		{4}	
{6}	{1}	{2}	{3}		{6}

Subgroups of the cyclical groups of improper rotations. The subgroups of the improper rotations can be constructed exactly as for the proper rotations.

From a list of the η powers of the generating element, such as (3), the power $(A_\alpha i)^p$ is selected as a generating element, and its powers constitute a group.

If p is even, then, since $i^2 = 1$, all the i's vanish and the subgroup is a group of proper rotations. Since it was shown that the order of a group of improper rotations is always even, there is always at least one subgroup of proper rotations.

If p is odd, then the powers are alternately improper rotations and proper rotations, and the subgroup is a group of improper rotations. Since the order η of the group is even, η/p, which is the order of the subgroup, must be even, so that the subgroup must contain improper and proper rotations in equal numbers. Such subgroups require several periods of elements like (5) for the selection of powers to end on A^η $(=1)$, and these subgroups turn out to be the group itself.

For the category $n = 4N$, groups cannot be decomposed into products involving inversion or reflection. The only nontrivial subgroups are those of proper rotations. The subgroup of greatest order is $(n/2)$, and other subgroups are subgroups of this one.

For the categories $n = 4N + 1$ and $n = 4N + 2$, the groups can be decomposed into a product of a proper rotation group and either $\{i\}$ or $\{m\}$, respectively. The proper rotation group can be decomposed into subgroups as outlined in the last section. These subgroups, and their products with $\{i\}$ and $\{m\}$, comprise the subgroups of the group.

The subgroups of the crystallographic cyclical groups of improper rotations are listed in Table 2.

Table 2. Subgroups of the crystallographic cyclical groups of improper rotations

Improper rotation group	Decomposition into group product	Order	Subgroups	
			Proper	Improper
$\{\bar{1}\}$	$\{1\}\{\bar{1}\}$	2	$\{1\}$	$\{\bar{1}\}$
$\{\bar{2}\}$	$\{1\}\{\bar{2}\}$	2	$\{1\}$	$\{\bar{2}\}$
$\{\bar{3}\}$	$\{3\}\{\bar{1}\}$	6	$\{1\}$ $\{3\}$	$\{\bar{1}\}$ $\{\bar{3}\}$
$\{\bar{4}\}$	—	4	$\{1\}$ $\{2\}$	$\{\bar{4}\}$
$\{\bar{6}\}$	$\{3\}\{\bar{2}\}$	6	$\{1\}$ $\{3\}$	$\{\bar{2}\}$ $\{\bar{6}\}$

The crystallographic cyclical rotation groups. A cyclical rotation group is a crystallographic group only if n has one of the permissible crystallographic values of 1, 2, 3, 4, or 6. The Schoenflies designations for the groups of proper rotations are C_1, C_2, C_3, C_4, and C_6, corresponding to the crystal classes 1, 2, 3, 4, and 6. The Schoenflies designations for the groups of improper rotations are C_1', C_2', C_3', C_4', and C_6', corresponding to crystal classes $\bar{1}$, $\bar{2}$, $\bar{3}$, $\bar{4}$, and $\bar{6}$. Note that the subscript n of C_n' refers to the order of the *axis* and not of the group; the order of the group C_3' is 6, not 3, since 3 is odd.

Groups of rotations about several axes

Since lattices are consistent only with 1-, 2-, 3-, 4-, and 6-fold axes, the basic symmetries of crystals must be composed of the groups $\{1\}$, $\{2\}$, $\{3\}$, $\{4\}$, $\{6\}$, and $\{\bar{1}\} = \{i\}$, $\{\bar{2}\} = \{m\}$, $\{\bar{3}\} = \{\bar{3}\}\{i\}$, $\{\bar{4}\}$, and $\{\bar{6}\} = \{3\}\{m\}$. All the permissible crystallographic groups must consist of these groups plus their combinations, that is, plus their products.

Since products can be readily formed when each element of the one group transforms the other group into itself, a knowledge of the geometrical meanings of the operations is required. These were discussed in earlier chapters. In general, one axis, and its operations, transform another axis, and its operations, into themselves only if the axes are parallel or perpendicular. Parallel combinations could result in acceptable combinations only when they are identical with possible rotations about the same axis, and hence can be disregarded since such groups have already been investigated.

Products of two proper rotation groups. A 2-fold axis perpendicular to any other axis transforms that axis into itself. Therefore the products $\{2\}\{n\}$ are groups. These are the dihedral groups designated D_n in Schoenflies notation. A dihedral group exists for each crystallographic value of n, specifically

$$
\begin{aligned}
\{2\}\{1\} \equiv \{2\} &\Leftrightarrow C_2,\\
\{2\}\{2\} &\Leftrightarrow D_2,\\
\{2\}\{3\} &\Leftrightarrow D_3,\\
\{2\}\{4\} &\Leftrightarrow D_4,\\
\{2\}\{6\} &\Leftrightarrow D_6.
\end{aligned}
$$

Note that the possibility $\{2\}\{1\}$ represents a trivial product, equivalent to the simple cyclical rotation group C_2.

The operations of these groups are found by forming the products of the operations of group $\{2\}$ with group $\{n\}$, that is, the products of $\{1, A_\pi\}$ with $\{1, B_\alpha, B_{2\alpha}, \cdots, B_{(n-1)\alpha}\}$. The product of each A and B element, which are rotations, is another rotation C. The characteristics of each product C can be found by using the Eulerian method as outlined in Chapter 4. The angle γ of the rotation C can be found by solving (16) of Chapter 4 for W;

$$\cos W = -\cos U \cos V + \sin U \sin V \cos w. \tag{19}$$

Here,
$$U = \alpha/2 = \pi/2 \quad \text{for group } \{2\}$$
$$V = \beta/2$$
$$W = \gamma/2$$
$$W = A \wedge B = \pi/2.$$

Substituting these values into (19) it reduces to

$$\cos W = -0 \cdot \cos V + 1 \cdot \sin V \cdot 0 \tag{20}$$
$$= 0;$$
$$\therefore \quad W = \pi/2,$$
$$\text{and so} \quad \gamma = \pi. \tag{21}$$

This requires the products, C, to be 2-fold operations, which, together with the element 1, constitute the operations of various 2-fold axes.

The Eulerian method can be used also for finding the angle these 2-fold axes, C, make with the original 2-fold axis A. To do this, an equation like (17) of Chapter 4 is solved for $v = 2\beta$, which is the angle between A and C. This equation is

$$\cos v = \frac{\cos V - \cos W \cos U}{\sin W \sin U}. \tag{22}$$

In this case this reduces to

$$\cos v = \frac{\cos V - \cos(\pi/2)\cos(\pi/2)}{\sin(\pi/2)\sin(\pi/2)}$$
$$= \frac{\cos V - 0 \cdot 0}{1 \cdot 1} \tag{23}$$
$$= \cos V.$$

Since $V = \beta/2$, this requires that

$$\cos v = \cos \beta/2;$$
$$\therefore \quad v = \beta/2. \tag{24}$$

As a consequence of this discussion it is seen that each product of the type $A_\pi B_\beta$ is another rotation C_π about an axis making an angle of $\beta/2$ with A_π.

The operations of the four crystallographic dihedral groups are given in the following sections:

$\{2\}\{2\} = 222$, *also designated* D_2, V, *or* Q. The elements of this product can be written

$$\begin{matrix} 1 & B_\pi \\ A_\pi & A_\pi B_\pi, \end{matrix} \tag{25}$$

which is the same as

$$\begin{matrix} 1 & B_\pi \\ A_\pi & C_\pi. \end{matrix} \tag{26}$$

This is illustrated in Fig. 1. Each 2-fold operation transforms the operations of the other 2-fold axes into themselves. Each of the three subgroups $\{1, A_\pi\}$, $\{1, B_\pi\}$, and $\{1, C_\pi\}$ is therefore transformed into itself by all other operations and so each is an invariant subgroup.

The subgroups of this group are obviously $\{1\}$, $\{1, A_\pi\}$, $\{1, B_\pi\}$, $\{1, C_\pi\}$, and $\{1, A_\pi\}\{1, B_\pi\}$, which can be expressed $\{1\}$, $\{{}^12\}$, $\{{}^22\}$, $\{{}^32\}$, and $\{{}^12\}\{{}^22\}$. A more compact listing is given in Table 4.

Group (25) is isomorphic with one of the two possible abstract groups of order 4. This group is known as the *four group*, or the *Vierergruppe*, or the *quadratic group*. Its Schoenflies symbol, commonly written D_2 to emphasize its relation to other dihedral groups, is also written V (for *Vierergruppe*) and Q (for quadratic group).

The other group of order 4 is the cyclical group $\{1, A, A^2, A^3\}$.

$\{2\}\{3\} = 32$, *also designated* D_3. The elements of this product can be written

$$\begin{matrix} 1 & B_{2\pi/3} & B_{-2\pi/3} \\ A_\pi & A_\pi B_{2\pi/3} & A_\pi B_{-2\pi/3}, \end{matrix} \tag{27}$$

which are the same as

$$\begin{matrix} 1 & B_{2\pi/3} & B_{-2\pi/3} \\ A_\pi & {}^1C_\pi & {}^2C_\pi. \end{matrix} \tag{28}$$

Here the presuperscripts on the C's denote two different axes. The elements of the group are illustrated in Fig. 2.

Figure 2 shows that, while A, ${}^1C$, and ${}^2C$ transform the subgroup $\{1, B_{2\pi/3}, B_{-2\pi/3}\}$ into itself, B does not transform A into itself. Rather B transforms A into ${}^2C$, ${}^1C$ into the reverse end of A, and ${}^2C$ into the reverse end of ${}^1C$. Thus each axis is transformed into the other end of another axis; i.e., each operation is transformed into the reverse of another operation. These statements are therefore equivalent to the transformations

$$\begin{aligned} B^{-1}(A)B &= {}^2C^{-1}, \\ B^{-1}({}^1C)B &= A^{-1}, \\ B^{-1}({}^2C)B &= {}^1C^{-1}. \end{aligned} \tag{29}$$

Since no operation of the group transforms opposite ends of these axes into themselves, these axes are said to be *polar*.

The subgroups of this group are the subgroups of $\{1, A\}$ and $\{1, B, B^2\}$, their transforms, and their products. They are listed in Table 4.

This group is isomorphic with one of the two possible abstract groups of order 6. The other is the cyclical group $\{1, A, A^2, A^3, A^4, A^5\}$.

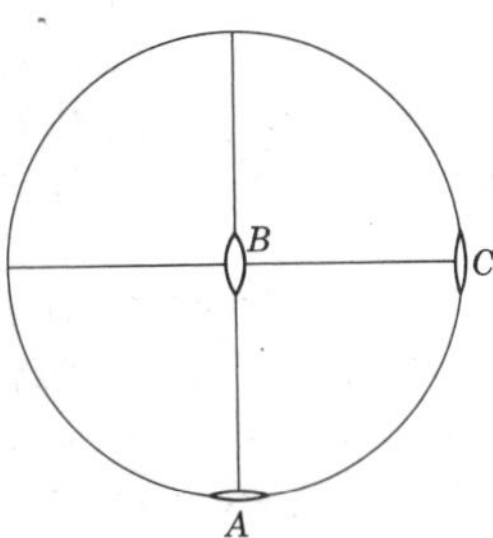

FIG. 1. Derivation of the elements of the group {2} {2}.

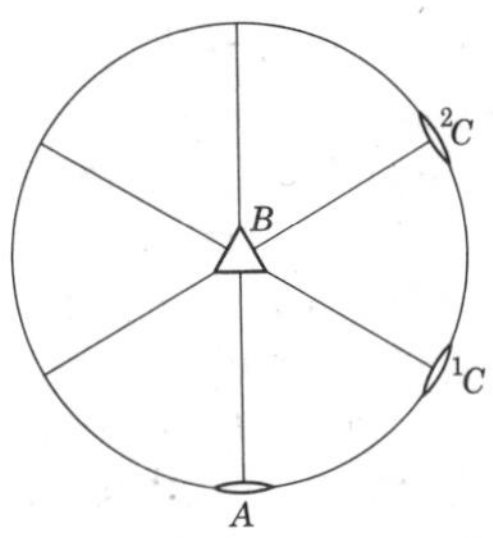

FIG. 2. Derivation of the elements of the group {2} {3}.

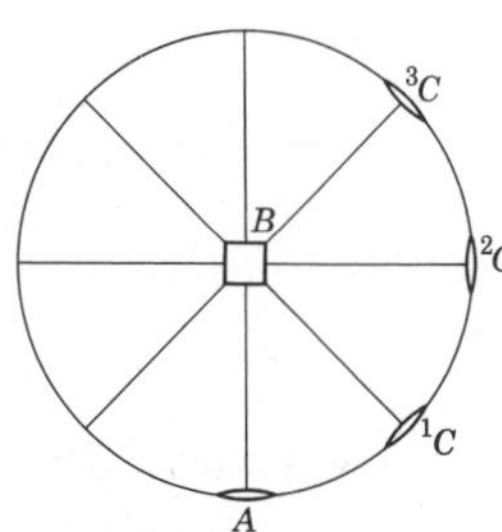

FIG. 3. Derivation of the elements of the group {2} {4}.

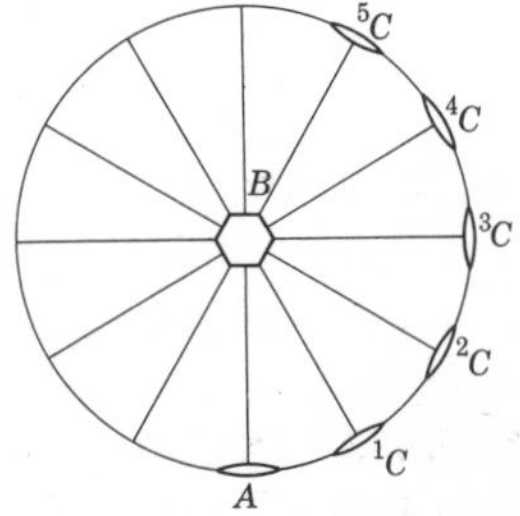

FIG. 4. Derivation of the elements of the group {2} {6}.

{2} {4} = 422, *also designated* D_4. The elements of this product can be written

$$\begin{matrix} 1 & B_{\pi/2} & B_{\pi} & B_{-\pi/2} \\ A_{\pi} & A_{\pi}B_{\pi/2} & A_{\pi}B_{\pi/2} & A_{\pi}B_{-\pi/2}, \end{matrix} \tag{30}$$

which are the same as

$$\begin{matrix} 1 & B_{\pi/2} & B_{\pi} & B_{-\pi/2} \\ A_{\pi} & {}^1C_{\pi} & {}^2C_{\pi} & {}^3C_{\pi}. \end{matrix} \tag{31}$$

These are illustrated in Fig. 3. The illustration shows that, while A, ${}^1C$, ${}^2C$, and ^3C transform B into itself, B does not transform the other operations into themselves. Rather,

$$\begin{aligned} B^{-1}\,(A)B &= {}^2C, \\ B^{-1}\,({}^1C)B &= {}^3C, \\ B^{-1}\,({}^2C)B &= A^{-1}, \\ B^{-1}\,({}^3C)B &= {}^1C^{-1}. \end{aligned} \tag{32}$$

At the same time, the operation B^2 transforms opposite ends of the same axis into itself. Each axis is therefore nonpolar.

The subgroups of this group are listed in Table 4.

This group is isomorphic with one of the five possible abstract groups of order 8.

$\{2\}\,\{6\} = 622$, *also designated* D_6. The elements of this product can be written

$$\begin{matrix} 1 & B_{2\pi/6} & B_{2\pi/3} & B_{\pi} & B_{-2\pi/3} & B_{-2\pi/6} \\ A_{\pi} & A_{\pi}B_{2\pi/6} & A_{\pi}B_{2\pi/3} & A_{\pi}B_{\pi} & A_{\pi}B_{-2\pi/3} & A_{\pi}B_{-2\pi/6}, \end{matrix} \tag{33}$$

which are the same as

$$\begin{matrix} 1 & B_{2\pi/6} & B_{2\pi/3} & B_{\pi} & B_{-2\pi/3} & B_{-2\pi/6} \\ A_{\pi} & {}^1C_{\pi} & {}^2C_{\pi} & {}^3C_{\pi} & {}^4C_{\pi} & {}^5C_{\pi}. \end{matrix} \tag{34}$$

These are illustrated in Fig. 4. The A and C axes of this group are transformed into their reverses by B_{π}, and so they are nonpolar.

The subgroups of this group are listed in Table 4.

The isometric rotation groups

$\{3\}\,\{2\}\,\{2\} = 23$, *also designated* T. One of the dihedral groups is unique in that its three nontrivial operations are orthogonal rotations through angle π. This is the group $\{2\}\,\{2\} = 222$, Fig. 1. The three rotations can be visualized as projecting normal to three faces of a cube, as shown in Fig. 5A. This group can obviously be transformed into itself by a 3-fold rotation through a cube diagonal, D, as suggested by Fig. 5A. The products of $\{1, D, D^2\}$ with $\{{}^A2\}\{{}^B2\}$ therefore form a group. Each operation of $\{1, D, D^2\}$ transforms $\{{}^A2\}\{{}^B2\}$ into itself.

When the combination $A_{\pi}D_{2\pi/3}$ is found according to Euler's construction, the result is $E_{-2\pi/3}$, as illustrated in Fig. 5A. The relative senses of the rotations are illustrated in Fig. 5B by the angles $U = \alpha/2$, $V = \beta/2$, and $W = \gamma/2$. It is evident that, if the sense of the rotation, looking toward D, is positive, then that looking toward E is negative. The sense of the rotation about E looking

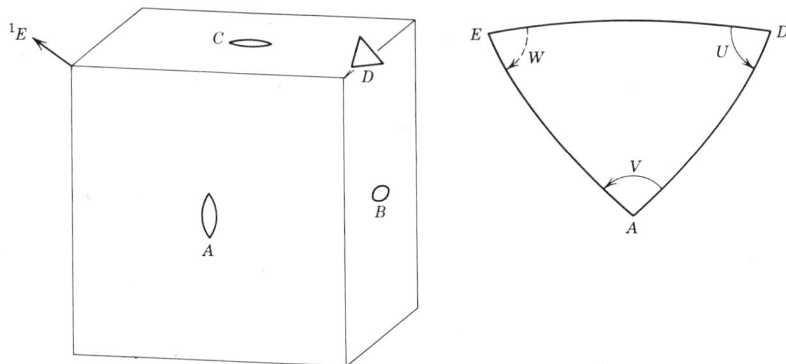

FIG. 5. Transformation of 222 into itself by 3-fold rotation at D, and the product $D_{2\pi/3} \cdot A_\pi = {}^1E_{-2\pi/3}$.

toward the opposite direction, however, is positive. This is consistent with the fact that the opposite end of E is the transform of D by B, as illustrated in Fig. 5A. The full set of operations of this group is found by multiplying the operations of $\{2\}\{2\}$, namely $\{1, A_\pi, B_\pi, C_\pi\}$, by $\{1, D_{2\pi/3}, D_{-2\pi/3}\}$. These operations are

$$\begin{array}{llll} 1 & A_\pi & B_\pi & C_\pi \\ D_{2\pi/3} & D_{2\pi/3}A_\pi & D_{2\pi/3}\,B_\pi & D_{2\pi/3}C_\pi \\ D_{-2\pi/3} & D_{-2\pi/3}A_\pi & D_{-2\pi/3}B_\pi & D_{-2\pi/3}C_\pi. \end{array} \tag{35}$$

When the products are formed by (17) of Chapter 4, this set of operations proves to be the same as

$$\begin{array}{llll} 1 & A_\pi & B_\pi & C_\pi \\ D_{2\pi/3} & {}^1E_{-2\pi/3} & {}^2E_{-2\pi/3} & {}^3E_{-2\pi/3} \\ D_{-2\pi/3} & {}^2E_{2\pi/3} & {}^2E_{2\pi/3} & {}^3E_{2\pi/3}. \end{array} \tag{36}$$

The arrangement of axes in this group is illustrated in Fig. 6. The subgroups of this group are listed in Table 4.

This group is called the tetrahedral group because it is the group of rotations of the tetrahedron.

$\{3\}\{2\}\{2\}\{2\} = 432$, *also designated O.* In the group 23 just formed, the 3-fold axes projecting from the opposite corners of a cube face are equivalent by the operation of the 2-fold axes, yet the particular *ends* of the 3-fold axes which project from the adjacent corners of a cube face are not equivalent by any operation of the group 23. This amounts to saying that no operation of the group 23 carried D_α into any E_α, although the several operations of the group do carry D_α into $E_{-\alpha}$. There still remains the possibility, then, of performing this transformation of the group 23 into itself.

There are two operations which carry the two adjacent cube face corners into one another. One is a rotation of $\pi/2$ normal to the center of a cube face.

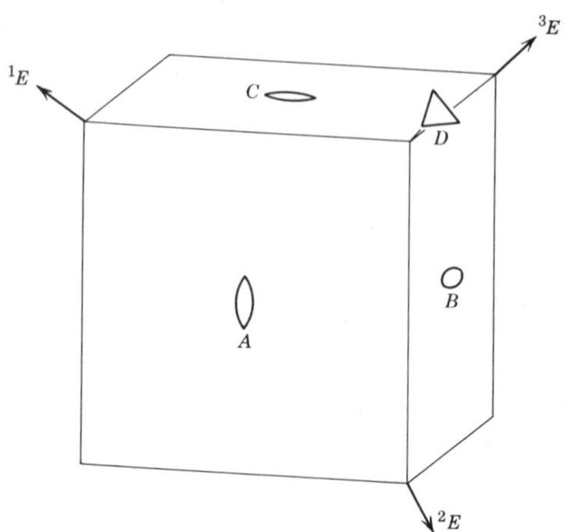

FIG. 6. The arrangement of axes in point group 23.

The other is a rotation of π through an axis F through the center of the cube edge and parallel to the diagonal of a cube face which does not share this edge. In Chapter 4 it was shown that these two rotations, and the 3-fold rotation in

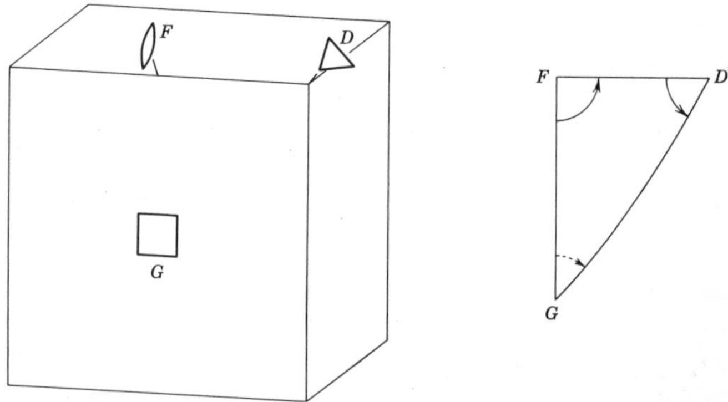

FIG. 7. Relation between rotations in point group 432.

question, are related, and this was indicated by the symbol 432. This is illustrated in Fig. 7.

To form this supergroup, the group $\{1, F_\pi\}$, located as shown in Fig. 7, must be multiplied by each of the 12 elements in (36), whose geometrical arrangement is indicated in Fig. 6. Since this must result in 12 new products, these are illustrated separately in Fig. 8. They are as follows:

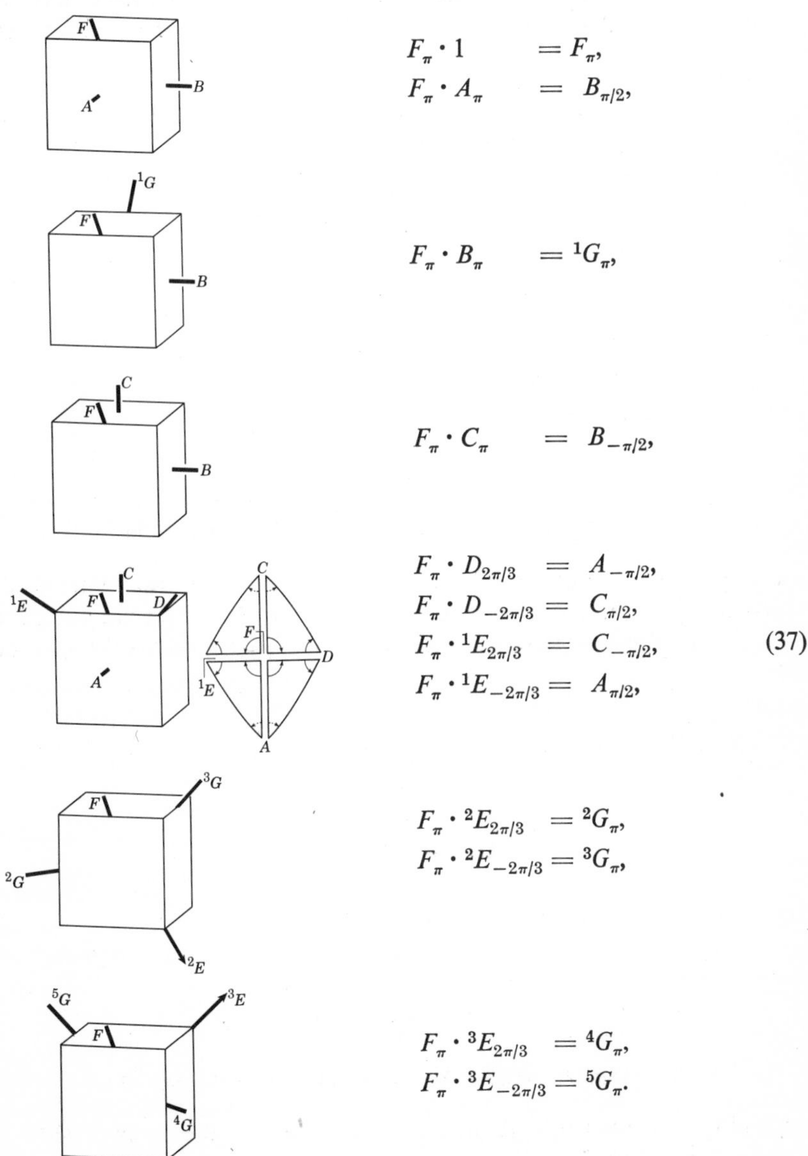

$$F_\pi \cdot 1 \quad = F_\pi,$$
$$F_\pi \cdot A_\pi \quad = B_{\pi/2},$$

$$F_\pi \cdot B_\pi \quad = {}^1G_\pi,$$

$$F_\pi \cdot C_\pi \quad = B_{-\pi/2},$$

$$\begin{aligned} F_\pi \cdot D_{2\pi/3} &= A_{-\pi/2}, \\ F_\pi \cdot D_{-2\pi/3} &= C_{\pi/2}, \\ F_\pi \cdot {}^1E_{2\pi/3} &= C_{-\pi/2}, \\ F_\pi \cdot {}^1E_{-2\pi/3} &= A_{\pi/2}, \end{aligned} \tag{37}$$

$$F_\pi \cdot {}^2E_{2\pi/3} = {}^2G_\pi,$$
$$F_\pi \cdot {}^2E_{-2\pi/3} = {}^3G_\pi,$$

$$F_\pi \cdot {}^3E_{2\pi/3} = {}^4G_\pi,$$
$$F_\pi \cdot {}^3E_{-2\pi/3} = {}^5G_\pi.$$

FIG. 8.

To appreciate the characteristics of the new group, the original elements and their products with $\{1, F_\pi\}$ should be rearranged so as to reveal the rotations about each axis. The elements of the new supergroup are then as follows:

$$\begin{array}{llll}
1 & & & \\
A_{\pi/2} & A_\pi & A_{-\pi/2} & \\
B_{\pi/2} & B_\pi & B_{-\pi/2} & \text{4-fold rotations,} \\
C_{\pi/2} & C_\pi & C_{-\pi/2} & \\
 & & & \\
D_{2\pi/3} & D_{-2\pi/3} & & \\
{}^1E_{2\pi/3} & {}^1E_{-2\pi/3} & & \text{3-fold rotations,} \\
{}^2E_{2\pi/3} & {}^2E_{-2\pi/3} & & \\
{}^3E_{2\pi/3} & {}^3E_{-2\pi/3} & & \\
 & & & \\
F_\pi & & & \\
{}^1G_\pi & & & \\
{}^2G_\pi & & & \text{2-fold rotations.} \\
{}^3G_\pi & & & \\
{}^4G_\pi & & & \\
{}^5G_\pi & & &
\end{array} \qquad (38)$$

This group contains 24 operations, which can be distributed to three 4-fold axes, four 3-fold axes, and six 2-fold axes. This is the group of rotations of an octahedron and is therefore called the octahedral group, which gives rise to the symbol O. It is currently symbolized by 432.

The subgroups of this group are listed in Table 4.

Groups of the second sort

The combination of two operations of the second sort is an operation of the first sort. This is readily seen if, for example, the operations of the second sort are expressed as rotoinversions. Let $A_{\alpha,i}$ and $B_{\beta,i}$ be any two such operations. Then their combination is

$$A_{\alpha,i}B_{\beta,i} = A_\alpha i B_\beta i. \qquad (39)$$

Now, the operation of inversion, i, has the property of transforming any rotation into itself, so that it is permutable with any operation of rotation. Since $i^2 = 1$, the product in (39) can therefore be reduced as follows:

$$\begin{aligned} A_{\alpha,i}B_{\beta,i} &= A_\alpha B_\beta ii \\ &= A_\alpha B_\beta. \end{aligned} \qquad (40)$$

This combination therefore is an operation of the first sort. *Therefore any group containing operations of the second sort also contains operations of the first sort.*

These operations of the first sort form a subgroup. This follows because they obey the group postulates. Specifically, the product of any two operations of the first sort is itself an operation of the first sort; these operations include identity; and, since they are already members of the supergroups, each has an inverse.

An important characteristic of the subgroup of operations of the first sort is that its index is always 2. This is equivalent to saying that the group of the second sort contains equal numbers of operations of the first sort and the second sort. To prove this, let the subgroup of operations of the first sort be represented by a's, specifically

$$\{g\} = 1, \quad a_2, \quad a_3, \quad \cdots, \quad a_n, \tag{41}$$

and let B be *any* operation of the second sort in the group. Then its products with (41) are

$$B\{g\} = B, \quad Ba_2, \quad Ba_3, \quad \cdots, \quad Ba_n, \tag{42}$$

There are as many products in (42) as in (41), and they are all of the form Ba_r. The B part of each such product can be expressed as a rotoinversion, $B_{\alpha,i}$, so that each product in (42) can be expressed as

$$\begin{aligned} B_{\alpha,i}a_r &= B_\alpha i a_r \\ &= B_\alpha \cdot a_r \cdot i. \end{aligned} \tag{43}$$

The part $B_\alpha a_r$ is an operation of the first sort, so that $B_\alpha a_r i$ is an operation of the second sort. Therefore all the products in (42) are operations of the second sort. Now this set contains *all* the operations of the second sort in the group. To prove this, select *any* operation C, which is a member of the group. Then, according to (40), CB is an operation of the first sort and so must be in (41). Let

$$CB = a_p, \tag{44}$$

that is, an operation in (41).

$$\therefore \qquad CBa_p^{-1} = 1, \tag{45}$$

$$\therefore \qquad Ba_p^{-1} = C^{-1}, \tag{46}$$

$$\therefore \qquad Ba_p^{-1}C^2 = C^{-1}C^2 = C. \tag{47}$$

But, according to (40), C^2 is an operation of the first sort and therefore must be included in (41). Let

$$C^2 = a_q. \tag{48}$$

Then (47) can be written

$$Ba_p a_q = C. \tag{49}$$

The product $a_p a_q$ is in (41). Let it be designated a_r. Then

$$Ba_r = C. \tag{50}$$

This proves that C is already in the set (42).

Several conclusions can be drawn from this:

1. *Any group of the second sort contains equal numbers of operations of the first sort and second sort.*

2. *In any group of the second sort, the operations of the first sort form a subgroup of index* 2.

3. *A group of the second sort can be formed from a group of the first sort by adding to it any operation of the second sort (and its products) which transforms the group into itself.*

4. *All groups of the second sort can be formed by starting with all groups of the first sort and adding to each, in turn, each possible operation of the second sort (and its products) which transforms the group into itself.* When this method is used to generate groups of the second sort, some of the groups based upon the same subgroup of the second sort are duplicates. This follows from (50). Some details of this situation are discussed below.

These conclusions are quite general. They apply to noncrystallographic and crystallographic groups, and to space groups as well as point groups.

Point groups of the second sort

General considerations. In Chapter 4 it was shown that any rotoinversion axis, except those for which $n = 4N$, can be decomposed into a combination of a rotation axis and an inversion, or a rotation axis and a reflection. Correspondingly, any possible operation, except those for which $n = 4N$, can be expressed as a combination of operations of a rotation and an inversion, or a rotation and a reflection. It follows that any group of the second sort, except those containing an operation of the second sort for which $n = 4N$, can be formed by adding operation i or m to a point group of the first sort in such a way that the new operation transforms the group into itself. This provides a method of forming point groups of the second sort. It corresponds to that followed in Chapter 6.

This method offers difficulties in the way of recognizing duplicates. Another method that avoids this difficulty and that takes full advantage of group theory is followed in this chapter.

Groups not containing *i*. As shown in a preceding section, any group of the second sort, $\{\bar{G}\}$, can be expressed as cosets of some proper subgroup $\{g\}$ of index 2, with some improper operation $\bar{n}$. This expansion is

$$\{\bar{G}\} = \{g\}, \ \bar{n}\{g\} \tag{51A}$$

$$= \{g\}, \{g\}\bar{n}. \tag{51B}$$

Since $\{g\}$ is of index 2, the left and right cosets $\bar{n}\{g\}$ and $\{g\}\bar{n}$ are the same, which assures that operation $\bar{n}$ transforms $\{g\}$ into itself. Now the products in (51*A*) and (51*B*) are similar to the set which occurs in a similar point group of the first sort, namely,

$$\{G\} = \{g\}, \ n\{g\} \tag{52A}$$

$$= \{g\}, \{g\}n. \tag{52A}$$

The subgroup $\{g\}$ occurs in both (51) and (52), and these two sets of elements differ only in that the multiplying element is $\bar{n}$ in (51) and n in (52). Both n and $\bar{n}$ represent operations of rotation about the same axis, so that they combine with the elements of $\{g\}$ in the same way as permitted by Euler's construction. Furthermore, if n is even, then the orders of n and $\bar{n}$ are the same, as pointed out in an earlier part of this chapter. (When n is odd the situation is different.) This means that the combinations of n with the elements of $\{g\}$ follow the same rules as the combinations of $\bar{n}$ with the elements of $\{g\}$. Therefore the two groups (51) and (52) are isomorphic.

This relation provides an easy way of constructing one category of groups of the second sort. *For every point group of the first sort, $\{G\}$, which can be expressed as a product of a subgroup $\{g\}$ of index 2, and an operation of the first sort, n, where n is even, there exists a corresponding point group of the second sort, $\{\bar{G}\}$, which can be expressed as a product of the same subgroup $\{g\}$ and the corresponding operation of the second sort, $\bar{n}$.*

This method is inapplicable to forming groups containing any operation $\bar{n}$ where n is odd. This is because the order of $\bar{n}$ is twice that of n when n is odd. Fortunately all groups that contain $\bar{n}$ when n is odd necessarily contain operation i, and such groups are easy to form, as outlined in the next section.

Thus only the odd orders of $\bar{n}$, when $\bar{n}$ is even, are permissible operations for this category. These permissible operations are specifically

$$\bar{2}\ (= m)$$

$$\bar{4}, \quad \bar{4}^3\ (= \bar{4}^{-1})$$

$$\bar{6}, \quad \bar{6}^3\ (= m), \quad \bar{6}^5\ (= \bar{6}^{-1}).$$

Since a group that contains operation p also contains operation p^{-1}, it is evident that different groups can be produced only when $\bar{n}$ is $\bar{2}$ (= m), $\bar{4}$, and $\bar{6}$.

As a consequence of this discussion it is apparent that all point groups of the second sort not containing operation *i* can be found by examining the subgroups of all the point groups of the first sort for subgroups of index 2. Whenever these occur, there exists a point group of the second sort which can be written

Table 3. Derivation of the crystallographic point groups of the second sort not containing operation *i*

Point group of the first sort	Expansion as cosets of subgroup of index 2	Expansion of corresponding point group of the second sort	Designation of point group of the second sort
1	—	—	—
2	2{1}	$\bar{2}$ {1}	*m*
3	—	—	—
4	4{2}	$\bar{4}$ {2}	$\bar{4}$
6	2{3}	$\bar{2}$ {3}	$\bar{6}$ $(=\frac{3}{m})$
222	2{2}	$\bar{2}$ {2}	*mm*2
32	2{3}	$\bar{2}$ {3}	3*m*
422	2{4}	$\bar{2}$ {4}	4*mm*
	4{222}	$\bar{4}$ {222}	$\bar{4}2m$
622	2{6}	$\bar{2}$ {6}	6*mm*
	6{32}	$\bar{6}$ {32}	$\bar{6}m2$ $(=\frac{3}{m}m2)$
23	—	—	—
432	4{23}	$\bar{4}$ {23}	$\bar{4}3m$

down by changing the remaining operation n to $\bar{n}$. This process is carried for the crystallographic point groups in Table 3.

The relation between the point groups of the first sort and those of the second sort formed from them by this method is interesting. Both groups have the same structure, but one has an element n and its products while the other has $\bar{n}$ and its products. If the elements of both groups were to be put into a single group, the new group would contain i. This can be shown by expressing n and $\bar{n}$ as rotoinversion and by recalling that, if $\bar{n}$ is an element of the group, so is $(\bar{n})^{-1}$:

$$\begin{aligned}(\bar{n})^{-1}n &= (A_{\alpha,i})^{-1}A_\alpha \\ &= (A_\alpha i)^{-1}A_\alpha \\ &= i^{-1}A_\alpha{}^{-1}A_\alpha \\ &= i^{-1} = i. \end{aligned} \tag{53}$$

Groups containing operation *i*. As pointed out above, a characteristic of the operation i is that it has the property of transforming any rotation into itself. Consequently an operation i placed at the intersection of the axes of a group of rotations has the property of transforming every rotation of the group into

Table 4. The 11 crystallographic point groups of the first sort, and their subgroups

Point group	Subgroups									
1	1										
2	$\boxed{1}$	2									
3	1		3								
4	1	$\boxed{2}$		4							
6	1	2	$\boxed{3}$		6						
222	1	$\boxed{2}$				222					
32	1	2	$\boxed{3}$				32				
422	1	2		$\boxed{4}$		$\boxed{222}$		422			
622	1	2	3		$\boxed{6}$	222	$\boxed{32}$		622		
23	1	2	3			222				23	
432	1	2	3	4		222	32	422		$\boxed{23}$	432
	1	2	3	4	6	222	32	422	622	23	432

Note: Subgroups of index 2 are enclosed in boxes.

itself. Therefore every distinct point group of the first sort can be transformed into a distinct point group of the second sort by adding to its operations the products of these operations with i. This amounts to multiplying each point group of the first sort, $\{G\}$, by the group of operations $\{1, i\}$.

The new groups formed in this way can be designated by the group product $\{G\}\,\{i\}$. The operations of each group are those of $\{G\}$ plus the products of $\{G\}$ with i. The operations of the 11 possible crystallographic point groups have already been listed in detail in the first part of this chapter. These correspond with (41). The products with i correspond with (42), where i is used for the particular operation B. The products Ba_r are then products of the form iA_α, where A_α is one of the rotational operations of $\{G\}$. Each of these products is a rotoinversion, because

$$iA_\alpha = A_\alpha i = A_{\alpha,i}. \tag{54}$$

For example,

$$i \cdot 3 = 3 \cdot i = \bar{3}. \tag{55}$$

Table 5. The 10 crystallographic point groups of the second sort not containing the operation *i*, and their subgroups

Point groups	Subgroups																	
m	1		m															
$\bar{4}$	1	2				$\bar{4}$												
$\bar{6}$	1		m	3				$\bar{6}$										
$mm2$	1	2	m							$mm2$								
$3m$	1		m	3								$3m$						
$4mm$	1	2	m		4					$mm2$			$4mm$					
$\bar{4}2m$	1	2	m			$\bar{4}$			222	$mm2$				$\bar{4}2m$				
$6mm$	1	2	m	3			6			$mm2$		$3m$			$6mm$			
$\bar{6}m2$	1	2	m	3				$\bar{6}$		$mm2$	32	$3m$				$\bar{6}m2$		
$\bar{4}3m$	1	2	m	3		$\bar{4}$			222	$mm2$		$3m$		$\bar{4}2m$			23	$\bar{4}3m$
	1	2	m	3	4	$\bar{4}$	6	$\bar{6}$	222	$mm2$	32	$3m$	$4mm$	$\bar{4}2m$	$6mm$	$\bar{6}m2$	23	$\bar{4}3m$

Table 6. The 11 crystallographic point groups of the second sort containing i, and their subgroups

Point group	Subgroups
$1 \cdot i = \bar{1}$	$1\ \bar{1}$
$2 \cdot i = \frac{2}{m}$	$1\ \bar{1}\ 2\ m\ \frac{2}{m}$
$3 \cdot i = \bar{3}$	$1\ \bar{1}\ \ 3\ \bar{3}$
$4 \cdot i = \frac{4}{m}$	$1\ \bar{1}\ 2\ m\ \frac{2}{m}\ \ 4\ \bar{4}\ \frac{4}{m}$
$6 \cdot i = \frac{6}{m}$	$1\ \bar{1}\ 2\ m\ \frac{2}{m}\ 3\ \bar{3}\ \ 6\ \bar{6}\ \frac{6}{m}$
$222 \cdot i = \frac{2}{m}\frac{2}{m}\frac{2}{m}$	$1\ \bar{1}\ 2\ m\ \frac{2}{m}\ \ 222\ mm2\ \frac{2}{m}\frac{2}{m}\frac{2}{m}$
$32 \cdot i = \bar{3}\frac{2}{m}$	$1\ \bar{1}\ 2\ m\ \frac{2}{m}\ 3\ \bar{3}\ \ 32\ 3m\ \bar{3}\frac{2}{m}$
$422 \cdot i = \frac{4}{m}\frac{2}{m}\frac{2}{m}$	$1\ \bar{1}\ 2\ m\ \frac{2}{m}\ \ 4\ \bar{4}\ \frac{4}{m}\ \ 222\ mm2\ \frac{2}{m}\frac{2}{m}\frac{2}{m}\ \ 422\ 4mm\ \bar{4}2m\ \frac{4}{m}\frac{2}{m}\frac{2}{m}$
$622 \cdot i = \frac{6}{m}\frac{2}{m}\frac{2}{m}$	$1\ \bar{1}\ 2\ m\ \frac{2}{m}\ 3\ \bar{3}\ \ 6\ \bar{6}\ \frac{6}{m}\ 222\ mm2\ \frac{2}{m}\frac{2}{m}\frac{2}{m}\ 32\ 3m\ \bar{3}\frac{2}{m}\ \ 622\ 6mm\ \bar{6}m2\ \frac{6}{m}\frac{2}{m}\frac{2}{m}$
$23 \cdot i = \frac{2}{m}\bar{3}$	$1\ \bar{1}\ 2\ m\ \frac{2}{m}\ 3\ \bar{3}\ \ 222\ mm2\ \frac{2}{m}\frac{2}{m}\frac{2}{m}\ \ 23\ \frac{2}{m}\bar{3}$
$432 \cdot i = \frac{4}{m}\bar{3}\frac{2}{m}$	$1\ \bar{1}\ 2\ m\ \frac{2}{m}\ 3\ \bar{3}\ 4\ \bar{4}\ \frac{4}{m}\ \ 222\ mm2\ \frac{2}{m}\frac{2}{m}\frac{2}{m}\ 32\ 3m\ \bar{3}\frac{2}{m}\ 422\ 4mm\ \bar{4}2m\ \frac{4}{m}\frac{2}{m}\frac{2}{m}\ \ 23\ \frac{2}{m}\bar{3}\ 432\ \bar{4}3m\ \frac{4}{m}\bar{3}\frac{2}{m}$
	$1\ \bar{1}\ 2\ m\ \frac{2}{m}\ 3\ \bar{3}\ 4\ \bar{4}\ \frac{4}{m}\ 6\ \bar{6}\ \frac{6}{m}\ 222\ mm2\ \frac{2}{m}\frac{2}{m}\frac{2}{m}\ 32\ 3m\ \bar{3}\frac{2}{m}\ 422\ 4mm\ \bar{4}2m\ \frac{4}{m}\frac{2}{m}\frac{2}{m}\ 622\ 6mm\ \bar{6}m2\ \frac{6}{m}\frac{2}{m}\frac{2}{m}\ 23\ \frac{2}{m}\bar{3}\ 432\ \bar{4}3m\ \frac{4}{m}\bar{3}\frac{2}{m}$

For the particular operation of the first sort, A_π, the product

$$i \cdot A_\pi = A_\pi \cdot i = m_\perp, \tag{56}$$

or

$$\bar{1} \cdot 2 = 2 \cdot \bar{1} = \bar{2}. \tag{57}$$

If, to the set of operations of each of the point groups of the first sort there are added the products with *i*, all possible point groups containing *i* are found. There are 11 crystallographic point groups of the first sort, listed in Table 4. Corresponding with these are 11 more crystallographic point groups of the second sort containing *i* as an operation. These are listed in Table 6. There are obviously no other crystallographic point groups of the second sort containing *i* as an operation.

The 32 point groups can evidently be separated into three categories: groups of the first sort, groups of the second sort not containing operations *i*, and groups of the second sort containing operation *i*. These point groups and their subgroups are listed in Tables 4, 5, and 6 respectively.

22 · Group theory applied to space symmetries

Groups of translations

When integers are combined by addition, they form a group in which zero plays the role of identity. A generalization of the set of integers is the set of translations which are integral multiples of a specific "unit" translation. In vector notation, the vectors of this set have the general form

$$\vec{T} = u\vec{t_1}, \tag{1}$$

where $\vec{t_1}$ is the unit vector and u is an integer. Any two vectors of form (1) can be combined by vector addition to give

$$u_1\vec{t_1} + u_2\vec{t_1} = (u_1 + u_2)\vec{t_1}. \tag{2}$$

The set of all such vectors forms a group because the set of integers u forms a group.

This set of vectors is confined to one dimension. A generalization to two dimensions is a set of vectors which is the vector sum of two noncollinear sets of vectors like (1), specifically,

$$\vec{T} = u\vec{t_1} + v\vec{t_2}. \tag{3}$$

A further generalization to three dimensions is a set of vectors which is the vector sum of three noncoplanar sets of vectors like (1), specifically,

$$\vec{T} = u\vec{t_1} + v\vec{t_2} + w\vec{t_3}. \tag{4}$$

The vectors in (1) correspond to the translations of a line lattice; those of (3) correspond to the translations of a plane lattice; and those of (4) correspond to the translations of a space lattice. The vectors of each of these sets form an infinite group with vector addition as the rule of combination and the null vector as the identity element.

If one wishes to use a product representation of combination, then one represents the addition of two vectors A and B as AB. With this notation, (4) can be expressed as

$$T = t_1{}^u t_2{}^v t_3{}^w \tag{5}$$

From this discussion it is evident that the translations of a lattice form a group. Any translation of the group transforms any other translation of the group into itself. Therefore any two translations are permutable. Hence a group of lattice translations is Abelian.

Space groups and their symmetry elements

Any group of operations containing a group of lattice translations in three dimensions as a subgroup is called a *space group*. Evidently a space group can be formed by starting with a translation group and adding to it operations that transform the translation group into itself. Since the operations must transform the translation group into itself, the lattice translations must constitute an invariant subgroup of every space group.

Any symmetrical lattice can be transformed into itself by its symmetry operations. Each of the 14 Bravais lattices can therefore be transformed into itself by its point-group symmetry operations. This means that each of the 14 Bravais lattices listed in Table 1 of Chapter 8 can be combined with its holohedral crystal class and also with its several merohedral crystal classes. There are 73 such combinations. Each combination corresponds to the product of a point group and a translation group, and therefore can be represented by a group product. Of the 230 space groups, 73 are simple group products of point groups and translation groups.

There are other operations than point-group operations, however, which can transform a group of translations into itself. Since any translation transforms a translation into itself, any translation can be added to a rotation or rotoinversion that transforms a group of lattice translations into itself without disturbing the transformation. It does not follow that the resulting operation (say a screw or glide) will make the new combination a group, however. The condition that the new translation-bearing operation is an acceptable symmetry operation is that, when combined with the other operations of the set, the result is an operation of the set. In particular, some power of a screw operation must be a lattice translation, and the square of a glide operation must be a lattice translation. It is this kind of restriction that limits the possible translations of screw and glide operations.

Furthermore, when various screw and glide operations are added to the lattice translations, their combinations must be members of the group. This feature of space groups will be discussed later.

Quotient groups

An interesting and useful feature associated with invariant subgroups can be stated in the following form:

Theorem: The cosets of an invariant subgroup form a group in which the subgroup is the identity element.

The identity element in this case is not 1, but the more general I. This more general kind of identity element was noted in the beginning of the discussion of group theory.

Let the group be G and the invariant subgroup g. Let the elements of g be $a_1, a_2, \cdots$, etc., and let the elements not in g be $B_2, B_3, \cdots$. Then the expansion of G into cosets of g is

$$G = g, \quad B_2g, \quad B_3g, \quad \cdots, \quad (B_1 = 1). \tag{6}$$

In detail the individual elements of the group are

$$\begin{array}{llllll} g = & a_1, & a_2, & a_3, & \cdots, & (B_1 = a_1 = 1) \\ B_2g = & B_2\ , & B_2a_2, & B_2a_3, & \cdots, & \\ B_3g = & B_3\ , & B_3a_2, & B_3a_3, & \cdots, & \\ \cdot & \cdot & \cdot & \cdot & \cdots, & \\ \cdot & \cdot & \cdot & \cdot & \cdots, & \\ \cdot & \cdot & \cdot & \cdot & \cdots, & \end{array} \tag{7}$$

Now, by $(B_ig)(B_jg)$ is meant all the distinct products that can be formed from elements of the ith row with elements of the jth row of (7). The theorem states that the elements of (6) form a group, according to the meaning of this kind of product. That this is so depends fundamentally on the feature that g is an invariant subgroup and therefore can be permuted with any B. To prove that the elements of (6) form a group, it must be proved that the group postulates are obeyed:

By virtue of the permissible permutation

$$B_ig = gB_i, \tag{8}$$

any product $(B_ig)(B_jg)$ can be reduced as follows:

$$\begin{aligned} (B_ig)(B_jg) &= B_iB_jgg \\ &= B_iB_jg. \end{aligned} \tag{9}$$

Since B_i and B_j are elements of the group G, their product B_iB_j is an element of the group. Let this product appear in the same coset as B_k; that is, let B_iB_j be equal to some general term in this coset; for example, let

$$B_iB_j = B_ka_p. \tag{10}$$

Then the right of (9) can be further reduced as follows:

$$\begin{aligned} (B_ig)(B_jg) &= B_iB_jg \\ &= B_ka_pg. \end{aligned} \tag{11}$$

Any element of a group transforms a group into itself, so that

$$a_p g = g. \tag{12}$$

Therefore, the right of (11) can be further reduced to

$$(B_i g)(B_j g) = B_k g. \tag{13}$$

Therefore the right side of (9) is a row of (7). This means that the individual terms of (6) form a closed set. Since

$$gg = g, \tag{14}$$

it follows that

$$(B_i g)g = B_i g, \tag{15}$$

so that the subgroup g functions as the identical element. The inverse of $B_i g$ is $B_i^{-1}g$, because

$$\begin{aligned}(B_i g)(B_i^{-1}g) &= B_i g B_i^{-1} g \\ &= B_i B_i^{-1} gg \\ &= gg = g.\end{aligned} \tag{16}$$

Thus the group postulates are obeyed and the theorem is proved.

The group of cosets is called a *quotient group* of G relative to g, or a *factor group* of g in G. It is symbolized by G/g.

Homomorphism

Array (7) displays the individual elements of group G in such a way that each row comprises a coset of the invariant group g. Consider a general product of two elements such as $(B_i a_r)(B_j a_s)$. Now, since g is an invariant subgroup of G, any B transforms g into itself, so that any $B^{-1}aB$ is in g. In particular, let

$$B_j^{-1} a_r B_j = a_t, \tag{17}$$

so that

$$a_r B_j = B_j a_t. \tag{18}$$

This permits the general product of two elements to be reduced to

$$\begin{aligned}(B_i a_r)(B_j a_s) &= B_i a_r B_j a_s \\ &= B_i B_j a_t a_s.\end{aligned} \tag{19}$$

According to (10) the right side of (19) can be reduced to

$$(B_i a_r)(B_j a_s) = B_k a_p a_t a_s. \tag{20}$$

Since any product of a's is in g, this is equivalent to

$$(B_i a_r)(B_j a_s) = B_k a_q. \tag{21}$$

This means that the general product $(B_i a_r)(B_j a_s)$ is in the same coset B_k as the product of its B's, which is the kth row.

In the light of this there is an interesting relation between the structures of the group G and its quotient group G/g. These groups can be compared as follows:

group G						group G/g
a_1	a_2	a_3	a_4	$\cdots$	a_r	g
B_2	B_2a_2	B_2a_3	B_2a_4	$\cdots$	B_2a_r	B_2g
B_3	B_3a_2	B_3a_3	B_3a_4	$\cdots$	B_3a_r	B_3g
B_4	B_4a_2	B_4a_3	B_4a_4	$\cdots$	B_4a_r	B_4g
$\cdot$	$\cdot$	$\cdot$	$\cdot$	$\cdots$	$\cdot$	$\cdot$
$\cdot$	$\cdot$	$\cdot$	$\cdot$	$\cdots$	$\cdot$	$\cdot$
B_s	B_sa_2	B_sa_3	B_sa_4	$\cdots$	B_sa_r	B_sg

$(B_1 = a_1 = 1)$

The set of elements in G forms a group, and the set of elements in G/g forms a group. Any of the r elements in a row of G corresponds to one element in G/g. Any of the several products in G consisting of one element of the B_ith row and one element of the B_jth row is a product in the row $B_iB_j = B_k$ (say). Since there are only r distinct products in this row, any of these r distinct products corresponds to the one product in G/g. To summarize, the following structural relation exists between G and G/g:

G	G/g
r elements B_i	correspond to one element B_ig
r elements B_j	correspond to one element B_jg
r products B_iB_j	correspond to one product B_iB_jg

This correspondence is a generalization of isomorphism. It is called *homomorphism*. G is said to bear an $r:1$ *homomorphism* to G/g, and the two groups are said to be *homomorphic* (i.e., they have a similar structure). (Homomorphism is sometimes called *multiple isomorphism*.)

Infinite groups

When a group contains an infinite number of operations, its order is infinite, and it is called an infinite group. For example, the translations of (1), (3), or (4) form infinite groups under vector addition.

Any group containing operations which have a translation component is an infinite group. Consider the group of operations which are powers of a glide reflection m_t:

$$1, \quad m_t, \quad m_t^{\,2}, \quad m_t^{\,3}, \quad m_t^{\,4}, \quad \cdots. \tag{22}$$

This can also be written

$$1, \quad mt, \quad m^2t^2, \quad m^3t^3, \quad m^4t^4, \quad \cdots. \tag{23}$$

Since

$$m^2 = 1, \tag{24}$$

(23) can be rewritten as

$$1, \quad mt, \quad t^2, \quad mt^3, \quad t^4, \quad \cdots. \tag{25}$$

Let

$$t^2 = T. \tag{26}$$

Then (25) can be represented by

$$1 \quad mt \quad T \quad mtT \quad T^2 \quad mtT^2 \quad \cdots. \tag{27}$$

This can be rearranged to emphasize the product aspect, as follows:

$$\begin{array}{ccccc} 1, & T, & T^2, & T^3, & \cdots, \\ mt, & mtT, & mtT^2, & mtT^3, & \cdots. \end{array} \tag{28}$$

With this arrangement it is evident that this group contains as a subgroup the powers of T. The group can be regarded as the product of operation mt with invariant subgroup $\{T\}$.

Now compare the operation of the group of glide reflections in (28) with the group of pure reflections. The comparison can be made as follows:

		group $\{m_t\}$			group $\{m\}$
1,	T,	T^2,	T^3,	$\cdots$	1
mt,	mtT,	mtT^2,	mtT^3,	$\cdots$	m

(29)

In this comparison it is evident that any of the infinite subgroup of elements T^n of $\{m_t\}$ corresponds to the identity of group $\{m\}$, that any of the infinite set of operations mtT^n of $\{m_t\}$ corresponds to the element m of group $\{m\}$, and that any product in $\{m_t\}$ occurs in the same line as the corresponding product in $\{m\}$. Thus group $\{m_t\}$ is homomorphic with group $\{m\}$.

Homomorphism is displayed in the comparison of any cyclical group of translation-bearing operations and the group of operations of its isogonal symmetry element. As a further, somewhat more complicated, example, compare the group $\{4_1\}$, based upon operation $A_{\pi/2,t}$, with group $\{4\}$, based upon operation $A_{\pi/2}$. Recalling that, for a 4-fold screw, $t^4 = T$, these two groups can be compared as follows:

Group $\{4_1\}$				Group $\{4\}$
1	T	T^2		1
$A_{\pi/2}t$	$A_{\pi/2}t\,T$	$A_{\pi/2}t\,T^2$	$\cdots$	$A_{\pi/2}$
$A^2_{\pi/2}t^2$	$A^2_{\pi/2}t^2T$	$A^2_{\pi/2}t^2T^2$	$\cdots$	$A^2_{\pi/2}$
$A^3_{\pi/2}t^3$	$A^3_{\pi/2}t^3T$	$A^3_{\pi/2}t^3T^2$	$\cdots$	$A^3_{\pi/2}$.

(30)

It is evident that $\{4_1\}$ is homomorphic with $\{4\}$. In this homomorphism the subgroup of lattice translations of $\{4_1\}$ corresponds with the identity of $\{4\}$.

In general, the group of operations of a screw or glide is homomorphic with the group of operations of the isogonal point-group symmetry element, and the lattice translations correspond with the identity of the point-group symmetry element. Another description of the relation of the two groups is as follows: The group of translations is an invariant subgroup. The quotient group of this subgroup has elements which are the cosets of the horizontal rows. This quotient group is isomorphous with the group of point-group operations.

Another interesting relation brought out by (30) is that the set of operations

$$\Gamma, \qquad A_{\pi/2}t, \qquad A^2_{\pi/2}t^2, \qquad A^3_{\pi/2}t^3, \tag{31}$$

where Γ is any translation in the subgroup $\{1, T, T^2, \cdots\}$, can be regarded as forming a kind of group. Fundamentally this is because the operations of (31) each consist of rotational and translational components. The rotational components form a group because they are a group of point-group operations $\{4\}$. The translational components also form a group provided that a combination like t^3t, which equals $t^4 = T$, is permitted to correspond to identity. In the language of a *modular algebra*, this can be done by noting that any translation is equal to 1 (modulo Γ), where Γ is any translation in the subgroup $\{1, T, T^2, \cdots\}$.

Construction of space groups

The relation between the group of operations of a point-group symmetry element and the quotient group of its isogonal space-group symmetry element is one of isomorphism, as just discussed. If the multiplication table of the group of the point-group symmetry element is known, the multiplication table of the quotient group of the space-group symmetry element is known to be the same. Furthermore, the rotational component of both the point-group and space-group operations in a corresponding coset are the same, whereas the translation components comprise an infinite group. The translation components can also be described as forming a finite group modulo Γ, where Γ is a lattice translation.

The relation that obtains between a group of symmetry operations of a space-group symmetry element and a group of symmetry operations of the isogonal point-group symmetry element can be readily extended to the relation between any group of space-group operations and the group of isogonal point-group operations. The rotational components of the space-group symmetry operations form a finite group which is identical with the group of isogonal point-group symmetry operations. But the space-group operations within a cell conform to the further requirement that their translation components form a group modulo Γ, that is, a group in which some lattice translation is regarded as functioning as identity.

To see how this is applied in the construction of space groups based upon a given point group, consider the construction of the space groups isogonal with point-group *mm*2 and based upon a primitive lattice. The structure of *mm*2 is given by the following multiplication table:

	1	${}^{x}m$	${}^{y}m$	${}^{z}2$
1	1	${}^{x}m$	${}^{y}m$	${}^{z}2$
${}^{x}m$	${}^{x}m$	1	${}^{z}2$	${}^{y}m$
${}^{y}m$	${}^{y}m$	${}^{z}2$	1	${}^{x}m$
${}^{z}2$	${}^{z}2$	${}^{y}m$	${}^{x}m$	1 .

(32)

The superscripts refer to coordinate axes. Thus, ${}^{x}m$ is a mirror perpendicular to X, while ${}^{z}2$ is a 2-fold axis parallel to Z.

The space-group symmetry operations must have a multiplication table for the rotational part of the group identical with (32). In addition, the operations within the cell must have translations obeying a table like (32), specifically,

	Γ	${}^{1}t$	${}^{2}t$	${}^{3}t$
Γ	Γ	${}^{1}t$	${}^{2}t$	${}^{3}t$
${}^{1}t$	${}^{1}t$	Γ	${}^{3}t$	${}^{2}t$
${}^{2}t$	${}^{2}t$	${}^{3}t$	Γ	${}^{1}t$
${}^{3}t$	${}^{3}t$	${}^{2}t$	${}^{1}t$	Γ .

(33)

For the purpose of finding the three translations of (33) it is sufficient to consider a general product from (32) like

$$ {}^{x}m \cdot {}^{y}m = {}^{z}2 \tag{34}$$

and the corresponding product from (33):

$$ {}^{1}t \cdot {}^{2}t = {}^{3}t \quad (\text{modulo } \Gamma). \tag{35}$$

Together these determine the combination

$$^{s}m_{\tau_1} \cdot {}^{s}m_{\tau_2} = A_{\pi,\tau_3}, \tag{36}$$

where the superscripts s indicate a possible separation of the mirror from the 2-fold screw. The permissible values of τ_1 are zero or half a lattice translation parallel to the plane ^{x}m, that is 0, $b/2$, or $c/2$. The permissible values of τ_2

Table 1. Determination of translations associated with space groups isogonal with $mm2$ based upon P

^{3}t (of $^{z}2$)	0	0	0	0	0	0	0	0
^{1}t (of ^{x}m)	0	$\frac{a}{2}$	$\frac{b}{2}$	$\frac{c}{2}$	$\frac{a}{2}+\frac{b}{2}$	$\frac{a}{2}+\frac{c}{2}$	$\frac{b}{2}+\frac{c}{2}$	$\frac{a}{2}+\frac{b}{2}+\frac{c}{2}$
^{2}t (of ^{y}m)	0	$\frac{a}{2}$	$\frac{b}{2}$	$\frac{c}{2}$	$\frac{a}{2}+\frac{b}{2}$	$\frac{a}{2}+\frac{c}{2}$	$\frac{b}{2}+\frac{c}{2}$	$\frac{a}{2}+\frac{b}{2}+\frac{c}{2}$
Designation	$mm2$	$^{s}ma2$	$b\,{}^{s}m2$	$cc2$	$^{s}b\,{}^{s}a2$	$^{s}cn2$	$n\,{}^{s}c2$	$^{s}n\,{}^{s}n2$
Space group	$Pmm2$	$Pma2$	$(Pbm2)$	$Pcc2$	$Pba2$	$Pcn2$	$(Pnc2)$	$Pnn2$
		Symmetrical in a, b				Symmetrical in a, b		

^{3}t (of $^{z}2$)	$\frac{c}{2}$	$\frac{c}{2}$	$\frac{c}{2}$	$\frac{c}{2}$	$\frac{c}{2}$	$\frac{c}{2}$	$\frac{c}{2}$	$\frac{c}{2}$
^{1}t (of ^{x}m)	0	$\frac{a}{2}$	$\frac{b}{2}$	$\frac{c}{2}$	$\frac{a}{2}+\frac{b}{2}$	$\frac{a}{2}+\frac{c}{2}$	$\frac{b}{2}+\frac{c}{2}$	$\frac{a}{2}+\frac{b}{2}+\frac{c}{2}$
^{2}t (of ^{y}m)	$\frac{c}{2}$	$\frac{a}{2}+\frac{c}{2}$	$\frac{b}{2}+\frac{c}{2}$		$\frac{a}{2}+\frac{b}{2}+\frac{c}{2}$	$\frac{a}{2}$	$\frac{b}{2}$	$\frac{a}{2}+\frac{b}{2}$
Designation	$mc2_1$	$^{s}mn2_1$	$b\,{}^{s}c2_1$	$cm2_1$	$^{s}b\,{}^{s}n2_1$	$^{s}ca2_1$	$n\,{}^{s}m2_1$	$^{s}n\,{}^{s}a2_1$
Space group	$Pmc2_1$	$Pmn2_1$	$Pbc2_1$	$(Pcm2_1)$	$Pbn2_1$	$(Pca2_1)$	$Pnm2_1$	$Pna2_1$
	Symmetrical in a, b ($Pmc2_1$–$(Pcm2_1)$)							
			Symmetrical in a, b ($Pbc2_1$–$(Pca2_1)$)					

are zero or half a lattice translation parallel to the plane ${}^{y}m$, that is 0, $a/2$, or $c/2$. The permissible values of τ_3 are zero or half a lattice translation parallel to c, that is 0 or $c/2$. Any other values occurring in satisfying (35) are to be attributed to the separations s of the planes from the axis. This computation is carried out in Table 1. If (35) is expressed as vector addition, it can be written in the form

$$\overrightarrow{{}^{1}t} + \overrightarrow{{}^{2}t} + \overrightarrow{{}^{3}t} = \Gamma. \tag{37}$$

All permissible values of ${}^{1}t$ are chosen in turn, namely 0, $a/2$, $b/2$, $c/2$, $a/2 + b/2$, $a/2 + c/2$, $b/2 + c/2$, and $a/2 + b/2 + c/2$. The table is divided into two parts. In the first part it is assumed that the axis isogonal with 2 is a pure rotation axis, so that ${}^{3}t = 0$. In the second part it is assumed that the axis isogonal with 2 is a screw, so that ${}^{3}t = c/2$.

Subgroups of space groups

It has been shown that any point group is isomorphic with the quotient groups of its several isogonal space groups. It follows that, to each subgroup in the point group, there corresponds a subgroup in the quotient group of each isogonal space group. The most obvious kind of subgroup in the space group is the one involving sets of operations of symmetry elements in the same unit cell and which corresponds to a subgroup of operations in the point group. All such subgroups of a space group necessarily have the same unit cell as the space group. These are the subgroups ordinarily listed in tabulations of space groups. But other subgroups with larger cells also exist. The whole collection of all subgroups, regardless of unit cell, are called "derivative symmetries."*

* M. J. Buerger, Derivative crystal structures, *J. Chem. Phys.*, *15* (1947), 1–16.

Index